ELEMENTS OF BIOLOGY

ELEMENTS OF BIOLOGY

Paul B. Weisz
Professor of Biology
Brown University

2D EDITION

McGRAW-HILL BOOK COMPANY

New York   St. Louis   San Francisco   Toronto   London   Sydney

Elements of Biology

This book is set in Fototronic Laurel.
The chapter titles are Venus Medium Extended.

To Stephanie, Sherry, and Peter

PREFACE

The pedagogic approach of this second edition is the same as that of the first; the guiding philosophy outlined in the latter is still fully valid:

"... A beginning course in biology should be analytical rather than merely descriptive. Instead of being an exercise in memorization, the course should convey understanding of some of the principles underlying living phenomena. Furthermore, the basic morphological unit of discussion might profitably be the molecule, with the basic physiological unit being the molecular reaction. One of the important aims should be to show, in so far as this can be shown, how the various microscopic and macroscopic attributes of living organisms ultimately result from molecules and their interactions.

A course of this kind need not necessarily delve deeply into details of actual chemistry. It is important only that the general *orientation* be molecular; the student should learn to think about living processes "from the molecule up," as it were. Where desired, of course, the conceptual framework may be augmented with as little or as much chemical detail as the student can profitably absorb. But the first essential is to provide at least the molecular conceptual framework. This in itself does not make a course any more advanced or more difficult than a traditional presentation. On the contrary, because it probes deeply and searches for molecular foundations, it makes the traditional far more meaningful and more satisfyingly comprehensible."

Unchanged also in this edition are the general level and scope of the presentation, even though the subject matter is now organized into seven parts instead of six and the chapter sequence is in some instances rearranged slightly. However, the most pronounced changes in this edition are those which, within individual chapters, update or strengthen the coverage of given topics. Such changes include, for example, an integrated introductory treatment of basic chemistry, to serve as a foundation for all later biochemical concepts (Chap. 3); a modernized account of genetic codes, messenger RNA, and genetics as a whole (Chaps. 16 and 23); an increased emphasis on cytology and histology (Chap. 5) and on types and morphology of organisms (Part 3). Moreover, the coverage of plant biology is greatly expanded; the book now contains a separate new section on plant tissues (Chap. 5), substantially augmented sections on the structure (Chaps. 8 and 9) and reproduction of plant and plantlike types (Chap. 21), a modernized account of photosynthesis (Chap. 11), a new section on the growth physiology of plants (Chap. 17), and a separate treatment of plant evolution (Chap. 25). Together with many other changes of smaller scope throughout the book, these revisions are designed to provide a good balance not only between botanical and zoological subject matter, but also more generally between the morphological-systematic and the biochemical-physiological areas of biology.

In conjunction with the changes in the text, numerous diagrams have been redesigned or redrawn and many photographs have been changed or newly added. Also, the lists of suggested readings have been brought up to date and the glossary has been expanded. Available with the text is a revised *Instructor's Manual* and, if the instructor so specifies to his students, a newly prepared *Study Guide*, written specifically for use with this edition.

Paul B. Weisz

CONTENTS

Part 2   *The Organization of Life*

Part 3   The World of Life

Part 5   The Functions of Life: Steady States

Part 6   *The Functions of Life: Reproduction*

Part 7 The Functions of Life: Adaptation

ELEMENTS OF BIOLOGY

THE NATURE OF SCIENCE

1

Our current civilization is so thoroughly permeated with science that, for many, the label "scientific" has become the highest badge of merit, the hallmark of progress, the dominant theme of the age of atoms and space. No human endeavor, so it is often claimed, can really be worthwhile or of basic significance unless it has a scientific foundation. Moreover, advertisements loudly proclaim the "scientific" nature of consumer goods, and their "scientifically proved" high quality is attested to by "scientific" experts. Human relations too are supposed to be "scientific" nowadays. Conversation and debate have become "scientific" discussions, and in a field such as sports, if one is a good athlete, he is a "scientific" athlete.

There are even those who claim to take their religion "scientifically" and those who stoutly maintain that literature, painting, and other artistic pursuits are reducible to "science," really. And then there are those who believe that science will eventually solve "everything" and that, if only the world were run more "scientifically," it would be a much better place.

Yet in contrast to this widespread confidence in things and activities which claim to be, and in a few cases actually are, scientific, large segments of society doubt and mistrust scientists as persons. To many, the scientist is somehow queer and "different." He is held to be naïve and more or less uninformed outside his specialty. He is pictured as a cold, godless calculating machine living in a strange, illusory world of his own.

Many circumstances in our civilization conspire to foster such false, stereotyped notions about science and scientists. However, no one who wishes to consider himself properly educated can afford to know about the meaning of science only what popular misconceptions, and "common knowledge," may have taught him. Especially is this true for one who is about to pursue studies in a modern science such as biology.

What then *is* the actual meaning of science? How did truly scientific undertakings develop, and how does science "work"? What can it do and, more especially, what can it not do? How does science differ from other forms of activity, and what place does it have in the scheme of modern culture?

The origin of science

Science began in the distant past, long before human history was being recorded. Its mother was tribal *magic*.

The same mother also gave birth to religion, and, probably even earlier, to art. Thus science, religion, and art have always been blood brothers. Their methods differ, but their aim is the same: to understand and interpret the universe and its workings and, from this, to promote the material and spiritual welfare of man where possible.

This was also the function of tribal magic. For long ages, magic was the rallying point of society, the central institution in which were concentrated the accumulated wisdom and experience of the day. The execution of magical procedures was in the hands of specially trained individuals, the medicine men and their equivalents. These were the forerunners of the scientists and the clergymen of today. How did science and religion grow out of magic? We may illustrate by means of an example.

Several thousand years ago, it was generally believed that magical rites were necessary to make wheat grow from planted seeds. In this particular instance, the rites took one of two forms. Either man intensified his sexual activity, in a solemn spring festival celebrated communally in the fields, or he abstained completely from sexual activity during the planting period.

The first procedure was an instance of *imitative* magic. The reasoning was that, since sowing seeds is like producing pregnancy in a woman, man could demonstrate to the soil what was wanted and so induce it to imitate man and be fertile. The second procedure, an instance of *contagious* magic, grew out of the assumption that only a limited amount of reproductive potency was available to living things. Consequently, if man did not use up his potency, that much more would become available for the soil. Depending on the tribe, the time, and the locality, either imitative or contagious magic might have been used to attain the same end, namely, to make the earth fruitful.

The fundamental weakness of magic was, of course, that it was unreliable. Sometimes it worked, and sometimes it did not work. Bad soil, bad grain, bad weather, and insect pests often must have defeated the best magic. In time, man must have realized that magical rites actually played no role in wheat growth, whereas soil conditions, grain quality, and good weather played very important roles. This was a momentous discovery—and a scientific one.

Magic became science when man accidentally found, or began to look for, situations which could be predictably controlled without magical rituals. In many situations where magic seemed to work successfully most of the time, man discovered an underlying scientific principle.

Yet there remained very many situations where magic did not work and where scientific principles could not be found. For example, in spite of good soil and good weather, wheat might not have grown because of virus or fungus infections. Such contingencies remained completely beyond understanding up to very modern times, and early man could only conclude that unseeable, uncontrollable "somethings" occasionally defeated his efforts. These somethings became spirits and gods. And unless prayers and sacrificial offerings maintained the good will of the gods, their wrath would undo human enterprise. Thus magical rituals evolved into primitively religious ones.

At this stage, medicine men ceased to be magicians and instead assumed the dual role of priest and scientist. Every personal or communal undertaking required both scientific and religious action: science, to put to use what was known; religion, to protect against possible failure by inducing the unknown to work on man's side.

In time, the "two-way" medicine man disappeared and made way for the specialized scientist and priest. In both religion and science, shades of the old magic lingered on for long periods. The religions still retain a high magical content today, and the sciences only recently dissociated from magic-derived pseudosciences such as alchemy, astrology, and the occult arts.

Throughout the early development of science and religion, emphasis was largely on practical matters. Science was primitively technological, and religion too was largely "applied," designed to deal with the concrete practical issues of the day. Man was preoccupied mainly with procuring food, shelter, and clothing, and science and religion served these necessities. Later, as a result of technological successes, more time became available for contemplation and cultural development, and this is when researchers and theorists appeared alongside the technologists, and theologians alongside the clergymen.

The forms of science

Today there are three types of scientists carrying on two kinds of science.

One kind of scientist may be symbolized as a man who sits by the river on nice afternoons and who whittles away at a stick and wonders about things. Strange as it may seem to some, the most powerful science stems from such whittlers. Whereas most people who just sit manage merely to be lazy, a few quietly boil with rare powers and make the wheels of the world go round. Thinker-scientists of this sort usually are not too well known by the general public, unless their thoughts prove to be of outstanding importance. Newton, Einstein, Darwin, and Freud are among the best known.

A second kind of scientist is the serious young man in the white coat, reading the dials of monster machines while lights flash and buzzers purr softly. This picture symbolizes the technician, the lab man, the trained expert who tests, experiments, and works out the implications of what the whittler has been thinking.

The third kind of scientist is a relatively new phenomenon. He goes to an office, dictates to secretaries, and spends a good part of his time in conferences or in handling contracts, budgets, and personnel. This symbolizes the businessman-scientist, who gets and allocates the funds which buy time and privacy for the whittler and machines for the lab man.

Note, however, that every scientist worthy of the name actually is a complex mixture of philosopher, technician, and businessman all rolled into one, and none is a "pure" type. But the relative emphasis varies greatly in different scientists.

Whatever type mixture he may be, a scientist works either in basic research, often called *pure science*, or in technology, often called *applied science*.

Basic research is done primarily to further man's understanding of nature. Possible practical applications of the findings are here completely disregarded. Scientists in this field are more frequently of the philosopher–lab-man type than in technology. They may be found principally in university laboratories and research institutes and, in lesser numbers, in industry and government. They have little to show for their efforts beyond the written accounts of their work; hence it is comparatively hard for them to convince nonscientists that they are doing anything essential. However, government and every enlightened industry today either support independent research or conduct such research. And the public is beginning to realize that pure science is the soil from which applied science must develop.

Technology is concerned primarily with applying the results of pure science to practical uses. No lesser inventiveness and genius are required in this field than in basic research, though here the genius is more of a commercial and less of a philosophical nature. Physicians, engineers, crime detectives, drug manufacturers, agricultural scientists, all are technologists. They have services and tangible products to sell; hence the public recognizes their worth rather readily.

Here again, note that no scientist is pure researcher or pure technologist. Mixtures are in evidence once more, with emphasis one way or the other. Moreover, technology is as much the fertilizer of basic research as the other way round. As new theories suggest new ways of applying them, so new ideas for doing things suggest further advances in research. Thus, in most research today, pure and applied science work hand in hand. Many conclusions of pure science cannot be tested before the technologist thinks up the means of testing. Conversely, before the technologist can produce desirable new products, years of basic research may first be required. In so far as every basic researcher must use equipment, however modest, he is also a technologist; and in so far as every technologist must understand how and why his products work, he is also a basic researcher.

It follows that any science shrivels whenever either of its two branches ceases to be effective. If for every dollar spent on science an immediate, tangible return is expected, and if the budding scientist is prevented from being a whittler by the necessity of producing something salable, then basic research will be in danger of drying up. And when that happens, technology too will become obsolete before long.

The procedure of science

Everything that is science ultimately has its basis in the *scientific method*. Both the powers and the limitations of science are defined by this method. And wherever the scientific method cannot be applied, there cannot be science.

Taken singly, most of the steps of the scientific method involve commonplace procedures carried out daily by every person. Taken together, they amount to the most powerful tool man has devised to know and to control nature.

OBSERVATION

All science begins with *observation*, the first step of the scientific method.

At once this delimits the scientific domain; something that cannot be observed cannot be investigated by science. However, observation need not be direct. Atomic nuclei and magnetism, for example, cannot be perceived directly through our sense organs, but their effects can be observed with instruments. Similarly, mind cannot be observed directly, but its effects can be, as expressed, for example, in behavior.

For reasons which will become clear presently, it is necessary, furthermore, that an observation be *repeatable*, actually or potentially. Anyone who doubts that objects fall back to the ground after being thrown into the air can convince himself of it by repeating the observation. One-time events on earth are outside science.

Correct observation is a most difficult art acquired only after long experience and many errors. Everybody observes, with eyes, ears, touch, and all other senses, but few observe correctly. Lawyers experienced with witnesses, artists who teach students to draw objects in plain view, and scientists who try to see nature all can testify to this.

This difficulty of observation lies largely in unsuspected bias. People forever see what they *want* to see or what they think they *ought* to see. It is extremely hard to rid oneself of such unconscious prejudice and to see just what is actually there, no more and no less. Past experience, "common knowledge," and often teachers can be subtle obstacles to correct observation, and even experienced scientists may not always avoid them. That is why a scientific observation is not taken at face value until several scientists have repeated the observation independently and have reported the same thing. That is also a major reason why one-time, unrepeatable events normally cannot be science.

A scientific piece of work is only as good as the original observation. Observational errors persist into everything that follows, and the effort may be defeated before it has properly begun.

PROBLEM

After an observation has been made, the second step of the scientific method is to define a *problem*. In other words, one asks a question about the observation. How does so and so come about? What is it that makes such and such happen in this or that fashion? Question-asking additionally distinguishes the scientist from the layman; everybody makes observations, but not everybody shows further curiosity.

More significantly, not everyone sees that there may actually be a problem connected with an observation. During thousands of years, even curious people simply took it for granted that a detached, unsupported object falls to the ground. It took genius to ask, "How come?" and few problems, indeed, have ever turned out to be more profound.

Thus scientists take nothing for granted, and they ask questions, even at the risk of irritating others. Question askers are notorious for getting themselves into trouble, and so it has always been with scientists. But they have to continue to ask questions if they are to remain scientists. And society has to expect annoying questions if it wishes to have science.

Anyone can ask questions. However, good questioning, like good observing, is a high art. To be valuable scientifically, a question must be *relevant*, and it must be *testable*. The difficulty is that it is often very hard or impossible to tell in advance whether a question is relevant or irrelevant, testable or untestable. If a man collapses on the street and passers-by want to help him, it may or may not be irrelevant to ask when he had his last meal. Without experience one cannot decide on the relevance of this question, and a wrong procedure might be followed.

As to the testability of questions, it is clear that proper testing techniques must be available, actually or potentially. This cannot always be guaranteed. For example, Einstein's fame rests, in part, on showing that it is impossible to test whether or not the earth moves through an "ether," an assumption held for many decades. All questions about an ether therefore become nonscientific, and we must reformulate associated problems until they become testable. Einstein did this, and he came up with relativity.

In general, science does best with "How?" or "What?" questions. "Why?" questions are more troublesome. Some of them can be rephrased to ask "How?" or "What?" But others such as "Why does the universe exist?" fall into the untestable category. These are outside the domain of science.

HYPOTHESIS

Having asked a proper question, the scientist proceeds to the third step of the scientific method. This involves the seemingly quite unscientific procedure of guessing. One guesses what the answer to the question might conceivably be. Scientists call this postulating a *hypothesis*.

Hypothesizing distinguishes the scientist still further from the layman. For while many people observe and ask questions, most stop there. Some do wonder about likely answers, and scientists are among these.

Of course, a given question may have thousands of *possible* answers but only one *right* answer. Chances are therefore excellent that a random guess will be wrong. The scientist will not know whether his guess was or was not correct until he has completed the fourth step of the scientific method, *experimentation*. It is the function of every experiment to test the validity of a scientific guess.

If experimentation shows that the first guess was wrong, the scientist then must formulate a new hypothesis and once more test for validity by performing new experiments. Clearly, the guessing and guess-testing might go on for years, and a right answer might never be found. This happens.

But here again, artistry, genius, and experience usually provide shortcuts. There are good guesses and bad ones, and the skilled scientist is generally able to decide at the outset that, of a multitude of possible answers, so and so many are unlikely answers. His knowledge of the field, his past experience, and the experience of others working on related problems normally allow him to reduce the many possibilities to a few likelihoods.

This is also the place where hunches, intuitions, and lucky accidents aid science enormously. In one famous case, so the story has it, the German chemist Kekulé went to bed one night after a fairly alcoholic party and dreamed of six monkeys chasing one another in a circle, the tail of one held in the teeth of the other. Practically our whole chemical industry is based on that dream, for it told the sleeping scientist what the long-sought structure of benzene was—as we now know, six carbon atoms "chasing" one another in a circle. And benzene is the fundamental parent substance for thousands of chemical products.

The ideal situation for which the scientist generally strives is to reduce his problem to just two distinct alternative possibilities, one of which, when tested by experiment, may then be answered with a clear "yes," the other with a clear "no." It is exceedingly difficult to streamline problems in this way, and with many it cannot be done. Very often the answer obtained is "maybe." However, if a clear yes or no does emerge, scientists speak of an elegant piece of work, and such performances often are milestones in science.

EXPERIMENT

Experimentation is the fourth step in the scientific method. At this point, science and nonscience finally and completely part company.

Most people observe, ask questions, and also guess at answers. But the layman stops here: "My answer is so logical, so reasonable, and it sounds so 'right' that it must be correct." The listener considers the argument, finds that it is indeed logical and reasonable, and is convinced. He then goes out and in his turn converts others. Before long, the whole world rejoices that it has the answer.

Now the small, killjoy voice of the scientist is heard in the background: "Where is the evidence?" Under such conditions in history, it has often been easier and more convenient to eradicate the scientist than to eradicate an emotionally fixed public opinion. But doing away with the scientist does not alter the fact that answers without evidence are at best unsupported opinions, at worst wishful thinking and fanatical illusions. Experimentation can provide the necessary evidence, and whosoever then experiments after guessing at answers becomes truly "scientific" in his approach, be he a professional scientist or not.

On the other hand, experiments do not guarantee a scientific conclusion. For there is ample room within experimentation and in succeeding steps to become unscientific again.

Experimentation is by far the hardest part of scientific procedure. There are no rules to follow; each experiment is a case unto itself. Knowledge and experience usually help technically, but to design the experiment, to decide on the means by which a hypothesis might best be tested, that separates the genius from the dilettante. The following example will illustrate the point:

Suppose you observe that a chemical substance X, which has accidentally spilled into a culture dish full of certain disease-causing bacteria, kills all the bacteria in that dish. Problem: Can drug X be used to protect human beings against these disease-causing bacteria? Hypothesis: yes. Experiment: You go to a hospital and find a patient with the particular bacterial disease and inject some of the drug into the patient.

Possible result 1: Two days later the patient is well. Conclusion: hypothesis confirmed. You proceed to market the drug at high prices. Shortly afterward, users of the drug die by the dozens, and you are tried and convicted for homicide.

Possible result 2: Two days later the patient is dead. Conclusion: The drug is worthless, and you abandon your project. A year later a colleague of yours is awarded the Nobel prize for having discovered a drug X which cures a certain bacterial disease in man—the same drug and the same disease in which you had been interested.

In this example, the so-called experiment was not an experiment at all.

First, no allowance was made for the possibility that people of different age, sex, eating habits, prior medical history, hereditary background, etc., might react differently to the same drug. Obviously, one would have to test the drug on many categories of carefully preselected patients, and there would have to be many patients in each such category. Besides, one would make the tests first on mice, or guinea pigs, or monkeys.

Second, the quantity of drug to be used was not determined. Clearly, a full range of dosages would have to be tested for each different category of patient. We tacitly assume, moreover, that the drug is a pure substance, i.e., that it does not contain traces of other chemicals which might obscure, or interfere with, the results. If impurities are suspected, whole sets of separate experiments would have to be made.

Third, and most importantly, no account was taken of the possibility that your patient might have become well, or have died, in any case, even without your injecting the drug. What is needed here is *experimental control;* for every group of patients injected *with* drug solution, a precisely equal group must be injected with plain solution, *without* the drug. Then, by comparing results in the control and the experimental groups, one can determine whether or not the recovery or death of patients is really attributable to the drug.

Note that every experiment requires at least two parallel tests or sets of tests identical in all respects except one. Of these parallel tests, one is the control series, and it provides a standard of reference for assessing the results of the experimental series. In drug experiments on people, not fewer than about 100,000 to

200,000 test cases, half of them controls, half of them experimentals, would be considered adequate. It should be easy to see why a single test on a single test case may give completely erroneous conclusions. Many repetitions of the same test, under as nearly identical conditions as possible, and at least one control test for each of the experimental tests—these are always prerequisite for any good experiment.

While an actual drug-testing program would be laborious, expensive, and time-consuming, the design of the experiment is nevertheless extremely simple. There are few steps to be gone through, and it is fairly clear what these steps must be. But there are many experiments such that the tests themselves may not take more than an hour or two, although thinking up appropriate, foolproof plans for the tests may have taken several years.

And despite a most ingenious design and a most careful execution, the result may still not be a clear yes or no. In a drug-testing experiment, for example, it is virtually certain that not 100 per cent of the experimental, drug-injected group will recover or 100 per cent of the untreated control group remain sick.

The actual results might be something like 70 per cent recovery in the experimentals and something like 20 per cent recovery in the controls. The experimentals here show that 30 per cent of the patients with that particular disease do not recover despite treatment, and the controls show that 20 per cent of the patients get well even without treatment. Moreover, if 70 out of every 100 experimental patients recover, then 20 out of these 70 were not actually helped by the drug, since, from the control data, they would have recovered even without treatment. Hence the drug is effective in only 70 per cent minus 20 per cent, or 50 per cent, of the cases.

Medically, this may be a major accomplishment, for having the drug is obviously better than not having it. But scientifically, one is confronted with an equivocal "maybe" result. It will probably lead to new research based on the new observation that some people respond to the drug and some do not and to the new problem of why and what can be done about it.

The result of any experiment represents *evidence*. That is, the original guess in answer to a problem is confirmed as correct or is invalidated. If invalidated, a new hypothesis, with new experiments, must be thought up. This is repeated until a hypothesis may be hit upon which can be supported with confirmatory experimental evidence.

As with legal evidence, scientific evidence can be strong and convincing, or merely suggestive, or poor. In any case, nothing has been proved. Depending on the strength of the evidence, one merely has a basis for regarding the original hypothesis with a certain degree of confidence.

Our new drug, for example, may be just what we claim it to be when we use it in this country. In another part of the world it might not work at all or it might work better. All we can confidently say is that our evidence is based on so and so many experiments with American patients, American bacteria, and American drugs and that under specified hospital conditions, with proper allowance for unspotted errors, the drug has an effectiveness of 50 per cent. Experimental results are never better or broader than the experiments themselves.

This is where many who have been properly scientific up to this point become unscientific. Their claims exceed the evidence; they mistake their partial answer for the whole answer; they contend to have proof for a fact, while all they actually have is some evidence for a hypothesis. There is always room for more and better evidence, or for new contradictory evidence, or indeed for better hypotheses.

THEORY

Experimental evidence is the basis for the fifth and final step in the scientific method, the formulation of a *theory*.

When a hypothesis has been supported by really convincing evidence, best obtained in many different laboratories and by many independent researchers, and when the total accumulated evidence is unquestionably reliable within carefully specified limits, then a theory may be proposed.

In our drug example, after substantial corroborating evidence has also been obtained from many other test localities, an acceptable theory would be the statement that "in such and such a bacterial disease, drug X is effective in 50 per cent of the cases."

This statement is considerably broader than the experiments on which it is based. Theories always are. The statement implies, for example, that drug X, regardless of who manufactures it, will be 50 per cent effective anywhere in the world, under any conditions, and can be used also for animals other than man.

Direct evidence for these extended implications does not exist. But inasmuch as drug X is already known to work within certain limits, the theory expresses the belief, the *probability*, that it may also work within certain wider limits.

To that extent every good theory has *predictive* value. It prophesies certain results. In contrast to nonscientific prophecies, scientific ones always have a substantial body of evidence to back them up. Moreover, the scientific prophecy does not say that something will certainly happen, but says only that something is *likely* to happen with a stated degree of probability.

A few theories have proved to be so universally valid and to have such a high degree of probability that they are spoken of as *natural laws*. For example, no exception has ever been found to the observation that an apple, if disconnected from a tree and not otherwise supported, will fall to the ground. A law of gravitation is based on such observations.

Yet even laws do not pronounce certainties. For all practical purposes, it may well be irrational to assume that some day an apple will rise from a tree, yet there simply is no evidence that can absolutely guarantee the future. Evidence can be used only to estimate probabilities.

Most theories actually have rather brief life spans. For example, if, in chickens, our drug X should be found to perform not with 50 per cent but with 80 per cent efficiency, then our original theory becomes untenable and obsolete. And the exception to the theory becomes a new observation, beginning a new cycle of scientific procedure.

Thus new research might show that chickens contain a natural booster substance in their blood which materially bolsters the action of the drug. This might lead to isolation, identification, and mass production of the booster substance, hence to worldwide improvement in curing the bacterial disease. And we would also have a new theory of drug action, based on the new evidence.

Thus science is never finished. One theory predicts, holds up well for a time, exceptions are found, and a new, more inclusive theory takes over—for a while. We may note in passing that old theories do not become incorrect but merely become obsolete. Development of a new airplane does not mean that earlier planes can no longer fly. New theories, like new airplanes, merely range farther and serve more efficiently than earlier ones, but the latter still serve for their original purposes. Science is steady progression, not sudden revolution.

Clearly, knowledge of the scientific method does not by itself make a good scientist, any more than knowledge of English grammar alone makes a Shakespeare. At the same time, the demands of the scientific method should make it evident that scientists cannot be the cold, inhuman precision machines they are so often, and so erroneously, pictured to be. Scientists are essentially artists, and they require a sensitivity of eye and of mind as great as that of any master painter, and an imagination and keen inventiveness as powerful as that of any master poet.

The limitations of science

Observing, problem-posing, hypothesizing, experimenting, and theorizing—this sequence of procedural steps is both the beginning and the end of science. To determine what science means in wider contexts, we must examine what scientific method implies and, more especially, what it does not imply.

THE SCIENTIFIC DOMAIN

First, scientific method defines the domain of science: *Anything to which the scientific method can be applied, now or in the future, is or will be science; anything to which the method cannot be applied is not science.*

This helps to clarify many a controversial issue. For example, does science have something to say about the concept of God? To determine this, we must find out if we can apply the scientific method.

Inasmuch as the whole universe and everything in it may be argued to be God's work, one may also argue that He is observable. It is possible, furthermore, to pose any number of problems, such as "Does He exist; is the universe indeed His doing?" and "Is He present everywhere and in everything?" One can also hypothesize; some might say "yes," some might say "no."

Can we design an experiment about God? To be reliable, we would need experimental control, i.e., two otherwise identical situations, one with God and one without. Now, what we wish to test is the hypothesis that God exists and is universal, i.e., that He is everywhere. Being a hypothesis thus far, this could be right or wrong.

If right, He would exist and exist everywhere; hence He would be present in *every* test we could possibly make. Thus we would never be able to devise a situation in which God is not present. But we need such a situation in order to have a controlled experiment.

But if the hypothesis is wrong, He would not exist, hence would be absent from every test we could possibly make. Therefore, we would never be able to devise a situation in which God *is* present. Yet we would need such a situation for a controlled experiment.

Right or wrong, our hypothesis is untestable either way, since we cannot run a controlled experiment. Hence we cannot apply the scientific method. The point is that the concept of God is outside the domain of science, and science cannot legitimately say anything about Him. He cannot be tested by science, because its method is inapplicable.

It should be carefully noted that this is a far cry from saying "Science disproves God," or "scientists must be godless; their method demands it." Nothing of the sort. Science specifically leaves anyone perfectly free to believe in any god whatsoever or in none. Many first-rate scientists are priests; many others are agnostics.

Science commits you to nothing more, and to nothing less, than adherence to the scientific method.

Such adherence, it may be noted, is a matter of faith, just as belief in God or confidence in the telephone directory is a matter of faith. Whatever other faiths they may or may not hold, all scientists certainly have strong faith in the scientific method. So do those laymen who feel that having electric lights and not having bubonic plague are good things.

THE SCIENTIFIC AIM

A second consequence of the scientific method is that it defines the aim and purpose of science: *The objective of science is to make and to use theories.*

Many would say that the objective of science is to discover truth, to find out facts. We must be very careful here about the meaning of words. "Truth" is popularly used in two senses. It may indicate a temporary correctness, as in saying "It is true that my hair is brown." Or it may indicate an absolute, eternal correctness, as in saying "In plane geometry, the sum of the angles in a triangle is 180°."

From the earlier discussion on the nature of scientific method, it should be clear that science cannot deal with truth of the absolute variety. Something absolute is finished, known completely, once and for all. But science is never finished. Its method is unable to determine the absolute. Besides, once something is already known absolutely, there is no further requirement for science, since nothing further needs to be found out. Science can only adduce evidence for temporary truths, and another term for "temporary truth" is "theory." Because the word "truth," if not laboriously qualified, is ambiguous, scientists try not to use it at all.

The words "fact" and "proof" have a similar drawback. Both may indicate either something absolute or something temporary. If absolute, they are not science; if temporary, we have the less ambiguous word "evidence." Thus, science is content to find evidence for theories, and it leaves truths, proofs, and facts to others.

Speaking of words, "theorizing" is often popularly taken to mean "just talk and speculation." Consider, however, how successfully theorizing builds bridges!

SCIENCE AND VALUES

A third important implication of the scientific method is that *it does not make value judgments or moral decisions.*

It is the user of scientific results who may place valuations on them. But the results by themselves do not carry built-in values. And nowhere in the scientific method is there a value-revealing step.

The consequences of this are vast. For example, the science which produced the atomic bomb and penicillin cannot, of itself, tell whether these products are good things or bad things. Every man must determine that for himself as best he can. The scientist who discusses the moral aspects of nuclear weapons can make weightier statements than a layman only in so far as he may know more about what damage such weapons may or may not do. This will certainly influence his opinions. But whatever opinion he gives, it will be a purely personal evaluation made as a citizen, and any other scientist—or layman—who is equally well informed about the capacities of the weapons may conceivably disagree completely. Human values are involved here; science is not.

In all other types of evaluations as well, science is silent and noncommittal. Beauty, love, evil, happiness, virtue, justice, liberty, property, financial worth, all these are human values which science cannot peg. To be sure, love, for example, might well be a subject of scientific research, and research might show much about what love is and how it works. But such research could never discover that love is wonderful, an evaluation clear to anyone who has done a certain amount of nonscientific research.

It also follows that it would be folly to strive for a strictly "scientific" way of life or to expect strictly "scientific" government. Certainly the role of science might profitably be enlarged in areas of personal and public life where science can make a legitimate contribution. But a completely scientific civilization, adhering strictly to the rules of the scientific method, could never tell, for example, whether it is right or wrong to commit murder, or whether it is good or bad to love one's neighbor. Science cannot and does not give such answers. To be sure, this does not imply that science does away with morals. It merely implies that science cannot determine whether or not one ought to have moral standards, or what particular set of moral standards one ought to live by.

THE SCIENTIFIC PHILOSOPHY

A fourth and most important consequence of the scientific method is that it determines the philosophical foundation on which scientific pursuits must be based.

Inasmuch as the domain of science is the whole material universe, science must inquire into the nature of the forces which govern the universe and all happenings in it. What makes given events in the universe take place? What determines which event out of several possible ones will occur? And what controls or guides the course of any event to a particular conclusion?

Questions of this kind seek to discover the "prime mover" of the universe. As such they are actually philosophic questions of concern not only in science but in all other areas of human thought as well. Depending on how man answers such questions, he will adopt a particular philosophy of nature and this philosophy will then guide him in his various undertakings. Scientific man too must try to find answers, and we already know the framework within which the scientific answers must be given: to be useful in science, any statement about the universe or its parts must be consistent with the procedure of the scientific method. Therefore, if a given philosophy of nature can be verified wholly or even partly through experimental analysis, it will be valuable scientifically. But a philosophy which cannot be so verified will be without value in science, even though it may well be valuable in other areas of human thought.

Vitalism versus mechanism.   In the course of history, two major answers have been proposed regarding the governing forces of the universe. These answers are incorporated in two systems of philosophy called *vitalism* and *mechanism*.

Vitalism is the doctrine of the supernatural. It holds, essentially, that the universe and all happenings in it are controlled by supernatural powers. Such powers have been variously called gods, spirits, or simply "vital forces." Their influence is held to determine the nature and guide the behavior of atoms, planets, stars, living things, and indeed all components of the universe. Clearly, most religious philosophies are vitalistic ones.

Whatever value a vitalistic philosophy might have elsewhere, it cannot have value in science. This is because the supernatural is by definition beyond reach of the natural. Inasmuch as the scientific method is a wholly natural procedure, it cannot be used for an investigation of the supernatural. We have already noted earlier, for example, that science cannot prove or disprove anything about God. Any other vitalistic conception is similarly untestable by experiment and is therefore unusable as a *scientific* philosophy of nature.

A philosophy which *is* usable in science is that of mechanism. In the mechanistic view, the prime mover of the universe is a set of natural laws, i.e., the laws of physics and chemistry. Experiments carried out in the course of several centuries have shown what some of these laws are, and any happening in the universe is held to be governed by the laws. The foundation of mechanism is therefore natural rather than supernatural and is amenable to experimental analysis.

On the basis of the total experimental experience, the mechanistic philosophy holds that if all physical and chemical phenomena in the universe can be accounted for, no other phenomena will remain. Therefore, the controlling agent of the material in the universe must reside within the material itself. Moreover, it must consist of physical and chemical events *only*. As a further consequence, the particular course of any happening must be guided automatically, by the way in which the natural laws permit physical and chemical events to occur within given materials. Note that biological materials are included here; life too must be a result of physical and chemical events *only*. The course of life must be automatically self-determined by the physical and chemical events occurring within living matter.

Clearly, these differences between vitalism and mechanism point up a conceptual conflict between religion and science. But note that the conflict is not necessarily irreconcilable. To bridge the conceptual gap between the two philosophies, one might ask how the natural laws of the universe came into being to begin with. A possible answer is that they were created by God. In this view, the universe ran vitalistically up to the time that natural laws were created and ran mechanistically thereafter. The mechanist must then admit the existence of a supernatural Creator at the beginning of time (even though he has no *scientific* basis for either affirming or denying this; mechanism cannot, by definition, tell anything about a time at which natural laws might not have been in operation). Correspondingly, the vitalist must admit that any direct influence of God over the universe must have ceased once His natural laws were in operation. These laws would run the universe adequately, and further supernatural control would therefore not be necessary (or demonstrable, so long as the natural laws continued to operate without change).

Thus it is not necessarily illogical to hold both scientific and religious philosophies at the same time. However, it is decidedly illogical to try to use vitalistic ideas as explanations of scientific problems. Correct science does demand that supernatural concepts be kept out of natural events, i.e., those which can be investigated by means of the scientific method. However much a vitalist he might be in his nonscientific thinking, man in his scientific thinking must be a mechanist. And if he is not, he ceases to be scientific.

Many people, some scientists included, actually find it exceedingly difficult to keep vitalism out of science. Biological events, undoubtedly the most complex of all known events in the universe, have in the past been particularly subject to attempts at vitalistic interpretation. How, it has been asked, can the beauty of a flower ever be understood simply as a series of physical and chemical events? How can an egg, transforming itself into a baby, be nothing more than a "mechanism" like a clock? And how can a man, who thinks and experiences visions of God, be conceivably regarded as nothing more than a piece of "machinery"? Mechanism *must* be inadequate as an explanation of life, it has been argued, and only something supernatural superimposed on the machine, some vital force, is likely to account for the fire of life.

In such replacements of mechanistic with mystical thought, the connotations of words often play a supporting role. For example, the words "mechanism" and "machine" usually bring to mind images of crude iron engines or clockworks. Such analogies tend to reinforce the suspicion of vitalists that those who regard living things as mere machinery must be simpleminded indeed. Consider, however, that the machines of today also include electronic computers which can learn, translate languages, compose music, play chess, make decisions, and improve their performance of such activities as they gather experience. In addition, theoretical knowledge now available would permit us to build a machine which could heal itself when injured and which could feed, sense, reproduce, and even evolve. Clearly, the term "mechanism" is not at all limited to crude, stupidly "mechanical" engines. And there is certainly nothing inherently simple-minded or reprehensible in the idea that living things are exquisitely complicated chemical mechanisms, some of which even have the capacity to think and to have visions of God.

On the contrary, if it could be shown that such a mechanistic view is at all justified, it would represent an enormous advance in our understanding of nature. In all the centuries of recorded history, vitalism in its various forms has hardly progressed beyond the mere initial assertion that living things are animated by supernatural forces. Just how such forces are presumed to do the animating has not been explained, nor have programs of inquiry been offered to find explanations. Actually, such inquiries are ruled out by definition, since natural man can never hope to fathom the supernatural. In the face of this closed door, mechanism provides the only way out for the curious. But is it justifiable to regard living things as pure mechanisms, even complicated chemical ones?

Notwithstanding the doubts expressed by some, a mechanistic interpretation of life is entirely justifiable and interjection of touches of vitalism is entirely unjustifiable. Science today *can* account for living properties in purely mechanistic terms. Moreover, biologists are well on their way to being able to create a truly living entity "in the test tube," solely by means of physical and chemical procedures obeying known natural laws. We shall discuss some of the requirements for such laboratory creation in the course of this book. Evidently, vitalistic "aids" to explain the mechanistic universe are not only unjustifiable but also unnecessary.

It may be noted in this connection that, historically, vitalism has tended to fill the gaps left by incomplete scientific knowledge. Early man was a complete vitalist, who for want of better knowledge regarded even inanimate objects as "animated" by supernatural spirits. As scientific insight later increased, progressively more of the universe ceased to be in the domain of the supernatural. Thus it happened repeatedly that phenomena originally thought to be supernatural were later shown to be explainable naturally. So it has been with living phenomena as well. And those today who may still be prompted to fill gaps in scientific knowledge with vitalism must be prepared to have red faces tomorrow. Incidentally, it might also be pointed out in passing that even confirmed vitalists find it prudent on occasion to become ardent believers in mechanism, whether they realize it or not. For example, few vitalists hesitate to accept the mechanistic administrations of a physician at the first signs of disorder in their "machinery."

We conclude that a mechanistic view of nature is one component of the philosophic attitude required in science. A second component may now be considered.

Teleology versus causalism. Even a casual observer must be impressed by the apparent nonrandomness of natural events. Every part of nature seems to follow a plan, and there is a distinct directedness to any given process. Living processes provide excellent instances of this. For example, developing eggs behave as if they knew exactly what the plan of the adult is to be. A chicken egg soon develops into an embryo with two wings and two legs, *as if* there existed a blueprint which specified that adult chickens should have two wings and two legs each. Moreover, since virtually all chicken eggs undergo the same course of growth, the impression of plan in development becomes reinforced strongly; one is led to conclude that the various parts of a chicken are there not just by random coincidence. Similarly, an earthworm which has been decapitated grows a new head, *as if* there were a plan which specified that every earthworm should have a head—not another tail and not two heads either, but one head.

All known natural processes, biological or otherwise, thus start at given beginnings and proceed to particular endpoints. This observation poses a philosophical problem: how is a starting condition directed toward a given terminal condition; how does a starting point appear to "know" what the endpoint is to be?

It will be noted that such questions have to do with a specific aspect of the more general problem of the controlling agents of the universe. We should expect, therefore, that two sets of answers would be available, one vitalistic and the other mechanistic. This is the case. In view of the discussion in the preceding section, a book of science such as this could properly disregard the vitalistic answers as inadmissible from the outset and proceed at once with an outline of the mechanistic position. It is nevertheless advisable to examine both positions, partly because such a procedure adds to an understanding of the nature and limitations of science, partly because it is important to be able to recognize vitalistic answers if and when they occur (as they occasionally still do) in what is supposed to be scientific thought.

According to vitalistic doctrines, natural events *appear* to be planned because they *are* planned. A supernatural "divine plan" is held to fix the fate of every part of the universe, and all events in nature, past, present, and future, are programmed in this plan. All nature is therefore directed toward a preordained goal, namely, the fulfillment of the divine plan. As a consequence, nothing happens by chance, but everything happens on purpose.

Being a vitalistic, experimentally untestable conception, the notion of purpose in natural events has no place in science. Does the universe exist for a purpose? Does man live for a purpose? You cannot hope for an answer from science, for science is not designed to tackle such questions. Moreover, if you already hold certain beliefs in these areas, you cannot expect science either to prove or to disprove them for you.

Yet many arguments have been attempted to show purpose from science. For example, it has been maintained by some that the whole purpose of the evolution of living things was to produce man. Here the evidence supporting the theory of evolution is invoked to prove that man was the predetermined goal from the very beginning.

This implies several things besides the conceit that man is the finest product of creation. It implies, for example, that nothing could ever come after man, for he is supposed to be the last word in living magnificence. As a matter of record, man is sorely plagued by an army of parasites which cannot live anywhere except inside people. And it is clear that you cannot have a man-requiring parasite before you have a man.

Many human parasites did evolve after man. Thus, the purpose argument would at best show that the whole purpose of evolution was to produce those living organisms which cause influenza, diphtheria, gonorrhea, and syphilis. This even the most ardent purpose arguer would probably not care to maintain.

If one is so inclined, he is of course perfectly free to believe that man is the pinnacle of it all. Then the rest of the universe with it billions of suns, including the living worlds which probably circle some of them, presumably are merely immense and fancy scenery for the microscopic stage on which man struts about. One may believe this, to be sure, but one cannot maintain that such beliefs are justified by evidence from science.

The essential point is that any purpose-implying argument, in this or in any other issue, stands on quicksand the moment science is invoked as a witness; for to say such and such is the goal, the ultimate purpose, is to state a belief and not a body of evidence adduced through the scientific method. Nowhere does this method include any purpose-revealing step.

The form of argumentation which takes recourse to purposes and supernatural planning is generally called *teleology*. In one system of teleology, the preordained plan exists outside natural objects, in an external Deity, for example. In another system, the plan resides within objects themselves. According to this view, a starting condition of an event proceeds toward a specific end condition because the starting object has built into it actual foreknowledge of what the end condition is to be. For example, the egg develops toward the goal of the adult because the egg *knows* what the adult state is to be. Similarly, evolution has occurred as it has because the participating starting chemicals had foreknowledge that the end should be man. Clearly, this and all other forms of teleology "explain" an end state by simply asserting it given at the beginning. And in thereby putting the future into the past, the effect before the cause, teleology negates time.

The scientifically useful alternative to teleology is called *causalism*. It has its foundations in mechanistic philosophy. Causalism denies foreknowledge of terminal states, preordination, purposes, goals, and fixed fates. It holds that natural events take place *sequentially*. Events occur only as other events *permit* them to occur, not as preordained goals or purposes make them occur. End states are consequences, not foregone conclusions, of beginning states. A headless earthworm regenerates a new head because conditions within the headless worm are such that only a head—*one* head— can develop. It becomes the task of the biologist to find out what these conditions are and to see if, by changing the conditions, two heads or another tail could not be produced. Scientists actually *can* obtain different end states by changing the conditions of initial states, and the idea of predetermined goals loses all validity in scientific thought.

(Care must therefore be taken in scientific endeavors not to fall unwittingly into the teleological trap. Consider often-heard statements such as: "the *purpose* of the heart is to pump blood"; "the ancestors of birds evolved wings *so that* they could fly"; "eggs have yolk *in order to* provide food for development." The last statement, for example, implies that eggs can "foresee" the nutritional problem in development and that food will be required; therefore, they proceed to store up some. In effect, eggs are given human mentality. The teleologist is always anthropocentric, that is, he implies that the natural events he discusses have minds like his. Substitute "and" for every "so that" or "in order to" and "function" for every "purpose" in biological statements and they become properly nonteleological.)

Clearly then, science in its present state of development must operate within carefully specified, self-imposed limits. The basic philosophic attitude must be mechanistic and causalistic, and we note that the results obtained through science are inherently without truth, without value, and without purpose.

But it is precisely because science is limited in this fashion that it advances. After centuries of earnest deliberation, mankind still does not agree on what truth is, values still change with the times and with places, and purposes remain as unfathomed as ever. On such shifting sands it has proved difficult to build a knowledge of nature. What little of nature we really know and are likely to know in the foreseeable future stands on the bedrock of science and its powerful tool, the scientific method.

The language of science

SCIENCE AS A WHOLE

Fundamentally, science is a *language*, a system of communication. Religion, art, politics, English, and French are among other such languages. Like them,

science enables man to travel into new countries of the mind and to understand and be understood in such countries. Like other languages, science too has its grammar—the scientific method; its authors and its literature—the scientists and their written work; and its various dialects or forms of expression—physics, chemistry, biology, etc.

Indeed, science is one of the few truly universal languages, understood all over the globe. Art, religion, and politics are also universal. But each of these languages has several forms, so that Baptists and Hindus, for example, have little in common either religiously, artistically, or politically. Science, however, has the same single form everywhere, and Baptists and Hindus do speak the same scientific language.

It should be clear that no one language is "truer" or "righter" than any other. There are only *different* languages, each serving its function in its own domain. Many an idea is an idiom of a specific language and is best expressed in that language. For example, the German "Kindergarten" has been imported as is into English and the American "baseball" has gone into the world without change. Likewise, one cannot discuss morality in the language of science, or thermodynamics in the language of religion, or artistic beauty in the language of politics; to the extent that each system of communication has specific idioms, there is no overlap or interchangeability among the systems.

On the other hand, many ideas can be expressed equally well in several languages. The English "water," the Latin "aqua," and the scientific "H_2O" are entirely equivalent, and no one of these is truer or righter than the others. They are merely different. Similarly, in one language man was created by God; in another man is a result of chance reactions among chemicals and of evolution. Again, neither the scientific nor the religious interpretation is the truer. If the theologian argues that everything was made by God, including scientists who think that man is the result of chance chemical reactions, then the scientist will argue back that chance chemical reactions created men with brains, including those theological brains which can conceive of a God who made everything. The impasse is permanent, and within their own systems of communication the scientist and the theologian are equally right. Many, of course, assume without warrant that it is the compelling duty of science to prove or disprove religious matters, and of religion, to prove or to disprove scientific matters.

The point is that there is no single "correct" formulation of any idea which spans various languages. There are only *different* formulations, and in given circumstances one or the other may be more useful, more satisfying, or more effective. Clearly, he who is adept in more than one language will be able to travel that much more widely and will be able to feel at ease in the company of more than one set of ideas.

We are, it appears, forever committed to multiple standards, according to the different systems of communication we use. But we have been in such a state all along, in many different ways. Thus, the color red means one thing politically, something else in a fall landscape, and is judged by a third standard in the fashion world. Or consider the different worth of the same dime to a child, to you, and to the United States Treasury. To be multilingual in his interpretation of the world has been the unique heritage of man from the beginning. Different proportions of the various languages may be mixed into the outlook of different individuals, but science, religion, art, politics, spoken language, all these and many more besides are always needed to make a full life.

BIOLOGY

Within the language of science, biology is an important dialect, permitting travel in the domain of *living things*. Man probably was a biologist before he was anything else. His own body in health and disease; the phenomena of birth, growth, and death; and the plants and other animals which gave him food, shelter, and clothing undoubtedly were matters of serious concern to even the first of his kind. The motives were sheer necessity and the requirements of survival. These same motives still prompt the same biological studies today; agriculture, medicine, and fields allied to them are the most important branches of modern applied biology. In addition, biology today is strongly experimental, and pure research is done extensively all over the world. Some of this research promotes biological technology; all of it increases our understanding of how living things are constructed and how they operate.

Over the decades, the frontiers of biological investigations have been pushed into smaller and smaller realms. Some 100 to 150 years ago, when modern biology began, the chief interest was the whole plant or the whole animal, how it lived, where it could be found, and how it was related to other whole living things. Such studies have been carried on ever since, but in addition, techniques gradually became available for the investigation of progressively smaller parts of the whole, their structures, their functions, and their relationships to one another. Thus it happened that during the past few decades, the frontiers of biology were pushed down to the chemical level. And while research with larger biological units continues as before, the newest biology attempts to interpret living operations in terms of the chemicals which compose living creatures.

Biology here merges with chemistry. Today there are already many signs that the next frontier will be the atoms which in their turn compose the chemicals, and biology tomorrow will undoubtedly merge with atomic physics. Such a trend is quite natural. Ultimately, living things are atomic things; penultimately, they are chemical things; and only on a large scale are they plants and animals. In the last analysis, therefore, biology must attempt to show how atoms and chemicals made out of atoms are put together to form, on the one hand, something like a rock or a piece of metal and, on the other, something like a flower or a human baby.

This book is an outline of how successful the attempt has been thus far.

Review questions

1. What are the aims and the limitations of science? Review fully. In what sense is science a language, and how does it differ from other, similar languages?

2. What characterizes the different present-day forms of science and the different specializations of scientists?

3. Review the steps of the scientific method and dis-

cuss the nature of each of these steps. Define controlled experiment.

4. How would you show by controlled experiment:

a. Whether or not temperature affects the rate of growth of living things?

b. Whether or not houseflies can perceive differently colored objects?

c. Whether or not plants use up some of the soil they grow in?

5. Suppose that it were found in question *4a* that, at an environmental temperature of 28°C, the growth of fertilized frog eggs into tadpoles occurs roughly twice as fast as at 18°C. What kinds of theories could such evidence suggest?

6. What are the historical and the modern relations of science and religion? Which of the ideas you have previously held about science should you now, after studying this chapter, regard as popular misconceptions?

7. Can you think of observations or problems which so far have not been investigated scientifically? Try to determine in each case whether or not such investigation is inherently possible. Why is mathematics not considered to be a science?

8. Describe the philosophic foundations of science. Define mechanism and causalism and contrast these systems of thought with those of vitalism and teleology. Can conceptual conflicts between science and religion be reconciled?

9. Consider the legal phrases "Do you swear to tell the truth and nothing but the truth?" and "Is it not a fact that on the night of . . .?" If phrases of this sort were to be used in a strictly scientific context, how should they properly be formulated?

10. Biology is called one of the *natural sciences*, all of which deal with the composition, properties, and behavior of matter in the universe. Which other sciences are customarily regarded as belonging to this category, and what distinguishes them from one another and from biology? What are *social sciences*? Do they too operate by the scientific method?

Suggested collateral readings

Beveridge, W. I. B.: "The Art of Scientific Investigation," Norton, New York, 1957.

Butterfield, H.: The Scientific Revolution, *Sci. Am.*, vol. 203, 1960.

Conant, J. B.: "On Understanding Science," Yale, New Haven, Conn., 1947.

————: "Science and Common Sense," Yale, New Haven, Conn., 1951.

————: "Modern Science and Modern Man," Columbia, New York, 1952.

Terman, L. M.: Are Scientists Different? *Sci. Am.*, vol. 192, 1955.

part **1**

The Basis of Life

In studying living things, it is well to find out at the start what a living thing is. In this set of chapters, therefore, we first examine the *nature* of life and look for the meaning of the term "living." We then examine the *chemical basis* of life, to determine what a living thing is ultimately made of. And lastly we examine the historical *origin* of life, to give us some understanding of how living things may have come into being.

THE NATURE OF LIFE

2

Life is an attribute of *organisms*, or individual living creatures. What does being "alive" actually mean? For example, what distinguishes a living organism from a dead one? The most obvious difference surely is that a living organism does certain things the dead one does not do. We may therefore conclude that the essence of "living" lies in characteristic activities, or processes, or *functions*.

What then is the difference between organisms, either living or dead, and inanimate objects like stones? Clearly, organisms are put together in such a way that the functions of life are or once were actually possible, whereas inanimate things are constructed in a way which makes living functions inherently impossible. Accordingly, the essence of "organism" lies in characteristic building materials and building patterns, or *structures*.

A living organism thus is what it is by virtue of its particular functions and its particular structures. The aim of this chapter is to identify these life-defining functions and structures.

Function and life

One of the principal activities of living organisms is *nutrition,* a process which provides the raw materials for maintenance of life. All living matter has an unceasing requirement for such raw materials, for the very act of living continuously uses up two basic commodities: energy and matter. In this respect a living organism is like a mechanical engine or indeed like any other action-performing system in the universe. Energy is needed to power the system, to make the parts operate, to keep activity going—in short, to maintain function. And matter is needed to replace parts, to repair breakdowns, to continue the system intact and able to function—in short, to maintain structure. Therefore, by its very nature as an action-performing unit, a "living" organism can remain alive only if it continuously expends energy and matter. These commodities must be replenished from the outside at least as fast as they are used up inside, and the replenishment function is nutrition.

The nutritional raw materials are *nutrients.* They are available in the general environment of the earth, partly in the physical environment of air, water, and land, partly in the biological environment of other organisms, living or dead. The role of nutrition is to transfer the required kinds and amounts of nutrients from the external environment into the living organism. As we shall see, different ways exist in which such nutritional transfers can be accomplished. Note generally that, as nutrition permits continuation of life, so life also permits continuation of nutrition; nourished living matter must already preexist if its further nutrition is to be possible.

As just noted, one of the basic roles of nutrients within a living organism is to supply energy. Nutrients are chemicals, and as such they contain chemical energy. Why this is so will become clear in the next chapter. For the present we need note only that all living matter runs on the chemical energy obtained from nutrients. How do nutrients actually supply energy? If chemicals are decomposed, that is, broken into smaller fragments, then the energy originally stored in the chemicals can be released. Many familiar engines operate on this principle. In a gasoline or steam engine, for example, fuel is burned, that is, the chemical structure of the fuel is decomposed. The burning process releases energy and this energy then drives the motor. The living "motor" is quite similar. First, nutrients function like fuels (and indeed nutrients and engine fuels are related chemically in very basic respects). Second, nutrients are decomposed in a way which is actually a form of burning. And third, the energy obtained through nutrient decomposition drives the living "machine."

In living organisms, the process of energy procurement through decomposition of nutrients is called *respiration.* It constitutes a second major activity of living matter and it is the basic power-generating process which maintains *all* living functions. Note that this includes nutrition and even respiration itself. Nutritional activities can be sustained only with the aid of respiratory energy, but respiration in turn depends on the fuel-providing process of nutrition. Moreover, respiration is itself an activity of life and thus must be sustained by respiration. In other words, energy made available by previous respiration is required to make further respiration possible.

The second basic role of nutrients is to serve as construction materials. The whole structure of the living organism must be built from and kept intact with nutrient "bricks." Thus the stuff which forms living matter is fundamentally the same as that which forms nutrients. This consideration leads to an interesting inference. If nutrients and living matter are basically equivalent and if nutrients are also respiratory fuels, is should follow that living matter should be able to use *itself* as fuel. This is indeed the case; all living matter is inherently self-decomposing and self-consuming. In this respect a living organism may be likened to an engine which is built out of steel and in which steel is also the fuel. As such an engine runs it burns up not only fuel supplied from the outside but also its own substance; the motor cannot tell the difference between external fuel and internal structural parts, because both are fundamentally the same. Such an engine would be quite unstable structurally and in fact would burn itself up very quickly. A living organism is similarly unstable structurally, but unlike a machine it counteracts this instability with the aid of nutrients. New structural parts are manufactured continually out of nutrients and the new parts replace those which burn away. Put another way, the structural damage resulting from the unceasing respiratory self-consumption is offset by an equally unceasing self-repair.

Respiration actually is not the only circumstance necessitating the use of nutrients as construction materials. For example, living matter frequently sustains structural damage through injuries from accidents and disease. Parts of the living structure also rub off, evaporate, and dissipate in other ways. Clearly, the structural *wear and tear* resulting unavoidably from the very activities of living has many forms and causes, and uninterrupted reconstruction must offset this wear and tear if the living structure is to persist. We note that living matter is never the same from moment to moment. As wear and tear and reconstruction occur side by side, the substance of living matter always "turns over"; although the basic structural pattern remains the same, every bit of the building material is replaced sooner or later. Moreover, if new building materials accumulate faster than old building materials wear away, the living organism will *grow*. Growth is a characteristic outcome of the use of nutrients in the construction of living matter.

The processes by which nutrients are fashioned into new structural parts of organisms may be referred to collectively as *synthesis* activities. They represent a third basic function of all living things. Like other functions of life, synthesis requires energy, and respiration must provide it. Thus respiration is both the main cause making synthesis necessary and the main means making it possible. In its own turn, synthesis maintains the structural apparatus required for respiration, for nutrition, and indeed for all other life functions as well.

The three functions of nutrition, respiration, and synthesis together constitute a broad living activity known as *metabolism* (Fig. 2.1). Taken as a whole, metabolism may be said to run the machinery of life. By running, the machinery may then carry out continued metabolism. As we have seen, a system which nourishes, respires, and synthesizes is capable of undertaking more nutrition, more respiration, and more synthesis.

But being *capable* of continued activity is not the same as *actually* continuing the activity. Actual continuation becomes possible only if the activity is *con-*

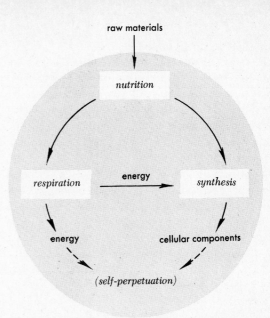

Fig. 2.1. The interrelations of the main processes of metabolism and the main results of metabolism.

trolled. In this respect, living matter is again like an engine. It is not enough that an engine can obtain fuel, can generate energy by burning fuel, and can be repaired. Continuous operation demands that the *rates* of fuel supply, of burning, and of repair be finely geared to one another, and that if one rate changes for some external or internal reason all other rates change appropriately. In other words, the various operations of the engine must remain harmonized internally and must be adjusted and readjusted in line with events that may occur externally. Continuous operation, in short, requires control. Just so, continuation of metabolism in living matter depends on control. Metabolism as such is not equivalent to "life," but *controlled* metabolism in a general sense is.

The necessary control is provided by *self-perpetuation*, a broadly inclusive set of processes. Self-perpetuation ensures that the metabolizing machinery continues to run indefinitely, without outside help, and despite internal and external happenings which might otherwise stop its operation. We may also note that, in carrying out this controlling role, self-perpetuation uses up respiratory energy and the products of synthesis. Controlled metabolism thus is as much a result of self-perpetuation as a prerequisite.

The most direct and immediate regulation of metabolism is brought about by self-perpetuative processes we may collectively call *steady-state controls*. Fundamentally, such controls permit a living organism to receive *information* from within itself and from the external environment and to act on this information in a self-preserving manner. The information is received in the form of *stimuli* and the self-preserving actions are *responses*. For example, with the aid of energy and building materials, steady-state controls may cause the organism to procure fresh nutrients when past supplies are used up; may adjust respiration and synthesis in rate and amount according to given requirements; may channel the energy of respiration into protective responses like movement; and may direct the repair of damaged parts or the construction of additional parts, as in growth. Taken together, such controls therefore preserve *optimum* operating conditions within living matter; they maintain a *steady* state. In this state a living organism may then remain intact and functioning as long as inherently possible.

But span of existence is invariably limited. We know that individual life rarely lasts longer than a century and in most cases actually ceases within a single year. Death is a built-in characteristic of living matter because, like all other parts of the organism, those which maintain steady states are themselves subject to breakdown, to respiratory or accidental destruction, to wear and tear generally. When some of its controls become inoperative for any such reason, the organism suffers *disease*. We may define disease as any structural or functional breakdown of steady-state controls, that is, a temporary *unsteady* state. Other, still intact controls may then initiate self-repair. In time, however, so many controls break down simultaneously that too few remain intact to effect repairs. The organism then is in an irreversibly unsteady state and it must die. In this regard the organism again resembles a machine; even the most carefully serviced apparatus eventually becomes scrap, and the destructive impact of the environment ultimately can never be denied.

But unlike a machine, living matter here outwits the environment. For before it dies, the organism may have brought into play a second major self-perpetua-

tive function, namely, *reproduction*. With the help of energy and raw materials, the living organism has enlarged, and such growth in size subsequently permits subdivision and growth in numbers. Reproduction in a sense anticipates and compensates for unavoidable individual death. Through reproduction over successive generations, the tradition of life may then be *inherited* and carried on indefinitely.

Reproduction implies a still poorly understood capacity of *rejuvenation*. The material out of which the offspring is made is part of the parent, hence is really just as old as the rest of the parent. Yet the one lives and the other dies. Evidently, there is a profound distinction between "old" and "aged." Reproduction also implies the capacity of *development*, for the offspring is almost always not only smaller than the parent but also less nearly complete in form and function.

Reproduction leads us to consider a third major self-perpetuative function, that of *adaptation*. As generation succeeds generation, long-term environmental changes are likely to have their effect on the living succession. In the course of thousands and millions of years, for example, climates may become altered profoundly; ice ages may come and go; mountains, oceans, vast tracts of land may appear and disappear. Moreover, living organisms themselves may in time alter the nature of a locality in major ways. Consequently, two related organisms many reproductive generations apart could find themselves in greatly different environments. And whereas the steady-state controls of the ancestor may have coped effectively with the early environment, these same controls, if inherited unchanged by the descendant, could be overpowered rapidly by the new environment. In the course of reproductive successions, therefore, organisms must change *with* the environment if they are to persist. They actually do change through adaptation. As we shall see later, this self-perpetuative function itself consists of several subfunctions, namely, *sex, heredity,* and *evolution*.

We may note, therefore, that self-perpetuation as a whole encompasses three major control activities (Fig. 2.2). Steady-state controls maintain optimum operating conditions within individual organisms as long as possible. Reproduction ensures a continuing

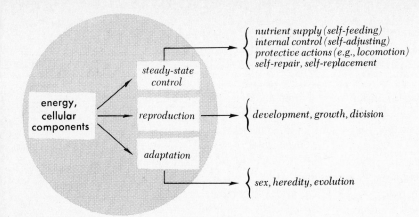

nutrient supply (self-feeding)
internal control (self-adjusting)
protective actions (e.g., locomotion)
self-repair, self-replacement

development, growth, division

sex, heredity, evolution

Fig. 2.2. The interrelations of the main processes of self-perpetuation and the main results of these processes.

succession of individual organisms. And adaptation molds and alters the members of this succession in step with the slowly changing nature of the environment. Self-perpetuation so adds the time dimension to metabolism; regardless of how the environment may change in time, self-perpetuation virtually guarantees the continuation of metabolism. Metabolism in turn makes possible uninterrupted self-perpetuation, and the system so able to metabolize and self-perpetuate can persist indefinitely; it becomes a "living" system.

To define, then, the fundamental meaning of "living," we may say that *any structure which metabolizes and self-perpetuates is alive.* And we may add that *the metabolic functions of nutrition, respiration, and synthesis make possible and are themselves made possible by the self-perpetuative functions of steady-state control, reproduction, and adaptation.*

A first implication of this definition is that, by their very nature, living systems collectively are a highly permanent form of matter, perhaps the most permanent in the universe. They are certainly the most enduring on earth. Every inanimate or dead object on earth sooner or later decomposes and crumbles to dust under the impact of the environment. But every living object metabolizes and self-perpetuates and so may avoid such a fate. We come to realize that living matter, though soft and weak to the touch, is actually far more durable than the strongest steel, far more permanent than the hardest granite. Oceans, mountains, even whole continents have come and gone several times during the last 2 billion years, but living

matter has persisted indestructibly during that time and, indeed, has become progressively more abundant.

A second implication is that any structure which does not satisfy the above definition in every particular is either inanimate or dead. Life must cease if even one of the fundamental functions of metabolism or self-perpetuation ceases; all these functions must be carried out simultaneously and interrelatedly. This criterion of life offers an instructive contrast to the operation of modern machines, many of which perform some of the functions also occurring in living organisms. As noted, for example, a machine may take on "nourishment" in the form of fuel and raw materials. The fuel may be "respired" to provide operating energy, and, with it, the raw materials may then be "synthesized" into nuts, bolts, and other structural components out of which such a machine might be built. If any one of these processes should stop, the machine would cease to operate even though it was still whole and intact.

Evidently, machines may carry out activities fully equivalent to those of metabolism. In view of such counterparts in inanimate nature, metabolism cannot be the special distinguishing feature of living nature. That distinguishing feature must lie, rather, in self-perpetuation. Note however that, like living systems, many "automated" machines have ingenious steady-state controls built into them. For example, such controls may make a machine automatically self-"feeding" and self-adjusting. But no machine is as yet self-protecting, self-repairing, or self-healing to any major extent, and no machine certainly is self-growing. On the other hand, it is known today how, theoretically, such a fully self-controlled, self-preserving machine could be built. If it is ever built, it will have steady-state controls conceivably quite as effective as the ones which have been standard equipment in living organisms for two billion years.

Machines resemble organisms further in that they die after a period of time, that is, enter so unsteady a state that they are beyond repair. But whereas living matter may reproduce before death, machines may not. It is in this capacity of reproduction that living systems differ most critically from inanimate systems. No machine self-reproduces, self-rejuvenates, or self-develops. However, it may be noted once again that the theoretical knowledge of how to build such a machine now exists. A device of this kind would metabolize, maintain steady states, and eventually "die," but it would reproduce before it died. It would be almost living. If it had the additional capacity of adaptation, it would be fully living. And here too the theoretical know-how is already available. On paper we may now design machines which could carry out "sexual" processes of a sort, which could pass on hereditary information to their self-reproduced "offspring," and which could "evolve" and change their properties in the course of many "generations."

Today, of course, such fully self-perpetuating machines do not—yet—exist in actuality. Living matter certainly may counteract the disruptive and destructive effect of the environment far more efficiently than any machine. It is primarily this which puts living objects into one category of matter and machines and all other inanimate objects into another. Nonliving objects are what they are because they cannot perform *all* the functions of metabolism and self-perpetuation. But if the time ever comes when machines *will* be able to carry out all these functions, then the essential distinction between "living" and "machine" will have disappeared.

This consideration brings us to a third implication of the definition above: the property of life basically does not depend on a particular substance. *Any* substance of whatever composition will be "living" provided that it metabolizes and self-perpetuates. It happens that only one such substance is now known. We call it "living matter," or often also *protoplasm*. It has certain clear-cut characteristics of compositions and makeup, as will be shown below, and it is molded into organisms. But if some day we should be able to build a fully metabolizing and self-perpetuating system out of nuts, bolts, and wires, then it too would have to be regarded as being truly alive. Similarly, if some day we should encounter on another planet out in space a metabolizing and self-perpetuating entity made up of hitherto completely unknown materials, it also would have to be considered living. It may not be "life as we know it," that is, life based on the earthly variety of protoplasm, but in any case it will be truly living if it metabolizes and self-perpetuates.

We may conclude, then, that an object is defined as living or nonliving on the basis of its functional properties, not its structural properties. On the other hand, structural properties determine whether an object is an "organism" or something inanimate; by virtue of its structure a chicken is an organism even if it is dead, but a stone is not an organism. Linguistically as well as biologically the root of "organism" is *organization*, a characteristic *structural order*. We shall examine this order in the following section.

Structure and organism

LEVELS OF ORGANIZATION

The smallest structural units of all matter, living matter included, are *subatomic particles*. The next larger units are *atoms*, each of which consists of subatomic particles. Atoms in turn form still larger combinations called *chemical compounds*, and the latter are variously joined together into even larger units, namely, *complexes of compounds*.

We may consider these units to form successively higher *levels of organization of matter*. Such levels form a *hierarchy* in which any given level contains all lower levels as components. Moreover, any given level is also a component of all higher levels. As noted, for example, atoms contain subatomic particles as components and atoms are themselves components of chemical compounds.

Complexes of compounds and all structural levels below them are encountered both in the nonliving and in the living world. In living matter, complexes of compounds often occur as microscopic and submicroscopic bodies called *organelles*. We shall identify some of them and their functions in later chapters. But note here that organelles as such do not qualify as living units. To reach the level of life, we must go beyond complexes of compounds to the next higher structural level, namely, the level of *cells*.

A cell is a specific combination of organelles, a microscopic bit of matter containing all the necessary apparatus for the performance of metabolism and self-perpetuation. A cell thus represents the smallest known structure that can be fully alive. It follows that a living organism must consist of at least one cell. Indeed, *unicellular* organisms probably constitute the majority of living creatures on earth. All other organisms are *multicellular,* each composed of from two up to hundreds of trillions of joined cells.

Several distinct levels of organization may be recognized within multicellular organisms. The simplest multicellular types consist of aggregations of comparatively small numbers of cells. If all such cells are more or less alike, the organism is often referred to as a *colony* of cells. If two or more different groups of cells are present, each such group may be called a *tissue*. Structurally more complex organisms not only contain several tissues, but some of the tissues may also be joined further into one or more units called *organs*. The most complex organisms contain not only many tissues and organs, but groups of organs may also form one or more structural combinations known as *organ systems*. We note that, in terms of structural levels, living organisms exhibit at least five degrees of complexity: the single-celled form, the colonial form, the organism with tissues, the type with organs, and the type with organ systems.

Beyond organisms of all kinds, several still higher levels of life may be distinguished. A few individual organisms of one kind together may make up a *family*. Groups of families of one kind may form a *society*. Groups of families, societies, or simply large numbers of organisms of one kind make up a geographically localized *population*. All populations of the same kind together form a *species*. Different species aggregate into a local *community*. And the sum of all local communities represents the whole living world (Fig. 2.3).

This hierarchial organization of matter into levels permits us to formulate a *structural* definition of life and nonlife. As we have seen, up to the level of the complex of compounds matter is nonliving. At all higher levels matter is living, provided that, at each such level, metabolic and self-perpetuative functions are carried out. To be living, a society, for example, must metabolize and self-perpetuate on its own level, as well as on every subordinate level down to that of the cell.

Moreover, as life is organized by levels, so is death. Structural death occurs when one level is disrupted or decomposed into the next lower. For example, if a tissue is disaggregated into separate cells, the tissue ceases to exist. Structural death of this sort always entails functional death also, that is, disruption of the metabolic and self-perpetuative processes of the affected level. But note that disruption of one level need not necessarily mean disruption of lower levels. If a tissue is decomposed into cells, the cells may carry on as individuals; if a family is disrupted, the member organisms still may survive on their own. On the other hand, death of one level does always entail death of higher levels. If many or all of its tissues are destroyed, the whole organ will be destroyed; if many or all of its families are dismembered, a society may cease to exist. In general, the situation is comparable to a pyramid of cards. Removal of a top card need not affect the rest of the pyramid, but removal of a bottom card usually topples the whole structure. We recognize that neither life nor death is a singular state but is organized and structured into levels.

Note, incidentally, that the hierarchy of levels provides a rough outline of the past history of matter. There is good reason to suspect that the universe as a whole began in the form of subatomic particles, which then aggregated into atoms and formed galaxies, stars, and planets. As will be shown in Chap. 4, the atoms of planets subsequently gave rise to chemical compounds and complexes of compounds. On earth, some of the complexes of compounds eventually produced living matter in the form of cells, and unicellular types later gave rise to multicellular types. Among the latter, colonial types arose first, forms with organ systems last. Considered historically, therefore, matter appears to have become organized progressively, level by level. The presently existing hierarchy is the direct result

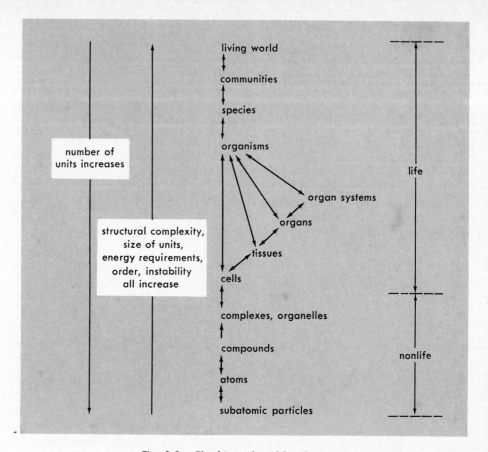

Fig. 2.3. The hierarchy of levels in the organization of matter.

and it still gives mute, built-in testimony of its own historical development.

Several important characteristics inherent in the structural hierarchy may now be pointed out. For example, each level of organization includes fewer units than any lower level. There are fewer communities than species, fewer cells than organelles; and there is only one living world, but there are uncountable numbers of subatomic particles. It should be clear also that each level is structurally more complex than lower ones; a given level combines the complexities of all lower levels and it has an additional complexity of its own. Moreover, each level exhibits new properties over and above those found at lower levels. For example, a cell exhibits the property of life in addition to the various properties of the organelles which compose it;

a multicellular organism with organs such as eyes and brains can see and distinguish objects, whereas its cells taken singly at best can only sense light.

We may note, furthermore, that a jump from one organizational level to the next can be achieved only at the expense of energy. It takes energy to build atoms into chemical compounds and it took energy to create cells out of chemical complexes. Similarly, energy is needed to produce tissues out of cells, societies out of families, or any other living level out of lower ones. Moreover, once a higher living level has been created, energy must continue to be expended thereafter to maintain that level. For example, if the energy supply to the cell, the organ, or the organism is stopped, death and decomposition soon follow and reversion to lower levels occurs. Similarly, maintenance of a family or a society requires work over and above that needed to maintain the organization of subordinate units.

Such energy expenditures represent the price which must be paid for the new properties obtained at the higher level. One of the new properties always is united, integrated function: nonaggregated structure means independent function and, by extension, *competition;* aggregated structure means joint function and, by extension, *cooperation.* Atoms, for example, may remain structurally independent, and they may then be in functional competition for other, suitable atoms with which they might aggregate. Once they do aggregate into a compound, they have lost structural independence and cannot but function unitedly, as a single cooperative unit. Similarly, cells may remain independent structurally and they may compete for space and raw materials. But if they aggregate into a multicellular unit, they surrender their independence and become a cooperative, integrated system.

This generalization applies at every other organizational level as well. The results on the human level are very familiar. Men may be independent and competing, or they may give up a measure of independence, form families and societies, and start cooperating. Note here that sociological laws governing human society are based on and are reflections of the more fundamental laws governing the organization of all matter, from atoms to the whole living world.

Note also that competition and cooperation are not in any basic sense willful, deliberate, planned, or thought out; atoms or cells neither think nor have political or economic motives. Structural units of any sort simply *function* as their internal makeup dictates. And the automatic result of such functioning among independent units may be competition; among aggregated units, cooperation. To be sure, human beings may *decide* to compete or to cooperate, but this merely channels, reinforces, makes conscious, and is superimposed on what they would necessarily do in any event.

SPECIALIZATION

If cooperation is a general new property gained at a higher level and if a price of energy must be paid to obtain this property, is the gain worth the price? It is,

for an important consequence of cooperation is *operational efficiency:* the cooperating aggregate functions more efficiently than its subordinated components separately and competitively. For example, a given number of separate cells must expend more energy and materials to survive than if that same number of cells were integrated into a tissue. Similarly for all other organizational levels.

The underlying reason for this difference is that, in the aggregate, duplication of effort may be avoided. Thus, in a set of separate cells, every cell is exposed to the environment on all sides and must therefore expend energy and materials on all sides to cope with the impact of the environment. However, if the same cells are aggregated into a multicellular unit such as a disk or a ball, only the outermost cells are in direct contact with the environment and inner cells then need not channel their resources into protective activities.

In addition to avoiding duplication of effort, aggregation also permits continuity of effort. Such continuity is not always possible in nonaggregated units. We may illustrate the general principle by contrasting unicellular and multicellular organisms, for example. A unicellular organism must necessarily carry out all survival functions within its one cell. In many instances, however, the performance of even one of these functions requires most or all of the capacity of the cell. In many cases, for example, the *entire* cell surface is designed to serve as a gateway for entering nutrients and departing wastes. The *entire* substance of the cell functions to distribute materials within it. And *all* parts of the cell may be required directly in locomotion or in feeding, for example (Fig. 2.4).

Very often, therefore, two such functions cannot be performed at the same time. Wherever locomotion and feeding *each* necessitate action by the *whole* cell surface, performance of one of these functions more or less precludes the simultaneous performance of the other. We shall find, moreover, that reproduction too involves the operational equipment of the *whole* cell, and in a unicellular organism this usually necessitates temporary suspension of both feeding and locomotion. Mutual exclusion of some functions by others is a common occurrence in all unicellular forms.

In multicellular forms, by contrast, continuity of effort becomes possible through *division of labor.* In only. For example, some cells may function in feeding, continuously so, and other cells may function in locomotion, again continuously so. Indeed, division of labor in many cases is so pronounced that given cells are permanently limited in functional capacity; they can perform *only* certain jobs and no others. Thus, nerve cells can conduct nerve impulses only and are quite unable to reproduce or move. Muscle cells can move by contracting, but they cannot reproduce. Most cells in many multicellular organisms have analogous limitations. Each group of cells is more or less restricted in its functional *versatility* and exhibits a particular *specialization*.

In a multicellular organism, therefore, an individual specialized cell does not and indeed cannot perform all the functions necessary for survival. This is why, when some cells are separated away from the whole organism, as in injury, for example, such cells must usually die. The specialized cell has lost independence mainly because it is not very versatile, because it can do only some of the jobs necessary for survival. The whole job of survival can be carried out only by the entire integrated multicellular system, which does possess the required versatility by virtue of its many differently specialized cells.

We may now understand the fundamental advantage of higher organizational levels generally and of multicellularity specifically. First, multicellularity makes possible division of labor, which avoids duplication of effort and permits continuity of effort. Second, division of labor leads to specialization, which permits any given effort to become highly effective. The overall result is an enormous saving of energy and materials, hence cheaper operation, and an enormous gain in efficiency. Basically, this gain of cheaper yet more efficient operation is what has favored more and more aggregation in matter generally and in living matter particularly; and this is why living history produced multicellular organisms, equipped successively with tissues, organs, and organ systems, rather than only bigger and better unicellular organisms.

Note that the specializations of one level determine the specializations of higher levels. If the cells composing a tissue are specialized as muscle cells, then the whole tissue will be specialized correspondingly for contraction and movement. If the organs of

Fig. 2.4. An amoeba. Like all other unicellular organisms, this protozoon carries out all metabolic and self-perpetuative functions within the confines of its single cell. Note nucleus (dark central body), excretory vacuole (light spherical body), and the pseudopods—fingerlike extensions which function in locomotion and feeding. (Carolina Biological Supply Co.)

such an organism, the total job of survival may be divided up into several subjobs and each subjob becomes the continuous responsibility of particular cells an organ system include teeth, stomach, and intestine, then, since the organs perform nutritional functions, the whole organ system will be specialized for nutrition. It follows that every organism as a whole is itself specialized, in line with the particular specializations of its subordinate parts. For example, every organism is able to live in a *particular* environment only and is able to pursue only a *particular* way of life. A fish must lead an aquatic existence, a tree cannot do without soil, and man too is specialized in his own way. He requires a terrestrial environment of particular properties, a social environment of variously specialized human beings, a community of wheat, cattle, and other food organisms. Thus the specializations of his body allow him to pursue no other but a characteristically human mode of life. And by being specialized, every organism in effect is a dependent, necessarily cooperating unit of a higher living level: the population, the whole species, the community of several species. These higher-level units are specialized in their own turn, according to the specializations of their members.

Note also that although all organisms are alike in general characteristics, they differ in specific characteristics because of specialization. Functionally, all organisms pursue life identically through metabolism and self-perpetuation; structurally, all organisms are composed of cells. But in each organism both the functions and the structures are in some respects specialized, and the specializations differ for different organisms. Evidently, there are many ways of making a living; and it is precisely because living matter is able to specialize that the problems of life can have different solutions in different cases.

In summary, the foregoing has shown that living units are organized structural aggregates at or above the cellular level of complexity, carrying out the functions of metabolism and self-perpetuation at every one of these levels. Energy must be expended to maintain the structural hierarchy, and the gain is greater division of labor and more specialization at successively higher levels. As a result of specialization, the versatility and independence of subordinate units is reduced, but the efficiency of maintaining life increases and the comparative cost in materials and energy decreases.

As noted, the lowest levels of the structural hierarchy are represented by subatomic particles, atoms, and compounds. We must now examine these levels in greater detail, for on them is based the whole living world.

Review questions

1. What is metabolism? Self-perpetuation? What are the principal component functions of these, and what specific roles do these functions play toward the maintenance of life?

2. What are the fundamental differences between inanimate and living systems?

3. Define organisms, living, cellular specialization, death.

4. Review the hierarchy of levels in the organization of matter, and discuss how living matter is characterized in terms of levels.

5. Review the relationship of levels of organization to aggregation, competition, cooperation, and operational efficiency.

6. In terms of cellular specializations, how does a cell of a single-celled organism differ from a cell of a multicellular organism?

7. Define organelle, cell, tissue, organ, organ system.

8. What are the functional advantages of specialization? Cite examples of specialization on the organism, society, species, and community levels of organization.

Suggested collateral readings

Bonner, J. T.: The Social Amebae, *Sci. Am.*, vol. 180, 1949.

————: Volvox, a Colony of Cells, *Sci. Am.*, vol. 182, 1950.

Kemeny, J. G.: Man Viewed as a Machine, *Sci. Am.*, vol. 192, 1955.

Moscona, A. A.: How Cells Associate, *Sci. Am.*, vol. 205, 1961.

Parker, G. H.: Criteria of Life, *Am. Scientist*, vol. 41, 1953.

Penrose, L. S.: Self-reproducing Machines, *Sci. Am.*, vol. 200, 1959.

THE CHEMICAL BASIS

3

It is now firmly established that, as already noted in the preceding chapter, living creatures ultimately consist entirely of chemicals. Also, there is little question that before living organisms existed on earth only chemicals were present; living matter originated out of chemicals. Basically, therefore, the story of life is a story of chemicals. This chapter provides an introduction to the latter.

Chemical substances

ATOMS

The universe is made up of 92 different basic kinds of materials called chemical elements. Iron, silver, gold, copper, and aluminum are some familiar examples. Some others, most of them present also in living matter, are listed in Table 1. Man has learned to create artificially several other elements in addition to the 92 kinds found in nature. Plutonium is an example of these man-made elements. Each element consists of particles called *atoms*. An atom may be said to be the very smallest complete unit of an element. For example, a gold atom is the basic unit of the element gold.

TABLE 1

Some common chemical elements

element	symbol	common valences
hydrogen	H	+1, 1
sodium	Na	+1
potassium	K	+1
chlorine	Cl	−1, 1
iodine	I	−1, 1
calcium	Ca	+2
magnesium	Mg	+2
sulfur	S	2
oxygen	O	2
copper	Cu	+1, +2
iron	Fe	+2, +3
carbon	C	2, 4
silicon	Si	4
aluminum	Al	3
nitrogen	N	3, 5
phosphorus	P	3, 5

Each element is given a chemical symbol, often the first or the first two letters of its English or Latin name. For example, the symbol for hydrogen is H, that for carbon is C, and that for silicon is Si. To represent one atom of an element, one simply writes the appropriate symbol. For example, the letter H stands for one atom of hydrogen. If more than one atom is to be indicated, the appropriate number is put before the atomic symbol. For example, 5 H stands for five separate hydrogen atoms.

Under specific conditions of temperature, pressure, and concentration, most atoms are able to attach and remain linked to certain other atoms. Such combinations of two or more atoms are called *compounds*. As we shall see presently, the atoms of a compound are held together by specific forces of attraction referred to as *chemical bonds*.

Each compound has a particular chemical name and a particular formula, both name and formula reflecting the kinds and numbers of atoms in the compound. For example, table salt is technically the compound "sodium chloride," which indicates the presence of sodium and chlorine. The formula NaCl also shows the quantitative ratio of these components: one sodium atom is bonded to one chlorine atom. Water is technically the compound "hydrogen oxide" with the formula H_2O, which indicates the presence of two hydrogen atoms for every one of oxygen. Note generally that the number of like atoms in a compound is indicated as a subscript. For example, iron oxide (Fe_2O_3) contains two iron atoms for every three oxygen atoms. A more complex compound is calcium phosphate, with the formula $Ca_3(PO_4)_2$. This is a shorthand notation for the following combination of atoms: three calcium atoms are bonded to two subcombinations, each of the latter consisting of one phosphorus and four oxygen atoms. Evidently 13 atoms altogether form one unit of the compound calcium phosphate.

If more than one unit of a compound is to be written in symbols, the appropriate number is put before the formula. For example, H_2O stands for a single unit of the compound water and 5 H_2O stands for five such units.

How do atoms form chemical bonds between them? In other words, how are compounds produced? To answer this, we must consider the internal structure of atoms.

COMPOUNDS

The atoms of all elements are constructed of components known as subatomic or *elementary particles*. Two kinds of such particles, *neutrons* and *protons*, occur in varying numbers in the center of an atom, where they form an *atomic nucleus*. Neutrons are electrically neutral; protons carry one unit of positive charge. The atomic nucleus as a whole consequently is electrically positive. Orbiting around the nucleus are given numbers of a third type of elementary particle, namely, *electrons*. Each electron carries one unit of negative electric charge, and there are exactly as many electrons present as there are protons in the nucleus. The electrons are maintained in orbit around the nucleus because the positively charged nucleus attracts the negatively charged electrons more or less strongly. Since the total positive charge equals the total negative charge, an atom as a whole is electrically neutral (Fig. 3.1).

Imagine now that two atoms, *A* and *B*, come exceedingly close to one another. If the nucleus of atom *A* attracts electrons strongly, it may attract not only

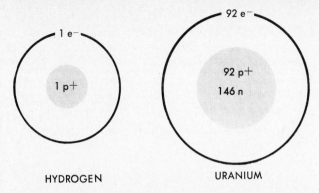

HYDROGEN   URANIUM

Fig. 3.1. The atomic structure of hydrogen and uranium, the lightest and heaviest natural atoms, respectively. The atomic nucleus of hydrogen consists of a single positively charged proton; neutrons are absent in this case. The nucleus of uranium contains 92 protons and 146 neutrons. The number of negatively charged electrons around the nucleus in each case equals the number of protons within the nucleus.

its own electrons but also those of atom *B*. If atom *B* happens to attract electrons rather less strongly, it may then happen that one or more of the *B* electrons become pulled away from *B* and become added to *A*. Atom *A*, now possessing additional electrons (hence additional negative electric charges), will therefore no longer be neutral but will be electrically negative. At the same time, atom *B*, which has lost electrons (hence has lost negative electric charges), also will no longer be electrically neutral but will be electropositive (because the positive charges in the *B* nucleus now are no longer fully neutralized by electrons). Atoms or groups of atoms which have gained or lost electrons are called *ions*. We may say, therefore, that close proximity between atoms may lead to a *transfer* of electrons among the atoms, hence to *ionization* of the atoms (Fig. 3.2).

Note that whenever an electron becomes transferred from one atom to another, *both* atoms become ions, and one of these is always electrically negative, the other electrically positive. Inasmuch as positively and negatively charged particles attract one another, a positive ion and a negative ion will similarly exert mutual attraction. It is this attraction which forms a chemical bond between the ions, and it is this bond which unites the ions as a compound.

Compounds formed as above by the transfer of electrons between atoms and the mutual attraction of the resulting ions are called *ionic compounds*. They represent a major category of chemical substances and we shall encounter them frequently in living matter. The chemical bonds within an ionic compound are referred to as ionic or *electrovalent bonds*. The number of such bonds in a compound relates directly to the number of electrons transferred. For example, an atom of sodium and an atom of chlorine may interact by the transfer of one electron from sodium to chlorine:

$$Na \xrightarrow{\quad e^- \quad} Na^+$$
$$Cl \xrightarrow{\qquad} Cl^-$$
$$\Big\} \longrightarrow Na^+Cl^-$$

The ionic compound sodium chloride results, consisting of a sodium ion and a chlorine ion. These two are held together by an attracting force generated by the transfer of one electron. We say that the compound possesses a single bond. Analogously, if compounds result from transfer of two, three, or more electrons, the compounds are said to possess double, triple, or multiple electrovalent bonds. In such electron transfers, atoms which tend to lose electrons and then become positively charged ions are otherwise known as *metals;*

Fig. 3.2. If atom A attracts electrons more strongly than atom B, then an electron of B may become *transferred* to A. Since *A* so gains a negative electric charge, it becomes ion A^-. At the same time *B* loses a negative charge and so becomes ion B^+. Having opposite charges, the two ions then attract each other and form the ionic compound A^-B^+.

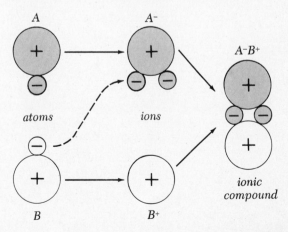

atoms which gain electrons and become negatively charged ions are *nonmetals*. Sodium is a metal, chlorine a nonmetal.

As noted, ionic compounds typically form when, in a group of atoms, some (viz., nonmetals) attract electrons very strongly whereas others (viz., metals) attract electrons quite weakly. What happens, however, if two or more atoms attract electrons with more or less equal strength? Imagine again an atom A and an atom B in close proximity (for example, A might be a chlorine atom and B might be another chlorine atom). The nucleus of A will attract some of the electrons of B, but the nucleus of B now also attracts some of the electrons of A with equal force. Clearly, an electronic "tug-of-war" will take place which neither atom can "win"; and without a decision, the mutual tugging will continue indefinitely. As a result, the atoms will in effect remain linked together, just as equally matched opponents of a real tug-of-war will remain linked by the mutual pull they exert on each other. In this case electrons will not be transferred and ions will not be formed. Instead, as each atom unsuccessfully attempts to "own" electrons of the other, electrons of both atoms will be *shared* in common (Fig. 3.3).

Electron-sharing represents a second major way in which compounds are formed. Compounds of this type are called *molecular compounds*, or simply *molecules*. The chemical bonds within molecules are known as *covalent bonds*, and their number is related directly to the number of electrons shared. For example, if two chlorine atoms are in close proximity, atom A will attract one electron of B and atom B will attract one electron of A. One electron *pair* will here be shared mutually by both atoms, and the attracting force generated by this shared pair represents a single covalent bond. In general, the number of covalent bonds in a molecule equals the number of shared electron pairs.

In addition to compounds in which all bonds are ionic or all are covalent, many compounds exist which are partly ionic and partly molecular. For example, in sulfuric acid, H_2SO_4, the SO_4 group is formed by covalent bonds and this group as a whole is joined with H_2 by electrovalent bonds. To be sure, a shorthand symbolization such as "H_2SO_4" indicates neither the kinds of bonds present nor their distribution within a compound. In the chapters to follow, it will not be necessary to distinguish between electrovalent and covalent bonds, but the position of bonds will need to be shown fairly often. We shall then symbolize a compound by means of a *structural* formula, in which the location of a bond (either electrovalent or covalent) is indicated as a short dash between appropriate atoms. For example,

NaCl   or Na—Cl
Cl$_2$ or Cl—Cl
H$_2$O   or H—O—H

Multiple dashes are used to signify double or triple bonds:

CO$_2$ or O=C=O
N$_2$ or N≡N

The chemical properties of a compound are determined by the *arrangement*, the *numbers*, and the *types* of atoms present. Two molecules, for example, may contain the same set of atoms; but if these are arranged differently, the molecules will have different properties. Thus the molecules

Fig. 3.3. If atom *A* attracts electrons just as strongly as atom *B*, then a mutual attraction between *A* and *B* may result in electron *sharing* and the formation of the molecular compound *AB*.

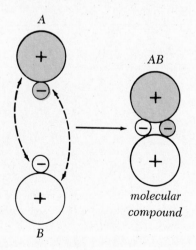

molecular compound

contain identical atoms, and both molecules may be written as C_4H_{10}. But since their atoms are bonded in different patterns, they are in fact different kinds of molecules with different properties. As we shall see, differences in the bonding patterns of otherwise similar molecules are particularly significant in the chemistry of living matter.

By virtue of its bonds, each compound has a greater or lesser *energy content*. As we have seen, forces of mutual electric attraction between atoms or ions produce the chemical bonds of a compound. These bonding forces, which hold atoms or ions together with a certain tenacity or strength, are said to represent *chemical energy* or *bond energy*. The greater the attracting force between two atoms or ions, the greater is the bond energy. The general concept of energy is roughly equivalent in meaning to work potential, or the capacity to do work. Bond energy therefore implies work, that is, the electrical work done by atoms which keeps them bonded together. Also, bond energy may be defined as the amount of work necessary to break a chemical bond. Two bonded atoms or ions will become disunited only if some external force pushes them apart and so breaks the bond. Such forcible separation requires work, or energy, and the amount of energy needed clearly must be at least great enough to overcome the attraction between the two atoms or ions. In other words, the energy required to break a bond equals the bond energy. Correspondingly, the total chemical energy of a compound may be defined as the energy required to break all the bonds in the compound.

By virtue of its bond energies, therefore, every compound represents a "package" of *stored* chemical energy. If a given amount of work is performed on the compound, the energy package can be opened. Some or all of the chemical energy can thereby be brought "out of storage" and can become available for the formation of new packages, that is, new compounds.

The clear implication is that compounds are not absolutely stable or permanent structures. On the contrary, if they are subjected to the impact of appropriate amounts of external energy, they may undergo chemical reactions and become different compounds as a result.

Chemical changes

REACTIONS

Any process which leads to changes in the number or the types or the arrangements of the atoms in one or more compounds may be regarded as a chemical reaction. Depending on the manner in which the structure of compounds becomes changed, four general categories of reactions may be distinguished.

First, two or more compounds may add together and form a single larger compound. This is a *synthesis* reaction. For example,

$$CO_2 + H_2O \longrightarrow H_2CO_3$$
carbon   *water*   *carbonic*
dioxide   *acid*

Reactions of this general type include the synthesis reactions which, as noted in the preceding chapter, represent a major metabolic activity of living matter.

Second, a given compound may break up into two or more smaller ones. This is a *decomposition* reaction, the reverse of synthesis. For example,

$$H_2CO_3 \longrightarrow H_2O + CO_2$$

Reactions of this general type include the decomposition reactions of respiration, another metabolic activity mentioned in the preceding chapter.

Third, one or more of the atoms or ions of one compound may trade places with one or more of the atoms or ions of another compound. This is an *exchange* reaction. For example,

$$H-Cl \;+\; Na-OH \longrightarrow H-OH \;+\; Na-Cl$$
hydrochloric   *sodium*   *water*   *sodium*
acid   *hydroxide*   *chloride*

Lastly, the numbers and types of atoms in a compound may remain the same, but the bonding pattern of the atoms changes. This is a *rearrangement* reaction. For example,

Note that in every equation illustrating a reaction, as above, the *total* numbers and types of atoms to the left of the arrow equal exactly the totals to the right of the arrow; in the reaction as a whole, atoms are neither gained nor lost. It is important to make sure that, whenever reactions are written out symbolically, the equations balance in this fashion.

Since a reaction makes, breaks, or rearranges the bonds between some of the atoms and since bonds represent chemical energy, *energy changes* are likely to accompany the reaction. For example, consider the reaction

$$A + B \longrightarrow C + D$$

and assume that all the bonds of A and B together contain *less* energy than all the bonds of C and D together. In other words, less energy is available in the bonds of the starting materials than is actually needed to form the bonds of the endproducts. An energy deficit exists in the starting materials, and under such circumstances the reaction will not occur unless the deficit is made up. It can be made up if the missing energy is supplied from an external source. For example, the starting materials may be heated. Then, so long as external energy continues to be supplied, the reaction may proceed:

$$A + B + energy \longrightarrow C + D$$

All reactions which *require* external energy as above are called *endergonic* or *endothermic* reactions. Synthesis reactions generally, including those in living matter, are of this type, and we may note that chemical synthesis tends to be expensive in terms of energy.

Consider now the alternative situation, in which the total bond energy of A and B together happens to be *greater* than the total bond energy of C and D together. In this case an excess of energy is available in the starting materials. Under such conditions the reaction will proceed and will *yield* energy to the external environment:

$$A + B \longrightarrow C + D + energy$$

Such a yield may manifest itself, for example, by a spontaneous heating-up of the reaction mixture.

All reactions which yield energy as above are called *exergonic* or *exothermic* reactions. Decomposi-

tion reactions, including respiratory decompositions in living matter, tend to be of this type. We may note here that, under suitably arranged conditions, the energy produced by decompositions may be used to make syntheses possible. This is a standard occurrence in the living world; as pointed out in Chap. 2, respiratory energy supports metabolic synthesis.

Energy requirements or yields also characterize exchange and rearrangement reactions, and we may therefore write generally, for reactions of all kinds:

$$starting\ materials \longrightarrow endproducts \pm energy$$

Evidently, the participants of a chemical reaction are not only the atoms of compounds but also the bond energies which form such compounds to begin with.

IONIC DISSOCIATION

Virtually all chemical reactions of biological interest take place in a water medium, that is, in *aqueous solution*. When put into water, molecular compounds may dissolve. If they do, they then exist as whole molecules. Given compounds may also *dissociate* to a greater or lesser extent, that is, break up into free individual ions. For example,

$$NaCl \xrightarrow{H_2O} Na^+ + Cl^-$$
sodium   sodium   chloride
chloride   ion   ion

$$CH_3COOH \xrightarrow{H_2O} CH_3COO^- + H^+$$
acetic   acetate   hydrogen
acid   ion   ion

$$NH_4OH \xrightarrow{H_2O} NH_4^+ + OH^-$$
ammonium   ammonium   hydroxyl
hydroxide   ion   ion

Inasmuch as dissociation produces equal amounts of positive and negative electric charges, solutions containing such dissociated compounds remain electrically neutral. However, the presence of free ions permits passage of electric currents through such solutions. Dissociated compounds are therefore also called *electrolytes*, and undissociated compounds are called *nonelectrolytes*.

Note that, in the second equation above, acetic acid dissociates in such a way that hydrogen ions are formed. This is what actually makes acetic acid an acid; any compound which dissociates to yield *hydrogen ions* is called an *acid*.

Analogously, any compound which dissociates to yield *hydroxyl ions*, OH⁻, as in the third equation above, is a *base* or an *alkali*.

A compound resulting from the chemical interaction of an acid and a base is a *salt*. Sodium chloride (NaCl) is a salt because it is formed by the interaction of hydrochloric acid (HCl) and sodium hydroxide (NaOH):

$$HCl + NaOH \longrightarrow NaCl + H_2O$$
$$\textit{acid} \quad \textit{base} \qquad \textit{salt}$$

Every ion-producer is either an acid or a base or a salt. We may distinguish between "strong" acids and "weak" acids, strong bases and weak bases, and strong salts and weak salts. The basis for such distinctions is the *extent* to which a given compound is dissociated. In a strong acid such as HCl, for example, all or virtually all the chemical units form ions in water. By contrast, in a weak acid such as CH_3COOH, only a few free ions are found; others remain in the form of intact, undissociated compounds. The situation is analogous for bases and salts. In other words, water breaks the bonds of different ion-producing compounds to different degrees. In the case of HCl, virtually all bonds of H are broken; in the case of CH_3COOH, only some are broken. Consequently, a

solution of acetic acid, for example, will contain partly whole CH_3COOH molecules and partly the free acetate and hydrogen ions.

It is often important to determine the acid or alkaline "strength" of a solution of given compounds, that is, the degree to which the compounds are dissociated. This can be done with appropriate electrical apparatus by measuring the relative number of free H⁺ and OH⁻ ions present in the solution; for the more of these ions are found, the more the acids and bases present are dissociated. The result is expressed as a number, called the pH of the solution. Numbers indicating pH range from 0 to 14. A pH of 7 indicates chemical neutrality; that is, the solution is neither acid nor basic because the number of H⁺ ions *equals* the number of OH⁻ ions. The *lower* than 7 the pH of a solution, the *more acid* it is; that is, there are more H⁺ ions present than OH⁻ ions. Conversely, the *higher* than 7 the pH, the *more alkaline* is a solution. Thus, a strong acidity is indicated by pH 0, and a strong alkalinity by pH 14 (Fig. 3.4).

Living material, which contains a mixture of variously dissociated acids, bases, and salts, has a pH usually very near neutrality. For example, the pH of human blood is 7.3. However, some types of living matter may be characteristically more acid (e.g., lemons) or basic. A living system does not tolerate significant variations of its normal acid-base balance, and its pH must remain within fairly narrow limits. If these limits should be exceeded, major chemical and physical disturbances would result which could be lethal.

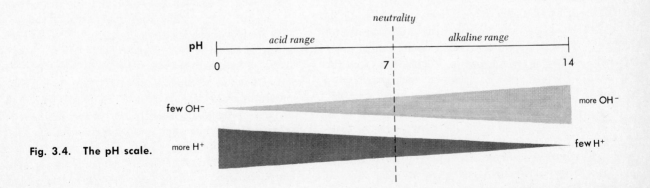

Fig. 3.4.   The pH scale.

CATALYSIS

Regardless of whether compounds are ionic or molecular, a chemical reaction is possible only if compounds are in actual or virtual *contact;* atoms must be in close proximity before bonds between them can break or form. The usual agency which brings compounds into contact is motion, particularly *heat* motion.

All atoms, ions, and molecules, regardless of whether they are in a gas, a liquid, or a solid, vibrate uninterruptedly in random back-and-forth movements. We feel these movements as heat and we measure them as temperature. A high temperature, for example, means that chemical units are in violent motion. Conversely, at $-273°C$, the theoretical absolute zero of temperature, heat is by definition entirely absent and all chemical units are stationary. But every known natural or experimentally produced material always contains at least some heat and the chemical units undergo more or less intense vibratory motions. Such motions produce collisions among the chemical units, and collision means contact. At a given temperature, therefore, chemical units have a characteristic collision rate, and the collision rate in turn determines the reaction rate of the units.

Ordinary room temperature often provides sufficient heat to agitate given chemical units enough to allow them to react. But for many reactions room heat is quite insufficient. For example, a mixture of fat and water reacts so slowly at room temperature that the result is quite unnoticeable. However, one can increase the molecular collisions, hence the speed of reaction, by subjecting the mixture to higher temperatures, e.g., over a flame.

Most chemical reactions characteristic of living material, like the fat-water reaction above, actually could occur only if environments were far hotter than room temperature. Yet at such temperatures living matter would quickly be killed. How then are living processes possible? How are enough collisions brought about despite the low temperatures at which living matter must exist and without additional heat? The answer lies in *catalysis:* the acceleration of reactions without heat, by means of so-called *catalysts.*

Catalysts are chemicals of very diverse kinds, and they are used frequently by chemists who wish to speed up a particular reaction without heating it.

Catalysts occur also in living matter, and these special ones are called *enzymes.* They are *proteins,* chemical compounds about which much more will be said later. For the present, note only that virtually every one of the thousands of reactions in living matter is speeded up enormously by a particular enzyme protein. Without such enzymes, the reactions could not occur fast enough at ordinary temperatures to sustain life. Thus enzymes are a device through which reactions requiring high temperatures in test tubes can occur at low temperatures in living matter.

How does an enzyme work? Best available evidence indicates that, like catalysts generally, an enzyme combines temporarily with the reacting compounds. Mutual contact of these compounds is then no longer a matter of chance collision but a matter of certainty. Hence reactions are faster.

The protein nature of enzymes is essential to this reaction-accelerating effect. Protein molecules are huge, and an almost unlimited number of different kinds of proteins exists. Accordingly, proteins have distinct molecular surfaces and the geometries of these surfaces differ as the internal structure of the proteins differs. The nature of the surface appears to be the key to enzyme action. Consider the reaction

$$\text{fatty acids} + \text{glycerin} \longrightarrow \text{fat} + \text{water}$$

Fatty acids have a given unique surface geometry, and so does glycerin. Enzymatic acceleration of this reaction may now occur if the surfaces of both fatty acids and glycerin happen to fit closely into the surface of a particular protein molecule. In other words, if the reacting molecules can become attached to a suitably shaped surface of an enzyme, then these molecules will be so close to each other that they may react chemically (Fig. 3.5). The enzyme itself remains almost passive here. It may provide a uniquely structured "platform" on which particular molecules may become trapped. Such trapping brings reacting molecules into contact far faster than chance collisions at that temperature; hence reactions are accelerated. Held by the enzyme, fatty acids and glycerin react and become fat and water and these endproducts then disengage from the enzyme surface. We may therefore think of an enzymatic reaction as a "lock-and-key" process. Only particularly shaped keys fit into particularly shaped locks. Just so, only certain types of compounds

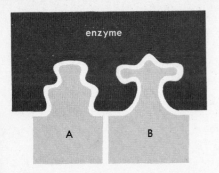

Fig. 3.5. The surfaces of molecules A and B fit into the surface of the enzyme. Reaction between A and B is thus speeded up, for contact between A and B does not depend on chance collision.

will establish a close fit with a given type of enzyme protein.

Differences in the surface configuration of different types of proteins undoubtedly account for the phenomenon of *enzyme specificity;* a given type of enzyme normally accelerates only one particular type of reaction. For example, the enzyme in the fatty acid-glycerin reaction above, called *lipase,* is specific and catalyzes *only* that particular reaction. In living matter, there are actually almost as many different kinds of enzymes as there are different kinds of reactions. This specificity of enzymes is an important corollary of the more general phenomenon of protein specificity, about which more will be said in Chap. 5. Because of protein specificity, some proteins are enzymes and some are not. If a protein happens to have a surface into which some other molecules could fit, then that protein could function as an enzyme in reactions involving those molecules.

Several other characteristics of enzymatic reactions may now be noted. Inasmuch as an enzyme essentially functions as a passive reaction platform, it is not itself changed by the reaction. It reappears unchanged at the end of the reaction, free to combine with a new set of starting molecules. Because of this, very small amounts of enzymes, used over and over, can catalyze large quantities of given raw materials.

Note also that a given enzyme can speed up a reaction in *either* direction. The reaction fat + water ⟶ fatty acids + glycerin is accelerated by the same enzyme, namely, lipase, that speeds up the reverse reac-

tion. This is understandable again if we keep in mind that enzymes are primarily passive reaction platforms. Thus, like heat, enzymes only influence reaction *speeds;* other factors govern the direction of a reaction, as we shall see presently.

Enzymes are often named according to the kinds of compounds they affect. For example, any enzyme accelerating reactions of compounds called carbohydrates may be referred to as a *carbohydrase.* Analogously, *proteinases* and *lipases* are enzymes which catalyze reactions of proteins and of fatty substances (= lipids), respectively. A suffix *-ase* always signifies that the substance in question is an enzyme. Note, however, that names of enzymes need not necessarily end in *-ase.*

In writing an enzymatic reaction symbolically, the name of the enzyme is conventionally put over the reaction arrow. Thus

$$\text{fatty acids} + \text{glycerin} \xrightarrow{\text{lipase}} \text{fat} + \text{water}$$

We have found that, like heat, enzymes increase the rate of contact among compounds and so they increase the rate of reactions. But heat and enzymes are not the only two conditions to do so. A third is the *concentration* of the compounds present.

MASS ACTION

Every chemical reaction has three basic attributes: it takes place at a certain *speed,* it proceeds in a certain *direction,* and it has a certain *duration.* What determines these attributes specifically for any given reaction?

As noted above, the speed of a reaction is determined by the environmental temperature and by catalysts. But it should be readily apparent that reaction speeds will depend also on the concentration of the reacting compounds present; for if the temperature and the enzymes remain constant, then the greater the concentration of the starting compounds, the more frequently will contacts among the compounds become possible and the faster will the reaction therefore be. We may say that, other factors being equal, *the speed of a reaction is proportional to the concentrations of the participating molecules.* This is known as the *law of mass action.*

This law actually predicts more than the speed of

reactions. By implication, it also predicts the direction and the duration of reactions. In principle, *all chemical reactions are reversible;* that is, if they can occur in one direction, they can also occur in the opposite direction. Suppose we consider again the reversible reaction

1 glycerin + 3 fatty acids $\rightleftharpoons$ 1 fat + 3 water

If glycerin, fatty acids, fat, and water molecules come into mutual contact, in which direction will the reaction proceed? Will fat form or will fat disappear? The law of mass action gives the answer: if glycerin and fatty acids are present in higher concentrations than fat and water, then the reaction will go to the *right;* but if fat and water are present in higher concentrations, then the reaction will proceed to the *left.* Put differently, if more collisions occur between glycerin and fatty acids, more fat and water will form; and if more collisions occur between fat and water, more glycerin and fatty acids will form.

Mass action clearly determines the direction of a reaction. How long will such a reaction continue in a given direction; that is, what is the duration of reaction? Suppose that we started out with high concentrations of glycerin and fatty acids and a zero concentration of fat and water:

glycerin + fatty acids $\longrightarrow$

The reaction proceeds to the right at a certain speed. But as glycerin and fatty acids are transformed, their concentrations decrease. And as the first few molecules of fat and water appear, they can react together and start some reaction to the *left:*

glycerin + fatty acids $\overrightarrow{\underleftarrow{}}$ fat + water

The *net* accumulation of fat will therefore now occur at a slower pace than at the beginning. With time, the net reaction to the right will become slower and slower; as more and more fat and water form, reacting increasingly to the left, less and less glycerin and fatty acids remain, reacting decreasingly to the right. An *equilibrium* will be reached when the left-hand reaction occurs as fast as the right-hand one. No further *net* increase of fat and water will take place thereafter, and the net reaction stops:

glycerin + fatty acids $\rightleftharpoons$ fat + water

In short, a reaction continues in a given direction until an equilibrium point is reached. At that point certain quantities of reactants are present, and so long as the equilibrium is maintained, the reaction in one direction occurs as fast as in the other. Hence the net quantities of all substances present do not change.

This holds if the reaction system is left to itself and nothing is added or removed. Suppose, however, that we removed fat (or water) as fast as it formed. Then, because fat (or water) is not allowed to accumulate, a reaction to the left cannot take place. The reaction to the right will therefore continue. An equilibrium point will not be reached, and all the glycerin and fatty acids present initially will eventually be converted into fat and water. The reaction to the right will proceed to completion and the yield of fat and water will then be maximal.

Reactions often proceed to completion, that is, to maximum yield, if one of the substances formed is an escaping gas ($\uparrow$) or a relatively insoluble precipitate ($\downarrow$); for either is equivalent to removing one of the endproducts as fast as it is formed. For example,

$$H_2CO_3 \longrightarrow H_2O + CO_2\uparrow$$
$$Ca^{++} + CO_3^= \longrightarrow CaCO_3\downarrow$$

Another way of preventing establishment of an equilibrium in the glycerin-fat reaction above would be to keep *adding* glycerin and fatty acids to the reaction system. The concentrations of glycerin and fatty acids then would always remain high and according to the law of mass action the reaction would always be "driven" to the right. More and more fat and water would form as more and more glycerin and fatty acids were added.

Note that the rules of mass action also apply to the energy changes of exergonic and endergonic reactions. Consider the reversible reaction

$A \rightleftharpoons B + energy$

Proceeding to the right, the reaction is exergonic. Energy here is as much an endproduct as *B,* and if energy escapes as fast as it is produced, the reaction to the right will not reach equilibrium but will proceed to completion. Equilibrium could be reached only if the reaction were completely energy-insulated, that is, if none of the energy produced could escape into the environment. Such insulation cannot be achieved in practice and reactions of this type always do tend to go to completion. The reverse reaction is endergonic. Here energy must be added continuously if all of *B* is to be converted into *A*. If the supply of energy is stopped prematurely, the reaction to the left will cease and the reverse reaction to the right will supervene and proceed to completion.

We may now conclude with the following summary. If chemical reactions occur in water, the participating substances can be acids, bases, or salts, dissociated to varying degrees, as well as whole, non-dissociated molecular compounds. The chemical changes among such compounds can be in the nature of syn-thesis, decomposition, exchange, or rearrangement. The speed of the reactions will be determined by the environmental temperature, by catalysts, and by mass action, and mass action will also determine the directions and durations of the reactions. Finally, as the reactions proceed, external energy will be required in an endergonic situation or will be released in an exergonic situation.

The foregoing account outlines the laws which govern events on the chemical levels of the hierarchy of matter. Our next objective is to examine how these chemical levels originally have given rise to and now form the foundations of the higher levels of life.

Review questions

1. Define element, atom, compound, ion, molecule, chemical energy, chemical bond, valence.

2. What is an electrovalent bond? How is such a bond formed? Explain in terms of atomic structure. What is a covalent bond? How is such a bond formed? Again explain in terms of atomic structure.

3. In what kinds of chemical reactions may compounds participate? Give specific examples.

4. Consider the following equation: $Ca(OH)_2 + 2 HCl \rightarrow CaCl_2 + 2 H_2O$. Identify the different atoms by name and determine the valence of each. Is this an exchange, synthesis, decomposition, or rearrangement reaction?

5. Define dissociation, acid, base, salt. Is H_2SO_4 an acid, a base, or a salt? How does sodium sulfate (Na_2SO_4) dissociate?

6. The magnesium ion is Mg^{++} and the nitrate ion is NO_3^-. Write the formulas for magnesium hydroxide, nitric acid, and magnesium nitrate.

7. What does the pH of a solution indicate? What would you expect the pH of a solution of NaCl to be? Of HCl? Of NaOH?

8. Review the role of environmental heat in chemical reactions. How does the external energy requirement differ for exergonic and endergonic reactions?

9. What is a catalyst? What is an enzyme and how does it work? Why is a carbohydrase ineffective in accelerating the reaction glycerin + fatty acids → fat + water? What kind of enzyme does such a reaction actually require? Review the general characteristics of enzymes.

10. State the law of mass action. How does this law govern the speed, the direction, and the amount of a chemical reaction? Under what conditions is a reaction reversible? Irreversible?

Suggested collateral readings

Frieden, E.: The Enzyme-Substrate Complex, *Sci. Am.,* vol. 201, 1959.

Pfeiffer, J. E.: Enzymes, *Sci. Am.,* vol. 179, 1948.

Roberts, J. D.: Organic Chemical Reactions, *Sci. Am.,* vol. 197, 1957.

Sienko, M. J., and R. A. Plane: "Chemistry," 2d ed., McGraw-Hill, New York, 1961.

THE ORIGIN OF LIFE

4

As already indicated earlier, life is believed to have originated through a series of events which raised the organization of inanimate matter to successively higher levels. Atoms combined into simple compounds, these combined into more elaborate ones, and the most elaborate eventually produced complexes which in turn aggregated into "living" units, namely, cells.

The details of these processes are at present known only partly. Some of the existing knowledge results from a backward projection of living types and living activities encountered today. For example, biologists deduce from viruses, bacteria, and other primitive existing forms what the earliest living forms might have been like. Other clues come from astronomy, physics, and geology, sciences which contribute information about the probable physical character of the ancient earth. Important data are also provided by ingenious chemical experiments designed to duplicate in the laboratory some of the steps which many millennia ago may have led to the beginning of life.

All this, supplemented here and there by reasonable speculation, today enables us to give a fairly plausible account of living origins. We shall trace these origins in this chapter.

Chemical evolution

THE EARLY EARTH

Living creatures on earth are a direct product of the earth. There is every reason to believe that living things owe their origin entirely to certain physical and chemical properties of the ancient earth. Nothing supernatural appeared to be involved—only time and natural physical and chemical laws operating within the peculiarly suitable earthly environment. Given such an environment, life probably *had* to happen. Put another way, once the earth had originated in its ancient form, with particular chemical and physical properties, it was then virtually *inevitable* that life would later originate on it also. The chemical and physical properties of the earth permitted certain chemical and physical reactions to occur, and one result of these reactions was something *living*. We may infer, moreover, that if other solar systems possess planets where chemical and physical conditions resemble those of the ancient earth, then life would originate on these other planets as well. Indeed, it is now believed strongly that life occurs not only on this earth but probably widely throughout the universe as well.

The life-producing chemical and physical properties of the early earth were a result of the way the earth and our solar system as a whole came into being to begin with. Available evidence indicates that the solar system is from 5 to 10 billion years old. Several hypotheses have been proposed to explain how the sun and the planets were formed. According to one, now widely accepted, the whole solar system started out as a hot, rapidly rotating ball of gas. This gas was made up of free atoms. Hydrogen atoms probably were the most abundant, and other, heavier kinds were present in lesser quantities. The sun was formed when most of this atomic gas, hence most of the hydrogen, gravitated toward the center of the ball. Even today, the sun is composed largely of hydrogen atoms. A swirling belt of gas remained outside the new sun. Eddies formed in this belt and in time it broke up into a few smaller gas clouds. These spinning spheres of fiery matter were the early planets.

The earth thus probably began as a glowing mass of free hydrogen and other types of atoms. These eventually became sorted out according to weight. Heavy ones, such as iron and nickel, sank toward the center of the earth, where they are still present today. Lighter atoms, such as silicon and aluminum, formed a middle shell. The very lightest, such as hydrogen, nitrogen, oxygen, and carbon, collected in the outermost layers.

At first, temperatures were probably too high for the formation of compounds—bonds would have been broken as fast as they might have formed. But under the influence of the cold of cosmic space, the earth began to cool down gradually. In time, temperatures became low enough to permit the formation of relatively stable bonds between atoms. Compounds then appeared in profusion and free atoms disappeared. With this we reach the beginning of the chemical history of the earth, which henceforth will accompany the physical history. As far as they are known or suspected, what were the life-producing chemical reactions?

THE FIRST COMPOUNDS

Among the lightest and most abundant materials in the surface gas of the early earth were atoms of hydrogen, and also atoms of oxygen, carbon, and nitrogen. Consequently, when temperatures became low enough to allow formation of compounds, the atoms of these four elements must have played a conspicuous role. (And it is therefore not a coincidence that, even today, some 95 per cent or so of the substance of every living creature consists of just these four elements.)

What simple compounds could have formed from the four elements? On the basis of their known chemical properties and their presumed relative abundance on the early earth, H, C, O, and N should have joined into some half dozen different combinations. At least three of these were of considerable significance in later events:

water, H—O—H, H_2O

methane, $H—\overset{\displaystyle H}{\underset{\displaystyle H}{C}}—H$, CH_4

ammonia, $H—N\big\langle\underset{\displaystyle H}{\overset{\displaystyle H}{}}$, NH_3

Temperatures were such that these three compounds persisted as gases, and the earth henceforth had an outer *atmosphere* containing large quantities of these three.

We have indirect evidence that the three gases actually came into being not only on the early earth but on other planets as well. For example, on the cold, distant planet Jupiter, water, methane, and ammonia are present today in the form of thick surface layers of permanently frozen solids. Apparently these compounds must have formed there as on earth, but at that great distance from the sun the surface of the planet probably froze before much additional chemical change could occur. On the hot earth, by contrast, the early compounds could interact further and give rise to new compounds later.

In time, as the gas ball which was the earth continued to cool, temperatures became low enough to allow some of the gases to liquefy and some of the liquids in turn to solidify. Heavy substances near the center of the earth probably tended to liquefy and solidify first. But the heat of the materials prevented complete solidification, and to this day the earth contains a hot, thickly flowing, deformable center. On the other hand, the middle shell of lighter substances did congeal, and a solid, gradually thickening crust developed. As the crust thickened and cooled, it wrinkled and folded and gave rise to the first mountain ranges. Overlying this crust was the outer atmospheric mantle, which at temperatures then prevailing still remained gaseous.

Then the rains started. All the water on earth up to this stage was in the atmosphere, forming clouds probably hundreds of miles thick. The solidifying crust underneath at first was sufficiently hot that any liquid water would boil away instantly. But eventually the crust became cool enough to hold water in liquid form. Then rain began falling in unceasing, centuries-long downpours. Basins and shallows filled up and torrential rivers tore down from the mountains. The oceans formed in this way.

Dissolved in these seas were quantities of the atmospheric CH_4 and NH_3, compounds which persist as gases at temperatures at which water is liquid. Also accumulating in the ocean were salts and minerals. At first there were none, but as the rivers eroded the mountainsides and dissolved them away and as violent tides battered the shores and reduced them to powder, salts and minerals came to be added to the ocean in increasing quantities. Moreover, massive submarine bursts of molten lava probably erupted frequently through the earth's crust, and they too added their substance to the mineral content of the world's waters. Thus the oceans acquired their saltiness relatively early and to a small extent they became saltier still during subsequent ages.

The formation of large bodies of liquid water containing the early atmospheric gases and many minerals in solution was the key event which made the later origin of life possible. Water was and is now the most abundant component of living matter. On an average, two-thirds and often as much as 90 per cent or more of anything living is water; and the presence of water in bulk over three-fourths of the earth's surface today is of profound importance in the economy of living things. This fundamental role of water in living matter traces primarily to two properties of water.

First, water is virtually the best of all possible solvents. It dissolves a greater variety of substances and greater quantities of each substance than practically any other liquid. This means that it is an excellent medium for chemical reactions. Chemical processes also occur in gases and solids, but many more can occur in liquids and much more readily. Since living processes are based on chemical processes, the abundant supply of liquid water on the early earth was a promising circumstance.

Second, water was originally the only good source of hydrogen and oxygen. Both elements have exceedingly useful properties, and the construction of a living system on a chemical basis virtually demands their availability. But, as noted, free hydrogen and free oxygen became unavailable soon after the origin of the earth. Water molecules then came to serve as the principal suppliers. Water remains today virtually the only usable source of hydrogen and one of the important sources of oxygen.

Thus, oceanic water set the stage for the formation of living matter. The actors on this stage were the various gases and minerals dissolved in water, plus water itself. And the title role was played by the carbon atoms of the gas methane.

EARLY ORGANIC COMPOUNDS

Properties of carbon.   Carbon is a most versatile element. It has a covalence of 4, which means that a carbon atom can form as many as four covalent bonds with other atoms. As noted, carbon is bonded to four hydrogens in methane. Any or all of these hydrogen atoms may be replaced rather readily by other atoms. For example, in reactions of methane with chlorine or chlorine-containing compounds, one may obtain new compounds such as CH_3Cl, CH_2Cl_2, $CHCl_3$, and CCl_4.

Apart from bonding possibilities such as these, carbon atoms may link directly to other carbon atoms, a most interesting and important bonding property. When carbon joins carbon, short or long *chains* of atoms may be formed.

To be sure, bare chains with open bonds do not exist as such, but they form parts of whole molecules in which various other atoms or groups of atoms are attached to the carbons. For example, if the carbons of two or more methane molecules are joined into a chain, then hydrogen atoms will be bonded to the carbons, as, for example, in

Alternatively, one or more types of atoms other than hydrogen may be attached to such chains.

Chains are by no means the only possible kinds of carbon-to-carbon combinations. If we imagine that one end of a carbon chain becomes connected to the other end, then a carbon *ring* will be the result. Benzene is one of such ring-containing compounds:

Many additional types of configurations exist. For example, carbon chains can be branched, rings and chains can become joined to one another, and any of these "patterns in carbon" can extend into three as well as two dimensions. Such carbon structures form molecular "skeletons," as it were, and the other atoms bonded to the carbons may be thought of as the "flesh" on the skeletons.

No other element even approaches the self-bonding versatility displayed by carbon. Clearly, carbon-to-carbon combinations introduce the possibility of tremendous *complexity* as well as *variety* into molecular structure. Actually, carbon-containing substances display more complexity and more variety than all other chemicals put together.

In view of these properties of carbon, the events which must have taken place in the oceans of the early earth are not difficult to envisage. Compounds like methane undoubtedly reacted with a good many of the other simple compounds present, and a large variety of different carbon-containing compounds must have come into existence. Included in these reactions must have been many in which compounds like methane were joined to one another or to other carbon-containing types. The result was the appearance of new kinds of compounds which contained two or more *linked* carbon atoms.

This development was a critical happening in the early history of living matter; the compounds with linked carbons eventually became the stuff out of which much of living matter was constructed. Today, carbon-to-carbon combinations occur almost exclusively within living matter or in materials derived from living and once-living matter. Accordingly, such complex carbon chemicals are called *organic compounds*. This contrasts with water, mineral substances, metallic materials, and other *inorganic compounds*, which do not contain linked carbons. As we shall see, living matter contains both organic and inorganic compounds.

What were some of the first organic compounds?

Compounds of carbon.   Among the numerous varieties of organic materials which undoubtedly formed in the early seas, five particular varieties came to have special significance in later events (as judged by hindsight from the vantage point of the present). These five varieties are:

1. sugars
2. glycerin
3. fatty acids
4. amino acids
5. nitrogen bases

Representations of the structural makeup of these compounds are given in Fig. 4.1. Note that in each case a carbon skeleton—either a chain or a ring structure—is the basis of the compound and that various groupings of hydrogen, oxygen, and nitrogen make up the remainder.

Sugars are members of a larger class of organic compounds known as *carbohydrates*. The carbon skeleton of a sugar is a relatively short chain. Chains consisting of five and six carbon atoms are particularly common in living matter. An important specific example of a C_5 sugar is *ribose* ($C_5H_{10}O_5$), and a specific example of a C_6 sugar is the widely occurring *glucose* ($C_6H_{12}O_6$). In sugars, as in carbohydrates generally, the only elements present are H, C, and O.

This is true also for glycerin, which contains three carbon atoms in a chain, and for the fatty acids. In the latter, however, the carbon chains may vary in length from 2 to 20 or more atoms. One end of a fatty acid molecule always terminates in a —COOH group, termed the *carboxyl* group, which endows the molecule with its acid properties (that is, the group may dissociate and yield H^+ ions).

Carboxyl groups also characterize the amino acids, which in addition carry nitrogen-containing *amino* groups, —NH_2. In an amino acid molecule, the carboxyl and amino groups are bonded to a carbon atom. To this atom is usually also attached a carbon skeleton which may vary in structure considerably. For exam-

Fig. 4.1.   The chemical structure of various types of compounds which are found in living systems today and which probably played conspicuous roles during the original formation of living systems. Glucose is one of many sugars. Purines and pyrimidines collectively may be referred to as nitrogen bases.

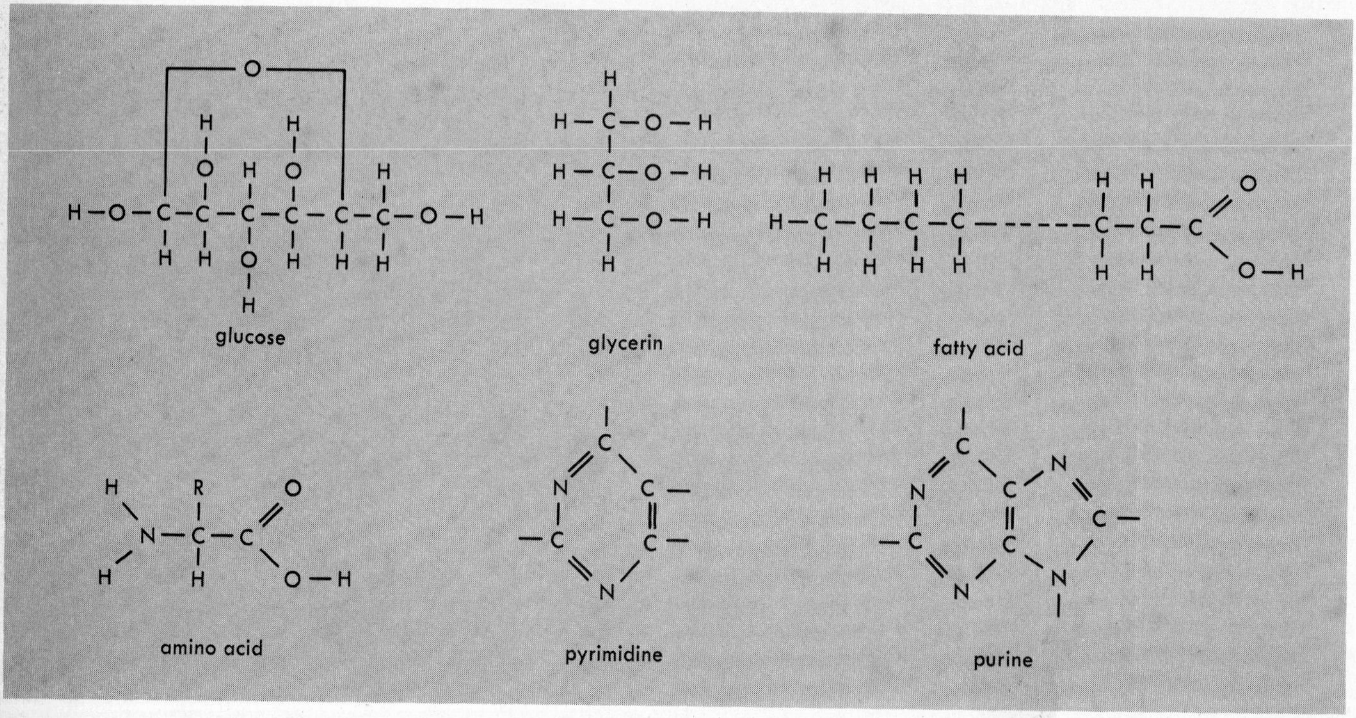

ple, it may consist of a few or of many carbon atoms and these may form either a chain, a ring, or a chain-ring combination (symbolized as —R— in Fig. 4.1).

Nitrogen is also an invariable component of the nitrogen bases, a group of compounds which includes two major subgroups, the *pyrimidines* and the *purines*. In both, the molecular skeleton is always a ring structure, the rings in these cases containing carbon as well as nitrogen atoms. A single carbon-nitrogen ring characterizes the pyrimidines; a double ring, the purines.

On the basis of these structural configurations and given the conditions which presumably prevailed on the primitive earth, we may guess how the five categories of organic compounds might have come into being. Simple chain compounds such as sugars, glycerin, and fatty acids could have formed through reactions of methane with itself and with water. Similarly, interactions of methane, water, and ammonia could have given rise to amino acids and conceivably also to nitrogen bases (Fig. 4.2).

However, regardless of how possible such events are on paper, we may well ask how likely it is that they really took place. What source, for example, would have supplied energy for these synthesis reactions?

Two different sources of energy were undoubtedly available. One of these was the sun. Although the dense cloud layers of water vapor at first must have prevented sunlight from reaching the earth's surface (which must have made the earth quite dark for long ages), the ultraviolet rays, X rays, and other high-energy radiations of the sun must have penetrated the clouds well. Some of this radiation could have provided the necessary energy for reactions among methane, ammonia, and water. Solar radiation certainly is known to support various chemical reactions today.

Moreover, a second energy source must have been the powerful electric discharges in lightning, which must have occurred almost continuously in the early cloud-laden, storm-lashed atmosphere. Like solar radiation, lightning is capable of energizing chemical reactions. Either lightning or solar energy could have acted directly on the gas molecules of the atmosphere, as still happens today to some extent. The resulting aerial chemicals could then have been washed down into the seas by rain. Alternatively, reactions could have taken

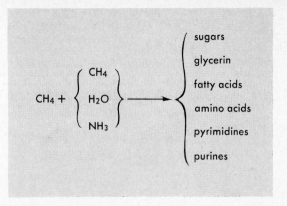

Fig. 4.2. Summary of early reactions. Interaction of methane with itself, water, and ammonia probably resulted in the compounds shown on the right.

place directly in the waters of the ocean, where methane and all other necessary ingredients were dissolved.

But even assuming that adequate energy sources and appropriate simple compounds might have been available, could organic materials really have formed? They could indeed, as was demonstrated in the early 1950s through dramatic and now classical laboratory experiments. In these experiments, the presumable environment of the early earth was duplicated in miniature. Into a flask were put inorganic mixtures containing water, methane gas, and ammonia gas, and electricity was discharged through these mixtures for several days to simulate the lightning discharges of the early earth. When the contents of the flask were then examined, many amino acids, fatty acids, and other simple organic compounds were actually found to be present.

Thus there is excellent reason to think that, under the impact of early energy sources, simple gases and other inorganic materials not only could but probably did react with one another and gave rise to a variety of organic compounds which accumulated in the ancient seas. These organic substances were not very complex as yet, but they contained the all-important carbon-to-carbon combinations. This was the key which was to open the door to life, for it made possible the later synthesis of even larger molecules, with larger carbon skeletons and many novel chemical properties.

LATER ORGANIC COMPOUNDS

Once started, the joining of carbon molecule to carbon molecule continued. Among the organic substances already present, some must have reacted with one another and with inorganic materials and highly complex new types of molecules must have become synthesized.

The main varieties. Specifically, sugars combined with one another, end to end. The result was a series of larger molecules containing very long carbon chains. These new molecules, called *polysaccharides*, still belonged to the general category of chemicals known as carbohydrates. Some of these polysaccharides are quite familiar. For example, *starch, cellulose,* and *glycogen* are polysaccharides. Each consists of hundreds of sugar molecules joined together. The early synthesis of polysaccharides was to prove important for the development of living systems, for, as we shall see, polysaccharides are useful nutrients which can serve both as energy-yielding fuels in respiration and as raw materials in synthesis. They still function in these capacities today.

In another series of reactions, glycerin combined with various fatty acids. *Fats* were formed in this manner. They too proved to be very good respiratory fuels and as raw materials in synthesis they came to be even more widely useful than polysaccharides.

Among the most important new compounds formed were the *proteins*. These consist of amino acids joined together in exceedingly complex ways. A tremendous number of amino acid molecules—in the order of 100,000 or more—can combine to form a protein, and the geometrical pattern of such unions can vary almost infinitely. As a result, proteins are not only among the largest molecules in existence but also among the most varied structurally.

Because of their structural variety, proteins could serve in two roles which came to be essential in the formation of living matter. First, differently structured proteins represented highly diverse building materials usable in many different construction jobs. As just noted above, polysaccharides and fats similarly served as raw materials in synthesis. But proteins constituted structural units of far greater diversity, and we now know by hindsight that only they actually could have made possible the construction of something so elaborate that it could have the properties of life. Even today, the structural differences between various organisms and the differences among the parts within a given organism are due primarily to the differences in the many protein building materials present.

Second, in addition to this structural role, proteins came to play a crucial functional role; some proteins could serve as enzymes and so could enormously speed up reactions among other molecules (see Chap. 3). We note that, with the appearance of the first proteins, the chemical tempo on the early earth could quicken substantially. Reactions which previously might have taken centuries now could occur within seconds or minutes. Living matter as it now exists can be sustained only through fast reactions, and enzymes make the necessary speed possible. Because "living" is strictly dependent on enzyme-accelerated reactions, we may conclude that proteins had to be present when life originated.

Two further groups of compounds of crucial future importance were formed from the nitrogen bases in the early seas. One of these groups comprised the *adenosine phosphates*. An adenosine phosphate molecule consists of three united parts, namely, a nitrogen base called *adenine*, the C_5 sugar *ribose*, and up to three *phosphate* groups:

$$\text{adenine} \quad + \quad \text{ribose} \quad + \quad \text{phosphates} \longrightarrow$$
$$\textit{(nitrogen base)} \quad (C_5 \textit{ sugar}) \quad \textit{(one, two, or three)}$$
$$\text{adenosine phosphates}$$

As at present, phosphate groups were inorganic mineral constituents of the ocean, and as such they could have combined readily with ribose and adenine molecules already in existence. The resulting adenosine phosphates then may have functioned in the same way they still do today, namely, as fundamental carriers of chemical energy.

More specifically, adenosine phosphates in living matter today serve to trap the energy produced in respiration. As pointed out in previous chapters, respiration involves a chemical decomposition of nutrients (for example, polysaccharides or fats), and such reactions are exergonic, or energy-yielding. When a decomposition reaction occurs in a test tube, any energy produced simply dissipates into the surroundings as heat; apart from raising the temperature, the energy is essentially lost and useless. In living matter, however, dissipation of respiratory energy is prevented by adenosine phosphates. In the presence of these molecules, energy resulting from nutrient decomposition does not become free as heat, but serves instead to form new chemical bonds within the structure of the adenosine phosphates. Put another way, bond energies from decomposing nutrients are transformed into bond energies within adenosine phosphate molecules. The latter thus come to accumulate and store energy. Indeed they serve as the central stores from which all living energy is drawn; every energy requirement in living matter, in synthesis and all other functions, is met directly by the chemical energy stored in adenosine phosphates. In a sense, therefore, adenosine phosphates in living matter serve like money in economics, as a common medium of exchange. All energy "profits" from respiration are converted into adenosine phosphates, and all energy expenditures in living activities are "paid for" out of these energy funds.

Conceivably, adenosine phosphates may have been of like significance in the early seas, before living matter existed. For example, if simple organic compounds already present underwent chemical decomposition, energy would have become available which could have been trapped in the adenosine phosphates. These could later become the energy donors for many new synthesis reactions. Since such reactions ultimately produced living matter, the original formation of adenosine phosphates must have been a most essential step on the chemical road leading to life.

A second group of compounds formed in part from nitrogen bases were the *nucleic acids*, discussed in the following section. The reactions which may have given rise to these and the various other compounds described are summarized in Fig. 4.3.

Nucleic acids. If any single entity could qualify as "the secret of life," that entity would unquestionably have to be the nucleic acids. To be sure, inasmuch as we can actually make such an identification today, it is really no longer possible to speak of any "secret." In any event, before nucleic acids had appeared on the early earth and regardless of what other substances might have been present, life could not possibly have originated. But after nucleic acids had appeared, the origin of life became a virtual certainty.

The structural units of nucleic acids are various nitrogen bases, various C_5 sugars, and phosphate groups. Clearly, the building blocks which make up nucleic acids and those which make up adenosine phosphates are quite similar. When a particular nitrogen base, a particular sugar, and one phosphate group are bonded together in a certain way, the result is a unit called a *nucleotide* (see Fig. 4.3). If hundreds and thousands of such nucleotide units are then joined in specific ways into long, chainlike compounds, the result is an exceedingly complex supermolecule called a *nucleic acid*. Evidently, nucleic acid molecules can be fully as large as or even larger than the most complex proteins.

Fig. 4.3. Summary of later chemical evolution. Interactions shown to the left of the arrows probably resulted in the compounds shown on the right.

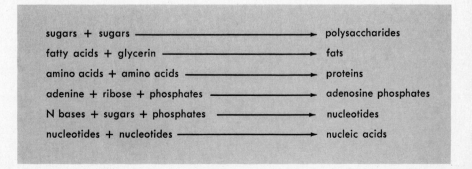

sugars + sugars ⟶ polysaccharides

fatty acids + glycerin ⟶ fats

amino acids + amino acids ⟶ proteins

adenine + ribose + phosphates ⟶ adenosine phosphates

N bases + sugars + phosphates ⟶ nucleotides

nucleotides + nucleotides ⟶ nucleic acids

Moreover, nucleic acids too exist in virtually unlimited numbers of structural varieties. These compounds are perhaps the most complex and most varied chemicals known.

As a result of their unparalleled complexity, the molecules exhibit three very remarkable properties. It is this which makes nucleic acids, far more so than any other single category of chemicals, the key to life.

Information codes.   Nucleic acids are known to function as chemical *information carriers*. The specific sequence of different nucleotides in a nucleic acid chain spells out information, just as the sequence of letters in a word spells out information. In a nucleic acid, the information is in chemical code. That is, a given segment of the chain, containing a particular sequence of nucleotides, stands for one element of a message; the adjoining segment, consisting of another particular sequence of nucleotides, stands for a second part of the message; etc. Therefore, depending on the specific nucleotide sequence a nucleic acid happens to have, the acid will carry a specific bit of information "written" in chemical code. Differently structured nucleic acids accordingly carry different bits of information.

How do we know that a nucleotide sequence really does represent information? And if it does, what does it "say"?

In the most general terms, any set of objects can justifiably be considered to contain information if the objects can bring about consistent effects. For example, a set of letters contains information when it consistently produces mental images of certain objects or ideas in a human viewer; a given set of dial positions on a motor contains information when it consistently makes the motor run at a particular speed. In the case of letters, the information is "written" in visual code; in the case of dials, the code may be mechanical or electrical, for example. Similarly, a set of atoms or groups of atoms may be regarded to contain chemically coded information which may make other atoms behave in particular ways. In this sense, a nucleotide sequence may likewise be said to contain information.

Research in recent years has shown what kind of information the nucleic acids actually carry. The compounds contain sets of instructions on *how to build proteins.* More specifically, a given sequence of nucleotides determines what *kinds* of amino acids will make

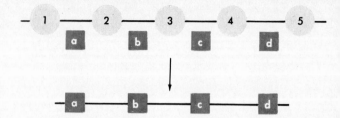

Fig. 4.4. Information codes and protein synthesis. If 1-2-3-4-5 represents a portion of a nucleic acid chain, the chemical characteristics of the nucleotide segment 1-2 could be such that only amino acid *a* could attach there. Similarly, only amino acid *b* might be able to attach to the nucleotide segment 2-3, amino acid *c* to the segment 3-4, etc. If then · the amino acids become linked to one another and form a protein, the sequence of the amino acids will have been determined by the coded information contained within the nucleic acid chain.

up a protein and in what *sequence* these amino acids will be joined. Imagine that a certain segment of a long nucleotide sequence is chemically so constituted that a particular kind of amino acid may become attached there. Similarly, the adjoining segment may permit another kind of amino acid—and only that kind—to become attached. In this manner, certain sequences of amino acids may become attached to given sequences of nucleotides; and when the amino acids then become linked together, the protein so formed will have been built according to the chemical instructions present in the nucleic acid. Put another way, a nucleic acid serves as a "blueprint" which specifies the amino acid sequence in a protein. Differently structured nucleic acids consequently control the formation of differently structured proteins (Fig. 4.4; see also Chap. 16 for a detailed discussion).

In all living creatures today, proteins are formed according to building instructions carried by nucleic acids. The significance of this is crucial, for, as noted, proteins are the principal building materials as well as the enzymes which control virtually all reactions in living matter. Therefore, the very nature of living matter both in its structural and its functional aspects is ultimately controlled by the nucleic acids. The particular nucleic acids serving in these regulating activities today are called *genes*. They are the fundamental agents which make possible the function of steady-state control, and indeed, as we shall see, they also make possible all other aspects of self-perpetuation.

The first nucleic acids on the early earth may have functioned in similar fashion. By their presence among reacting chemicals, they could well have controlled the synthesis of proteins. And to the extent that the proteins then served as enzymes in other reactions, these reactions would so have come under the indirect control of the nucleic acids. Such reaction control in itself did not yet constitute life, but it proved to be a critical factor in the eventual creation of life.

Reproduction. The nucleic acids also played a second major role. These compounds were, as under proper conditions they still are today, *replicating* molecules; that is, they could make exact replicas of themselves and so they could *reproduce*. At first glance it may seem utterly fantastic that a mere molecule should be able by its own efforts to make a copy of itself, But, as modern research shows, the process is no more unbelievable than that mere molecules should carry coded instructions on how to make other molecules. Indeed, nucleic acid reproduction is simply another instance of building other molecules according to coded information. In this case the "other molecules" are nucleic acids themselves.

Imagine again a long sequence of nucleotide units. Such a sequence automatically has built into it information about its own chemical structure, just as a sentence of words has built into it information about its own grammatical structure. If the sentence is to be reproduced, duplicate sets of words will have to be lined up in a sequence which matches that of the original sentence. In such a duplicating process, information transfer takes place. A man or a machine must first become informed about the structure of the existing sentence. Then, on the basis of this information, he or it must select appropriate duplicate words from a large pool of possible words and must put the selected words into the correct sequence. The new sentence now contains the information also present in the old.

Similarly, if a nucleotide sequence is to be reproduced, a duplicate set of individual nucleotides must be joined in a sequence which matches the original sequence exactly. The remarkable and quite unique property of nucleotide sequences is that they may carry out their own duplication, without intervention of any other controlling agency; under appropriate conditions they may select and arrange duplicate nucleotides on their own. Nucleic acids are said to be *self-duplicating*. In a given nucleotide sequence, for example, nucleotide 1 may attach to itself another nucleotide 1, if such a duplicate unit happens to be present in the vicinity as a raw material; nucleotide 2 similarly permits attachment of another nucleotide 2. In this manner, and provided that all needed duplicate nucleotides are available as raw materials, an existing molecule of nucleic acid may control the lineup of a matching set of nucleotides. If the matching set then links together into a chain, an exact replica of the original nucleic acid will have formed (Fig. 4.5).

In rough outline, this is how nucleic acid repro-

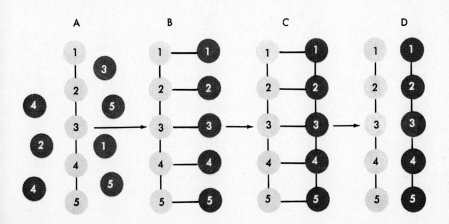

Fig. 4.5. Diagrammatic symbolization of nucleic acid reproduction. *A,* a preexisting nucleic acid molecule (light shading) surrounded by raw materials needed for the construction of a nucleic acid duplicate (dark shading). *B,* a raw material of a given type has affinity for a corresponding component of a nucleic acid, and the raw materials therefore attach in matching sequence to the preexisting nucleic acid. *C,* the correctly positioned raw materials link up with one another. *D,* the new nucleic acid molecule so created separates from the original "model." Model and replica are identical in composition.

duction is believed to occur now (see Chap. 16 for further detail) and to have occurred in the early seas. Essentially, the process represents a shortcut of the original process of nucleic acid creation. The first nucleic acids probably came into existence through random joining of random nucleotides. But with the appearance of the first nucleic acids, blueprints became available which could accelerate the subsequent formation of more nucleic acids. Each slowly and randomly created first nucleic acid could serve as a model for the rapid and no longer random creation of an exact duplicate. The duplicate could then serve as a model in its turn. In this way, descendants of the first nucleic acids have followed one another in an unbroken succession of molecular generations right down to the present.

Moreover, as one nucleic acid generation gave rise to the next, it passed on its information on how to construct particular proteins. With this *inherited* information, each generation of nucleic acids could re-create the protein types of its ancestors and so could exercise the same control over the same enzyme-dependent reactions. This repeated and controlled recurrence of a given set of chemical processes, generation after generation, later was to become a major characteristic of life.

Mutation.   Indirectly through their reproduction, nucleic acids also displayed a third property which later became a characteristic of life. As a class, nucleic acids are exceedingly stable molecules. That is, unlike most other kinds of compounds, nucleic acids are not easily affected by the many physical and chemical hazards encountered on earth. Occasionally, however, minor structural changes may be produced by various chemical and physical agents. When an alteration of this sort takes place, the altered nucleic acid molecule is itself very stable and, during its later reproduction, the changed condition is transmitted faithfully into the replica. Such stable changes, inheritable from one nucleic acid generation to the next, are called *mutations*. Because "mutation" means altered nucleic acid structure, it also means altered information content; once a nucleic acid has mutated, it will henceforth control the production of a different type of protein.

We may infer, therefore, that nucleic acid repro-

duction on the early earth produced not merely a succession of identical molecules, but that some of the descendant molecules became different from the ancestral types through occasional mutations. A single ancestral type so could in the course of time give rise to altogether new and diverse types such as had never existed before. The new *mutants* could then control the formation of new and diverse types of proteins. As a result, new sets of enzyme-requiring reactions came under the ultimate control of nucleic acids.

Evidently, the origin of nucleic acids introduced a radically novel dimension into the chemistry of the earth. First, the molecules possessed a structure large and stable enough to serve as a repository of information which could determine protein structure. Second, nucleic acids also carried information about their own structure, and they were replicable. This led to a succession of molecular generations with the same properties, hence to a perpetuation of given enzyme-requiring reactions over long periods of time. As a result, some of the chemistry of the earth ceased to occur randomly and became oriented into fixed, controlled, and persisting channels. Third, nucleic acids were complex enough to stay intact as stable wholes despite the introduction of occasional structural errors. This made the molecules mutable and led to the occasional appearance of new nucleic acids displaying new properties; that is, a mechanism became available which could deflect the channeled chemistry of the earth into new channels.

Indeed, with the formation of nucleic acids, all the basic ingredients for the eventual origin of a living entity were assembled. Events up to this point may be described collectively as *chemical evolution:* the production and gradual accumulation in the early seas of all the various compounds which later came to function as components of living matter. As we have seen, the most essential of these compounds included at least seven categories of substances, namely, inorganic materials such as water and dissolved mineral substances, and organic materials such as carbohydrates, fats, proteins, adenosine phosphates, and nucleic acids.

The events which followed may be described as *biological evolution:* the actual putting together of the chemical components into the first living units, namely, *cells.*

Biological evolution

If we say that the biological evolution of cells followed chemical evolution, this does not mean that chemical evolution simply stopped at one point and biological evolution then took over. On the contrary, chemical evolution continued and indeed goes on even now. What is meant instead is that at some stage of chemical evolution an *additional* kind of creation took hold. Molecules no longer gave rise just to new molecules only, but some of the molecules also produced something entirely new, something hitherto completely nonexistent, namely, fully living cells. These in turn then produced more cells through processes of multiplication which are still going on today. Thus the new dimension of biological evolution became *superimposed* on the still continuing older dimension of chemical evolution.

How did the first cells arise?

THE FIRST CELLS

In general outline, the creation of the first cells may be envisaged to have occurred in the following way. By one means or another, sets of all the key compounds already present in the early ocean must have collected together in tiny spaces, and each set of materials so accumulated must have remained aggregated in a cohesive drop. By virtue of the various properties of the aggregated materials, the drop would have been alive.

It is probably unlikely that aggregation of the necessary compounds could have occurred directly in the open ocean. The concentration of compounds must have been quite low and the open water must therefore have been too dilute a solution to provide a reasonable chance for the coming together and the staying together of just the right set of materials. It is more plausible to assume that the critical aggregations took place along the shores of the ocean. Organic compounds which had formed in the ocean could have been washed to the shore, where solid ground would have provided surfaces to which some of the molecules could have adhered. Other molecules of the same or of different types might or might not have become added later. The concentrations of the molecules so would have increased slowly, a process which would have been reinforced by considerable evaporation of water in the tide zone.

Indeed, it is not necessary to assume that nucleic acids, proteins, and large molecules generally had to be formed first in the open ocean and then had to become aggregated along the shore. On the contrary, it is quite possible that the first aggregations involved only the relatively simple organic compounds. Large molecules later could have become synthesized directly within, and indeed as a consequence of, the simple accumulations. We know that synthesis of large molecules requires close proximity of all needed raw materials. Thus if high enough concentrations of the simpler ingredients could have accumulated in microscopic pockets along the shore, complex molecules like nucleic acids might have formed first in such pockets. The nucleic acids themselves then could have directed the synthesis of the first proteins, again right within the aggregations already present. Some of the proteins would subsequently have acted as enzymes and so would have facilitated the rapid formation of a wealth of new compounds, e.g., polysaccharides out of sugar raw materials.

Moreover, some of the proteins and also some of the fats and carbohydrates would have represented building materials. These could have become organized into a structural framework which ramified through and around the aggregated drop. Many proteins are known to precipitate out of solution and to form solid granules or threadlike fibrils, for example. Also, mixtures containing proteins or protein-fat complexes may, as a consequence of their physical state, form membranous surface films (e.g., like the "skins" on custards). Thus the aggregated drops on the ocean shore could well have developed external boundary membranes and some measure of internal scaffolding. They would henceforth have been distinctly individual units marked off from the surrounding ocean water, and they would have remained individualized even if they absorbed more water and were later washed back into the open ocean. Indeed such units would have been primitive cells (Fig. 4.6).

It is not necessary to assume that cells were formed exclusively by the processes just described or

Fig. 4.6. The possible origin of the first cells. Appropriate chemical ingredients might have accumulated by adsorption in microscopic pockets along the seashore (1) and these ingredients could have become concentrated progressively (2). Under relatively dry conditions and perhaps with the aid of ATP, which might have been present, nucleic acids and proteins could have become synthesized (3). The proteins would then have permitted the occurrence of enzymatically accelerated reactions and the formation of structural membranes and internal fibrils (4). Finally, primitive cellular compartments might have been washed out to sea (5).

even that the above outline corresponds in detail to the actual events of the distant past. The important consideration at this stage of knowledge is mainly that we *can* envisage plausible sets of events through which cells might have formed. Whatever the actual events may have been, chance undoubtedly must have played a role; many aggregations probably never succeeded in becoming complete cells, and those that did owed their creation to the chance accumulation of the right ingredients. But in another sense, cell formation was not simply an enormously "lucky accident," a one-time occurrence of very remote probability. On the contrary, given an early earth so constituted that certain compounds could form and given these compounds and their special properties, then cell formation *had* to take place sooner or later, repeatedly and inevitably. The only element of chance here was time; the uncertainty was not in the nature of "if," but in the nature of "when" and "how often." Best estimates at present suggest that the first cells probably arose at least 2 billion years ago.

All aggregates which did become living cells must necessarily have shared the same general chemical composition. They all must have contained at least water, various mineral substances, carbohydrates, fats, proteins, adenosine phosphates, and nucleic acids. We now know that only aggregates possessing these substances would have displayed the collection of properties we call "life." It is not a coincidence that all living

things today still must, and do, possess the same seven categories of components.

That these chemical components actually did endow the first cells with the properties of life can be demonstrated readily. As noted above, many of the reactions among the cellular chemicals required the use of raw materials, that is, inorganic and simple organic compounds present abundantly in the early ocean. Such oceanic materials in effect were nutrients, and absorption of nutrients by the early cells represented a simple form of *nutrition*. Within the cells, some of the nutrients could be decomposed through enzymatic reactions, and the resulting energy could be packaged into adenosine phosphate molecules. In this way *respiration* became established as a continuing function. With various nutrients and with energy drawn from adenosine phosphates, *synthesis* reactions were then possible. These could produce more of all the cellular chemicals that could not be obtained directly from the ocean as preexisting nutrients. Structural repair and cellular growth so could occur. In short, the first cells could metabolize.

Moreover, by virtue of their nucleic acids, some of which now were genes, the cells could also self-perpetuate. Genes controlled protein synthesis, hence enzyme synthesis, and so they controlled all enzyme-dependent reactions, that is, virtually all chemical reactions in a cell. In effect, genes became the ultimate controllers of *steady state*. Genes also reproduced, and by regulating synthesis reactions they controlled the growth of cells. These activities of genes eventually made possible cellular *reproduction,* namely, the division of a cell into smaller offspring. Each such offspring cell still possessed all the characteristics of its parent, including an identical set of genes. Finally, because genes could mutate, cells of later generations could become different from their ancestors. This circumstance became the basis for evolution, and for *adaptation* generally as we shall see.

Clearly, by virtue of their makeup, early cells could perform all the functions of self-perpetuation in conjunction with those of metabolism. With the appearance of the first cells, therefore, the border domain between the nonliving and the living had been traversed. Henceforth the earth possessed entities which were clearly alive: single-celled *organisms.*

NUTRITIONAL EVOLUTION

As early living cells reproduced and multiplied, their numbers must have increased rapidly. This growth in numbers then must have brought about an increasingly severe drain on the free nutrients present in the ocean; more and more cells simply came to use up more and more food molecules.

But the rate of food production from water, methane, and ammonia did not increase correspondingly. On the contrary, this rate decreased and eventually became zero, for the environmental conditions which originally made such food production possible ultimately ceased to exist. After the permanent cloud layers in the early atmosphere had become converted into the waters of the oceans, lightning could no longer occur as abundantly as before. As a result, a principal energy source for combining water, methane, and ammonia into food molecules became unavailable. Moreover, high-energy solar radiation also became gradually unavailable on the earth surface, for such radiation was increasingly blocked off by a slowly forming radiation screen in the atmosphere. Living activities, respiration in particular, contributed greatly to the development of such a screen. One of the by-products of respiration was, and still is, carbon dioxide. As ever-growing populations of cells released more and more of this gas, some of it dissolved in the ocean

and the remainder escaped into the atmosphere. Thus a gas not previously present in appreciable quantities began to accumulate, and atmospheric carbon dioxide is known to prevent penetration of some of the high-energy radiation from space. We note that the activities of living matter in part were themselves responsible for the eventual cessation of the original process of food production.

Consequently, as cells continued to withdraw food molecules from the sea, it became only a question of time until the ocean would be completely empty of dissolved organic compounds, as empty of them as it is today. At present only inorganic materials are dissolved in the water. Furthermore, as supplies of free organic molecules began to dwindle, the distinct prospect loomed large that the ever-increasing multitude of cells would soon nourish itself into starvation. But we know that the early cells did not succumb. On the contrary, through their capacity of evolution they could avoid extinction and could adapt to the changing environmental conditions. They did so by evolving altogether new methods of procuring foods, methods which did not depend on free organic materials dissolved in the ocean.

Heterotrophism. One of the first evolutionary responses to dwindling food supplies may have been the development of *parasitism.* If foods could not be obtained from the open ocean, they still could be obtained within the bodies of living cells. Thus, a small cell could solve its food supply problem if it could manage to penetrate right into a larger cell and use the foods accumulated in such a host. Methods of invading, or infecting, cellular hosts undoubtedly evolved early, and today numerous groups of organisms still are infective and parasitic.

For many of the early organisms, parasitism undoubtedly was an effective new way of life. Another new way which required relatively little evolutionary adjustment was *saprotrophism.* Here an organism drew food molecules not from the decreasing supply in the ocean but from the bodies of dead cells or disintegrated cellular material. Many early organisms probably adopted this comparatively easy method of getting food and became the ancestors of the many modern saprotrophic types. Note that organic *decay* is a result of the nutrient-gathering activities of saprotrophic organisms. Before the evolution of saprotrophism, decay was unknown on earth. Today, saprotrophic types —especially bacterial saprotrophs—are so abundant that virtually any substance begins to decay almost immediately after exposure to air or water.

A third new process which permitted survival despite dwindling food supplies was *holotrophism,* i.e., the process of *eating* other living cells whole. This became possible through evolution of cellular mouths or equivalent engulfing structures, of devices to extract usable food molecules from the swallowed organisms, and of means of hunting for food organisms. Note, incidentally, that the difference between cellular eating and cellular parasitism is largely defined by the final result. In both cases, one cell gets inside another, but in one instance the larger host lives off the guest and in the other instance the guest lives off the host.

But all three of these new food-gathering procedures were ultimately self-limiting. Parasitism, saprotrophism, and holotrophism, collectively known as *heterotrophic* forms of nutrition, merely changed the distribution of already existing organic matter; they did not add any new food to the global supply. Clearly, if totally new food sources had not become available, life would have had to cease sooner or later.

Autotrophism.   What was needed, fundamentally, was a new way of making organic substances, preferably right within cells. The original way, in which sun and lightning formed food compounds out of materials such as methane, ammonia, and water, ultimately became inadequate, as noted. But the raw materials for a new process were still available in abundance. Water was in inexhaustible supply and, in addition to methane, there now existed an even better source of carbon directly within cells: carbon dioxide, byproduct of respiration. Given CO_2 and water, organic molecules could be manufactured in cells, provided that new external sources of energy could be found. Organisms which did evolve means of using external energy sources in the production of their own organic compounds are known collectively as *autotrophs.* Two principal types of autotrophs came into existence.

Chemosynthesizers.   Some of the early organisms found new external sources of energy in sulfur, in iron, in

nitrogen, and in a number of other metallic and non-metallic materials obtainable from the environment. Several groups of the early organisms must have evolved in such a way that they could absorb various inorganic molecules and make them undergo various exergonic chemical reactions. Energy so became available, and this energy was then used within the cells to combine CO_2 and water into food molecules (specifically, carbohydrates). The whole process is called *chemosynthesis* (Fig. 4.7).

Judging from the results some 2 billion years later, early chemosynthesis apparently was only a limited solution of the energy- and food-supply problem. Possibly it depended too much on particular inorganic materials available only in particular localities. A more generally useful solution required a steady, more nearly universal external energy source. Such a source was the sun.

Fig. 4.7.   The general pattern of chemosynthesis. With energy obtained from inorganic nutrients, the organism creates new organic nutrients out of carbon dioxide and water.

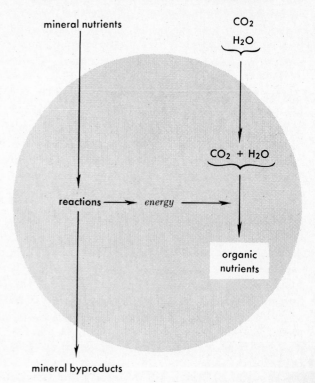

Photosynthesizers. Although lightning and high-energy solar radiations became inadequate as energy sources, solar radiation of lower energy content, especially *light,* still beamed down to earth as predictably and dependably as could be desired. If sunlight could be used, the energy problem, hence the food problem, could be solved. Sunlight actually did become the ultimate energy supplier for the vast majority of organisms, and it has played that role ever since.

Utilization of light energy within cells requires a cellular light-trapping device. Many kinds of photosensitive compounds are known to be able to absorb light and to trap more or less of its energy. Early cells may have manufactured various types of such compounds among the many new materials produced by cellular synthesis. One of these light-trapping substances has been perpetuated to the very present. It is green and we call it *chlorophyll.* By means of it, cells are able to trap some of the energy of sunlight and use the energy to transform CO_2 and water into organic food compounds. This food-procuring process is called *photosynthesis* (Fig. 4.8).

With a new source of organic compounds assured by photosynthesis, it did not matter that free molecular foods in the ocean finally disappeared. Photosynthesizing cells could make foods for themselves; holotrophic organisms could eat such cells and then each other; parasites could invade photosynthesizers or eaters; and saprotrophs in turn could find foods in the dead bodies of any of these. Consequently, excepting only the chemosynthesizers, which made their own foods, all other organisms were saved from starvation by photosynthesis. Today, photosynthesis still supports all living creatures except the chemosynthesizers.

We note that, sooner or later after the appearance of the first cells, five kinds of food-getting methods were evolved: parasitism, saprotrophism, holotrophism, chemosynthesis, and photosynthesis. Only the last two added to the net global supply of foods. There is good evidence that many individual organisms could obtain food by more than one of the five methods. For example, it must have been quite common for a single-celled organism to be able to eat *as well as* to photosynthesize. Numerous descendants of such types still exist today.

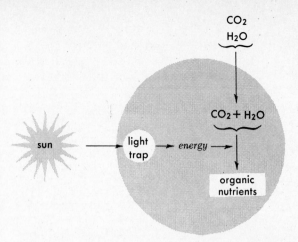

Fig. 4.8. The general pattern of photosynthesis. With energy obtained from the sun and by means of energy-trapping molecules such as chlorophyll, the organism creates organic nutrients out of carbon dioxide and water.

THE OXYGEN REVOLUTION

As photosynthesis occurred to an ever-increasing extent, it brought about far-reaching changes in the physical environment of the early earth. As we shall see later, a byproduct of photosynthesis is free molecular oxygen (O_2), a highly reactive gas which combines readily with other substances. Therefore, as increasingly large amounts of free oxygen escaped from photosynthesizing cells into the ocean and from there into the atmosphere, the gas must have reacted promptly with everything it could. This probably initiated a slow, profound "oxygen revolution" on earth (Fig. 4.9).

Oxygen probably reacted with methane and transformed it into carbon dioxide:

$$CH_4 + 2\,O_2 \longrightarrow CO_2 + 2\,H_2O$$

Oxygen also must have reacted with ammonia and molecular nitrogen (N_2) must have formed:

$$4\,NH_3 + 3\,O_2 \longrightarrow 2\,N_2 + 6\,H_2O$$

These events ultimately transformed the ancient atmosphere into the modern one, which no longer contains methane and ammonia. Instead, it consists mainly of water vapor, carbon dioxide, and molecular nitrogen, plus large quantities of free molecular oxygen itself.

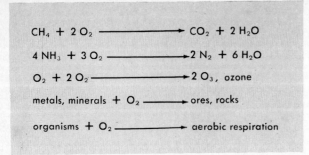

$$CH_4 + 2 O_2 \longrightarrow CO_2 + 2 H_2O$$

$$4 NH_3 + 3 O_2 \longrightarrow 2 N_2 + 6 H_2O$$

$$O_2 + 2 O_2 \longrightarrow 2 O_3, \text{ ozone}$$

$$\text{metals, minerals} + O_2 \longrightarrow \text{ores, rocks}$$

$$\text{organisms} + O_2 \longrightarrow \text{aerobic respiration}$$

Fig. 4.9. The "oxygen revolution." Oxygen resulting from photosynthesis reacted with other materials as shown and brought about the changes indicated.

At higher altitudes, under the impact of high-energy radiation from space, oxygen molecules combined with one another. The result was a layer of *ozone* (O_3). This layer, several miles up, has been in existence ever since. Ozone formed an even better screen than carbon dioxide against deep penetration of high-energy radiation. Consequently, organisms which evolved after the establishment of the ozone layer lived in an environment more or less completely free of high-energy radiation. This is why modern advanced organisms are comparatively unadapted to such radiation and are killed by even small doses of it. By contrast, the earliest organisms had evolved before the large-scale formation of ozone and had become more or less well adapted to space radiation. Some of their modern relatives (e.g., bacteria) still display this radiation resistance. They now can withstand exposures to X rays and similar radiation that would kill an army of men.

Free oxygen also reacted with the solid crust of the earth and converted most pure metals and mineral substances into *oxides*, the familiar ores and rocks of which much of the land surface is now made. A few relatively unreactive metals like gold resisted the action of oxygen, but others could not. And if today we wish to obtain pure iron or aluminum, for example, we must smelt or otherwise process appropriate ores to separate out the firmly bound oxygen.

Furthermore, free oxygen made possible a new, much more efficient form of respiration. The earliest cells decomposed food molecules without oxygen, a method of energy liberation called *fermentation*, or *anaerobic* (without air) respiration. However, if oxygen is available, it may participate in respiration. The amount of energy then obtained per unit amount of food consumed is much greater than in fermentation. When free environmental oxygen began to accumulate in quantity, newly evolving organisms developed means to utilize this gas. An *aerobic* (with air) form of respiration then came into existence, and it soon became the standard way of extracting energy from foods.

We note that the effects and activities of the early organisms greatly altered the physical characteristics of the earth and also the biological characteristics of the organisms themselves. So it has been ever since, even if never again so dramatically and incisively: the physical earth creates and influences the development of the biological earth, and the biological earth then reciprocates by influencing the development of the physical earth.

EARLY ORGANISMS

The above clearly implies that, through nutritional evolution and other evolutionary responses to environmental changes, organisms which descended from the first cells gradually came to differ from one another. Can we deduce how these developing differences ultimately produced the basic types of organisms which form the living world of today? In a general way we can, as the following sections will show.

Cells and viruses. In the earliest cells, gene-forming nucleic acid molecules probably were suspended free within the cell substance or were aggregated into tiny clumps. It must have happened on occasion that such clumps escaped from a cell into the open ocean, perhaps after an accidental rupture in the boundary membrane of a cell or after cell death. In this free state, a nucleic acid clump would have been simply a lifeless chemical aggregate. But it must have happened often that such inert aggregates by accident met up with other early cells and entered them. Within these host cells, the inert aggregates could become active again, i.e., the living machinery of the host could again provide the means for nucleic acid control activities and reproduction.

Such nucleic acid clumps, escaped from one cell, existing free for a time in an inert state, and then reentering and being reactivated by another cell, may have been the ancestors of the modern *viruses*. Viruses today behave exactly that way. First, they consist mainly of nucleic acids, the only other structural component being an external mantle of protein (Fig. 4.10). Note therefore that viruses are *not* cells and *not* organisms; they are considerably less than cells or organisms. Second, we know that at least some viruses arise as fragments broken off from the nucleic acid components of a given cell. Such fragments then direct the cell to manufacture protein mantles around them. The so-formed viruses subsequently escape from the host, often disintegrating the host cell in the process. Then they exist free in air or water. We know also that all modern viruses are quite inert in the free state and that they become reactivated if, and only if, they enter some new cell. In such infections, a virus may use the living apparatus of the host cell for renewed virus formation. Viruses can therefore be regarded as infective parasites, and we may note that the first viruslike units could have originated as soon as cells themselves were in existence.

Types of organisms. Among the early single-celled organisms, two main structural types came to have particular significance in later evolution. As already noted briefly, the first cells probably possessed freely suspended gene-forming nucleic acids. These compounds usually became associated closely with proteins, forming complexes we now call *nucleoproteins*. In some of the descendants of the early cells, the nucleoproteins apparently aggregated together into loose clumps. In each cell, such a clump then remained embedded within the cell substance and in direct contact with it.

The group of organisms characterized by this type of internal cellular arrangement may be referred to collectively as the *Monera*. Representatives of this group are still in existence today; the most familiar of the Monera are the *bacteria* (Fig. 4.11). The exact ancestry of modern bacteria is somewhat in doubt. However, in structure as well as function, bacteria now living are very close to our conception of what the first Monera might have been like. Conceivably, therefore, the latter may have been the ancestors of modern bacteria.

Another group now living and probably descended

Fig. 4.10. The shape and structure of modern viruses. Virus types of many other shapes are known. The diagram shows the typical composition of viruses, with nucleic acid in the center and a protein shell on the outside. The photograph is an electron micrograph. (Photograph courtesy of Dr. R. M. Herriott and Dr. J. L. Barlow, Johns Hopkins University, and *J. Gen. Physiol.*, vol. 36, p. 17.)

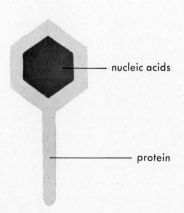

nucleic acids

protein

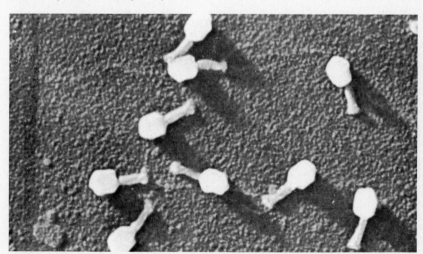

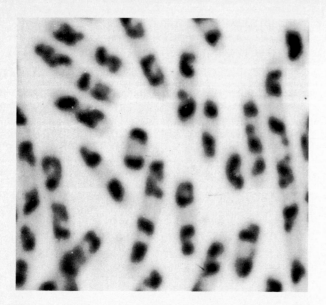

Fig. 4.11. The dispersed nucleic acid of bacteria. The name of the bacteria shown here is *Escherichia coli*. Some of the cells occur as single individuals; others are joined into chains. Staining makes the nucleic acids appear as dark bodies. Note the dispersion of these bodies throughout the cytoplasm of a bacterial cell. (Courtesy of the Society of American Bacteriologists, from A. G. Smith, *J. Bacteriol.*, vol. 59, 1950.)

from the first Monera are the *blue-green algae.* These primitive organisms resemble bacteria in many ways, including the way in which the gene-containing nucleoprotein is arranged within their cells. We may say, therefore, that the first cells on earth probably gave rise to an early group of Monera and that these in turn were the ancestors of the modern Monera, represented today chiefly by the bacteria and the blue-green algae.

As judged from these living forms, the Monera evolved four of the five methods of nutrition. Blue-green algae are largely photosynthetic, and bacteria are either photosynthetic, chemosynthetic, parasitic, or saprotrophic. Evidently, all methods except holotrophic eating evolved in the group. We may note also that Monera as a whole largely remained single-celled. Some bacteria and many blue-greens do form colonies of cells, often in the shape of filaments (see Chap. 8), but most Monera still base their present success on

the advantages of unicellularity: microscopic size, hence very rapid reproduction, huge numbers of individuals, and global distribution. As is well known, many kinds of bacteria compete very successfully even with man.

In a second major cellular type descended from the first cells, the gene-containing nucleoprotein clumps in each cell also condensed together into a central mass. But in addition a fine membrane formed around this mass, and as a result the nucleoprotein was no longer in direct contact with the rest of the cell substance. Such a membrane-enclosed nucleoprotein aggregate within a cell is now known as a cell *nucleus.* Early cells which evolved a distinct gene-containing nucleus may be referred to collectively as the *Protista* (Fig. 4.12).

These organisms are represented today by four major groups, namely, the *algae,* the *fungi,* the *slime molds,* and the *protozoa.* The latter are almost entirely unicellular. But in the first three groups only the ancient, primitive members are single-celled, and types which evolved later are variously multicellular. Such later types form simple and complex colonies and, in some highly advanced cases, also tissues. Nutritionally, four methods are in evidence, namely, photosynthesis, holotrophism, saprotrophism, and parasitism. Chemosynthesis apparently did not evolve. Some of the primitive unicellular algae now living may obtain nutrients by two or more of these methods. For example, a given individual may photosynthesize, or eat, or subsist as a saprotroph. Such multiple capacities may have been quite standard among the ancestral Protista. Most later descendants, however, retained only one or two of the different methods and lost the others. Thus, apart from the primitive members just mentioned, all other algae are exclusively photosynthetic; fungi and slime molds are saprotrophic or parasitic; and protozoa are holotrophic or parasitic.

For long ages, Monera and Protista were the only organisms in existence. Eventually, perhaps some 800 or 900 millions years ago (the exact time is unknown), certain of the Protista then living gave rise to a basically new category of organisms. These were holotrophic and multicellular, and the multicellularity exhibited new degrees of complexity; it included the organ level and later also the organ system level of organization.

Types so characterized have since become highly successful; the category as a whole is called *Metazoa* and the organisms in it are *animals*. Much later, about 400 million years ago, a second basic new category evolved from ancient Protista. This category is called *Metaphyta* and it comprises the *plants*. A good deal of evidence indicates that the specific ancestors of the Metaphyta were certain of the photosynthetic, multicellular algae. Photosynthesis remained as a characteristic of plants, and the multicellularity has become as complex as in animals; Metaphyta possess organs in all cases and organ systems in the most advanced cases.

We may conclude that the living world today is a collection of modern Monera, Protista, Metazoa, and Metaphyta. As we have seen, Monera and Protista trace their ancestry independently and more or less directly to the first cells, and from different Protista then arose animals and, independently at a later time, plants (see Fig. 4.12).

In this chapter we have outlined the major stages of the earth's early chemical and later biological his-tory (Fig. 4.13). Actually, no one point in this history qualifies as a "beginning" of life. The cell was the important product of the first 3 billion years, and we regard this product as having been alive. But the earlier organic compounds dissolved in the ocean already possessed the properties which eventually made life possible. Such compounds in turn owed their particular characteristics to the properties of various simpler compounds. The potential of life clearly traces back to the original individual atoms, and the creation of life out of atoms was but a step-by-step exploitation of their properties.

Thus, unlike Athena, who sprang fully formed and armed from Zeus's head, life did not burst forth from the ocean finished and ready. Instead, life *developed*, and here is perhaps the most dramatic illustration that small beginnings may have surprisingly large endings. Development has been the hallmark of life ever since; life today is still unceasingly forming and molding. Indeed, it will never be finally "finished" until its last spark is extinguished.

Fig. 4.12.   The four main categories of organisms and their probable evolutionary interrelations.

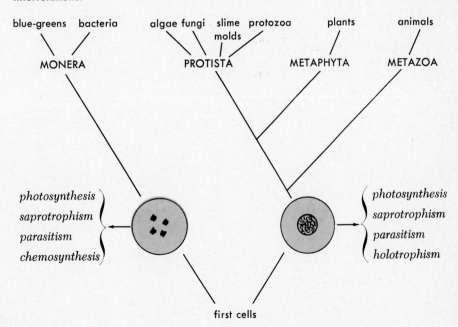

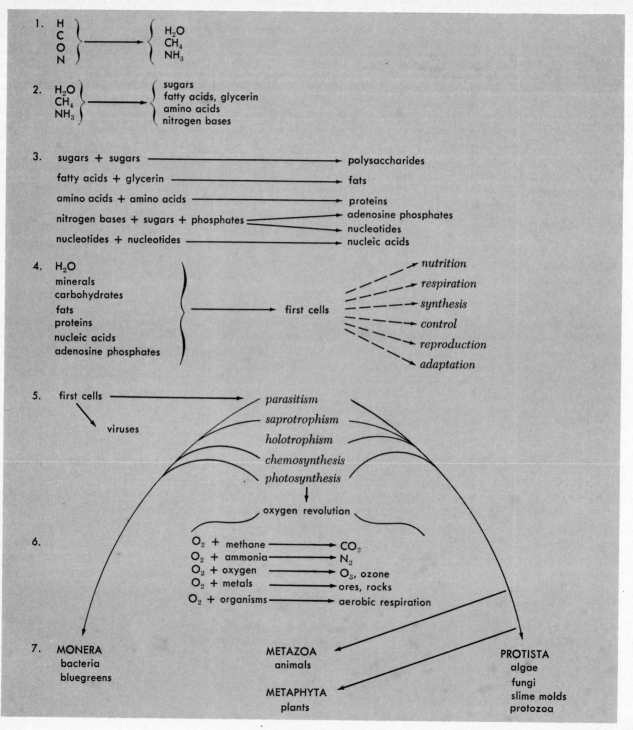

Fig. 4.13. Overall summary of the events described in this chapter.

Review questions

1. Which gases in the early atmosphere of the earth may have contributed to the formation of simple organic compounds? What were some of these compounds and what evidence do we have that they could actually have formed?

2. Review the role of (*a*) temperature, (*b*) water, (*c*) organic compounds, and (*d*) enzymes in the origin of life.

3. Review the chemical composition of carbohydrates, fats, proteins, and nucleic acids. What are sugars, amino bases, and adenosine phosphates?

4. What are the principal properties of nucleic acids and what roles have these properties probably played in the origin of life? What are genes?

5. How may the first cells have evolved? What are viruses and how could they have evolved?

6. What distinguishes moneran and protistan cell types and how could both have arisen from the first cells?

7. What are nutrients? What factors may have contributed to their disappearance from the early ocean and in what different ways did early organisms then obtain foods? Review the general nature of each of these ways.

8. What were the physical characteristics of the earth at the time it formed, before life originated, and after life originated? Review the principal events of the oxygen revolution.

9. Review the whole step-by-step sequence of events by which cellular life is now believed to have originated.

Suggested collateral readings

Gamov, G.: The Origin and Evolution of the Universe, *Am. Scientist*, vol. 39, 1951.

Miller, S. L.: A Production of Amino Acids under Possible Primitive Earth Conditions, *Science*, vol. 117, 1953.

Urey, H.: The Origin of the Earth, *Sci. Am.*, vol. 187, 1952.

Wald, G.: The Origin of Life, *Sci. Am.*, vol. 191, 1954.

part **2**

The Organization of Life

In this part we examine the structure of the living hierarchy in some detail. Our first concern is the internal make-up of living matter as such and the specific way living matter is organized into *cells* and into *organisms* generally. Individual organisms do not exist in isolation but are components of higher-level units such as families, populations, and especially *species* and *communities*. The internal organization of these larger units is our second subject of discussion. Groups like communities live in, and indeed are greatly influenced by, geographic localities which serve as homes, or *habitats*. The nature of such habitats is determined by global forces which affect the whole *environment*. These highest levels, encompassing all living matter on earth, constitute the final topic in this series of chapters.

CELL AND ORGANISM

5

An important conclusion of biological studies is that no living unit is ever exactly like any other. Moreover, no unit is ever exactly the same from moment to moment, for living matter is not a static, passive material. In a cell, for example, new substances enter continuously; wastes and manufactured products leave continuously; and substances in the cell interior are continuously transformed chemically and redistributed physically. As a result, living matter is in persistent internal turmoil. To the human observer a tree may appear to be a rather placid, inactive structure; but if the cellular components of the tree could be seen, they would all be noted to be constant, violent motion, colliding with one another and interacting and changing. Consequently, the tree as a whole changes continuously, and so indeed does every kind of living material.

However, despite such differences between living units and changes within living units, all units nevertheless share certain very basic features. Representing the universal heritage passed on by the very first cells on earth, the common features are partly *chemical*, partly *physical*, and partly *biological*. We shall examine each of these three aspects of living matter in this chapter.

Chemical organization

ELEMENTS AND COMPOUNDS

Four of the most widely distributed chemical elements on earth make up approximately 95 per cent of the weight of living matter: oxygen, 62 per cent; carbon, 20 per cent; hydrogen, 10 per cent; and nitrogen, 3 per cent. About 30 other elements contribute the remaining 5 per cent of the weight. The elements listed in Table 2 occur in virtually all types of cells. Trace amounts of others are found only in particular types, and still other elements may become incorporated into living matter accidentally, along with nutrient materials. All these elements, we recall, are present in the ocean; having originated in water, living matter still reflects the composition and content of water.

Virtually all the elements occur in the form of compounds. As already noted, cells consist of two great classes of compounds: mineral, or *inorganic*, compounds and more or less complex carbon-containing *organic* compounds.

Directly or indirectly, all inorganic compounds of living matter are of mineral origin, that is, they are

TABLE 2

The relative abundance of chemical elements in living matter

element	symbol	weight, per cent
oxygen	O	62
carbon	C	20
hydrogen	H	10
nitrogen	N	3
calcium	Ca	2.50
phosphorus	P	1.14
chlorine	Cl	0.16
sulfur	S	0.14
potassium	K	0.11
sodium	Na	0.10
magnesium	Mg	0.07
iodine	I	0.014
iron	Fe	0.010
		99.244
trace elements		0.756
		100.00

supplied in finished form by the external physical environment. *Water,* the most abundant cellular mineral, is present in amounts ranging from 5 to 90 or more per cent. For example, the water content of certain plant seeds is 5 to 10 per cent; of bone and of timber, 40 to 50 per cent; of muscle, 75 per cent; of brain, milk, and mushrooms, 80 to 90 per cent; and of algae and jellyfish, 90 to 95 or more per cent. As a general average, living matter is about 65 to 75 per cent water, overall.

Mineral solids constitute the other inorganic components of cells. Such solids are present in amounts ranging from about 1 to 5 per cent, on an average. A considerable fraction of the minerals may exist in the form of hard bulk deposits, which often are silicon- or calcium-containing substances. For example, the surface cells of certain grasses are reinforced externally with glasslike silica; the hard part of bone is largely a deposit of calcium phosphate; clam shells consist of calcium carbonate. Other minerals are in solution, either as free ions or combined with organic compounds. In general, the minerals of cells are also major constituents of the ocean and of rocks and ores. This is not a coincidence, for rocks are dissolved by water, water finds its way into the ocean and into soil, and living matter draws its mineral supplies from these sources.

Cells contain hundreds of different categories of organic constituents. Of these, four broad categories in particular are found in all types of cells, and they form the organic basis of living matter. We have already identified the four categories in the last chapter: *carbohydrates,* which include sugars and polysaccharides; *lipids,* which include fatty acids, fats, and derivatives of these; *proteins,* which comprise amino acid complexes; and *nitrogen base derivatives,* which include adenosine phosphates and nucleic acids.

Like mineral compounds, some of these organic substances may contribute to the formation of hard parts. For example, wood, horn, and *chitin* (the external covering of insects, many fungi, and of numerous other organisms) are predominantly organic. More generally, however, organic materials are dissolved or suspended in cellular water. Their relative abundance varies considerably for different types of cells and for different types of organisms. For example, an animal such as man contains about 15 per cent protein, about 15 per cent fat, and other organic components to the extent of about 1 per cent. In virtually all cases, the inorganic matter (mainly water) far outweighs the organic. It is also generally true that, per unit weight, plant cells contain less organic matter and more water than animal cells (Fig. 5.1).

ORGANIC COMPOUNDS

Carbohydrates.   Organic compounds in this group are so called because they consist of carbon and of hydrogen and oxygen in a 2:1 ratio, as in water. The general atomic composition of the simplest carbohydrates may be represented as $(CH_2O)_n$, where n is any whole number. If n equals 5, the carbohydrate may be a sugar such as *ribose* $(C_5H_{10}O_5)$. If n equals 6, sugars such as glucose, fructose, and galactose result, all widely encountered among cells and all having the formula $C_6H_{12}O_6$. Note again that differences between such compounds lie not in the numbers and types of atoms present, but in the patterns in which the atoms are bonded together.

Carbohydrates such as ribose and glucose are collectively called *monosaccharides*, because each represents a single sugar unit. If two monosaccharides become joined, a "double sugar" or *disaccharide* results. For example, a combination of two glucose units forms the disaccharide *maltose*, malt sugar; a combination of glucose and fructose forms *sucrose*, the cane or beet sugar used familiarly as a sweetening agent; and a union of glucose and galactose forms *lactose*, milk sugar. All three of these disaccharides have the formula $C_{12}H_{22}O_{11}$, and their formation is described by the same equation:

$$2\ C_6H_{12}O_6 \longrightarrow H_2O + C_{12}H_{22}O_{11}$$

Two or more disaccharide molecules may combine into even larger carbohydrates, producing the "multiple sugars" or *polysaccharides* already referred to in Chap. 4. Among important polysaccharides are *cellulose* (about 2,000 glucose units), *glycogen* (hundreds or thousands of glucose units), and *starch* (about 300 to 1,000 glucose units).

The cellular functions of the specific carbohydrates here named illustrate the general functions of carbo-

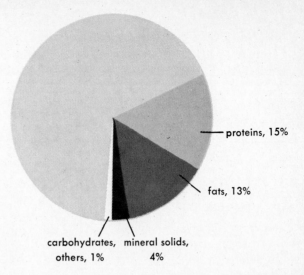

Fig. 5.1.   The average overall composition of animal cells.

Labels: proteins, 15%; fats, 13%; carbohydrates, others, 1%; mineral solids, 4%

hydrates as a group. For example, ribose is a structural component of adenosine phosphates and some nucleic acids; cellulose is deposited as a supporting wall around plant cells; starch, glycogen, and the disaccharides serve largely as storage foods in cells, usable either as donors of chemical energy or as raw materials in synthesis reactions; and glucose is the principal form in which carbohydrates are transported from cell to cell, as in the sap of plants and the blood of animals.

Lipids.   It will be recalled from earlier chapters that a fat molecule is formed by a combination of one glycerin molecule and three fatty acid molecules. A fatty acid in turn is a carbon chain carrying a terminal carboxyl (—COOH) group. The properties of a fat are determined largely by the nature of the fatty acids it contains. If the acids are long carbon chains, the fat is likely to be a hard *tallow*. If they are short chains, the fat tends to be a volatile liquid or a semiliquid *oil*. Chemically related to fats are the *waxes*, in which long fatty acids are joined to certain compounds other than glycerin. Also related to fats are *sterols*, complex ring structures which form the molecular framework of a number of vitamins and hormones.

In living matter, fats and fatty acids function as important storage foods and thus as potential energy donors and as raw materials for synthesis. Also, these lipids are major structural components of cells. For example, they play a particularly significant role in the formation of bounding membranes, where they probably contribute to controlling the movement of materials into and out of cells.

Proteins. As noted in Chap. 4, proteins are made up of *amino acids,* which may be symbolized generally as

$$NH_2—RCH—COOH$$

Here —COOH is the *carboxyl* group, —NH_2 is the *amino* group, and R represents a ring or a chain of carbons holding H, OH, and other atoms. Amino acids consequently differ according to the nature of their R portions. In living matter, only 23 different kinds of such R portions are found. Hence there are just 23 different natural types of amino acids.

Long chains of joined amino acids form proteins. Consider how varied such chains can be:

1. A protein may contain any or all of the 23 different *types* of amino acids.

2. A protein may contain virtually any *number* of each of these types of amino acids.

3. The specific *sequence* in which given numbers and types of amino acids are joined into a chain can vary almost without restriction.

4. The chains can be *folded* two- and three-dimensionally in virtually any imaginable pattern.

Forming a protein is somewhat comparable to forming words and sentences from an alphabet of letters. In the English language, 26 different letter symbols can be ordered practically at will to form an infinite variety of combinations. In proteins, the "letter symbols" are 23 different types of amino acids. And unlike real sentences, the protein "sentences" need not remain strung out in straight lines but can be branched and folded in practically any direction and form. Clearly, the number of theoretically possible proteins is astronomical.

Indeed, no two types of living organisms contain exactly the same types of proteins. This is not the case for carbohydrates or fats. Even a highly complex carbohydrate, for example, is the same whether we obtain it from mushrooms or mangoes, from mice or from men. A given lipid, similarly, is the same lipid regardless of where we find it. Not so for proteins,

however. Even twin organisms have slightly different proteins. The structural differences between proteins are the greater the more unrelated two organisms are evolutionarily. We say that proteins have a high degree of *specificity:* the proteins of a given living unit have a unit-"specific" character; that is, they are unique for that unit.

Protein specificity has major well-known consequences. For example, transfer of protein from one organism into the cells of another amounts to the introduction of foreign bodies and disease may result. Thus, the proteins of plant pollen may produce allergy in man. Blood of one person mixed with blood of another, if not of compatible type, may produce protein shock and death. Bacteria, partly because their proteins differ from those of other organisms, may produce many diseases if they infect given hosts. And portions of one organism, when grafted onto another organism, normally do not heal into place because the two sets of proteins differ. Moreover, because proteins are specific, enzymes are specific. Different enzymes represent structurally different proteins, and that is why any given enzyme can catalyze only one particular type of reaction.

As a result of their complicated geometrical makeup, proteins are extremely sensitive to chemical and physical influences. Excessive heat, pressure, electricity, heavy metals, and many other agents disrupt some of the bonds in a folded amino acid chain, and the protein molecule then loses its specific geometrical arrangement. Such changes in physical configuration are called *denaturation.* If the environmental effect is mild and of brief duration, denaturation may be temporary and the protein may subsequently revert to its original *native* state. But if the environmental effect is drastic and persisting, then denaturation becomes permanent and irreversible and the protein will be *coagulated* (like boiled egg white). Any biological property a protein may have in the native state is usually lost after denaturation. For example, specific enzyme function depends on specific protein configuration; and if the latter is lost, the former is likely to be lost as well. This is also a major reason why undue heat or virtually any undue environmental change kills living matter.

Nucleic acids.   We have found in Chap. 4 that these most critical constituents of cells are made up of *nucleotides,* a nucleotide being a nitrogen-base–sugar–phosphate complex.

The nitrogen base of a nucleotide can be one of five different kinds: *adenine, guanine, cytosine, thymine,* and *uracil.* The first two are purines, the last three, pyrimidines (see Fig. 4.1 for the basic molecular structure). Thus, depending on which one of these purines or pyrimidines is present in a given nucleotide, five different types of nucleotides may be distinguished.

The sugar of a nucleotide can be one of two kinds. One kind is *ribose,* the other is *deoxyribose.* The principal difference between these two 5-carbon sugars is indicated by their names: "deoxy"-ribose contains one oxygen atom less than ribose. Therefore, according to the kind of sugar present, two types of nucleotides may be distinguished: *ribose nucleotides* and *deoxyribose nucleotides.*

If we now classify nucleotides on the basis of both their nitrogen-base content and their sugar content, we find that eight major varieties of nucleotides actually exist:

ribose nucleotides	deoxyribose nucleotides
adenine-ribose-phosphate	adenine-deoxyribose-phosphate
guanine-ribose-phosphate	guanine-deoxyribose-phosphate
cytosine-ribose-phosphate	cytosine-deoxyribose-phosphate
uracil-ribose-phosphate	thymine-deoxyribose-phosphate

Note that adenine, guanine, and cytosine occur in both groups of nucleotides. But uracil is found only in association with ribose, and thymine, only in association with deoxyribose.

Hundreds of nucleotides joined together into a chain form a nucleic acid molecule. In any such molecule, all nucleotides present are *either* ribose nucleotides *or* deoxyribose nucleotides, but not both. On this basis, we may distinguish between *ribose nucleic acid, RNA* for short, composed entirely of ribose nucleotides, and *deoxyribose nucleic acid, DNA* for short, composed entirely of deoxyribose nucleotides. DNA specifically is the type of nucleic acid which forms genes and which probably played the key role during the origin of life.

Available evidence indicates that a DNA molecule is actually a *double chain of nucleotides,* one chain parallel to the other. In each single chain, the nucleotide units appear to be joined in such a way that the phosphate group of one unit links to the sugar of the next and that the purines and pyrimidines stick out laterally. If we symbolize a nucleotide as *P—D—N,* where *P* stands for phosphate, *D* for deoxyribose, and *N* for nitrogen base, then in a single chain

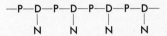

The evidence further suggests that two such single chains are linked into a double chain by the two sets of *N*s, which are held together pairwise by comparatively weak chemical bonds:

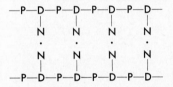

Four different —*N · N*— combinations occur in DNA, as outlined in Fig. 5.2. Note that *adenine is always paired with thymine, guanine always with cytosine.* There is no limit to the number of times each of these four combinations can occur in a long double chain. Nor, apparently, are there restrictions on their sequence. Thus *A · T, T · A, G · C,* and *C · G* may be regarded as an alphabet of four symbols, and "words" of any length may be constructed by using these symbols as often as desired and in any order.

Fig. 5.2.   The Watson-Crick model of DNA structure. *P,* phosphate; *D,* deoxyribose; *A, T, G, C,* purines and pyrimidines. A *P—D—A* unit represents one of the nucleotides. In this —*P—D—P—D*— double chain, four kinds of purine-pyrimidine pairs are possible, namely, *A·T, T·A, G·C,* and *C·G.* Each of the four may occur very many times, and the sequence of the pairs may vary in unlimited fashion.

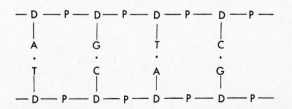

Evidently, the possible number of compositionally different DNAs is practically unlimited. This is reminiscent of the "alphabet" of amino acids out of which is formed a virtually unlimited number of different proteins. A final structural characteristic of DNA is that its double chain is not straight but spiraled (Fig. 5.3).

The structure of DNA as outlined here is known as the *Watson-Crick model,* after the investigators who proposed it. The model answers three important questions. First, it shows that DNAs can be just as *specific* as proteins: different sequences of nitrogen-base pairs would represent different DNAs. This accounts for the observation that no two organisms have exactly identical genes, genes being composed of DNA. Variations in gene types are actually just as great as variations in protein types, as is to be expected if the function of nucleic acids is to control protein synthesis. Second, the Watson-Crick model shows how DNA might actually accomplish control of protein synthesis. Third, the model suggests how DNA could reproduce. We shall deal with these functional aspects of nucleic acids in Chap. 16.

Other constituents. Special mention may here again be made of the *adenosine phosphates.* As pointed out in Chap. 4, these compounds consist of the nitrogen base adenine, the C_5 sugar ribose, and one, two, or three phosphate groups. The latter are attached to the ribose in a serial string. Depending on the actual number of phosphates (Ⓟ) so attached, three types of adenosine phosphates may be distinguished:

adenine-ribose-Ⓟ   *adenosine monophosphate,* or *AMP*
adenine-ribose-Ⓟ-Ⓟ   *adenosine diphosphate,* or *ADP*
adenine-ribose-Ⓟ-Ⓟ-Ⓟ *adenosine triphosphate,* or *ATP*

Fig. 5.3. A DNA double chain is spiraled as shown in this diagram. The two spirals symbolize the —P—D—P—D— chains, and the connections between the spirals represent the purine-pyrimidine pairs.

Of these, ADP and ATP particularly serve in respiration. ADP differs from ATP only in having one phosphate group less. Thus, if a third phosphate group is added to ADP, ATP will be formed. Such an addition requires a great deal of energy. The necessary energy actually is made available by respiratory decomposition of organic nutrients. In other words, the energy from decomposing nutrients serves to convert ADP into ATP. The latter so "stores" energy and may function subsequently as an energy donor (see Chap. 14).

Carbohydrates, lipids, proteins, and nitrogen-base derivatives such as nucleic acids and adenosine phosphates form the organic bulk of living matter. However, hundreds of other types of organic substances exist in cells. Although such substances are often present in very small quantities only, they may nevertheless be of extreme importance in the maintenance of life. We shall encounter several such compounds in subsequent chapters.

Note again that all these various compounds, both inorganic and organic, represent far more than a passive collection of chemicals; being chemicals, they *react.* The water medium dissolves many of the other components, and we already know that these exist partly as dissociated ions, partly as molecules. Many proteins present function as enzymes, and they, plus the temperature of the environment, permit numerous chemical reactions at various speeds, in various directions, and in various amounts. As a result of such reactions, energy exchanges occur, concentrations change, and chemical compositions as such become changed. New sets of reactions then become possible among the altered constituents, and such reactions alter chemical conditions in turn. If, as is normally the case, changes in the external environment occur at the same time, the diverse chemical events in cells will be affected accordingly. Living matter consequently is forever in chemical flux.

We know, furthermore, that living matter contains numerous materials which are not dissolved in water but which remain in suspension. These materials include, for example, fats and very large molecules such as some of the polysaccharides, the proteins, and the nucleic acids. Because it consists partly of dissolved and partly of suspended components, the living substance exhibits a particular *physical* organization superimposed on and resulting from the chemical organization. We now turn our attention to these physical characteristics of living matter.

Physical organization

COLLOIDS

Any liquid system in which particles of other material are present can be classified as belonging to one of three categories, depending on the size of the particles. If the particles are small enough to dissolve in the liquid medium, then the system is a true *solution.* Crystals can readily form from it, and such a system is therefore also called a *crystalloid.* If the particles are very large, e.g., the size of soil grains, they soon settle out by gravity at the bottom of a container. Such a system is a coarse *suspension.* But if all particles are of intermediate size, they neither form a solution nor settle out. Such a system is a *colloid.*

Living matter is largely a colloidal system. It consists of a *liquid phase,* namely, water containing dissolved ions and small molecules, and a *dispersed phase,* namely, large undissolved molecules such as fats, proteins, and others. What prevents the colloidal particles in living matter from settling out?

The molecules of a liquid, as of any other material, are in constant vibratory motion, the more so the higher the temperature (see Chap. 3). When the liquid freezes, this molecular motion is reduced sharply. Above the boiling point, molecules move so rapidly that many escape; that is, the liquid vaporizes. If dispersed particles are present in a liquid, they are buffeted and bombarded constantly by the molecules of the liquid. Very large particles are unaffected by these tiny forces, and they fall straight to the bottom of a container. But smaller bodies of colloidal size may be pushed back and forth, up and down. Gravitational pull may thereby be counteracted partly or wholly and the particles thus may be kept suspended. This random movement of small particles, called *Brownian motion,* is easily demonstrable under the microscope.

Brownian movement aids in keeping colloidal particles from settling out, but they cannot remain suspended by this force alone. Colloids stay dispersed mainly because of their *electrical charges.* All solid particles of a given colloidal system are either electropositive or electronegative. Since like charges repel, the particles are kept apart. If the charge is neutralized by electricity of opposite type, the colloid particles do settle out (Fig. 5.4).

Cellular colloids undergo reversible *sol-gel transformations,* also called *phase reversals.* If large numbers of colloidal particles are added to the system or, alternatively, if water is gradually withdrawn, the particles are brought closer together and come into contact with one another eventually. Rod-shaped particles then pile up like a log jam; round or irregular particles interlock in intricate ways. In effect, the original dispersed phase now is a continuous spongelike network which holds water within its meshes, in discontinuous droplets. This is the *gel* state of a colloid. The quasi-solid, pliable aspect of living matter, as in skin, or of protein colloids generally, as in jello and gelatin, is due to the gel condition. We may understand, therefore, how even organisms like jellyfish, which contain as much as 90 per

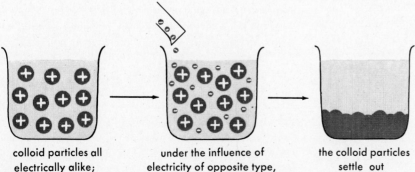

colloid particles all
electrically alike;

under the influence of
electricity of opposite type,

the colloid particles
settle out

Fig. 5.4. Colloid particles carry similar electric charges—in this illustration positive ones (left). These charges make the particles repel one another and thus keep them suspended. If electricity of the opposite type is added (middle), the colloid charges are neutralized and the particles settle out (right).

cent or more water, can maintain definite form and shape.

Conversely, addition of water to a colloidal system or removal of dispersed particles results in greater fluidity, the *sol* state of a colloid (Fig. 5.5). In cells, sol and gel states alternate normally and repeatedly with local variations of particle concentrations. Increased temperature may convert a gel into a sol; at higher temperature, colloidal particles in a gel become more agitated and the gelled meshwork is disrupted (e.g., liquefaction of jello by heating). Many other physical and chemical influences, such as low or high pH or pressure, affect sol-gel conditions.

Migratory movements occur in colloids, and also in true solutions, as a direct result of the thermal agitation of the particles. If ions, molecules, or colloidal particles are unevenly distributed, more collisions take place in more concentrated regions. For example, if a particle in the circle in Fig. 5.6 is displaced by heat motion or by Brownian bombardment *toward* a region of higher concentration, it will soon be stopped in its track by collision with other particles. But if it is displaced *away* from a high concentration, its movement will not be interrupted as soon, since neighboring particles are farther apart. On an average, therefore,

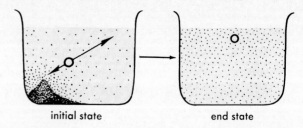

initial state   end state

Fig. 5.6. Diffusion. In the initial state, particles are distributed unevenly (left). A given particle (for example, the circled one) will therefore have more freedom of movement in the direction of lower concentrations. This eventually leads to an even distribution of particles, as in the end state shown at right.

a greater number of particles is displaced into more dilute regions than into more concentrated ones. In time, particles throughout the system will become distributed evenly. This equalization resulting from migration of particles is called *diffusion*.

Diffusion plays an important role in living matter. For example, it happens often inside a cell that particles are unevenly distributed. Diffusion will then tend to equalize the distribution. Evidently, this is one way through which materials in cells can migrate about.

An important property of living matter resulting from its colloidal makeup is that, as the following will show, it tends to form *membranes*.

MEMBRANES AND PERMEABILITY

The boundary between a colloidal system and a different medium (air, water, solid surfaces, or another colloid of different type) is called an *interface*. The molecules there are usually subjected to complex physical forces which act on and from both sides of the interface. The result is that the molecules at the interface pack together tightly and become *oriented* in layers. A so-called interfacial membrane forms (e.g., the "skins" on puddings, custards, boiled milk). On the surfaces of cells, such molecular skins are called *plasma membranes*. If the plasma membrane on the surface of a cell is punctured, a new membrane develops over the opening within seconds, before appreciable amounts of the interior can flow out.

Plasma membranes are the gateways through which the molecular traffic into and out of living mat-

Fig. 5.5. Phase reversals. A gel may be transformed into a sol by either addition of more liquid (top) or withdrawal of solid particles. And a sol may be transformed into a gel by either addition of more solid particles (bottom) or withdrawal of liquid.

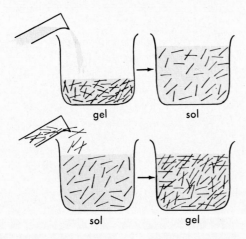

gel   sol

sol   gel

ter must pass. How do materials get through such membranes?

Plasma membranes have different *permeability* to different substances. Most membranes are completely permeable to water; that is, water molecules can pass through freely in either direction. As for other materials, organic or inorganic, there is no rule by which their passage potential can be determined beforehand. In general, three classes of materials can be distinguished: those that can pass through a membrane in either direction, those that can pass in one direction but not in the other; and those that cannot penetrate at all. These categories vary considerably for different membranes.

In the past, traffic through living membranes has been compared with traffic through nonliving ones like cellophane. Such nonliving membranes let water or small ions through, but not proteins, for example. Particle penetration here can be explained rather readily in terms of diffusion. Ions, for example, would strike the barrier; most of them would bounce off, but some would pass through *pores* in the membrane. If the ion concentration were greater on one side of the membrane than on the other, more ions on an average would migrate into the dilute side, thus equalizing concentrations.

However, a hypothesis postulating diffusion through pores is generally inadequate for living membranes. If cellular membranes were indeed passive, inert films with holes like cellophane, then it should not matter if such a membrane were poisoned; being nonliving, it could not be affected by a poison. But experiments actually show that the activity of cellular membranes *is* stopped or severely impaired by poisons, indicating that such membranes are not simply passive films. Moreover, if living membranes actually contained small holes, then the size of a particle should determine whether or not it could pass through such holes. However, particle size is often of little importance. For example, under certain conditions large protein molecules may pass through a given membrane whereas very small molecules sometimes may not. Again, the molecules of the three sugars glucose, fructose, and galactose, all $C_6H_{12}O_6$, have the same size, yet they are passed through living membranes at substantially different speeds.

Clearly, membranes are highly *selective;* they act as if they "knew" which substances to transmit and which to reject. Moreover, it is now known that active, energy-consuming work is often done by a living membrane in transmitting materials and that complex chemical reactions take place in the process. Therefore, rather than visualize a passive membrane with small holes, we are led to consider plasma films as dynamic structures in which entering or leaving particles are actively "handed" across from one side to the other.

Accordingly, if we encounter a situation where materials other than water pass through a living membrane, we will be quite wrong if we simply say offhandedly that this can be explained "by diffusion." Diffusion does play some role in most cases, but active work by the membrane usually plays an at least equally important role.

Membranes also account for a final property we must discuss.

OSMOSIS

When a membrane separates one colloid from another or from a different kind of medium, it often happens that some of the particles present on either side cannot go through the membrane. Suppose that one side contains a very low concentration of such particles (side *A* in Fig. 5.7), and the other side a very high

Fig. 5.7.   Osmosis. In the initial state, because *A* is less concentrated than *B*, water will be pulled from *A* into *B*. This eventually leads to the isotonic end state, where concentrations in *A* and *B* are equal. From this point on, no further net migration of water occurs (i.e., just as much water moves from *A* into *B* as from *B* into *A*). A semipermeable membrane is represented by *x*.

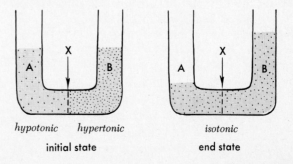

hypotonic hypertonic	isotonic
initial state	**end state**

concentration (side *B*, Fig. 5.7). What events occur in such a system?

1. In the beginning, relatively more water molecules are in contact with the membrane *X* on the *A* side than on the *B* side, since fewer of the solid particles occupy membrane space on the *A* surface than on the *B* surface.

2. Therefore, more water molecules, on an average, are transmitted through the membrane from *A* to *B* than from *B* to *A*.

3. As a result, the water content decreases in *A* and increases in *B*. Particles in *A* become crowded into a smaller and smaller volume, and more and more of them therefore take up membrane space on the *A* surface. On the *B* side, the increasing water content permits the spreading of the particles into progressively larger volumes, thus reducing particle concentration along the *B* surface of the membrane.

4. A stage will be reached at which the number of particles along the *A* surface equals that along the *B* surface. From then on, the number of water molecules transmitted from *A* to *B* equals the number transmitted from *B* to *A*. Thereafter, no further *net* shift of water occurs.

This *movement of water is called osmosis.*

Note that the amount of osmosis depends on the *concentration differential*, the relative *numbers* of particles in *A* and *B*. If the difference in particle number is great enough (for example, if *A* contains pure water only and *B* contains water and a large number of particles), then the *A* side may dehydrate completely and collapse, while the *B* side might burst and so collapse also. The side which loses water in osmosis is generally said to be *hypotonic*, and the side which gains water, *hypertonic*. When neither side gains or loses water, that is, when both sides contain equal concentrations of particles and thus are in osmotic equilibrium, they are said to be *isotonic* to each other.

Note that the net effect of osmosis is to pull water *into* the region of higher colloidal concentration, from the hypotonic to the hypertonic side. The process will continue until the two sides are isotonic. And note that osmosis will occur whenever certain particles cannot or do not pass through a membrane. Then nothing migrates through the membrane except *water* (plus any particles present which *can* diffuse through).

Like diffusion, osmosis plays an important role in living matter. It is one agency by which water is distributed and redistributed across membranes. As in diffusion also, care must be taken in explaining given membrane phenomena simply as "osmosis." Sometimes the event in question actually is osmosis, but many times it is not. In this connection, it is particularly poor practice simply to dismiss given events at membranes unthinkingly as "diffusion and osmosis."

We may conclude generally that, in its physical organization, living matter is a mixed colloidal system bounded by variously permeable membranes, undergoing localized sol-gel transformations, and being kept in constant internal motion by molecular bombardments, by diffusion displacements, and by osmotic forces. As a result of these properties, living matter is subjected to a continuous physical flux equally as profound as the chemical flux. Indeed, physical changes initiate chemical ones, and vice versa; and from any small-scale point of view, living matter is therefore never the same from moment to moment.

Superimposed on and resulting from its chemical and physical organization, living matter also displays a highly characteristic *biological* organization. We already know that this organization has the form of cells, tissues, organs, and organ systems. In the following section we shall examine these biological units of structure.

Biological organization

CELLS

The generalization that all living organisms consist of cells and cell products is known as the *cell theory*. Principal credit for its formulation is usually given to the German biologists Schleiden and Schwann, whose work was published in 1838. But the French biologist Dutrochet had made substantially the same generalization as early as 1824. The cell theory rapidly became one of the fundamental cornerstones of modern biological science, and with minor qualifications, it still has that status today.

The basic design. Examination of living or killed cells under various kinds of microscopes shows that cells vary considerably in size, ranging in diameter from about 2 microns to as much as several millimeters and more (1 micron, $1\mu = 1/1,000$ mm). However, the order of size of the vast majority of cells is remarkably uniform. A diameter of 5 to 15 microns is fairly characteristic of cells generally. We surmise that, notwithstanding the exceptions, cells can be neither much smaller nor much larger than a certain norm. Too small a size presumably would not provide enough room to accommodate the necessary parts, and too large a size would increase the maintenance problem and at the same time reduce the efficiency of compact operation.

The two fundamental subdivisions of most cells are the *nucleus* and the living substance surrounding the nucleus, called the *cytoplasm*. The nucleus is bounded by a *nuclear membrane*, the cytoplasm by a *cell membrane*, also called *plasma membrane*. Surrounding the cell membrane in many cases is a *cell wall* (Fig. 5.8). The general term *organelle* may be applied to distinct cellular bodies such as the nucleus, the various membranes, and other structures we shall encounter below.

Most cells contain a single nucleus each, but there are many exceptions. As already noted in Chap. 4, bacteria and blue-green algae do not contain distinct nuclei at all. Conversely, many other single-celled organisms normally contain more than one nucleus. *Binucleate* and *multinucleate* cells are found with some frequency among multicellular organisms also.

There are exceptions too concerning the individuality of cells, normally maintained by the cell membrane. In certain cases among plant and animal tissues, cell membranes at first form boundaries between individual cells. But at a later stage of development these boundaries dissolve, the result being a fused, continuous living mass with nuclei dispersed through it. Such a structure, in which cellular individuality has been lost, is called a *coenocyte* in plants and a *syncytium* in animals.

Despite variations in the number of nuclei or the occasional loss of the structural discreteness of cells, the fundamentally cellular character of living matter is undeniable even in such exceptional cases. And in all other cases the cellular character is unequivocal, for there we deal with distinct bits of living matter, each bounded by a plasma membrane and often a cell wall and containing one nucleus.

Nucleus and cytoplasm.   A nucleus typically consists of three kinds of components: the more or less gel-like nuclear sap, or *nucleoplasm*, in which are suspended the *chromosomes*, and one or more *nucleoli* (Fig. 5.9). The chromosomes are the principal nuclear structures. Indeed, a nucleus as a whole may be regarded primarily as a protective housing for these slender, thread-like organelles. Chemically, chromosomes consist largely of protein and of nucleic acids, intimately associated into complexes called *nucleoproteins*. DNA is the principal nucleic acid of the nucleoproteins, but RNA is

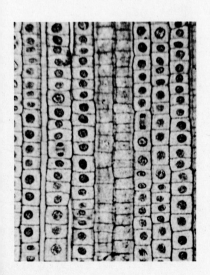
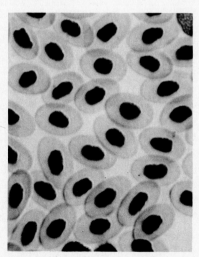

Fig. 5.8.   The general structure of cells. The photos show cells from the root of a plant (left) and red blood cells of a bird. Note the darkly stained nucleus in the center of the cells. (Photo of root cells, courtesy of Dr. M. S. Fuller, University of California; photo of blood cells, General Biological Supply House, Inc.)

also present. Functionally, chromosomes are the carriers of the genes which, as noted on previous occasions, are the ultimate controllers of cellular processes. Monera do not contain formed nuclei, as we have seen, and thus they may not contain formed chromosomes; but all cell types contain genes.

Chromosomes are conspicuous only during cell reproduction, when they become thickly coated with additional nucleoprotein. At other times such coats are absent and chromosomes then are very fine filaments not easily identifiable within the nuclear sap. The exact number of chromosomes within each cell nucleus is an important species-specific trait. For example, cells of human beings contain 46 chromosomes each. Analogously, cells of every other type of organism have their own characteristic chromosome number. A cell rarely contains more than in the order of 100 chromosomes. Therefore, since there are several million different kinds of organisms, many kinds share the same chromosome number. To be sure, possession of the same *numbers* of chromosomes does not mean possession of the same *types*.

A nucleolus ("little nucleus") is a spherical organelle which also consists largely of nucleoprotein. But the only type of nucleic acid present here is RNA. As we shall see in a later chapter, nucleoli are derivatives of chromosomes and they appear to play an important role in the control of protein synthesis within cells. Given cell types contain a fixed number of nucleoli per nucleus.

The whole nucleus is separated from the surrounding cytoplasm by the nuclear membrane. This organelle, like most other living membranes, is constructed mainly of proteins and lipids. It governs the vital traffic of materials between cytoplasm and nucleus.

If the nucleus, by virtue of its genes, is the control center of cellular functions, then the cytoplasm is the executive center. In it the directives of the nucleus are carried out. But it should be emphasized at once that such a functional distinction between nucleus and cytoplasm should not be taken too rigorously. Although the nucleus primarily controls, it also executes many directives of the cytoplasm; and although the cytoplasm primarily executes, it also influences many nuclear processes. As we shall see later, a vital reciprocal interdependence binds nucleus and cytoplasm, and experi-

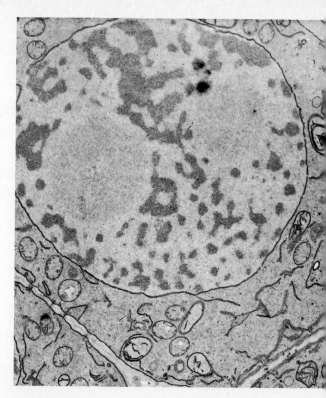

Fig. 5.9. Electron micrograph of a cell nucleus. The whole round structure covering most of the photograph is the nucleus; cytoplasm is outside it. Note the nuclear bounding membrane. Within the nucleus, the dark patches are the gene-containing chromatin and the two large, rounded, clear areas are nucleoli. (Courtesy of Dr. W. G. Whaley, University of Texas, and *Am. J. Botany,* vol. 47, p. 401.)

ment has repeatedly shown that one cannot long survive without the other.

Cytoplasm consists of a semifluid ground substance, which is in a sol or a gel state at different times and in different cellular regions, and in which are suspended large numbers of various organelles. These may have the shape of granules, rodlets, filaments, or droplets. The following are cytoplasmic organelles widespread among many or all cell types:

Mitochondria. Found in all nonmoneran cells, these round or filamentous organelles contain adenosine phosphates and respiratory enzymes, that is, enzymes required in energy-producing reactions. Mitochondria are

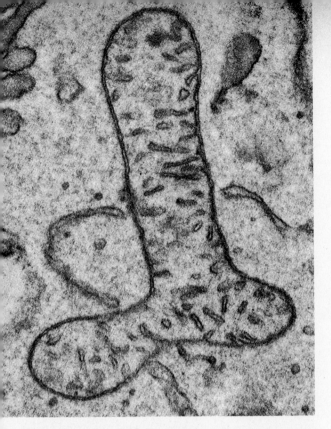

Fig. 5.10. Electron micrograph of a mitochondrion. Note the double-layered mitochondrial membrane and the infoldings of the inner layer of the membrane. (Courtesy of Dr. W. G. Whaley, University of Texas, and *Am. J. Botany*, vol. 47, p. 401.)

the principal chemical "factories" in which cellular respiration is carried out (Fig. 5.10).

Ribosomes. These organelles are exceedingly tiny granules, visible under the electron microscope (Fig. 5.11). Present in all cells studied, ribosomes contain RNA (hence the "ribo-" portion of their name) and enzymes required particularly in protein synthesis. Ribosomes are the principal "factories" in which cellular proteins are manufactured.

Golgi bodies. These structures are probably universal in cells, and they appear variously as complexes of droplets or as stacks of thin platelike layers, or as mixtures of these and other configurations (Fig. 5.12). Golgi bodies are believed to function in the manufacture of cellular secretion products, for these organelles are particularly conspicuous in actively secreting

cells. For example, whenever gland cells are producing their characteristic secretions, the Golgi bodies of such cells become very prominent.

Plastids. These round, oval, or disk-shaped organelles are found in most photosynthesizing cells. A plastid may contain pigments, and if one of the pigments is *chlorophyll,* then the plastid is given the name *chloroplast.* In addition to chlorophyll and other pigments, chloroplasts also contain nucleoprotein, enzymes, and indeed the whole chemical machinery required in photosynthesis (Fig. 5.13).

Centrioles. In the cells of some algae, some fungi, and all animals, a single small granule is located just outside the cell nucleus. As will be shown later, such centrioles function in cell production.

Apart from the organelles just listed, cytoplasm generally contains additional *granules,* and fluid-filled droplets bounded by membranes, called *vacuoles.* Such cytoplasmic granules and vacuoles perform a large variety of functions. They may be vehicles transporting raw materials from the cell surface to interior processing centers (e.g., *food vacuoles*) or finished products in the opposite direction (e.g., *secretion granules*); they may be places of storage (e.g., *starch granules, fat vacuoles, water vacuoles, pigment granules*); they may

Fig. 5.11. Electron micrograph of portion of cytoplasm showing ribosomes (fine dark granules). (Courtesy of Dr. W. G. Whaley, University of Texas, and *Am. J. Botany*, vol. 47, p. 401.)

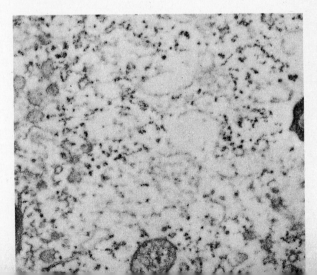

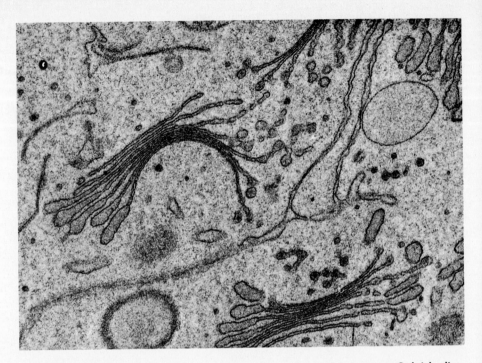

Fig. 5.12. Electron micrograph of portion of cytoplasm showing two Golgi bodies. Each such body consists of stacks of parallel membranous layers. (Courtesy of Dr. W. G. Whaley, University of Texas.)

be vehicles transporting waste materials to points of elimination (e.g., *excretory vacuoles*); or they may be special processing centers themselves.

In addition to all these, cytoplasm may or may not contain a variety of long, thin *fibrils* made predominantly out of protein (e.g., contractile *myofibrils*, conducting *neurofibrils*). Various other organelles, unique to given cell types and serving unique functions, may also be present. In general, every function a cell performs, common or not, is based on a particular organelle in which the machinery for that function is housed.

Cytoplasm as a whole is normally in motion. Irregular eddying and streaming occur at some times, and at others the substance of a cell is subjected to cyclical currents, a movement known as *cyclosis*. Most of the organelles, the nucleus included, are swept along passively in these streams. The specific cause of such motions is unknown, but there is little doubt that they are a reflection of the uninterrupted chemical and physical changes which take place on the molecular

level. Whatever the specific causes may be, the apparently random movements might give the impression that nothing is fixed within a cell and that cytoplasm is simply a collection of loose organelles suspended in "soup."

But this impression is erroneous, as examination under the electron microscope shows. The ground substance of cytoplasm, which under the light microscope does appear to be a fluid, structureless soup, actually turns out to be highly structured and organized. A network of exceedingly fine membranes can be shown to traverse the cytoplasm from plasma membrane to nuclear membrane and in many cases also from cell to cell. This network is known as the *endoplasmic reticulum* (Fig. 5.14). Linked to it are the nucleus, the mitochondria, the ribosomes, and all the other cytoplasmic organelles. Thus, little is really "loose" in a cell. When cytoplasm as a whole streams and moves, the endoplasmic reticulum streams and moves too and the organelles are carried along, still held to the ultramicroscopic network. Evidently, even though the contents of a cell may shift position and the cell as a whole may be deformable, an orderly structural integration of the interior persists nevertheless. Indeed, this is essential if cellular functions are to be orderly and integrated.

The cell surface.   Every cell as a whole is bounded by a *cell membrane.* Composed predominantly of protein and lipid substances, this important structure is far more than a passive outer skin. It is an active, highly selective, semipermeable membrane which regulates the entry and exit of materials into and out of a cell. The membrane therefore plays a critical role in all cell functions, since directly or indirectly every cell function necessitates *absorption* of materials from the exterior, *excretion* of materials from the interior, or both. We

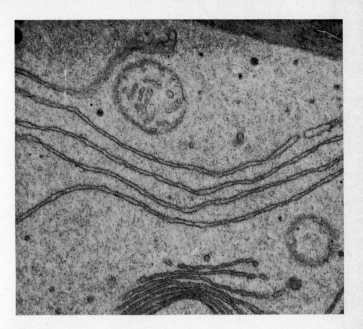

Fig. 5.14.   Electron micrograph showing portion of endo-plasmic reticulum. Note that the reticulum consists of an array of double membranes. (Courtesy of Dr. W. G. Whaley, University of Texas.)

shall have occasion in many later contexts to consider some of the specific activities of cell membranes.

Nearly all plant cells possess a *cell wall* of cellulose, situated around the cell membrane (Fig 5.15). A *primary cell wall* is that part of the wall which is formed while a cell grows and develops. Mature, nongrowing cells often deposit additional materials on the inner

Fig. 5.13.   Electron micrograph showing section through a whole chloroplast. Note layered structure and more densely layered regions called grana. A granum is a functional unit in which photosynthesis takes place. (Courtesy of Dr. A. J. Hodge, California Institute of Technology, and *J. Biophys. Biochem. Cytol.,* vol. 1, p. 605.)

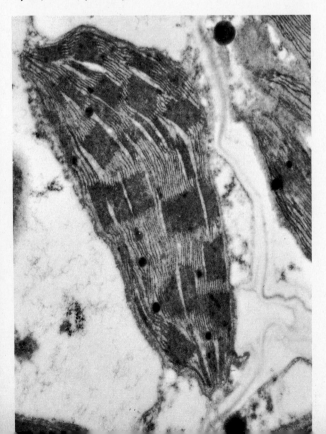

Fig. 5.15.   Diagram of a plant cell showing cell walls.

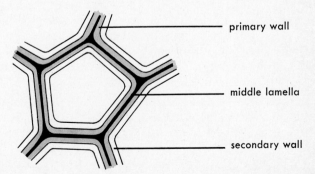

— primary wall

— middle lamella

— secondary wall

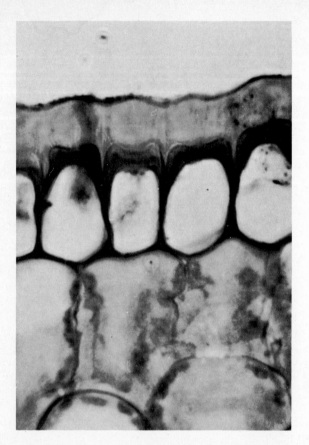

Fig. 5.16. Portion of a leaf showing epidermal cells with thick, dark walls and a waxy cuticle on their exposed surfaces. (Courtesy of Dr. M. S. Fuller, University of California.)

shells of lime, glass (silica), or organic substances are among other external covers manufactured by many cell types.

Many kinds of cells have the capacity of locomotion, and among these, many are equipped with distinct locomotor structures on the cell surface. Such structures are principally *flagella*, long, slender projections. The base of a flagellum is anchored in the cytoplasm of a cell, on a distinct granule known as a *kinetosome* or *basal granule*. This granule controls the motion of the flagellum. In most cases, a cell bears from one to four flagella, all originating from the same surface region. But in some cases the number is very much larger and each flagellum then originates at a separate surface point. Such flagella are usually called *cilia* (Fig. 5.17). Cilia and flagella are found widely among Protista, where they are the major means of propulsion and of creating food-bearing currents in the external water environment. Cilia and flagella are also widespread among plants and animals. For example,

Fig. 5.17. The ciliate protozoon *Tetrahymena* stained to show the cilia and their arrangement on the body surface. Note the basal granules. (Courtesy of Dr. Norman Williams, Iowa State University.)

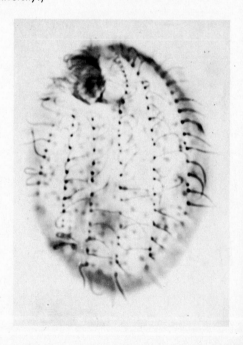

surfaces of their primary walls, and such additions form a *secondary cell wall*. Adjacent plant cells are held together by a thin layer of cementing material, called a *middle lamella*. Plant cells exposed directly to the external air secrete *cuticles* on their exposed surfaces, in addition to cell walls. Such cuticles are made of waxy and fatty materials and they make the exposed cells relatively impermeable to water (Fig. 5.16).

Walls of cellulose and cuticles of wax are not found among animal cells, but in many cases animal cells too surround themselves with walls or cuticles. For example, a coat of *chitin* is found on the skin cells of insects and many other invertebrates. Analogously, the surface cells of mammalian skin and hair secrete external coats made of the protein *keratin*. Skeletal the sperm cells of all but the most advanced plants move by means of flagella. Many embryos, larvae, and small adult animals move by means of ciliated skins. And many animal tissue cells, like those lining the ducts of the breathing and reproductive systems, possess ciliated surfaces.

The above outlines some of the main organizational features of cells generally. As we have seen, certain of the components of the nucleus, the cytoplasm, or the cell surface may be associated directly with well-circumscribed cell functions. Photosynthesis and respiration, for example, are distinct functions performed in distinct cytoplasmic structures; see Table 3 for a summary of such correlations. But many cell functions cannot be localized so neatly. For example, cell reproduction requires the cooperative activity of many or all of the cellular organelles. Functions of this kind cannot be referred to any particular part of a cell, but must be referred to the cell as a whole.

TABLE 3

Some structural components of cells and their correlated functions

structure	function
nucleus	
chromosomes	ultimate control of cell activities
nucleolus	auxiliary to protein synthesis
nuclear membrane	traffic control to and from cytoplasm
cytoplasm	
mitochondria	site of respiration
ribosomes	site of protein synthesis
Golgi bodies	site of secretion synthesis
chloroplasts	site of photosynthesis
centrioles	auxiliary to cell division
granules } vacuoles }	transport, storage, processing centers
fibrils	contraction, conduction
surface	
plasma membrane	traffic control to and from cell
cell walls } cuticles }	protection, support, cell shape
cilia } flagella }	locomotion, current creation

Note in this connection that, whereas many cell structures are bulky enough to be visible under the microscope, even more are not visible; individual molecules in a cell "function" no less than larger molecular aggregates. Note also that *each* cellular structure performs a function, and as the structures differ among cells, so do the functions; different cells are differently *specialized*.

TISSUES, ORGANS, ORGAN SYSTEMS

A tissue may be defined as an aggregation of cells in which each *cooperates* with all others in the performance of a particular group function. Tissues may be highly or less highly specialized, according to the degree of specialization of the component cells. An organ is an aggregation of tissues all of which cooperate in their turn in the performance of a group function. Analogously, an organ system is a cooperating aggregation of organs. As pointed out in Chap. 2, multicellular organisms differ in structural complexity according to whether they contain tissues only, or tissues and organs only, or tissues and organs as well as organ systems. We shall examine the general organization of the most advanced multicellular types, in which all these levels of complexity are represented.

The plant pattern. The principal tissue types of an advanced plant such as a flowering herb may be identified in the stem or the root. In these body parts the tissues are arranged in a concentric, radially symmetrical pattern (Fig. 5.18).

The outermost tissue is the *epidermis*, a protective cover one cell layer thick. In the epidermal cells of the stem, the parts of the cell walls which face the atmosphere are usually thickened by the deposition of waxy cuticles (see Fig. 5.16). At numerous points in the stem epidermis, *guard cells* are present. These are crescent-shaped, and they are paired in such a way that the concave side of one faces the concave side of another. Along these concave sides the cell walls are thicker than elsewhere. The pore enclosed by two such paired cells is a *stoma* (Fig. 5.19).

A stoma can open or close when the water volume increases or decreases within a pair of guard cells. These cells usually are the only epidermal cells that

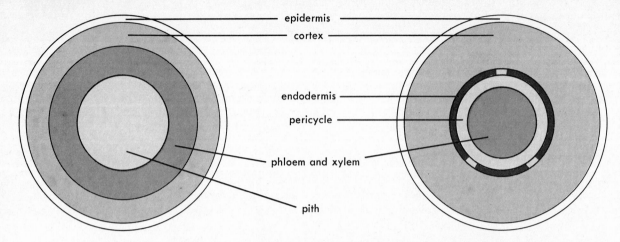

Fig. 5.18. **The typical arrangement of the tissues in a stem (left) and a root (right).** Phloem, xylem, pericycle, and pith are components of the stele.

contain chloroplasts and carry on photosynthesis. During the day, photosynthesis takes place and carbohydrates are produced. These foodstuffs increase the concentration of particles within the guard cells. As a result, water from surrounding epidermal cells is drawn osmotically into the guard cells. The cells swell up and the thin outer portions of the cell walls curve out farther under the increased water pressure. This pulls the inner thicker portions of the walls apart and the stoma opens. Conversely, when carbohydrates are being used up, as at night, the water volume of the guard cells

decreases. Their elastic walls then revert to the original position and the stoma closes. Guard-cell movements control the entry and exit of atmospheric gases through the body surface of the plant.

The cells of the root epidermis do not possess waxy cuticles, and guard cells are absent also. However, present in places are so-called *root-hair cells*, which carry fingerlike extensions of the cell cytoplasm on the side exposed to soil (Fig. 5.20). Such "hairs" greatly increase the surface area of the cells, a significant feature in nutrient absorption.

Fig. 5.19. **Surface view of epidermis showing a pair of chloroplast-containing guard cells enclosing a stoma.** (Ward's Natural Science Establishment, Inc.)

Fig. 5.20. **Root epidermis with root hairs.** (Courtesy of Dr. M. S. Fuller, University of California.)

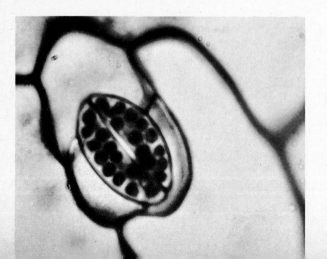

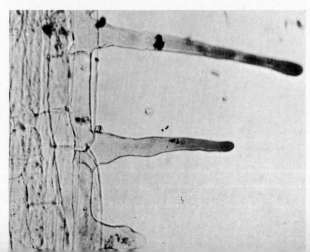

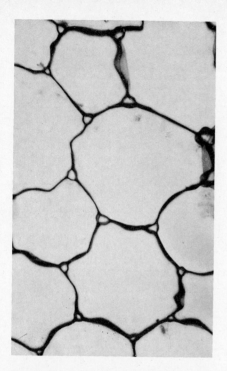

Fig. 5.21.   Parenchyma. (Courtesy of Dr. M. S. Fuller, University of California.)

Underneath the epidermis is a tissue called the *cortex*. It is composed of several layers of so-called *parenchyma cells,* a relatively unspecialized cell type found also in other tissues as we shall see (Fig. 5.21). The cortex is green and food-producing in stems, non-green and food-storing in roots. In both root and stem, the cortex also transports water. Adjacent to the innermost layer of the cortex is the *endodermis* tissue. In most stems the endodermis is developed very incompletely, and in some it may not be present at all. But in roots the endodermis is usually quite prominent. It is composed of a single layer of fairly large cells, most of them impregnated on their outer surfaces with a waterproofing material called *suberin* (Fig. 5.22). In certain regions of the root, small groups of endodermis cells do not manufacture suberin. These are called *passage cells;* as we shall see later, they play an important role in water transport through the root.

Toward the inside of the endodermis is a group of tissues known collectively as the *stele.* The outermost tissue of the stele, directly adjacent to the endodermis, is the *pericycle.* In most stems the pericycle, like the endodermis, is developed very incompletely and in some stems it may not be present at all. But in roots

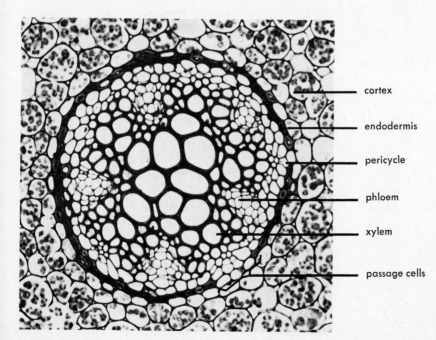

cortex

endodermis

pericycle

phloem

xylem

passage cells

Fig. 5.22. The central tissues in the stele of a buttercup root. The stele includes all the tissues within the endodermis. See also Fig. 9.12. (Courtesy of Dr. M. S. Fuller, University of California.)

the pericycle is fairly conspicuous, being composed here of one or more layers of parenchyma cells (see Fig. 5.22).

Toward the inside of the pericycle, a second tissue of the stele is the *phloem*. This is a highly composite and specialized tissue; it is composed of several types of cells, including parenchyma cells and so-called *companion cells* and *sieve-tube cells*. The latter are placed end to end, in vertical columns called *sieve tubes*. These extend uninterruptedly through root and stem into the leaves. When sieve-tube cells mature, their nuclei disintegrate and disappear. The adjacent companion cells then apparently control the activities of the remaining sieve-tube cytoplasm. Where sieve-tube cells adjoin top and bottom, performations develop in the cell walls. Such perforated areas are *sieve plates;* they presumably facilitate the passage of organic nutrients through a sieve tube. Food conduction is in fact the principal function of sieve tubes and of phloem tissue as a whole. Because of this, phloem is referred to as one of the two *vascular* tissues of plants (Fig. 5.23).

The other vascular tissue is *xylem*, also part of the stele and located typically toward the inside of phloem.

Fig. 5.23. Diagrammatic representation of a unit of phloem tissue. Note the nucleated companion cell, the sieve plates, and the nonnucleated sieve tube. Cytoplasm fills the sieve tube.

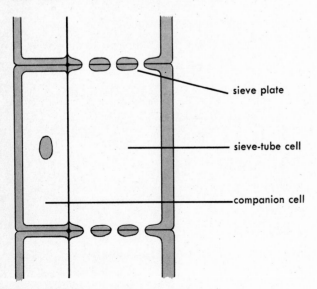

sieve plate

sieve-tube cell

companion cell

Like phloem, xylem is highly composite and specialized. Among its various components are parenchyma cells, as well as *tracheids* and *vessels*. Tracheids are elongated, spindle-shaped, thick-walled cells which form vertical columns extending from root to leaf. During the development of tracheids all interior living matter disintegrates, and the remaining cell walls then enclose only water. Vertical columns of thick-walled cells also constitute the early developmental stages of vessels. In later stages, the living matter as well as the top and bottom sections of the walls of the cells disintegrate, leaving a mature vessel as a hollow, water-filled tube (Fig. 5.24). Both tracheids and vessels function in vertical water conduction, and also in mechanical support of the plant as a whole; the thick walls of the tracheids and vessels in xylem lend rigidity to the plant body. When large quantities of xylem are present in a plant, this tissue is identifiable with the naked eye as *wood*.

The last of the basic tissues of the stele is the *pith*. It is not present in roots, and in stems it is located right at the center, surrounded by xylem. Pith is composed of parenchyma cells which store food (Fig. 5.25).

Clearly, these various tissues are not "just there," but are organized in a definite geometrical pattern. Because of this pattern, functional cooperation among the tissues becomes possible. The main cooperative functions of the tissues are, in the stem, support against gravity, conduction, and manufacture of organic nutrients; and in the root, support in soil, conduction, and absorption of inorganic nutrients. As noted, several tissues which cooperate functionally can be designated as an organ, and stems and roots actually are two of the kinds of organs found in a plant.

Two other sets of organs occur in vascular plants, namely, *leaves* and *reproductive organs*. As we shall see later, these are formed largely from the same kinds of cells and tissues present in stems and roots. In at least one instance among plants, several whole organs cooperate functionally and form the still more complex organization of an organ system. This is the case in cones and flowers. As we shall find, these consist of several reproductive and other associated organs, all contributing to the one overall function of propagation.

More than just one type of organ system is characteristic of advanced animals.

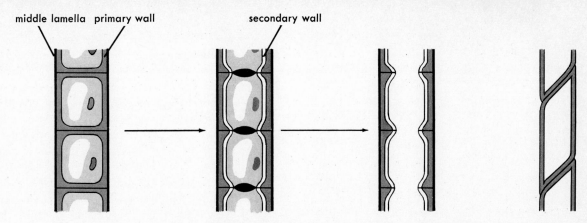

middle lamella primary wall   secondary wall

Fig. 5.24.   Sequence on left, the development of a xylem vessel. Far right, diagram of a tracheid, another component of xylem.

The animal pattern. Two general classes of animal tissues may be distinguished, namely, *connective tissues* and *epithelia*. Often not included in these two groups are three specific tissues, *blood, nerve tissue,* and *muscle tissue.*

In connective tissues, the cells are usually separated from one another by greater or lesser amounts of intercellular spaces which are variously filled with fluid and solid materials. Another identifying characteristic is the relatively unspecialized nature of the cells. With appropriate stimulation, they may transform from one connective-tissue cell type into another. In these respects, the cells are roughly equivalent to the parenchyma and parenchymalike cells of plants.

In so-called *loose connective tissues,* the most conspicuous components are large numbers of threadlike fibers, some of them tough and strong, some of them elastic. These fibers are suspended in fluid and form an irregular, loosely arranged meshwork (Fig. 5.26). The cells of the tissue are dispersed throughout the mesh and are of various types. Many are spindle-shaped *fibrocytes,* believed to be the chief fiber-forming cells. Others are *histiocytes,* capable of amoeboid locomotion and of engulfing foreign bodies (e.g., bacteria in infected regions). Also present are *pigment cells, fat cells,* and *mesenchyme cells.* The latter are embryonic, undeveloped, and relatively quite unspecialized; they may develop into any of the other cell types of the tissue.

By virtue of its cellular components, loose connective tissue functions in food storage and in body defense; and by virtue of its fibers, the tissue is a major binding agent which holds one body part to another. For example, the tissue connects skin to underlying muscle;

Fig. 5.25.   Section through a bean stem. (Ripon Microslides.)

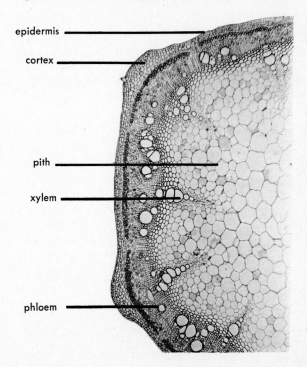

epidermis

cortex

pith

xylem

phloem

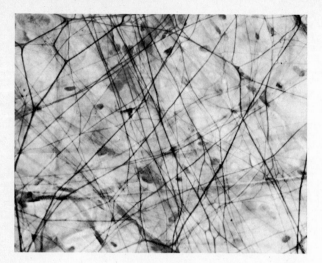

Fig. 5.26.   Loose connective tissue. Note the conspicuous fibers forming a meshwork, and the cells (small dark dots) embedded in the meshwork. (General Biological Supply House, Inc.)

the tough fibers provide connecting strength, yet the elastic fibers still permit the skin to slide over the muscle to some extent. In man, fat stored in loose connective tissue under the skin is responsible for the generally rounded contours of females and is partly responsible for the obese appearance of overweight persons.

Variant types of loose connective tissue may be distinguished on the basis of differences in the relative quantities of the cellular and the fibrous components. For example, *tendons* are dense tissues containing only fibrocytes and tough fibers, the fibers being arranged as closely packed parallel bundles (Fig. 5.27). Tendons typically connect muscles to cartilage or bone. A *ligament* is similar to a tendon, except that both tough and elastic fibers are present and that these are arranged in more or less irregular manner. Another variant of loose connective tissue is *adipose tissue*, in which fat cells are the most abundant components. Each fat cell contains a large fat droplet which fills almost the entire cellular space. A large collection of such cells has the external appearance of a continuous mass of fat. Still other variants of loose connective tissue are known.

In so-called *hard connective tissues*, the cellular components secrete organic and, especially, inorganic materials which form a solid precipitate around the cells. Thus the cells appear as islands embedded in hard intercellular deposits. The chief variants of this tissue type are *cartilage* and *bone* (Fig. 5.28). Calcium phosphate is the main inorganic constituent of bone. The functions of cartilage and bone are twofold; they support (e.g., the long bony rods of the appendages, which hold other tissues around them) and they protect (e.g., the flat bony plates of the skull, which cover the underlying brain).

As these examples indicate, connective tissues as a whole serve largely in forming the structural scaffolding of the animal body. Primarily functional parts of the body are formed chiefly by the epithelial tissues. An epithelium is a tissue in which the cells are cemented directly to one another and so form a single-layered sheet, a multilayered sheet, or an irregular, compact, three-dimensional aggregate.

Sheets consisting of a single layer of cells are called *simple epithelia*. Distinctions among them are made principally on the basis of cell shape; the cells may be *flattened* as in membranes, or *cuboidal* as in ducts, or *columnar* as in the inner lining of the gut (Fig. 5.29). If several epithelial layers are stacked into a multilayered sheet, the term *stratified epithelium* is often applied. The epidermis, that is, the outermost tissue of

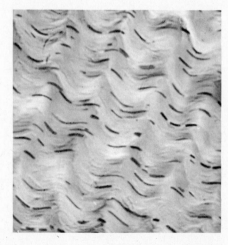

Fig. 5.27.   Photomicrograph of a tendon. Note the parallel arrangement of the fibers and the cells (dark spots) among the fibers.

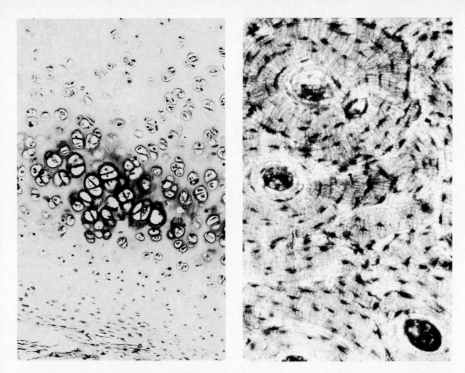

Fig. 5.28.   Left, section through cartilage. Note the many cartilage-producing cells, surrounded by their own secretions. Right, section through bone. Bone-producing cells are located in the dark patches, arranged in concentric patterns. Hard bone substance, light in the photo, surrounds the cells. (Left, General Biological Supply House, Inc.; right, Ward's Natural Science Establishment, Inc.)

the skin, is a good example of a stratified epithelium.

In contrast to the connective tissues, the epithelia are all fairly highly and permanently specialized. Once their cells are mature, they do not thereafter change in their basic structural characteristics. Also, by the time maturity is reached, the cells have acquired given fixed functions which are then performed throughout the life of the animal.

In most respects quite like an epithelium is *muscle tissue*, undoubtedly the most abundant tissue in most animals. In a man, as much as two-thirds of the total body weight is muscle weight. Muscle is also one of the most characteristically "animal" tissues, and there is no general body function that does not involve muscular contraction in some way.

Three types of muscle tissue may be distinguished: *smooth* muscle, which is generally not connected with the skeleton and is not under voluntary nervous control; *striated* muscle, which does connect with the skeleton and can be controlled voluntarily; and *cardiac* muscle, the specially structured contractile tissue of the heart (Fig. 5.30).

Fig. 5.29.   Section through the intestinal mucosa of a frog, a simple columnar epithelium lining the inner surface of the gut wall. (General Biological Supply House, Inc.)

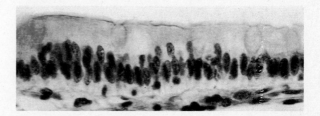

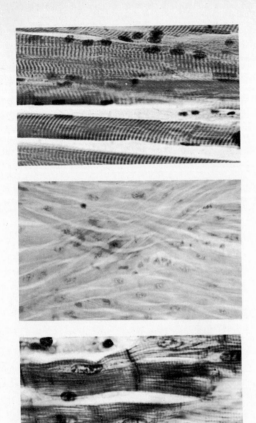

Fig. 5.30.   Top, a few fibers of skeletal muscle. Note the cross striations and the many nuclei within each fiber. Middle, smooth muscle. Note the spindle-shaped cells. Bottom, heart muscle. Note the branched fibers, the nuclei, the faint longitudinal fibrils within each fiber, and the faint cross striations. (General Biological Supply House, Inc.)

Living muscles are never completely relaxed. Mild contractions occur all the time, groups of cells working in relays. A definite *muscle tone* is thereby maintained, and it is through this that muscles preserve body shape and posture and provide structural support in general. (Note here that numerous animals, e.g., worms, do not possess skeletons; muscles then are the principal supporting structures.) Stronger contractions, above and beyond tonic ones, produce movement of internal organs or locomotion.

The manner in which various tissues are joined

cooperatively into an organ may be illustrated by considering a structure such as the small intestine (Fig. 5.31).

The wall of this organ consists of four main layers formed by at least six or seven different tissues. The innermost layer is the *mucosa*, composed principally of a simple columnar epithelium (see Fig. 5.29). Its chief function is to complete the digestion of foods and to absorb the digested nutrients from the cavity of the gut. Adjoining the mucosa outside is the *submucosa*, a layer of loose connective tissue in which are present numerous blood vessels, lymph vessels, and nerve fibers. The principal function of the submucosa is to transfer nutrients from the mucosa into the blood and lymph streams for further distribution into other parts of the body. Surrounding the submucosa is the *muscularis*, the chief muscle tissue of the gut wall. This tissue is composed of smooth muscle, and it contains an inner circular and an outer longitudinal sublayer. More nerve tissue is present between these two muscle layers. The muscularis maintains the tubular shape of the gut, and it also produces a series of gut movements which play important roles in digestion. The outermost layer of the intestinal wall is the *serosa*, composed of an inner sublayer of loose connective tissue and an outer sublayer of simple flat epithelium. The serosa as a whole is the limiting membrane of the gut, and it is continuous with the membranes which keep the entire intestine in place within the body.

All these component tissues of the small intestine cooperate in performing the one group function of food processing. An array of other organs, each similarly constructed out of two or more tissues, carries out other functions of food processing. Included here are, for example, mouth, stomach, liver, pancreas, salivary glands, large intestine, and others. Together these organs constitute a specialized organ system, namely, the *alimentary system*.

The most complex animals, man included, possess a total of ten organ systems:

the *integumentary* system, including skin and skin appendages such as hair, feathers, scales, nails, and skin glands, which serves as outer cover and protective device for the whole animal

the *circulatory*, *breathing*, and *excretory* systems, which ferry foods, gases, and wastes between the skin and the body interior, and within the interior

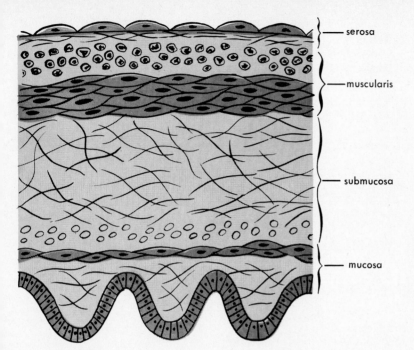

— serosa

— muscularis

— submucosa

— mucosa

Fig. 5.31. Cross section through a portion of the intestinal wall, diagrammatic. The four principal tissue layers are indicated. Note that the mucosa is usually far more extensively folded than suggested in the diagram.

the *alimentary* system, which processes available foods into usable ones

the *skeletal* and *muscular* systems, which provide support, protection, and the means of motion

the *reproductive* system, which propagates the animal

the *nervous* and *endocrine* systems, which coordinate the activities of all organs and systems into a harmonious pattern

In given animal groups, some or others of these systems may not be present. As already noted, for example, worms of all kinds do not possess skeletal systems. Vertebrates and insects are the principal groups which possess endocrine systems. Many primitive animals do not possess circulatory or breathing or excretory systems. In all such animals, as indeed also in plants, the functions which are performed elsewhere

by systems are performed by individual cells or individual tissues or individual organs.

All the various parts of an organism, from atoms to organ systems, are united physically to form a distinct whole, clearly separated from other such wholes. The individual organism so becomes the most readily identifiable "unit" of the living world. Yet, notwithstanding this physical discreteness, we know that the biological organization of living matter does not stop with the organism; each organism is itself but a component of higher levels of organization. Moreover, the invisible biological bonds which unite organisms on these higher levels are just as real and powerful as the more material bonds between units within an organism. The structure of these higher levels and the nature of their bonds will be the subjects of the next chapters.

Review questions

1. What are inorganic compounds? Organic compounds? What principal classes of each occur in living matter and in what relative amounts? Which of these substances are electrolytes and which are nonelectrolytes?

2. Review the chemical composition and molecular structure of carbohydrates. What are monosaccharides, disaccharides, and polysaccharides? Give examples of each. What are fats and fatty acids? In what kinds of reactions

may carbohydrates and fats participate and what general roles do they play in living matter?

3. What are proteins and how are they constructed? What is protein specificity? How is a coagulated protein different from a native or a denatured protein? Review the general biological roles of proteins.

4. What is the chemical composition and molecular structure of nucleic acids? In chemical terms, what are DNA and RNA? What is their relation to nucleoproteins? How are nucleotides related to DNA and RNA? What different kinds of nucleotides occur in living matter?

5. What is a colloidal system? How does such a system differ from a solution? Review the properties of colloidal systems.

6. Define diffusion and show how and under what conditions this process will occur. What is the biological significance of diffusion?

7. Define osmosis. Show how and under what condi-tions this process will occur. Distinguish carefully between osmosis and diffusion. Cite examples of biological situations characterized by isotonicity, hypertonicity, and hypotonicity.

8. What are the structural subdivisions of cells? What are the main components of each of these subdivisions, where are they found, and what functions do they carry out?

9. Review the structural and functional characteristics of cell types among plants. Which cell types function primarily in conduction? In mechanical support? What cell types are unique to roots? To aerial portions of a plant? Describe the tissue composition of an organ such as a stem.

10. What basic types of tissues are characteristic of animals? Describe the structural characteristics and principal variants of these tissues and give examples. Show how such tissues are combined to form specific organs. Name the organ systems of man and for each list some of the organs which compose it.

Suggested collateral readings

Brachet, J.: The Living Cell, *Sci. Am.*, vol. 205, 1961.

Bushwell, A. M., and W. H. Rodebush: Water, *Sci. Am.*, vol. 194, 1956.

Crick, F. H. C.: Nucleic Acids, *Sci. Am.*, vol. 197, 1957.

Doty, P.: Proteins, *Sci. Am.*, vol. 197, 1957.

Gross, J.: Collagen, *Sci. Am.*, vol. 204, 1961.

Holter, H.: How Things Get into Cells, *Sci. Am.*, vol. 205, 1961.

Satir, P.: Cilia, *Sci. Am.*, vol. 204, 1961.

Schmitt, F. O.: Giant Molecules in Cells and Tissues, *Sci. Am.*, vol. 197, 1957.

Solomon, A. K.: Pores in the Cell Membrane, *Sci. Am.*, vol. 203, 1960.

Stein, W. H., and S. Moore: The Chemical Structure of Proteins, *Sci. Am.*, vol. 202, 1961.

SPECIES AND COMMUNITY

Being a specialized entity, every organism depends on other organisms for some essential product or process; no organism can survive entirely by itself. Cooperative aggregations of organisms are as ancient as organisms themselves, and as the ones evolved, so did the others. Moreover, the same principles and consequences of aggregation described previously for organizational levels below the organism hold also for the levels above.

In this chapter, we shall deal with two major levels above the organism, the *species* and the *community*. As one of the specialized groupings under the species level, we shall also examine the *society*, and as one of the expressions of community living, we shall discuss parasitism and other forms of *symbiosis*.

The species

THE NATURE OF A SPECIES

The smallest organizational group formed by organisms of the same kind is the *family*. This is a rather temporary type of association characteristic of only very few kinds of organisms, namely, some of the vertebrate animals (see below). Also more or less temporary and typical of only certain animal organisms are larger associations of families of the same kind into *tribes* or *herds*. But, whether or not like organisms form families and herds, they always form a next higher grouping, namely, local *populations*.

A population is a relatively permanent association of organisms of the same kind. It is encountered among all types of organisms; the dandelions in a field, the pines in a forest, the earthworms in a plot of soil, the minnows in a pond, and the people in a village—all are examples of local populations. Individual organisms multiply and die, emigrate or immigrate, but collectively the population persists. It may split into subpopulations or it may fuse with adjacent sister populations, yet the basic characteristics of the group as a whole do not thereby change. Structurally, the geographic extent of a population may vary vastly, from the space in a laboratory test tube to a space of continental or oceanic proportions. Likewise, population density may vary greatly. Functionally, the fundamental unifying link of a population is that *its members interbreed more or less preferentially with one another*. However, fairly frequent interbreeding with members of sister populations does occur in addition. A population thus is a reproductively cohesive unit, integrated more loosely with other such units.

The sum of all the populations of the same kind and therefore the sum of all the organisms of the same kind forms a *species*. For example, all the corn plants on earth, all the bullfrogs on earth, all the human beings on earth, each group represents a species. Even more so than the population, the species is a universal, very permanent grouping.

The identifying feature of a species is that the member organisms usually interbreed *only* with one another and *not* with members of other species. Whereas cross-mating occurs more or less freely *within* a species, it does not generally occur *between* species. For example, bullfrogs from any part of the world may mate with bullfrogs from any other part. Similarly, grass frogs may mate with other grass frogs—and only grass frogs. But even though bullfrogs and grass frogs may, and often do, inhabit the same pond, they never interbreed. They represent two different species.

Evidently, some kind of *reproductive barrier* exists between species. In many cases, as between bullfrogs and grass frogs, the barrier is *biological* and interbreed-

ing then is impossible regardless of how close the organisms are. Bullfrogs and grass frogs have incompatible structures and functions and sperms from one cannot successfully fertilize the eggs of the other. In numerous other cases, the eggs and sperms of different species *are* compatible, yet effective biological barriers still exist. For example, the breeding season in one group may occur a few weeks earlier or later than in another, or the members of one group may be active only at night, those of another only in the daytime. Interbreeding will be impossible under such circumstances.

In still other instances, the reproductive barriers are not biological but *environmental*. Impassable mountains, unfordable rivers, pronounced climatic differences, or merely great distances between one territory and another may make contact between groups impossible and reproductive isolation will be the consequence. In given cases, interbreeding might still occur if the isolating condition were removed, but in nature such removals do not normally occur. Therefore, when two different species *do not* interbreed in nature, this does not always mean that they *cannot* interbreed. In many cases, members of different species may be brought together in the laboratory and there they interbreed perfectly well. For example, swordtails and platys, two species of tropical fish (Fig. 6.1), may have offspring in the laboratory quite readily. But in nature they almost never do because they normally live in different parts of a river and simply do not meet.

The development of new environmental isolating conditions is the usual cause of *speciation*, i.e., the origin of new species by the splitting of one into two. For example, if an original parent species ranges over a given large territory, physical barriers may arise in the course of time which may prevent interbreeding between populations at opposite ends of the territory. With reproductive contact so lost, evolution in the now isolated populations may henceforth follow entirely different courses. In effect, the parental species will be split into two new ones. At first, the descendant species will still be rather similar structurally and functionally. In time, however, evolutionary changes are likely to introduce progressively pronounced differences, including biological barriers to interbreeding. These would add to and reinforce the environmental ones already

Fig. 6.1. Platyfish female at top, swordfish male at bottom. These animals belong to different species, and in nature they do not interbreed. But they can and do interbreed in the laboratory. (Courtesy of the Genetics Laboratory, New York Zoological Society.)

in existence. Speciation by this means is the principal way in which new species evolve. Such a process takes, on an average, about 1 million years.

VARIATIONS

In each species, a basic set of structural and functional characteristics is common to all member organisms. For example, no matter in what way or to what degree human beings might differ, they never differ so much that their human status cannot be recognized. Because such common and unique traits do exist, species can be used as fundamental units in classifying organisms (see Chap. 8). However, superimposed on the common traits, differences among the member organisms are equally characteristic of species. We say that the organisms within a species exhibit individual *variations*.

Two classes of variations may be distinguished, *inheritable* and *noninheritable* ones. The first are produced by gene mutations and are controlled by genes. They may therefore be transmitted to offspring. Noninheritable variations are the result of developmental processes within organisms and are not controlled genetically. They therefore disappear from a species with the death of the individuals which exhibit them. Evidently, only inheritable variations can be significant in species evolution. If a man is an athlete, his muscular system is likely to be developed much more than that of the average person. This is an individual variation and a noninheritable one. The degree of muscular development does not depend on heredity, primarily, but only on whether or not a person goes in for athletics. On the other hand, the blood type, the skin color, and the hair color are examples of hereditary variations. They are part of the genetic inheritance from parents and earlier forebears and will, in turn, influence the traits of future offspring generations (Fig. 6.2).

In many and probably in the majority of instances, the variations within a species are correlated with variations in the environment. Among birds and mammals, for example, man not excepted, clear-cut structural differences accompany differences in climatic temperatures. In warm climates, for example, individuals of many animal species tend to have smaller body size, longer ears, tails, and other protrusions, and darker body colors than fellow members of the species living in cold climates. Such structural variations are said to be *adaptive;* that is, they are advantageous to the individuals in the different environments. Smaller bodies and longer ears, for example, make for a large body surface relative to the body volume. Under such conditions evaporation from the skin surface is rapid and the cooling effect of this enhanced evaporation is of considerable benefit in a warm climate. The converse is true in the cool climate. In many instances it may be very difficult to recognize the adaptive value of a variation. And some variations conceivably may be *nonadaptive*, without inherent advantage to the possessors. Human eye color may possibly (but not certainly) be in this category.

Variations within a species may be exceedingly pronounced. Two individuals may be so different structurally and functionally that their common traits become evident only through the most careful study. Familiar examples of this are found in insect societies. These often consist of kings, queens, drones, soldiers, workers, and other "castes," all structurally and functionally very dissimilar. Such instances of great variation indicate a high degree of *specialization* of individuals. In insect societies, for example, each of the

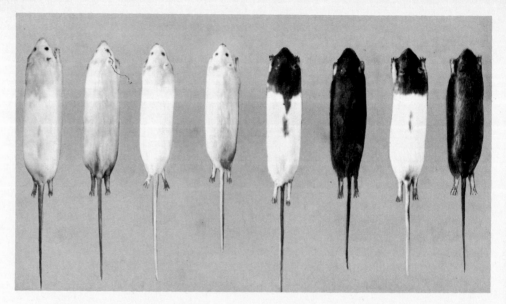

Fig. 6.2. **Inheritable variations.** These are litter-mate rats, produced by the same two parents. Considerable variation in coat color is evident. Such differences arise because even brothers and sisters of the same family may be different genetically. Hereditary (i.e., gene-controlled) variations tend to be more pronounced, the less related the given members of a species. (American Museum of Natural History.)

different types of individuals is specialized to perform only certain jobs and the survival of the society depends on the cooperation of the different members. In one form or another, a high degree of individual variation and specialization is always characteristic of societies, as the following section will show.

Societies

A society is subordinated to the species; it is a special type of population *within* a species. In most cases, the only identifying feature of a population (apart from localized geography) is the preferential interbreeding of the member organisms. In some cases, however, a population is a far more closely knit group, the unifying link being not only interbreeding but also a particularly great structural or functional interdependence of the member organisms. Such a strongly cooperating group is a *social* population.

Societies are characteristic only of animals. Also, all societies have evolved independently of one another and the most advanced societies occur in the most advanced animals: insects and vertebrates.

INSECT SOCIETIES

Highly developed societies occur among termites, ants, bees, and wasps. In these, each member organism is structurally adapted from birth to carry out specific functions in the society. Insect societies, organized somewhat differently in each of the four groups just named, operate in fixed, stereotyped, largely unlearned behavior patterns. In its rigid, inflexible ways, the insect society resembles a human dictatorship, except that among insects there is no dictator, no rule by force. Each member is guided by inherited, instinctive reactions and is unable to carry out any functions other than those for which built-in instincts exist. Insects *can* learn, though only to a limited extent. For example, a bee may be taught to respond differently to different colors and scents, and it may learn a new route to its hive if the hive has been moved.

Social insects have this in common: they build intricate *nests*, and their societies are stratified into *structurally* distinct castes. In each of the four groups, different species form societies of different degrees of complexity. A quite complex society is encountered among honeybees.

A colony of honeybees (Fig. 6.3) is made up of three social ranks: a *queen*, tens or hundreds of male *drones*, and from 20,000 to 80,000 *workers*. The queen and the stingless drones are fertile, and their main functions are reproductive. The smaller-bodied workers are all sterile females. They build the hive, ward off enemies, collect food, feed the queen and the drones, and nurse the young.

When a hive becomes overcrowded, the queen together with some drones and several thousand workers secedes from the colony. The emigrants swarm out and settle temporarily in a tree or other suitable place until a new hive is found. In the old hive, meanwhile, the workers which remain behind raise a small batch of the old queen's eggs in large, specially built honeycomb cells. These eggs develop into new queens. The first one to emerge from its cell immediately searches out the other queen cells and stings their occupants to death. If two new queens happen to emerge at the same time, they at once engage in mortal combat until one remains victorious. The young queen, her succession now undisputed, soon mates with one of the drones. In a nuptial flight high into the air, she receives mil-

Fig. 6.4.   A nurse bee feeds and cleans the larvae in the brood cells. (Copyright © Walt Disney Productions.)

lions of sperms which are stored in a receptacle in her abdomen. The sperms from this single mating last through the entire egg-laying career of the queen.

Among the eggs laid individually into honeycomb cells (Fig. 6.4), some escape fertilization, even in a young queen. None is fertilized in an older queen once her sperm store is exhausted. Unfertilized eggs develop into drones. Fatherless development of this sort, or *natural parthenogenesis,* is widespread among social insects and a number of other animal types, e.g., rotifers, water fleas, brine shrimp. Fertilized eggs develop into larvae and these either into queens or into workers, depending on the type of food the larvae receive from their worker nurses. Larvae to be raised into workers are fed a "regular" diet of plant pollen and honey. Queens form when the larvae receive an especially rich royal jelly, containing pollen, honey, and comparatively huge amounts of certain vitamins. But new queens are not raised while the original queen remains in the hive, healthy and fertile. If the queen produces eggs faster than honeycomb cells can be built, she receives less food from her attendants. Egg production then slows down. Conversely, if she is behind in her egg laying, she is fed more intensively.

Fig. 6.3.   **Honeybees.** Worker on left, queen in middle, drone on right. (U.S. Department of Agriculture.)

In the six weeks or so of its life, a worker bee does not perform the same duties continuously. The age of a bee determines what work it can do; housekeeping tasks are performed by young bees, food-collecting trips are made by older ones. On a food-collecting trip, the bee gathers pollen, rich in protein, and nectar, a thin sugar solution. Pollen is carried home in *pollen baskets* on the hind legs. Nectar is swallowed into the *honey crop*, a specialized part of the alimentary tract, where saliva partially digests the sugar of nectar. On arriving at the hive, the bee first passes a security check on the way in, then unloads its pollen into one cell, and regurgitates its nectar into another. Other bees which happen by pack the pollen tight and start converting nectar into honey. They rapidly beat their wings close to a nectar-filled cell, a process which is continued until most of the water has evaporated. Every now and then a bee samples the product (probably more a matter of hunger than of professional pride in the work). And when the honey is just right (or when all the bees standing by have had their fill?) the cell is sealed up with wax. This is the principal food store for the winter. Pollen is unobtainable at that time and, being perishable, cannot be stored as readily.

Bees and other social insects possess remarkable powers of orientation and communication. On food-collecting trips, bees have been shown to navigate by the sun. They are able to relate the position of their hive with the direction of polarized light coming from the sun; hence they may steer a beeline course home from any compass point. On arrival in its hive, a scouting bee which has found a food-yielding field of flowers communicates with its fellow workers by means of an *abdominal dance,* a side-to-side wiggle of the hind portion of the bee's body. The violence of the dance gives information about the richness of the food source. Flight distance is indicated by the duration of the dance, and flight direction, by the specific body orientation the dancing bee assumes on the honeycomb surface.

In winter, bees cling together in compact masses. Animals in the center always work their way out; those near the surface work their way in. A clump of bees thereby withstands freezing, even when exposed to very low temperatures. Smoke calms bees, as is well known. The animals react to smoke by rushing to their food stores and gorging themselves with honey. They are too busy at that time to sting an intruder. This is probably an inherited adaptive response to fire. Smoke might indicate a burning tree, and it is of obvious advantage if the bees are well fed when they are forced to abandon their nest. Similarly adaptive is the expulsion of all drones from the colony at the approach of winter. Not contributing to the well-being of the colony, males merely use up food which is at a premium in the cold season. Reactions such as these might appear to be thought out. Yet bees probably do not "reason" at all (Fig. 6.5).

Among insect societies generally, the fixed nature of each individual constitutes a potential long-range disadvantage. Death of a queen bee and the destruction of honeycomb cells which contain larvae still young enough to be reared into queens usually spell the end of a bee colony; new workers are not produced, and old ones die out. Destructive social crises of this sort are offset by the establishment of numerous colonies

Fig. 6.5. A marching column of army ants. If such a column is made to travel in a circle, as in the photo, then these ants will continue to circle endlessly. Unless they are diverted by an outside force, they may march themselves to death. Each ant evidently is governed by inherited instinct so completely that it is capable only of following the ant before it and is incapable of thinking itself out of an even slightly altered situation. (American Museum of Natural History.)

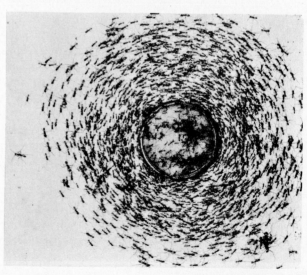

and by enormous reproduction rates. The safety of the species lies in the number of its individuals. We recognize, however, that it would be immediately advantageous if, in addition to safety through numbers, the society were organized more flexibly; if each member could perform the functions of every other member and if the colony as a whole could learn to adopt new ways of life in the face of changed environmental conditions. Flexible social organization is actually in evidence to greater or less degree among vertebrate groups.

VERTEBRATE SOCIETIES

In contrast to insects (and disregarding the differences between males and females), the members of vertebrate societies are structurally more or less alike at birth. Individual variations largely develop later and they are not primarily structural as in insects, but functional. Thus they may involve variation in physical strength, in developed skills, in mental capacity, and in some cases in social tradition. As in insects, on the other hand, the main determiner of behavior is inherited instinct, tempered here with a more or less thin veneer of *learning* and *reasoning*. Learning goes hand in hand with *training*, and both are made possible largely by *family* groupings. The subdivision of the advanced vertebrate society into family units is one of its main distinctions.

Schools of fish, flocks of birds, packs of European wolves, herds of deer are some of the most primitive of the associations among vertebrates. Functional variation of individuals is not particularly pronounced here. In travel, the individual which happens to be in the lead position, usually a male, guides the group temporarily. Other males, often stationed along the outskirts of the group, may take the lead in frequent rotation. The advantages of such associations are largely protective. Many eyes see more than two; a closely huddled herd stays warm; a group is more effective in attack and in defense. Family life within such groups may or may not be evident. There is hardly any in schools of fish. But a duck or a doe trains its young. Families tend to maintain their own physical space within the society. For example, in a herd of seals resting on an island, males take up stations at more or less

Fig. 6.6. A group of fur seals on an island in the far north. Note the polygamous, familial organization: a single male, several females, and their young. (Courtesy of V. B. Scheffer, U.S. Fish and Wildlife Service.)

regular intervals and each male gathers his family around him. The individual patriarch jealously guards his territory, driving off bachelor males and keeping a sharp eye on his females (Fig 6.6). Social life among beavers is more cooperative and rather more advanced. Several families may pool their efforts in woodcutting and dam building. All share the benefits of this teamwork, which clearly serves more than mere protection.

Social herding very often is associated with extensive animal *migrations*. These may be undertaken in search of richer or safer pastures, in response to seasonal changes in climate, or to reach geographically fixed breeding grounds. Eels, seals, salmon, and many types of birds are among familiar migrants. When not migrating, solitary individuals or families of these animals may be dispersed widely over a considerable territory. At specific times, as if on cue, individuals draw together from far and near to a common jumping-off point, and then they travel together to their destination, as a band.

Not all vertebrate societies migrate and not in all cases are families grouped into herds. Solitary families are common among both monogamous and polygamous species. Fish such as sticklebacks, birds such as parrots, and mammals such as bears and wolverines are monogamous and may mate for life. Such family groups are organized like human families.

Solitary polygamous families may approach the numerical proportions of flocks or herds, as in chickens. Such a group is usually made up of a single dominant male, a series of females, their young, and sometimes a few unrelated young bachelor males. The rule of the dominant male is frequently challenged by the bachelors. If one of these succeeds in defeating his opponent in battle, the loyalty of the females is transferred to the winner. In this way the group is assured of continuously fit, healthy leadership.

An interesting social organization exists among the females of a polygamous family. In a flock of chickens, for example, hens are ranked according to a definite *peck order*. A given hen may peck without danger all hens below her in social rank but may be pecked in turn by all hens above her in the scale. If a new hen is introduced into the flock, she undertakes, or is made to undertake, a pecking contest with each fellow hen. Winning here and losing there, she soon finds her level in the society. A high ranking carries with it certain advantages, such as getting first to the food trough and obtaining a position of prestige on the perch. Very high-ranking birds often are so aggressive that they persistently reject the attentions of the rooster. More submissive hens then produce most of the offspring. Social rankings of a similar nature are found also among female elephants as well as in most other polygamous families.

The success of vertebrate societies as a whole lies primarily in the functional versatility of the individual. In the insect society, as we have noted, reproduction of the majority is suppressed, and reproduction of the minority serves not only toward the new formation of individuals, but also toward the new formation of the whole society. Thus, among insects, the fate of the society hinges on the fate of a single female, and her genes alone provide continuity from one social generation to the next. By contrast, virtually all members of a vertebrate society are reproducers. Social continuity consequently is the responsibility of many, and reproduction of any one individual is less vital for the propagation of the society.

Although insect and vertebrate societies differ in origin and internal organization, remarkably similar patterns of social behavior are in evidence. For example, ant societies exist which make deliberate war, others which practice slavery, and still others which pursue agriculture and domesticate other organisms. Such ants and man are unique in these respects among animals.

Society in all its forms, like the population generally, is subordinated to the larger species. Populations of social and nonsocial organisms in turn are subordinated to the local community, an aggregation that occupies our attention next.

Communities

A community is a local association of populations of several *different* species. A pond with its various plant and various animal populations is a community; so is a forest, a meadow, a section of ocean shore, or a village with its people, trees, grasses, bacteria, cats, dogs, and other organisms. Note that a community almost always contains plants as well as animals and indeed also Monera and Protista, a virtual necessity for community survival. The sum total of all communities makes up the whole living world.

The boundaries between communities are not primarily biological, as between species, but are primarily geographical and environmental. And the *kind* of community likely to be found in a given territory depends largely on the physical and chemical nature of that territory. For this reason, we shall discuss the different specific types of communities in the next chapter, in a context which stresses the environmental aspects of the living world. Here we shall deal with the general characteristics of all types of communities and with the forces which govern their structure.

CYCLES AND BALANCES

Like other living entities, a community grows, develops, passes through a relatively stable mature phase, reproduces and ultimately dies. The time scale is in hundreds and thousands of years.

Such communal life cycles result from an interplay between organisms and their environment. Being specialized, different organisms are adapted to, and must therefore live in, different environments. The physical characteristics of a given region consequently determine what types of organisms can settle there originally. Temperature, winds, amount of rainfall, the chemical composition of the surroundings, latitude and altitude, soil conditions, and other similar factors decisively influence what kinds of plants will be able to survive in a given locale. Vegetation in turn, as well as the physical characteristics of the locale, have a selective effect on the types of animals that may successfully settle in the region.

By its very presence, however, a given set of organisms gradually alters local conditions. Raw materials are withdrawn from the environment in large quantities, and metabolic wastes are returned. To the extent that these wastes differ from the original raw materials, the environment becomes altered. Moreover, the parts of dead organisms also return to the environment, but not necessarily in the same place, nor necessarily in the same form, in which they were obtained. In time, organisms thus bring about profound redistributions and alterations of vast quantities of the earth's substance.

This means that later generations of the original organisms may find the changed local environment no longer suitable, and the members of the community must resettle elsewhere or die out. A new community of different plants and animals may come to occupy the territory, and as this community now alters the area according to its own specialization, type replacement, or *communal succession,* may eventually follow once more. We note how closely the nonliving and the biological components of the environment are interlinked; change in one produces change in the other.

In a community, as on all other levels of living organization, *turnover* as above occurs continuously. Individuals of the various populations emigrate or die out and are replaced by others. The important point is that this flux is automatically self-adjusting. As a result the community remains internally *balanced* and exhibits a numerical steady state; that is, in all populations present, the numbers of individuals remain relatively constant. In a large, permanent pond, for example, the number of algae, frogs, minnows, and any other organisms, plant or animal, will be more or less the same from decade to decade. Annual fluctuations are common, but over longer periods of time, constancies of numbers are characteristic in most natural communities.

Three main factors create and control these striking numerical balances: *food, reproduction,* and *protection.* They are the principal links which make the members of a community interdependent.

COMMUNAL INTERDEPENDENCE

In every stable community, green plants produce their own food and grow; herbivorous animals eat the plants; carnivorous animals eat each other or herbivores; the elimination products and the dead bodies of all plants and all animals replenish the ocean or the soil; and this, plus solar energy and raw materials from the environment, then makes new plant growth possible (Fig. 6.7).

In such cycles, a pound of soil does not make a pound of new living plant matter; for many of the components of soil are completely unusable in the construction of the living matter of plants. Similarly, a pound of plant food cannot make a pound of new living animal matter; for much of what a plant consists, cellulose, for example, cannot be digested or used otherwise by animals. Therefore, as raw materials are transferred from soil to plants and from plants to animals, these transfers are not 100 per cent efficient. More than a pound of soil is needed to make a pound of plant matter, and more than a pound of plant matter is needed to make a pound of animal matter. Similarly, more than 300 pounds of antelope meat or even lion meat is required to produce a 300-pound lion.

This inescapable condition leads to the establishment of *food pyramids* in the community (Fig. 6.8). So many tons of soil can support only so many *fewer* tons of grass. Grass in turn supports herbivores which together weigh less than the grass. And only a relatively small weight of carnivores can find sustenance in such a community. Several acres of ground thus might just suffice to support a 150-pound man. Such a pyramid of total weights also delineates a pyramid of individual numbers and individual sizes, for prey is generally smaller than predator; hence the balanced community may contain millions of individual grasses, but only one man.

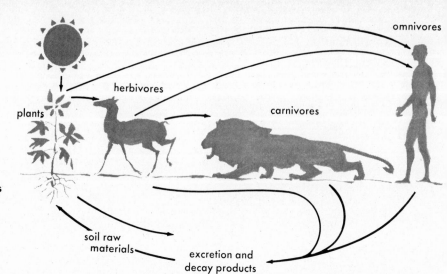

Fig. 6.7. The basic nutritional links in a community.

Pyramids of this sort are one of the most potent factors in balancing communal populations; significant variations of numbers at any level of a pyramid entail automatic adjustments at every other level. For example, overpopulation of carnivores soon results in the depletion of herbivores, since a greater number of herbivores is eaten. This depletion leads to starvation of carnivores, hence to a reduction of their numbers. Underpopulation of carnivores then results in overpopulation of herbivores, since fewer herbivores are

eaten. But the fewer carnivores can be well fed. They may therefore reproduce relatively rapidly, and this increases their numbers again. As a general result, although the numbers of all kinds of organisms undergo short-term fluctuations, the total quantities remain relatively constant over the long term.

The reproductive interdependence within a community is illustrated clearly by the pollinating activity of insects. In some well-known cases of remarkable specialization, a given insect visits only one or a few specific flower types for pollen and nectar, and the flower in turn is structurally adapted to facilitate entry of the insect (e.g., the liplike petals of snapdragon flowers). Such intimate cooperation indicates that the animal and the plant have evolved together, in close correlation. It is fairly obvious how such interdependence contributes to population balance: reduction of the insect population brings with it reduced plant pollination, hence reduction of the plant population, and vice versa. Similarly significant in balancing the size of plant populations is the seed-dispersing activity of birds and mammals.

Other examples of reproductive dependence are many. Birds such as cuckoos lay eggs in nests of other birds. Insects such as gall wasps embed their eggs deep in the tissues of particular plants, where the hatching larvae find food and protection. Other insects deposit eggs on or under the skin of various animals. Certain

Fig. 6.8. The general pattern of food pyramids. Soil and ocean support plant life; herbivorous animals subsist on the plants; and carnivorous animals subsist on the herbivores.

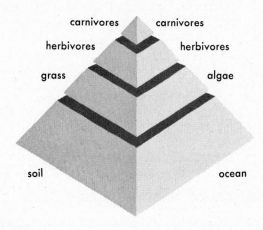

wasps, for example, kill tarantulas and lay their eggs in them.

Numerous examples also give evidence of the protective interdependence of the organisms within a community. For instance, the many ways in which forests and grasslands house and hide large and small animals are commonplace. Protective devices here usually involve *camouflage* of body colors or of body shapes. Probably the most remarkable instance of color camouflage is the phenomenon of *mimicry*, widespread particularly among butterflies and moths. In certain of these animals, pigmentation patterns exist which are virtually indistinguishable from those of other, unrelated species. Usually those species are mimicked which are strong or fast and have few natural enemies. The advantage is that an animal resembling even superficially another more powerful one will be protected too, by scaring off potential enemies.

Insects also display a variety of structural camouflages. For example, the individuals of certain species possess the detailed shape of leaves, of branches, or of thorns (Fig. 6.9). This serves not only defensively, but also as a disguise against potential victims.

Other protective devices vary widely in type. Various birds and some mammals mimic the song and voice of other species, either defensively or as an aggressive lure. The hermit crab protects its soft abdomen in an empty snail shell of appropriate size. Schools of small pilot fish scout ahead of large sharks, leading their protectors to likely prey. Significant protection is also provided by man, through domestication, game laws, parks, and sanctuaries.

These various examples illustrate how the member populations of a community are specialized nutritionally, reproductively, and protectively. Carnivorous populations cannot sustain themselves on plant food and not even on every kind of animal food. Herbivorous populations require plants and are incapable of hunting for animals. The populations of green plants depend on soil or ocean, and the populations of saprotrophs cannot do without dead organisms. These are profound specializations in structure and function, and

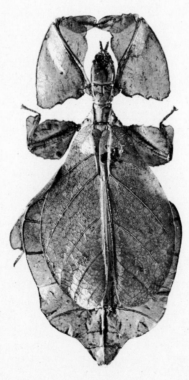

Fig. 6.9. The shape of many insects mimics that of plant parts on which these animals habitually live. Left, a praying mantis, colored green, resembling a thin stem. Right, a leaf insect, whose resemblance to a leaf is exceptionally striking. (U.S. Department of Agriculture.)

they imply loss of individual self-sufficiency as well as a need for cooperative interdependence. Communal associations of populations evidently are a necessity. They are but extensions, on a higher biological level, of the necessarily cooperative aggregation of cells into tissues, organs, and organisms.

Indeed, the development of "community" appears to be as integral a part of organic evolution as the development of individual organisms. Events were probably *not* such that a particular organism first evolved structurally and functionally in a certain way and then happened to find the right community into which it could fit. Rather, the community probably existed from the very beginning, and all its member populations evolved together; the community itself evolved. The histories of the bumblebee and the snapdragon are linked as intimately as the histories of every man's hand and foot.

A community within a given territory includes not only free-living organisms in loose cooperative association but also organisms which live together in more or less permanent *physical* contact. Two individuals of different species may be joined so intimately that one lives right *within* the other. All such instances of physically intimate living together of members of different species are instances of *symbiosis,* a special form of communal life.

Symbiosis

THE PATTERN

A free association in which an animal habitually shelters under a plant might, in a relatively simple evolutionary step, become an association in which the animal and the plant have entered a more permanent protective union. A plant which depends on some animal for seed dispersal might advantageously live in, or on, the animal altogether, not only at the time of seed production but throughout life. A soil bacterium or a scavenging protozoon living on the undigested elimination products of larger forms might find a surer food supply if it could adapt to an existence right in the gut cavity of its supplier.

Among ancestral populations of free-living forms, ample opportunity existed for the development of such symbiotic relationships. These opportunities were exploited to the full, and many associations arose in which two organisms of different species came to live together in intimate, lasting physical contact. Today there is no major group of organisms which does not include symbiotic species, and there is probably no individual organism which does not play *host* to at least one *symbiont.*

Symbionts affect each other in different ways. Thus, *mutualism* describes a relationship in which both associated partners derive some benefit, often a vital one, from living together. *Commensalism* benefits one of the partners, and the other is neither helped nor harmed by the association. *Parasitism* is of advantage to the parasite but is detrimental to the host to greater or lesser extent. These categories intergrade imperceptibly, and in many boundary cases clear-cut distinctions cannot be made.

An example of a mutualistic association is the tickbird-rhinoceros relationship. The tickbird feeds on skin parasites of the rhinoceros, and in return the latter is relieved of irritation and obtains warning of danger when the sharp-eyed bird flies off temporarily to the security of the nearest tree.

Another example is the mutualistic symbiosis of sea anemones and hermit crabs. Sea anemones attach themselves to empty snail shells, and hermit crabs use these shells as protective housing. The sea anemone, an exceedingly slow mover by itself, is thus carried about on the shell of the hermit crab—an obvious advantage to the anemone in its search for food and in geographic dispersal. The hermit crab in turn benefits from the disguise. Moreover, since the anemone is not a dainty eater, scraps of food become available to the crab when the anemone catches prey.

Mutualism is also encountered among animals which harbor billions of intestinal bacteria in the lower gut. The bacteria draw freely on materials not digested or not digestible by the host, and their activities initiate fecal decay. The host generally benefits from the auxiliary digestion carried out by the bacteria and in many instances is also dependent on certain of the bacterial byproducts. For example, mammals obtain many vitamins in the form of "waste" materials released by the bacterial symbionts of the gut.

Commensalism is illustrated by a species of small

tropical fish which finds shelter in the cloaca of sea cucumbers. The fish darts out for food and returns, to the utter indifference of the host. The so-called suckerfish (Fig. 6.10) possesses a dorsal fin which is modified into a holdfast device. By means of it, the fish attaches to the underside of sharks and thereby secures scraps of food, wide geographic dispersal, and protection. The shark neither benefits nor suffers in any respect. Barnacles may attach to the skin of whales, an association which secures geographic distribution and wider feeding opportunities for the sessile crustaceans. In this instance, a trend toward parasitism is in evidence, for in some cases the barnacles send rootlike processes into the whale, outgrowths which eat away bits of host tissue.

Parasitism is actually the most stable and most widespread form of symbiosis.

PARASITISM

Parasitic ways of life. It has probably become apparent in the above that symbiosis revolves largely, though not exclusively, around the problem of food. We might suspect, therefore, that symbiosis in general and parasitism in particular would be most prevalent among organisms in which competition for food is most intense. This is actually the case. Although some parasitic green plants do exist (e.g., mistletoes, Fig. 6.11), photosynthesizing organisms by and large are not under competitive pressure for basic nutrients; air, water, and sunlight are present everywhere in inexhaustible quantities. Parasitism flourishes primarily among organisms

Fig. 6.11. Mistletoe, parasitic on branch of pine tree. (U.S. Forest Service.)

which must obtain food from others: in viruses, in bacteria, in fungi, and in animals.

All viruses are parasitic. Of the bacteria, those which are not photosynthetic or saprotrophic are parasitic. Among fungi, some are saprotrophic, the rest are parasitic. And in animals, many major groups are wholly parasitic; virtually all others include important parasitic subgroups.

As we have seen in Chap. 4, parasitism is almost as old as life itself. So advantageous and economical is the parasitic mode of living that many parasites may be infested with smaller parasites of their own and these in turn may support still smaller ones. For example, a mammal may harbor parasitic worms; these may be invaded by parasitic bacteria; and the bacteria may be infected by *bacteriophages,* viruses which parasitize bacteria (Fig. 6.12). *Hyperparasitism* of this sort, namely, one parasite inside another, is very common. It represents a natural exploitation of the very condition of parasitism. Inasmuch as the parasite is generally smaller than the host and inasmuch as one host may support many parasites, parasitic and hyperparasitic relationships form inverted food pyramids contained within the pyramids of the larger community.

The first problem a potential parasite faces is the defense mobilized by a potential host. Attachment to

Fig. 6.10. Commensalistic symbiosis. Shark with three suckerfish attached to underside. (New York Zoological Society.)

Fig. 6.12. **Electron micrograph of the remnants of a bacterium after attack by bacteriophages.** The virus parasites are the small rodlets with knobbed ends. (R. W. G. Wyckoff, "Electron Microscopy," Interscience Publishers, Inc., 1949.)

cannot pick a host at random, even if many similar ones offer the same types of nutrients. During the evolution of a parasite, structural and functional specializations have developed in adaptation to particular hosts only. Thus, most parasites enter a host's body by fixed routes, then settle in fixed regions, as if, in the course of time, they had learned to channel their attack through points of weakness characteristic of particular hosts.

Once established in the body of a host, the parasite may pursue a life of comparative ease. Embedded in food, it needs no locomotor equipment, few sense organs, no fast nervous reflexes. Indeed, structural and

Fig. 6.13. **A caterpillar of a sphinx moth, parasitized by the pupae of another insect species.** (Courtesy of E. W. Teale.)

the outer body surface can be prevented only with difficulty, particularly if the host does not possess limbs. Numerous *ectoparasites* exploit this possibility (Fig. 6.13). Equipped with suckers, clamps, or adhesive surfaces, they hold onto skin or hair, and with the aid of cutting, biting, or sucking mouth parts, or with rootlike outgrowths, they feed on the body fluids of the host. Examples are leeches, lice, ticks, mites, lampreys, and many fungi.

Endoparasites, within the body of the host, must breach more formidable defenses. Cellular enzymes of a host, digestive juices and strong acids in the alimentary tract, antibodies in the blood, white blood cells, and other cells which engulf foreign bodies in amoeboid fashion—these are among the defensive agents which guard against the invader. Overcoming such defenses means *specialization:* development of resistant outer coverings, as in bacteria and fungi; tough cuticles, as in most parasitic worms; development of cyst walls and calcareous capsules; development of hooks or clamps with which to hold onto the gut wall; development of enzymes which, when secreted, erode a path through host tissues.

Specialization of the parasite also involves the selection of *specific* hosts. Highly advanced parasites

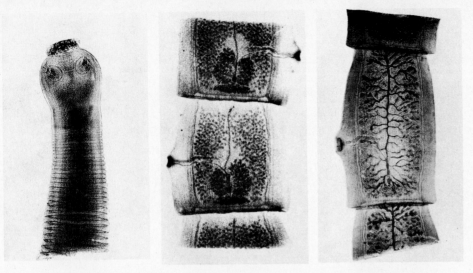

Fig. 6.14.   Tapeworm. Left, head. Middle, segmental sections near middle of body. Right, segmental sections near hind end of body. Tree-shaped structures in middle and right are reproductive organs. Note testes filling segments in middle and genital pores opening on the sides of the segments. The uterus filled with eggs is conspicuous in right. (General Biological Supply House, Inc.)

functional *simplification* is a nearly universal characteristic of parasites.

A simplified design is pronounced in *tapeworms*, for example. These parasites (Fig. 6.14) possess only a highly reduced nervous system, a reduced muscular system, and not even a vestige of a digestive system. Almost like blotting paper, the worms soak up through their body walls the food juices of the host gut.

Simplification is probably an adaptive advantage, for the simplified condition of the parasite may be more economical than the fully developed condition of the free-living ancestor. A tapeworm, for example, being structurally simplified, may concentrate all its resources into parasitizing the host, and it need not divert energy and materials into maintaining elaborate nervous, muscular, or digestive systems, which are unnecessary anyway in this parasitic way of life.

Parasite reproduction.   In one respect parasites are far from simplified: reproduction. In this function they are as prolific as the most prolific free-living forms. The practical necessity of this is correlated with a major problem confronting the parasite, particularly the endoparasite, namely, how to get from one host to another.

Parasites succeed in two ways, both of which involve reproduction: *active transfer* and *passive transfer*. In the former, one stage of the life cycle of the parasite is free-living *and* motile; that is, this active stage transfers from one host to another through its own powers of locomotion. For example, the adult may be parasitic, and the free-living embryo or larva may be capable of locomotion. Or the larva may be the parasite, the adult then being free-living and capable of locomotion.

Passive transfer is encountered among parasites in which *no* stage of the life cycle is capable of locomotion. Propagation here is accomplished by wind, by water, or by *intermediate hosts*. The last offer a means of transfer which is not quite as chancy as random distribution by wind or water. What is involved here is well illustrated in the propagation of tapeworms (Fig. 6.15).

These parasites of man, like numerous others, exploit one of the easiest routes into and out of the host, namely, the alimentary tract. Entering through

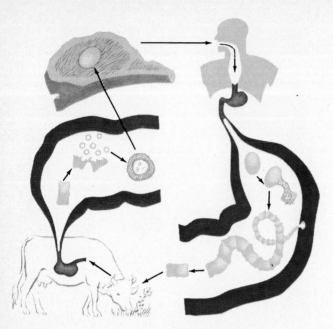

Fig. 6.15. The life cycle of a tapeworm. Ripe sections of the worm pass with the feces from the human gut. Eggs are released from these sections in the gut of cattle. Tapeworm embryos then encapsulate in beef muscle, and the embryos become adults in the intestine of man.

the host's mouth by way of eaten food and leaving through the anus by way of feces, some, like tapeworms, spend their adult life directly in the gut cavity of the host. Others utilize the gut as a springboard from which to invade interior tissues. The problem is to transfer offspring from one human host to another by passive means. Tapeworms accomplish a first phase of this readily; namely, mature eggs are released to the outside with the host's feces.

Since man does not eat feces, the eggs evidently cannot reach new human hosts directly. However, tapeworms ingeniously take advantage of the food pyramids of which man is a member: man eats beef, and cattle eat grass. A ready-made pathway from grass to man thus exists, and the transfer chain becomes complete if, as happens on occasion, human feces are deposited on grass. Tapeworm eggs clinging to such vegetation may then be eaten by cattle.

In the intestine of a cow, a tapeworm egg develops into an embryo, and such an embryo bores a path through the gut wall into the cow's bloodstream. From there the embryo is carried into beef muscle, where it encapsulates and matures. If man then eats raw or partially cooked beef, the capsule surrounding the young tapeworm is digested away in the human gut, and the free worm now hooks on to the intestinal wall of its new host.

This history illustrates a very widely occurring phenomenon. Many kinds of parasites utilize well-established food pyramids in transferring to new hosts. Often there is more than one intermediate host, and by such means parasites have solved their transfer problems most successfully. So successfully, indeed, that there are many more individual parasites in existence than free-living organisms.

A community consists of various kinds of free-living and various kinds of symbiotic populations. Which particular ones of each type actually compose a given community, hence the very nature of the community itself, is determined largely by the type of *environment* in which organisms exist. We shall examine the different communal environments in the following chapter.

Review questions

1. What is a population, a society, a species? Make sure that you understand the interrelation of these units.

2. How do new species arise and in what general ways are two sister species different?

3. What are individual variations? Distinguish between inheritable and noninheritable variations and give examples of each. What are adaptive variations?

4. Review the organization of some insect and vertebrate societies and contrast these organizations. What is the social significance of family groupings and where do the

latter occur? What is the significance of animal migrations? Of peck orders?

5. Define community, communal succession, food pyramid, mimicry. Review the nutritional, reproductive, and protective links which hold the members of a community together.

6. How are long-range numerical population balances maintained? In what ways are populations, species, and communities specialized?

7. What are the various forms of symbiosis and how are they defined? Give concrete examples of each.

8. What is hyperparasitism, ectoparasitism, endoparasitism?

9. What general structural and functional characteristics distinguish parasites from free-living organisms? How do parasites transfer from host to host?

10. Describe the life cycles of tapeworms and review the general significance of intermediate hosts.

Suggested collateral readings

Burnet, F. M.: Viruses, *Sci. Am.*, vol. 184, 1951.

Frisch, K. von: Dialects in the Language of Bees, *Sci. Am.*, vol. 207, 1962.

Guhl, A. M.: The Social Order of Chickens, *Sci. Am.*, vol. 194, 1956.

Luria, S. E.: The T2 Mystery, *Sci. Am.*, vol. 192, 1955.

Lwoff, A.: The Life Cycle of a Virus, *Sci. Am.*, vol. 190, 1954.

Sahlins, M. D.: The Origin of Society, *Sci. Am.*, vol. 203, 1960.

Schneirla, T. C., and G. Piel: The Army Ant, *Sci. Am.*, vol. 178, 1948.

Smith, R. F., and W. W. Allen: Insect Control and the Balance of Nature, *Sci. Am.*, vol. 190, 1954.

HABITAT AND ENVIRONMENT

Different localities harbor different kinds of communities, and an inquiry into the nature of these various communal homes, or *habitats*, forms our first topic. The second topic deals with the physical, chemical, and geological forces which affect the habitats and the organisms in them and which actually govern environmental conditions on the entire earth. In other words, we shall examine the large-scale nature of the *global environment*.

The communal habitats

With the possible exception of the most arid deserts, the high frozen mountain peaks, and the perpetually icebound polar regions, probably no place on earth is devoid of life. The large subdivisions of this planetary home are the *aquatic* and the *terrestrial* habitats. Both range from equator to pole and from a few thousand feet below to a few thousand feet above sea level. *Ocean* and *fresh water* are the principal components of the aquatic habitat, and *air* and *soil* of the terrestrial.

THE OCEANIC HABITAT

The ocean basin.   All ocean basins have roughly the form of an inverted hat (Fig. 7.1). A gently sloping *continental shelf* stretches away from the coast line for an average distance of about 100 miles (discounting often extreme deviations from this average). The angle of descent then changes more or less abruptly, and the shelf grades over into a steep *continental slope.* Characteristically, this slope is scored deeply by gorges and canyons, carved out by slow rivers of mud and sand discharging from estuaries. Several thousand feet down, the continental slope levels off into the ocean floor, a more or less horizontal expanse known as the *abyssal plain.* Mountains rise from it in places, with peaks sometimes so high that they rear up above sea level as islands. Elsewhere, the plain may be scarred by deep rifts, e.g., the deeps just east of the Philippines and Japan which, plunging 35,000 feet down, are the lowest parts of the earth's crust.

Each subdivision of the "wall" of such a basin represents a distinct subenvironment of the ocean and is inhabited by specially adapted communities of organisms. Moreover, the water itself which fills the basin is subdivided by the sun into two major subenvironments. Acting directly or via the overlying medium of air, the sun produces "weather" in the surface layers of the sea—waves, current, storm, evaporation, seasons, daily climatic rhythms, and other

changes. Deep water is not so affected. Moreover, sunlight penetrates into water only to an average depth of about 250 feet and to at most 600 feet in certain seas. Below this sunlit top layer, the ocean is eternally and completely dark. The most significant consequence of this is that photosynthesizing vegetation can exist only in the uppermost layers of the sea. Animal life directly dependent on plant foods therefore must remain near the surface too. As a result, the top 250 feet or so of the oceans contains a concentration of living matter as dense as any on earth.

On the basis of its relationship to these various environments, marine life has been classified into three general categories: *plankton, nekton,* and *benthos.* Plankton includes all passively drifting or floating forms. Most of them are microscopic and are found largely in the surface waters of the sea. Even though some of these forms possess locomotor systems, they are nevertheless too weak or too small to counteract currents and movements of water. Nekton comprises the active swimmers, capable of changing stations at will. All nektonic types are therefore animals, and they are found in all waters, along the surface as well as in the sea depths. The benthos consists of crawling, creeping, and sessile organisms along the sides and the bottom of the ocean basin.

The surface waters.   The predominant marine flora in the sunlit layers is planktonic. It consists of teeming

Fig. 7.1.   The structure of an ocean basin.

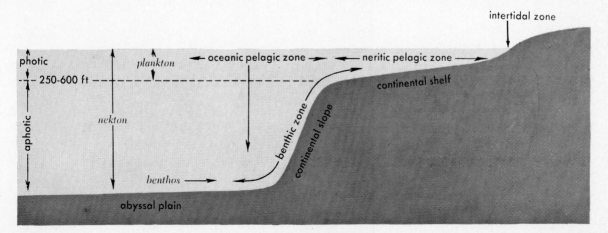

trillions of algae which as a group probably photosynthesize more food than all other photosynthesizing organisms combined. This marine vegetation represents the richest pasture on earth; directly or indirectly, it forms the nutritional basis of all marine life.

Most of the algal types included in this "grass of the sea" are microscopic and they remain afloat by buoyancy. Unquestionably the most abundant are the *diatoms*. Each of these single-celled algae is enclosed within a delicate, intricately sculptured, silicon-containing shell (Fig. 7.2). Reddish algal *dinoflagellates* also abound in surface waters, sometimes in populations so dense that they tint acre upon acre of ocean with a coppery hue (e.g., "red" tides). Other marine algae include many types of variously pigmented forms, and some of these, as well as countless numbers of marine bacteria, are bioluminescent. They emit flashes of cold light, which dot the night seascape with a billion pinpoints of greenish fire.

In certain circumscribed regions (e.g., the Sargasso Sea in the mid-Atlantic) are also present larger, multicellular algae—flat, sheetlike seaweeds, often equipped with specialized air bladders which aid in keeping the organisms afloat. Such seaweeds may sometimes aggregate in considerable numbers over wide areas, particularly if a region is ringed in by ocean currents and therefore remains relatively isolated and stagnant.

Living side by side with the plankton flora in the surface waters is the plankton fauna: protozoa, eggs, larvae, tiny shrimp, and countless other small animals carried along by surface drift. They feed directly on the microscopic vegetation. A good part of the nekton, largely fishes and marine mammals, lives in these surface waters too, feeding either on the plankton or on one another.

Nearer to shore, in the waters above the continental shelf, even a bottom dweller is likely to be within the range of sunlight. The problem therefore is not so much to remain afloat as to remain attached to solid ground, for close to shore the force of waves and of ground swells is considerable. And in the tide zone, an even more profound problem is the ebbing of water twice daily and the consequent rhythmic alternation between aquatic and essentially terrestrial

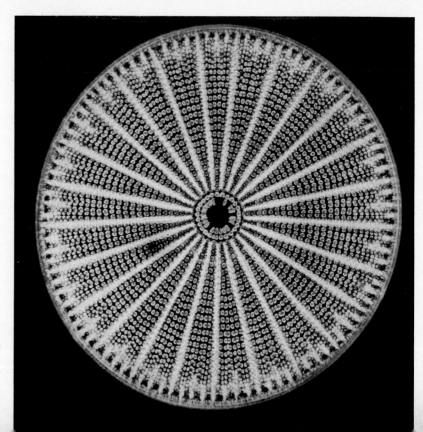

Fig. 7.2. The finely sculptured silica shell of a diatom. Other examples of these single-celled components of plankton are illustrated in Chap. 8, Fig. 8.9. (General Biological Supply House, Inc.)

conditions. Also, in waters in and for miles beyond estuaries, fresh water discharging from rivers mixes with ocean water, a circumstance introducing additional environmental inconstancies. Being the meeting ground of water, land, and air, the tide zone is actually among the most violently changing environments on earth.

Vegetation in these coastal waters is again largely algal. In addition to the planktonic types, attached forms abound. Most of these are equipped with specialized holdfasts which anchor the algae to underlying ground. The animals in this region include numerous planktonic forms, nektonic forms (largely fish), and an abundance of sessile and creeping types which are variously adapted to rocky, muddy, or sandy bottoms. These animals make use of all conceivable dwelling sites: tide pools left on rock by ebbing water, crevices and hollows in and under rock, burrows in sand or mud, the sheltered water among vegetation and among sessile animal growths, empty shells and other skeletons of dead animals, and flotsam and jetsam along the shore and in deeper water.

The deep waters. The contrast between the surface environments within reach of the sun and those underneath is dramatic. As the former are forever fluctuating, so are the latter perennially steady and relatively unchanging. The deep ocean is still little explored, and for many this "last frontier" has acquired a romance and mystery all its own. Several unique physical conditions characterize this world of the sea depths.

First, the region is one of eternal night. In the total absence of sunlight, the waters are pervaded with a perpetual blackness of a kind found nowhere else on earth.

Second, seasons and changing weather are practically absent. Localized climatic changes do occur as a result of occasional submarine volcanic activity or, more regularly, through deep-sea currents. These produce large-scale shifts of water masses and, incidentally, bring oxygen to even the deepest parts of the ocean. Being beyond the influence of the sun, the deep waters are cold, unchangingly so. Temperatures range from about 10°C at the top of the dark zone to about 1°C along the abyssal plain.

Third, water pressure increases steadily from the surface down, 1 atmosphere (atm) for every 33 feet of descent. Thus, in the deepest trenches of the ocean, the pressure is about a thousand times as great as at sea level.

And fourth, a continuous slow rain of the dead remnants of surface organisms drifts down toward the sea bottom. Much of this material, particularly the organic fraction, dissolves completely during the descent. But much microscopic mineral matter reaches the abyssal plain, where it forms ever-thickening layers of ooze. Accumulating over the millennia, the older layers eventually compress into rock. Vertical-bore samples of such rock have revealed a great deal of the past history of the oceans and their once-living surface inhabitants.

Contrary to early beliefs that life should be impossible in such an environment, a surprisingly rich diversity of organisms has been found to exist virtually everywhere in the free water and along the floor of the deep sea. Apart from containing bacteria and perhaps fungi, the community is characteristically *animal*—photosynthesizing organisms are confined to the sunlit surface. Virtually all animal groups are represented, many by—to us—strange and bizarre types uniquely adapted to the locale (Fig. 7.3).

Because the principal organisms present are animals, the deep sea is the most fiercely competitive environment on earth. The very structure of the animals underscores their violently carnivorous, "eat-or-be-eaten" mode of existence. For example, most of the fishes have enormous mouths equipped with long, razor-sharp teeth, and many can swallow fish larger than themselves.

Since the environment is pitch-black, one of the critical problems for these animals is to *find* food to begin with. A highly developed pressure sense provides one solution. Turbulence in the water created by nearby animals can be recognized and, depending on the nature of the turbulence, may be acted upon either by flight or by approach.

Another important adaptation to the dark is bioluminescence. Many of the deep-sea animals possess light-producing organs on the body surface, of different shapes, sizes, and distributions in different species. The light patterns emitted may include a variety of colors and probably serve partly in species recognition. Iden-

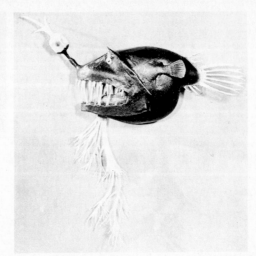

Fig. 7.3. **Deep-sea fishes.** Three kinds of oceanic angler fishes are shown. The animal at left is a female. The structure above the eye is a parasitic male, which is carried about permanently attached. This neatly solves the problem of finding mating partners in the dark. The "beard" of the animal in middle is probably luminescent. Many of these large-mouthed, dagger-toothed fishes are surprisingly small. For example, the animal at right would fit comfortably into the palm of a human hand. (American Museum of Natural History.)

tification of a suitable mate, for example, must be a serious problem in an environment where everything appears equally black. Another function of the light undoubtedly is to warn or to lure. Some of the bioluminescent lures have evolved to a high degree of perfection. Certain fish, for example, carry a "lantern" on a stalk protruding from the snout (see Fig. 7.3). An inquisitive animal attracted to the light of the lantern will discover too late that it has headed straight into powerful jaws.

THE FRESHWATER HABITAT

Physically and biologically, the link between ocean and land is the fresh water. Rivers and lakes were the original invasion routes over which some of the descendants of ancestral marine organisms reached land and, in the process, evolved into terrestrial forms. Certain of the migrant types never completed the transition but settled along the way, in fresh water.

Among such organisms, some adapted to the brackish water in estuaries and river mouths or to a life spent partly in the ocean, partly in fresh water (e.g., salmon, eels). Very many types could leave the ocean entirely and adapt to an exclusively freshwater existence. The descendants of these organisms include representatives of virtually all groups present in the ocean. Certain of the freshwater types later managed to gain a foothold on land. Of these, some continued to spend part of their lives in or near fresh water (e.g., mosses, frogs), but more became wholly terrestrial. And among the terrestrial forms, some subsequently returned to water and adapted secondarily to an aquatic existence (e.g., reed grasses, many insects). Thus, organisms which inhabit the fresh water today constitute a rich and major subdivision of the biological world.

Three main conditions distinguish the freshwater environment from the ocean environment. First, the salt content is substantially lower. If an organism has evolved in and still lives in the sea, the internal salt concentration of its body matches that of the marine environment. If such an organism moves to fresh water, the external salt concentrations will be much lower than the internal. As a result, water will be pulled by osmosis from the environment through the body surface into the organism. The amount of water in the organism will therefore tend to increase and the substance of cells will tend to become diluted.

Freshwater organisms evidently require, and they actually possess, means of counteracting this tendency of shipping too much water. Excretory systems, and also digestive systems and gills, serve in this water-balancing function. In animals inhabiting estuaries, where external salt concentrations fluctuate almost continuously, and in organisms whose life cycle includes both marine and freshwater phases, water- and salt-balancing mechanisms are particularly well developed.

A second general condition characterizing much of the freshwater environment is the presence of strong, swift currents. Except in large lakes, passively floating life so typical of the ocean surface is therefore not likely to be encountered. On the contrary, the premium will be either on maintaining firm anchorage along the shores and bottoms of rivers or on ability to resist and to overcome the force of currents by muscle power.

Indeed, freshwater plants are strongly rooted, and freshwater animals generally are powerful swimmers. The eggs of such animals are enveloped by sticky jelly coats which adhere firmly to plants or other objects in the water. And even the young are strongly muscled from the moment they hatch.

A third major distinction between fresh water and ocean is that the former, with the exception of only the very large lakes, is affected much more by climate and weather than is any part of the latter. Bodies of fresh water often freeze over in winter and may dry up completely in summer. Water temperatures change not only seasonally but also daily, frequently to a considerable extent. Gales or flood conditions may bring bottom mud and silt to the surface and upset the freshwater habitat in major ways. A large number of factors may alter flow conditions and produce, for example, stagnant water or significantly altered chemical content or situations facilitating infectious epidemics. We note that the fresh water shares the environmental inconstancies of the land in very large measure.

THE TERRESTRIAL HABITAT

That land environments differ vastly in character is eminently clear to a land dweller as efficient and far-ranging as man. It should also be clear that, regardless of which particular subdivision of the terrestrial environment one considers, the sustaining foundations of all land life are *air* and, directly or indirectly, also *soil*.

Like air, soil is itself a terrestrial home, providing a habitat for a vast array of subsurface organisms. And by creating the conditions necessary for the survival of all other terrestrial organisms, soil becomes a major agency which transforms terrestrial environments into life-sustaining "habitats." Two other agencies play a vital role here: annual *temperature* and *rainfall*. As these vary with geographic latitude and altitude, they divide the soil-covered land surface into a number of distinct habitat zones, or *biomes: desert, grassland, rain forest, deciduous forest, taiga,* and *tundra.*

In the tropics are found representatives of the first three of the six biomes just named. They are characterized here by comparatively high annual temperatures and by daily temperature variations which are greater than the seasonal variations. Differences in the amount of precipitation largely account for the different nature of these habitats.

A *desert* usually has less than 10 inches of rain per year, concentrated largely in a few heavy cloudbursts. Desert life is well adapted to this. Plants, for example, grow, bloom, are fertilized, and produce seeds, all within a matter of days after a rain. Since the growing season is thus greatly restricted, such plants stay relatively small. Leaf surfaces are often reduced to spines and thorns, minimizing water loss by evaporation. Desert animals too are generally small, and they include many burrowing forms which may escape the direct rays of the sun under the ground surface.

Grassland, as everyone well knows, is not an exclusively tropical biome but extends into much of the temperate zone as well. The more or less synonymous terms "prairie," "pampas," "steppe," "puszta," and many other regional designations underscore the wide distribution of this biome. The common feature of all grasslands is intermittent, erratic rainfall, amounting to about 10 to 40 inches annually. Grassland probably supports more species of animals than any other ter-

Fig. 7.4. The habitat of the rain forest. Many dozens of different plant types, coexisting in dense formations, are generally characteristic of it. (National Park Service.)

much of the rain water, and a good deal of the wind. As a result, the forest floor is exceedingly humid and quite dark, and it is populated by plants requiring only a minimum of light. Animal communities too are stratified vertically, according to the several very different habitats offered between canopy and ground. The tropical rain forest is singularly quiet during the day, but it erupts into a cacophony of sound at night, when the largely nocturnal fauna becomes active.

In the temperate zone, apart from extensive grasslands and occasional deserts, the most characteristic biome is the *deciduous forest*. The fundamental climatic conditions here are cold winters, warm summers, and well-spaced rains bringing some 30 to 40 inches of precipitation per year. The biome is characterized also by seasonal temperature variations which are greater than the daily variations. Winter makes the growing season discontinuous, and the flora is adapted to this. Trees are largely deciduous, that is, they shed their leaves and hibernate; and small annual plants produce seeds which withstand the cold weather. A deciduous forest differs from a rain forest in that trees are spaced farther apart and in that far fewer species are represented. Compared with the hundreds of tree types in the one, there may be only some ten or twenty in the other.

North of the deciduous forests and the grasslands, across Canada, northern Europe, and Siberia, stretches the *taiga* (Fig. 7.5). This is a biome of long, severe

restrial habitat. Different kinds of mammals are particularly conspicuous.

In those tropical and subtropical regions where torrential rains fall practically every day and where a well-defined rainy season characterizes the winter, plant growth continues the year round. Lush *rain forests* have developed here (Fig. 7.4), typified particularly by the communal coexistence of up to several hundred different species of trees. Rain forests are the "jungles" of the adventure tale. They cover much of central Africa, south and southeast Asia, Central America, and the Amazon basin of South America. Trees in such forests are normally so crowded together that they form a continuous overhead canopy of branches and foliage, which cuts off practically all the sunlight,

Fig. 7.5. The habitat of the taiga. Note the predominance of a single species of tree over large areas, characteristic of the taiga generally. (National Park Service.)

Fig. 7.6.   The habitat of the tundra. Note complete absence of trees in both views. (Courtesy of U. C. Nelson and H. C. Oberholser, U.S. Fish and Wildlife Service.)

winters and of growing seasons limited largely to the few months of summer. Hardy conifers, spruce in particular, are most representative of the flora, and moose, wolves, and bears of the fauna. The taiga is preeminently a zone of forests. These differ from other types of forests in that they usually consist of a single species

of tree. Thus, over a large area, spruce, for example, may be the only kind of tree present. Another conifer species might be found in an adjacent, equally large area. Occasional stands of hardy deciduous trees are often intermingled with conifers. An accident of geography makes the taiga a habitat characteristic of the northern hemisphere only: little land exists in corresponding latitudes of the southern hemisphere.

The same circumstance makes the *tundra,* most polar of terrestrial biomes, a predominantly northern phenomenon (Fig. 7.6). Much of the tundra lies within the Arctic Circle. Hence its climate is cold and there may be continuous night during the winter season and continuous daylight, of comparatively low intensity, during the summer. Some distance below the surface, the ground is permanently frozen. Above ground, frost can form even during the summer—plants often freeze solid and remain dormant until they thaw out again. The growing season is very brief, as in the desert, but in the tundra the limiting factor is temperature, not water supply. Plants are low, ground-hugging forms, and trees are absent. Lichens, mosses, coniferous and other shrubby growths, and herbs with brilliantly colored flowers, all blooming simultaneously during the growing season, are characteristic of the habitat. Conspicuous among the animals are hordes of insects, particularly flies, and a considerable variety of mammals: caribou, arctic hares, lemmings, foxes, musk oxen, and polar bears. Birds are largely migratory, leaving for more southern latitudes with the coming of winter.

Life does not end at the northern margin of the tundra but extends farther into the ice and bleak rock of the soilless polar region. Polar life is almost exclusively animal. And it is not really terrestrial anyway but is based on the sea (e.g., walrus, seals, penguins).

The horizontal sequence of biomes between equator and pole is repeated more or less exactly in a vertical direction, along the slopes of mountains (Fig. 7.7). Thus, habitat zones which are spread over thousands of miles latitudinally are telescoped altitudinally into a few thousand feet.

The foregoing should make it clear that the nature of any kind of habitat, hence the nature of its living communities, is determined by a few persistently recurring variables. Among them are solar light, solar

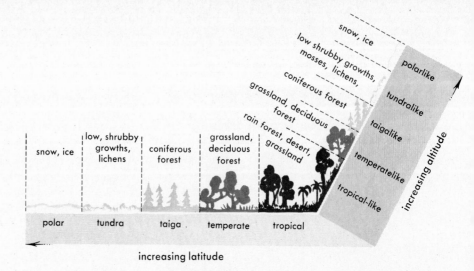

Fig. 7.7.   The sequence of habitat zones between equator and pole is repeated altitudinally between the foot and the top of a mountain.

heat, geographic latitude, vertical depth and altitude, rainfall, wind and water currents, and the chemical composition of the locale. Variables like these are of global importance, and together they add up to the large-scale "environment."

With this we reach the highest organizational level on earth: the earth itself as a unit, with its integrated living and nonliving components.

The global environment

The most important single observation we can make about the earthly environment as a whole is that it is forever changing, on every scale from the submicroscopic to the global. As a direct consequence, living matter too must constantly change: it must adjust internally if it is to maintain steady states; it must reproduce if it is to offset environmental destruction; and it must evolve if it is to stay adapted to its surroundings. As we have seen, the very origin of living matter was itself a result of environmental change, and organisms subsequently became a powerful cause of continued change.

The fundamental reason for uninterrupted environmental change is that the earth as a whole, hence also living matter and every other component, is an *open system*. Such systems exchange materials, energy, or both with their surroundings. By contrast, a *closed system* exchanges nothing with its surroundings. On earth, to be sure, the amounts of material entering from space or leaving into space are negligible. However, *energy* both enters and leaves, and this makes the earth an open system. Most importantly, various forms of solar energy—heat, light, X rays, electric rays, ultraviolet rays, and many others—beam to earth uninterruptedly; and enormous amounts of energy radiate out, principally in the form of heat. As a result, the earth's material substance can never attain static equilibrium; so long as the sun shines and the earth spins, energy flux creates balance-upsetting disturbances. Every imbalance creates new imbalances of its own, and, as a general consequence, the earth's environment is forever changing.

Such changes, being produced primarily by sun and planetary motion, occur predominantly in rhythmic, patterned *cycles*. Daily and seasonal climatic cycles are familiar examples. Other environmental cycles may be less readily discernible, particularly if their scale is too vast or too minute of if they occur too fast or too slowly for direct observation. Living matter is interposed into these cycles; and as the earth's components circulate, some of these components become raw materials in living metabolism.

The global environment consists of three main subdivisions. The *hydrosphere* includes all liquid components, namely, the water in oceans, lakes, rivers, and on land. The *lithosphere* comprises the solid components, that is, the rocky substance of the continents. And the *atmosphere* is the gaseous mantle which envelops the hydrosphere and the lithosphere. Living organisms require inorganic substances from each of these subdivisions. The hydrosphere supplies liquid *water;* the lithosphere supplies all other *minerals;* and the atmosphere supplies *oxygen, nitrogen,* and *carbon dioxide.* Together, these inorganic materials provide all the chemical elements needed in the construction and maintenance of living matter (Fig. 7.8). Moreover, in addition to being sources of supply, the three subdivisions of the environment also affect living matter in various other ways, as outlined in the following.

THE HYDROSPHERE

Water is the most abundant mineral of the planet. It covers some 73 per cent of the earth's surface entirely and it is a major constituent of the lithosphere and the atmosphere. As shown in Chap. 5, water is also the most abundant component of living matter.

Fig. 7.8. The material contributions of each of the three subdivisions of the environment to the maintenance of living matter.

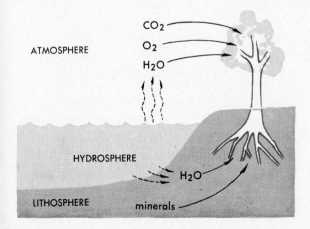

Fig. 7.9. The global water cycle. Evaporated water eventually returns to earth through precipitation.

The basic cycle which moves and conserves water in the environment is quite familiar. Solar energy evaporates water from the hydrosphere into the atmosphere. Subsequent cooling and condensation of the vapor at higher altitudes produces clouds, and precipitation as rain or snow then returns the water to the hydrosphere. This is the most massive process of any kind on earth, consuming more energy and moving more material than any other (Fig. 7.9).

Living organisms are interposed extensively in this cycle, and indeed they contribute substantially to its continuance. Aquatic organisms absorb water directly from their liquid environment and they excrete some of it back while they live. After death the remainder, still in the form of liquid water, is returned through decay. Terrestrial organisms absorb liquid water from the reservoir present in soil and in bodies of fresh water. Plants and animals move such water through their bodies and in the process they retain required quantities. The remainder is excreted, partly as liquid water but more particularly as water vapor which raises the moisture content of the atmosphere. After terrestrial organisms die, any liquid water in their bodies again returns to the hydrosphere through decay.

Water influences living matter not only through its function as a prime nutrient but also through its effect on virtually all aspects of climate and weather. In the ocean, for example, water warmed in the tropics becomes light and rises to the surface, whereas cool polar water sinks. These up-down displacements bring about massive horizontal shifts of water between equator and pole. The rotation of the earth introduces east-west displacements. These effects, reinforced substantially by similarly patterned wind-producing air movements, result in *oceanic currents*. The latter influence climatic conditions not only within the seas, but also in the air and on land.

Another climatic effect is a result of the thermal properties of water. Of all liquids, water is one of the slowest to heat or cool, and it stores a very large amount of heat energy. The oceans thus become huge reservoirs of solar heat. The result is that sea air chilled by night becomes less cold because of *heat radiation* from water warmed by day. Conversely, sea air warmed by day becomes less hot because of *heat absorption* by water cooled by night. Warm or cool onshore winds then moderate the inland climate in daily patterns. Analogous but more profound effects are produced by heat radiation and absorption in seasonal summer and winter patterns.

Thirdly, global climate over long periods of time is determined by the relative amount of water locked into *polar ice*. Temperature variations averaging only a few degrees over the years, produced by still poorly understood geophysical changes, suffice for major advance or retreat of polar ice. During the last million years, "ice ages" have developed and waned rhythmically, and warm *interglacial* periods, characterized by ice-free poles, have intervened between successive advances of ice. Four glaciation cycles have occurred, each lasting in the order of 60,000 to 200,000 years. At the present time, the earth is slowly emerging from the last ice age, which reached its peak some 50,000 to 20,000 years ago. As polar ice is melting, water levels are now rising and coast lines are gradually being submerged. If trends during the past 50 years are reliable indications, the earth appears to be warming up generally. Deserts are presently expanding; snow lines on mountains are receding to higher altitudes; in given localities, more days of the year are snow-free; and the flora and fauna native to given latitudes are slowly spreading poleward. It is difficult to be sure whether these changes are merely part of a short warm cycle or are really indicative of a long-range trend.

All these various cyclic changes in the hydrosphere have profound impact on living organisms. By influencing temperature, humidity, amount of precipitation, winds, waves, currents, and indeed the very presence or absence of water in given localities, they play a major role in determining what kinds and amounts of organisms may live there.

THE LITHOSPHERE

This subdivision of the environment affects living matter in two basic ways. First, as already pointed out above, it is the exclusive source of most *mineral* nutrients; and second, it forms the bulk component of *soil*, required specifically by terrestrial plants.

Minerals and cycles. Like the world's water, the rocky substance of the earth's surface moves in gigantic cycles, but here the rate of circulation is measured in thousands and millions of years. Such cycles are produced by the rising and lowering of land. Major parts of continents, or indeed whole continents, may be lifted higher when the land is pushed up from below or is pressed from the sides by adjacent portions of the earth crust. Changes of this sort take place exceedingly slowly. They are counteracted, equally slowly, by leveling of high land through erosion.

The most dramatic instance of such cycles is *mountain building* and *mountain leveling*. Presently the youngest, hence the highest, mountain ranges are the Himalayas, the Rockies, the Andes, and the Alps. All of them were thrown up some 70 million years ago, and we may note that the earth's crust in these regions is not completely settled even now.

Quite apart from the tremendous upheaval caused by mountain formation itself, such an event has long-lasting climatic consequences. A high, massive mountain barrier is likely to interfere drastically with continental air circulation. For example, moisture-laden ocean winds may no longer be able to pass across the barrier. Continual rain will therefore fall on the near side and the region may become lush and fertile. By contrast, the far side will be arid and desert conditions are likely to develop (Fig. 7.10). The following are two good examples: fertile California on the ocean side of the Sierras and the deserts of Arizona and New Mexico on the other side; fertile India on the ocean side of the Himalayas and the belt of deserts north of them. Organisms living on either side of a newly formed mountain range must adapt to the new environmental conditions by evolution. As we shall see, periods of extensive mountain building have always been followed by major evolutionary turnover among organisms (Chap. 25).

In time, even the highest mountains wear away and high land becomes lowered. Such changes are brought about in part by actual geologic sinking of land and in part by actions of the hydrosphere and the atmosphere. These actions usually take the form of *erosion* and *dissolution* of rock. Many erosional processes are quite familiar. For example, water and gravity produce shearing, canyon-cutting rivers (Fig. 7.11). Water and high temperatures produce corrosive humidity. Water and low temperatures produce grinding, rock-pulverizing glaciers. And as freezing water expands in rocky crevices, it carves boulders and stones off the face of a mountain. Water, wind, and sun in time so reduce mountain to hill and hill eventually to plain. Together with geologic sinking, these processes often may make land lie so low that substantial parts of it become overrun by the ocean.

Accompanying such physical changes are chemical ones. First, the chemical action of water, and also chemical processes which accompany the decay of dead terrestrial organisms, are major erosional factors.

Fig. 7.11. The cutting, erosional effect of a river. This canyon was channeled out by the stream flowing through it. (U.S. Department of Agriculture.)

Fig. 7.10. The effect of a mountain on climate. A mountain deflects moisture-rich ocean winds upward and causes rain to remain confined to the slope facing the ocean. That slope will therefore be fertile, but the far slope will become a desert.

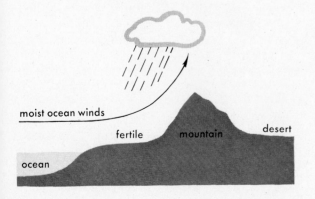

They contribute to breaking large stones into smaller ones and small pebbles into tiny sand grains and microscopic rock fragments. Chemical erosion so plays a principal role in the formation of the rocky components of *soil*.

Second, whenever water is in contact with rock, it dissolves small quantities of it and so acquires a *mineral* content. Accordingly, as rainwater runs off high land, it becomes progressively laden with minerals. Streams and rivers form, and these irrigate adjacent areas and contribute to the water content of soil. Rain adds water directly to soil. In soil, the water leaches more minerals out of the many rock fragments present and the total supply then serves as the mineral source for terrestrial organisms. After the organisms die and decay, the mineral ions of their bodies return to the soil.

Dissolved soil minerals eventually drain back into rivers, and rivers drain into the ocean. Therefore, as the lithosphere is slowly being denuded of mineral compounds, the hydrosphere fills with them. It was partly by this means that the early seas on earth acquired their original saltiness, and as the global water cycle now continues, it makes the oceans even saltier. Organisms in the sea freely use the mineral ions as metabolites.

The death of marine organisms subsequently helps to complete the global mineral cycle. Many plants and animals use mineral nutrients in the construction of protective shells and supporting bones. After these organisms die, their bodies sink down toward the sea floor, in a slow, steady rain. All organic and some of the inorganic matter dissolves during the descent, but much of the mineral substance persists in solid form and reaches the sea bottom. So abundant and uninterrupted is this rain that it forms gradually thickening layers of ooze over huge tracts of the sea floor. In the course of millennia, the older, deeper layers of the

ooze may compress into rock. The global lithospheric cycle then becomes complete when a section of sea bottom or low-lying land generally is subjected to new uplifting forces. High ground or mountains are thereby regenerated and such parts as were sea floor originally may be thrust up as new land in the process (Fig. 7.12).

Soil.   As noted, the lithosphere plays a special role in the life of land plants in that it contributes importantly to the formation of soil. This complex material serves in plant maintenance in two major ways: it provides mechanical *anchorage* for plants, without hindering growth and aeration of roots; and it holds water and mineral ions, the source from which land plants must obtain supplies of these *inorganic nutrients.*

Soil consists principally of two components. One is *sand,* that is, tiny eroded particles of rock. Such rock fragments generally have rough, jagged textures, and when they pack together they still leave small air spaces between them. Extremely small rock particles

Fig. 7.12.   The global mineral cycle. Minerals absorbed by terrestrial plants and animals return to soil by excretion and death. Rivers carry soil minerals into the ocean, where some of them are deposited at the bottom. Portions of sea bottom may then be uplifted geologically, and the new land so formed reintroduces minerals into a global cycle.

may pack together very tightly, leaving hardly any air spaces. This kind of sand is called *clay*. The other component of soil is *humus*. It consists of complex organic materials produced by the decay of previously present living matter. Humus to some extent binds the sand particles together and gives soil its crumbly, water-retaining characteristics.

Actually, soil is not an essential medium for plant maintenance. For example, floating aquatic plants do very well without it. Moreover, land plants too can be maintained adequately without soil if they are immersed in mineral-rich water. Such procedures are called *hydroponic* cultures. Evidently, so long as the environment provides water and minerals at all, it does not matter too much through what medium the plant obtains these materials. On land, soil happens to be the usual and the cheapest, hence the most treasured, large-scale supplier. And it has the additional, very essential property of anchoring plants mechanically, without halting the continuous expansion of root systems.

General references to "soil" are usually references to the *topsoil*, the upper, most valuable layer. Topsoils differ widely in color, according to the types of minerals and humus components contained in them. The roots of small plants are embedded entirely in topsoil. Larger plants send their roots into the extensive subjacent layer, the *subsoil*. Here the proportion of clay may be higher than in topsoil and subsoil may therefore be relatively dense. Also, the proportion of humus may be reduced. Subsoil is usually underlain by *loose rock*, and this layer extends down to the continuous *bedrock* of the continent (Fig. 7.13).

The quality of topsoil depends on a wide variety of factors. A good topsoil is neither too dense to prevent the growth of roots nor too loose to be blown away or washed away. Also, a good soil contains a high proportion of water-retaining humus and is underlain by a substantial layer of subsoil, which prevents water from draining away too fast. The chemical value of a soil depends on its usable mineral content. We have already referred to three major ways by which these nutrients are replenished: inflow of new mineral-laden water, direct chemical dissolution of soil particles by soil water, and decay of dead plants and animals. Decay not only returns minerals but also adds new

organic substances, and it so raises the humus content of soil. These relatively slow natural processes of replenishment may be augmented by man, through conservation procedures designed to prevent nutritional exhaustion of soil. For example, he may add mineral-rich *fertilizers* to soil. He may let soils *rest* for one or more seasons. He may grow crops and, instead of

Fig. 7.13. Profile of soil. Note dark topsoil, underlain by light-colored layer of subsoil. Streaked layers of clay lie under the subsoil, and the clay merges into rock near the bottom of the photo. (U.S. Department of Agriculture.)

harvesting them, may plow them right back into the ground. Or he may adopt a program of *crop rotation*, whereby different crops are planted in successive seasons, each crop requiring different sets of soil minerals.

Some natural replenishment of soil minerals is accomplished also by certain bacteria, and we shall see in the next section how this occurs.

THE ATMOSPHERE

Like the hydrosphere, the atmosphere as a whole is subjected to physical cycles by the sun and the spin of the earth. Warmed equatorial air rises and cooled polar air sinks, and the axial rotation of the earth shifts air masses laterally. The resulting global air currents basically have the same general pattern as the ocean currents, and the winds of the former strongly reinforce the latter. Also, the motions of air substantially influence climatic conditions, hence living organisms.

Of much greater significance to organisms, however, are the chemical cycles of the atmosphere. Air consists mainly of oxygen, O_2 (about 20 per cent); carbon dioxide, CO_2 (about 0.03 per cent); nitrogen, N_2 (about 79 per cent); water (in varying amounts, depending on climatic conditions); and minute traces of inert gases (helium, neon, krypton, argon, xenon). Excepting the inert gases, all these components of air

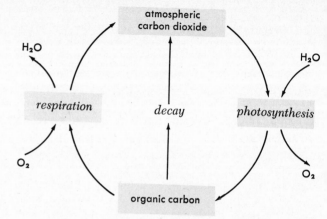

Fig. 7.15.   The carbon cycle.

serve as nutrients and each circulates in a global cycle in which organisms play a conspicuous role.

Atmospheric oxygen enters living organisms as a respiratory gas, and in the course of respiration it combines with hydrogen and forms water (see Chap. 14). Such water then becomes part of the general water supply of organisms. Photosynthesis requires water as a raw material, and in the course of photosynthesis the oxygen part of water is again liberated. Gaseous oxygen so leaves living organisms as a byproduct of photosynthesis and reenters the atmosphere (Fig. 7.14).

Atmospheric carbon dioxide is the principal carbon source of living matter. This gas enters the living world through photosynthesis, in which it is a fundamental raw material. Photosynthesis converts CO_2 into foods and these then serve living organisms in two ways. Some of the foods are used in respiration, which returns CO_2 to the environment as a byproduct. The remaining foods become part of the structure of organisms. After death, living matter decays by bacterial action and CO_2 is released in the process (Fig. 7.15). Note that the CO_2 content of air also increases through combustion of industrial fuels, through forest and other fires, and to some extent also through occasional additions from the interior of the earth (e.g., volcanic eruptions).

Atmospheric N_2 is the principal nitrogen source for living organisms (Fig. 7.16). However, aerial nitrogen is rather inert chemically and the majority of

Fig. 7.14.   The oxygen cycle.

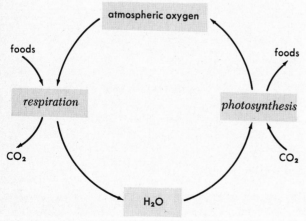

organisms actually cannot use it directly. For example, man obtains an abundance of aerial nitrogen with every breath, yet all of it is again exhaled, unchanged and unused. The situation is essentially similar in most other organisms. Only certain bacteria, the so-called *nitrogen-fixing bacteria*, may utilize atmospheric N_2 directly. Such "fixed" bacterial nitrogen then becomes available to plants in usable form. Plants also absorb mineral nitrates (NO_3^-) from soil and convert these ions into usable organic nitrogen (e.g., amino groups, $-NH_2$). Such organic nitrogen becomes part of plant structure. Animals ultimately depend on plant foods for their own source of usable nitrogen. After plants and animals die they decay, and as a result the nitrogen of their bodies appears in soil or ocean in the form of ammonia (NH_3). This compound is subsequently used as a nutrient by specialized *nitrifying bacteria*. They convert ammonia to nitrates, the latter representing the principal source of mineral nitrogen in soil and ocean. As noted, nitrates also accumulate through rock dissolution, through addition of fertilizers by man, and in other ways. The nitrate supply in the environment then serves plants and in part also so-called *denitrifying bacteria*. These organisms change nitrates back into molecular atmospheric nitrogen, N_2, and the nitrogen cycle becomes complete in this manner.

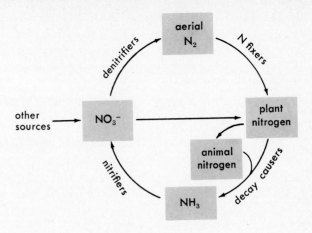

Fig. 7.16. The nitrogen cycle.

As this and the preceding chapters have shown, the living organization is an integral part of the makeup of the earth as a whole, on all levels from electrons to the global environment. The most conspicuous unit undoubtedly is the individual organism. Accordingly, it is appropriate to consider next the specific kinds of organisms that actually exhibit the living organization here described.

Review questions

1. What is the structure of an ocean basin? What are the major subenvironments in such a basin, and what role does the sun play in creating some of these subenvironments? What physical conditions characterize the various subenvironments?

2. Define plankton, nekton, and benthos. Give specific examples of each. Where in the ocean are each of these types of organisms found? What physical and biological conditions characterize the sea depths?

3. Review the essential physical differences between oceanic and freshwater environments. What major types of organisms occur in fresh water, and in what general ways are they adapted to this environment? What major types of organisms are terrestrial?

4. What are the main terrestrial habitats and what physical and biological conditions characterize each of them? In what way are latitudinal terrestrial habitats related to altitudinal habitats?

5. Review the global water cycle. What forces maintain it? How do organisms participate in this cycle? In what different ways does the world's water influence climates?

6. How does the formation of mountains influence climates? Cite examples. In what ways is the global lithospheric cycle of nutritional importance? Review the general pattern of mineral cycles.

7. What are the principal components of soil? In what ways does soil serve in the maintenance of plant life? What factors determine the quality of a soil? What are hydro-

ponics? Review the ways in which soil minerals are replenished.

8. What is the chemical composition of the atmosphere? Which of these components do not play a role in the maintenance of organisms?

9. Review (*a*) the oxygen cycle, (*b*) the carbon cycle.

Show how these cycles are interlinked with each other and with the global water cycle.

10. Review the global nitrogen cycle. How many different groups of bacteria aid in the maintenance of this cycle? What is the role of decay in the atmospheric, lithospheric, and hydrospheric cycles?

Suggested collateral readings

Cole, L. C.: The Ecosphere, *Sci. Am.*, vol. 198, 1958.

Kamen, M. D.: Discoveries in Nitrogen Fixation, *Sci. Am.*, vol. 188, 1953.

Kellogg, C. E.: Soil, *Sci. Am.*, vol. 183, 1950.

Munk, W.: The Circulation of the Oceans, *Sci. Am.*, vol. 193, 1955.

Öpik, E. J.: Climate and the Changing Sun, *Sci. Am.*, vol. 198, 1958.

Pequegnat, W. E.: Whales, Plankton, and Man, *Sci. Am.*, vol. 198, 1958.

Plass, G. N.: Carbon Dioxide and Climate, *Sci. Am.*, vol. 201, 1959.

Ryther, F. H.: The Sargasso Sea, *Sci. Am.*, vol. 194, 1956.

Walford, L. A.: The Deep-sea Layers of Life, *Sci. Am.*, vol. 185, 1951.

Went, F. W.: The Ecology of Desert Plants, *Sci. Am.*, vol. 192, 1955.

part **3**

The World of Life

This series of chapters is devoted to an examination of the main groups of organisms in existence today, their habits, structures, and internal organization. A preliminary objective will be to become familiar with the ways in which main groups are named and distinguished. Subsequently, each of the groups so identified will be studied systematically, with attention also on the principal subgroups.

Note that this part of the book serves a dual role. First, it leads to an appreciation of the vast diversity of the living creatures on earth. This promotes an understanding of how life is achieved in often highly different ways and under enormously varied environmental circumstances. Second, these chapters also provide the essential background for the remainder of the book. The processes of life, namely, metabolism and self-perpetuation, reside in specific individual organisms. Therefore, if the processes are to be understood, it is clearly necessary that their containers themselves be known and understood.

MONERA AND PROTISTA

Organisms can be classified into more or less well-defined types or categories. The biological subscience dealing with classification is called *taxonomy* or *systematics*. In the first part of this chapter we shall examine the general scheme of taxonomic classification and the major groups of organisms actually identified within this scheme. In the second and third parts, we shall concern ourselves particularly with the groups known as the Monera and Protista.

Kinds of organisms

CLASSIFICATION

Organisms are named and distinguished on the basis of their specializations in *structure, function, development,* and *evolutionary history.* The procedure of classifying organisms makes use of a universally recognized hierarchy of *taxonomic ranks.* In this hierarchy, any given rank usually contains several categories of lower ranks as components. If certain specializations are common to a large group of organisms, this group may be assigned a particular taxonomic rank. Within such a rank, several smaller groups of organisms can usually be distinguished on the basis of finer differences in their specializations, and such smaller groups are then assigned the next lower rank. Each such lower-ranking group in turn may be subclassified further into a succession of progressively lower ranks.

Within the living world as a whole, the highest taxonomic rank usually recognized is the *kingdom.* By tradition going back several centuries, organisms are classified into two kingdoms, namely, the plant kingdom and the animal kingdom. It is highly questionable whether this tradition is still justifiable today, and there are good reasons to name the major groups in a different way. We shall return to this point below.

The highest rank within a kingdom is the *phylum;* a kingdom contains several phyla. The phylum rank describes a broad grouping of historically usually closely related organisms, all characterized by fairly similar structural and functional body organization. For example, all sponges, or all mollusks, as a group represent a phylum. Note that, strictly speaking, the name "phylum" is applied only to animal organisms; the equivalent term for plants is *division.* But for convenience, and because in certain instances the distinction between "plant" and "animal" is far from clear (see below), we shall use the term "phylum" uniformly throughout this book.

Within a phylum, the next highest rank is the *class.* For example, sponges may be subdivided into classes on the basis of their skeletons, one group having calcium skeletons, another silicon skeletons, and a third horny skeletons. Similarly, the phylum *Chordata* includes all animals which possess an internal skeleton, the *notochord,* at least as embryos. This phylum contains the class of *mammals.* Such animals share the possession of a notochord with all other chordate classes, e.g., the birds, the reptiles, and the fishes. But mammals are set off from other chordate classes by their possession of hair and by their nursing young with milk. Each other class has its own distinguishing features.

Using such criteria of likenesses and differences among and within groups, one may recognize *orders* within a class, *families* within an order, *genera* within a family, and *species* within a genus. The species normally is the lowest unit. We have already seen in

Chap. 6 how this important rank is characterized. Because the species encompasses all organisms of the same kind and because it is a fundamental and reasonably permanent level of organization in nature, it can also become the base on which the whole pyramid of technical classification is built.

According to international rules, a species is always identified by *two* technical names. For example, the species of grass frogs is known technically as *Rana pipiens;* the species to which we belong is *Homo sapiens.* Such species names are always underlined or printed in italics, and the first name is capitalized. This first name always identifies the genus to which the species belongs. Thus, the human species belongs to the genus *Homo* and the grass-frog species to the genus *Rana. Homo sapiens* happens to be the only presently living species within the genus *Homo,* but the genus *Rana* contains *Rana pipiens* as well as many other frog species.

Sometimes it is desirable to make finer distinctions between two consecutive ranks. In that case an additional rank may be interpolated between the original two and the prefix "sub-" or "super-" is then added to one of the main ranks. For example, between an order and a family, the order may contain several *suborders,* each suborder several *superfamilies,* and each superfamily several families. (Note, incidentally, that the taxonomic meaning of the term "family" differs from the social meaning.)

A complete classification of an organism tells a great deal about the nature of that organism. For example, suppose we knew nothing else about corn plants and men except their taxonomic classifications. Then we would know that the characteristics of these organisms are as listed in Table 4. Evidently, even brief taxonomic characterizations such as these place an organism rather well, and we may note that a full, detailed classification would describe an organism completely.

Within a phylum, the member organisms often differ radically in their ways of life. Consider, for example, the different ways of a fish and a man. Nevertheless, all organisms within a phylum use the same kinds of structures in solving the different problems of their different environments. Thus the fins of a fish

TABLE 4
Classification of corn plants and men

taxonomic rank	corn plant	man
phylum	Tracheophyta: plants with vascular tissues	Chordata: animals with notochords
subphylum	Pteropsida: types with large leaves	Vertebrata: types with vertebral columns
superclass	Spermatophyta: seed producers	Tetrapoda: terrestrial; four limbs, bony skeletons
class	Angiospermae: flowering plants: seeds inside fruits	Mammalia: types with hair and milk glands
subclass	Monocotyledonae: parallel-veined leaves; single seed leaf; flower parts in threes or multiples	Eutheria: offspring develop within female parent, nourished by placenta
order	Graminales: grasses	Primates: fingers; flat nails
family	Graminaceae: leaves in two rows on round or flattened stem	Hominidae: upright posture; flat face; stereoscopic vision; large brains; hands and feet
genus	Zea: corn plants	Homo: double-curved spine; long life span and long youth
species	*Zea mays:* cultivated, domesticated corn plants	*Homo sapiens:* well-developed chins; high forehead; thin skull bones

and the arms of a man are basically the same kinds of structures, evolved from one common ancestral type of body appendage.

In some cases it is not universally agreed whether a given group of organisms represents a distinct phylum or a superphylum containing several smaller phyla or a class within a larger phylum. Indeed, general agreement among biologists becomes better with the lower taxonomic ranks and worse with the higher ranks. The higher rank categories actually are being reshuffled more or less constantly. This is probably as it should be, for these rankings incorporate our knowledge of the evolution of organisms and as this knowledge improves the rank categories must be adjusted accordingly. A specific instance of such an adjustment will be considered presently.

THE MAJOR LIVING GROUPS

Within the framework of the taxonomic system outlined above, how are existing organisms actually classified?

As noted above, it is rather doubtful whether the simple subdivision of the living world into plant and animal kingdoms is still adequate today. Work during the past few decades has shown that certain groups of organisms really fit into neither the plant nor the animal category and should in fact be regarded as something else. At the same time, several other groups fit into both categories. For example, bacteria really have very little in common with either plants or animals, and certain unicellular flagellate organisms can be regarded equally well as plants or animals.

A basic difficulty in this connection is that it is practically impossible to define "plant" or "animal" in adequate fashion. Every fundamental feature customarily used to define "plant" is encountered among at least some "animals" also, and vice versa. To be sure, no one has much difficulty in deciding whether advanced organisms like cabbages and cats are plants or animals. But such a difficulty does exist with primitive organisms, i.e., those closely related to the ancestral types which gave rise to both cabbages and cats. Such ancestral types possessed both plantlike and animal-like features *simultaneously,* as is true of their primitive descendants today. And if we go even farther back in time, the very first organisms on earth probably possessed neither plantlike nor animal-like features at all, as is again true of their present-day descendants.

The point is that plants and animals, clearly so recognizable, were not in existence right from the beginning. Rather, some of the early organisms *evolved* in plantlike or animal-like directions, slowly and gradually; and a definite, finalized "plant" status or "animal" status was attained only relatively late in evolutionary history. Therefore, a division of the living world merely into plant and animal kingdoms is too simple. It does not take into account this gradual evolutionary development, and it allows no place for those primitive organisms which still are neither "plant" nor "animal" or which are both.

In view of this, attempts have been made in recent years to establish alternative classifications which do reflect our present knowledge of evolution. One such alternative scheme, in part already referred to in Chap. 4, recognizes not two but four basic categories of organisms: *Monera, Protista, Metaphyta,* and *Metazoa.* Each of these has a taxonomic rank roughly equivalent to a kingdom, although it may not be desirable to use this rank designation so long as it is technically still reserved for "plants" and "animals."

The probable evolutionary interrelation of the four categories has been outlined in Chap. 4. Note that, in this four-part classification, every living creature has a proper place. Monera and Protista include organisms which are plantlike, animal-like, neither, or both, as well as some of the organisms traditionally regarded as "true" plants (e.g., advanced algae) and "true" animals (e.g., most protozoa). And the Metaphyta and Metazoa include the remainder of the "true" plants and animals. Throughout the remainder of this book, an otherwise unqualified reference to "plants" is specifically to Metaphyta; similarly, a reference to "animals" is specifically to Metazoa.

Another point may be emphasized in this context. All available evidence indicates that living evolution has the general pattern of a greatly branching *bush* (Fig. 8.1). All presently living organisms are *contemporaries,* appearing at the uppermost branch tips of the bush. Ancestral types, mostly long extinct, appear lower on the bush, where branches join. Thus, a particular common ancestor may give rise to *several* different types of descendants, each inheriting the characteristics of the common ancestor and evolving innovations of its own. And a particular descendant living today may become a common ancestor of new and different types living tomorrow.

Fig. 8.1. The bush pattern of evolution. The uppermost tips of the branches represent currently living forms, and branches terminating below the top represent extinct forms. Fork points such as *B* and *C* are ancestral types. *B* is more ancient and of higher taxonomic rank than *C*. *A* represents the archancestor of all living types.

A corollary of the above is that the pattern of evolution is *not* that of a "ladder" or a "scale." Many uninformed persons still speak of a "scale of evolution," implying a straight-line progression from one organism directly to the next, usually from some "low" type like an alga or a protozoon to some "high" type like a tree or a man. Such statements are based on wholly erroneous notions. A glance at Fig. 8.1 shows that a straight-line "scale" simply does not exist; only a branching pattern is in line with the actual evidence. Moreover, trees and men did not descend from algae and protozoa. Instead, all these organisms are modern contemporaries which have evolved, coequally and along entirely separate paths, from some ancient, long-extinct protistan ancestor. Finally, among currently living organisms, there simply are no "higher" and "lower" types, since all rank equally high (or equally low) on the evolutionary bush. There are only *different* types, with different histories and different characteristics.

With these various considerations as a general background, we may now proceed in this and subsequent chapters to a more specific study of the Monera, the Protista, the Metaphyta, and the Metazoa.

Monera

These organisms are distinguished from all other forms of life largely by negative features. For example, a moneran cell does *not* possess an organized nucleus with a distinct surrounding membrane, so characteristic of all other cell types. Gene-containing DNA protein forms one or more clumps, and these clumps do *not* contain chromosomes of the type found in other organisms. Such features of nonpossession may reflect the evolutionary antiquity of the moneran stock. Evidently, at the time this stock arose the internal elaboration and specialization of cellular structure had not yet progressed very far.

The Monera are basically unicellular, but in some cases the cells are aggregated together into colonies and other multicellular masses. Two phyla are included in the category, the *bacteria* and the *blue-green algae*.

PHYLUM SCHIZOPHYTA

bacteria (2,000 species)

As a group, bacteria represent the smallest cells now in existence. The tiniest of them are smaller even than certain gigantic viruses, and the largest are not substantially larger than very small cells of other organisms. Bacteria usually possess a cell wall, made of polysaccharides, proteins, and frequently also lipids. Many bacteria occur as single cells, but many others grow in clumps, forming chains, plates, or compact aggregates. Many also possess exceedingly fine surface flagella which endow them with a certain amount of self-powered mobility. On the basis of shape, three kinds of bacteria may be distinguished. A *coccus* is a spherical type, a *bacillus* a rod-shaped type, and a *spirillum* a coiled type (Fig. 8.2).

Some bacteria are chemosynthesizers or photosynthesizers, and these produce their own food. The photosynthesizing types possess unique varieties of chlorophyll, including one called *bacteriochlorophyll*. These forms do not possess chloroplasts. Instead, the bacteriochlorophyll is located in tiny granules dispersed throughout the cytoplasm. Bioluminescence is fairly common within the phylum.

Most bacteria depend on other organisms for food. Of these, some are free-living saprotrophs in soil or ocean, and the rest are parasitic, commensalistic, or mutualistic symbionts. Also, some bacteria must have oxygen for respiration, others can do without it and respire by fermentation, and still others may survive both with and without oxygen. In most of these types,

Fig. 8.2. Bacteria. Left, cocci, growing in chains; middle, bacilli; right, spirilla. (General Biological Supply House, Inc.)

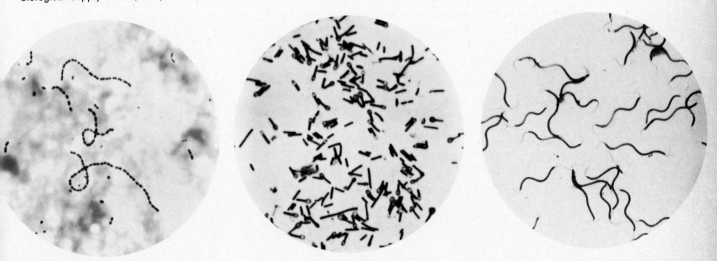

reserve foods are stored in the form of the polysaccharide *glycogen*.

Bacteria reproduce by cell division. This is an enormously effective process, for under good conditions bacterial cells may divide every 20 minutes or so. A single bacterium so may produce 1 million offspring in just 6 to 7 hours. It may be easily appreciated, therefore, that bacteria probably outnumber all other living organisms on earth.

Three groups of bacteria are of major significance to all other life on earth: those which, in soil and ocean, bring about *decay;* those which are *nitrogen-fixing, nitrifying,* and *denitrifying* and which therefore provide nitrogen usable by other organisms and contribute to maintenance of the global nitrogen cycle; and those parasitic bacteria which produce disease, the *pathogenic* bacteria.

Evidently, the phylum is highly diversified. In spite of the exceedingly small size of the individual bacterium, there is certainly nothing "simple" about it. Its molecular and chemical complexity is quite as great as that of any other cell type, and it often lives in a way and in an environment in which few other organisms can. Indeed, if man is challenged in his dominance by anything living, his greatest challenger is probably the bacterium.

PHYLUM CYANOPHYTA
blue-green algae (2,500 species)

This phylum name is somewhat misleading, since many of the designated organisms are not actually blue-green, but are of red, yellow, green, blue, and various intermediate shades. These colors are produced by several pigments. A variety of chlorophyll called *chlorophyll a* is usually present, and in addition there are other colored substances, including a blue *phyco-cyanin* and a red *phycoerythrin* pigment. The last two are quite unique to the phylum, occurring in no other.

The cells of cyanophytes are equipped with walls containing *cellulose* and, like bacterial cells, they lack a nuclear membrane internally. Chloroplasts are absent but, as in photosynthetic bacteria, the chlorophyll molecules are in granules dispersed through the cytoplasm. Again like certain bacteria, many cyanophytes may fix atmospheric nitrogen and many are bioluminescent. Food is stored in the form of a unique type of starch called *cyanophycean starch.*

Cyanophytes occur in virtually all environments

Fig. 8.3. Blue-green algae. Left, two colonies of *Gloeocapsa;* right, portion of a colony of *Nostoc.* Note the gelatinous envelopes in both views. (Left, courtesy of Dr. M. S. Fuller, University of California, Berkeley; right, General Biological Supply House, Inc.)

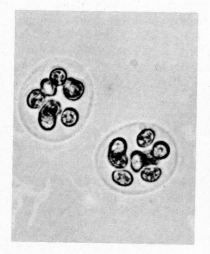
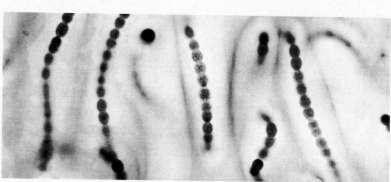

containing water. Many blue-greens grow as single cells, but many are multicellular. Such organisms usually form filaments or cellular aggregates of various other shapes. Colonies of this sort are often embedded in a gelatinous material secreted by the cells (Fig. 8.3).

Protista

This category includes an enormous assemblage of types, all believed to be more or less direct descendants of very early cells which had evolved a true cell nucleus, with a membrane separating the gene-containing nucleoproteins from the cytoplasm. Moreover, several other characteristics of the modern Protista must have been evolutionary "inventions" of the protistan ancestors (Fig. 8.4).

First, in addition to a *nuclear membrane*, the protistan nucleus contains genetic nucleoproteins organized in the form of clearly identifiable *chromosomes*. Also present within the nucleus are *nucleoli*.

Second, unlike moneran cells, protistan cells divide by a method called *mitotic division*. More will be said about it in Chap. 20, but we may note here that this method depends on the presence of chromosomes.

Third, the protistan ancestors probably "invented" most of the cytoplasmic organelles described in Chap. 5. This includes *centrioles*, various *vacuoles*, *fibrils*, *chloroplasts* in photosynthetic cells, and also the *basal granules* and the surface *flagella* attached to them. Flagella are very common throughout the Protista. Many unicellular protists under certain conditions can cast off their flagella and may then propel themselves by *amoeboid* locomotion. At some later time, flagella may be regrown.

Fourth, as already pointed out in Chap. 4, ancestral Protista probably could nourish themselves either by photosynthesis or by saprotrophism or by holotrophism or by symbiosis. Some primitive modern Protista still retain this multiplicity of choices. More advanced types have concentrated on one of these methods and have lost the others.

Fifth, primitive modern Protista are basically unicellular, like their presumable ancestors. But the more advanced members in each major protistan group have

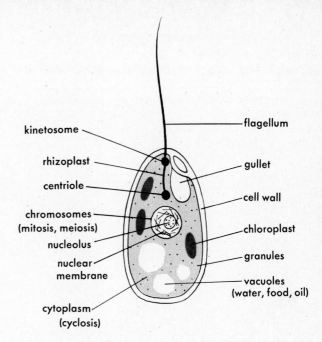

Fig. 8.4. Diagrammatic representation of the basic protistan cell type.

become multicellular and in some cases have attained the tissue level of organization.

Protista today include the *algae*, the *fungi*, the *slime molds*, and the *protozoa*.

ALGAE

As a group, algae may be regarded as a superphylum containing several distinct phyla. Although structural features provide useful distinctions between the algal phyla, the main differences are primarily biochemical: types of chlorophyll and other pigments present, the chemical composition of the cell wall, and the chemical nature of stored foods. On the basis of their chlorophyll content, three main groups of algae may be recognized. All three possess chlorophyll *a*, but in addition, one possesses chlorophyll *b*, the second chlorophyll *c* (or in some cases *e*), and the third chlorophyll *d*. In conjunction with other pigments present, these chlorophylls produce characteristic visible colors: some shade of green in the *a* plus *b* types, brown in the *a* plus

TABLE 5
Comparative biochemical characteristics of algae

group	phylum	chlorophyll	food-storage compounds	cell walls
green line	Chlorophyta	*a, b*	starch	cellulose
	Charophyta	*a, b*	starch	cellulose
	Euglenophyta	*a, b*	paramylum, fats	usually none
brown line	Chrysophyta	*a, c (e)*	leucosin, fats	cellulose, silica, or none
	Pyrrophyta	*a, c*	starch, polysaccharides, fats	cellulose or none
	Phaeophyta	*a, c*	laminarin, mannitol	cellulose, algin
red line	Rhodophyta	*a, d*	floridean starch	cellulose

c types, and red in the *a* plus *d* types. We may therefore distinguish a *green line*, a *brown line*, and a *red line* of algae (Table 5).

The green line.

PHYLUM CHLOROPHYTA
green algae (about 6,000 species)

The phylum is identified by chlorophylls *a* and *b*, by other pigments called *carotenes* and *xanthophylls*, by comparatively rigid cell walls containing cellulose, by reserve foods stored as starch, and by flagellate cells or stages which bear two (or more rarely four) equally long anterior flagella. These characteristics occur in precisely this combination only in the green algae and the Metaphyta. Early stocks of the former are therefore believed to have been in the specific ancestors of the latter.

Primitive flagellate algae are represented by green, single-celled types such as *Chlamydomonas*. Very closely related is *Polytoma*, which is virtually identical to *Chlamydomonas* except that it is colorless and nonphotosynthetic (Fig. 8.5). It lives as a saprotroph. As we shall see, paired types of this sort are also encountered among most of the other algal phyla. Undoubtedly, such paired photosynthetic and colorless forms represent branch lines descended from a relatively recent common ancestor, one line having retained and the other lost the photosynthetic method of nutrition. In certain cases, experiment may duplicate such evolutionary processes. For example, it has been possible to convert given photosynthetic algae into variant strains which lack chlorophyll. Such animal-like variants thrive perfectly well if a ready-made source of food is supplied from the outside. Very probably, experiments of this sort also simulate the ancient natural process through which original flagellate protists may have given rise separately to plantlike and animal-like descendants.

Cells rather like *Chlamydomonas* form flagellate colonies, which are usually composed of fixed numbers of cells—4, 8, 16, 32, 64, or larger multiples. If there are relatively few cells, they form disks or cup-shaped

Fig. 8.5. Diagrammatic representation of *Chlamydomonas*, a unicellular, flagellate, green alga. Note the large, cup-shaped chloroplast, an organelle which is absent in the related nonphotosynthetic type *Polytoma*.

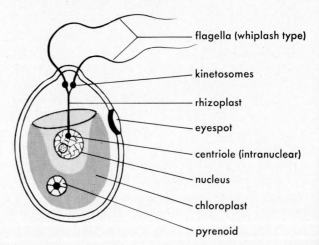

— flagella (whiplash type)

— kinetosomes

— rhizoplast

— eyespot

— centriole (intranuclear)

— nucleus

— chloroplast

— pyrenoid

colonies; and if the cell number is comparatively large, the colony is usually a hollow sphere, as in *Volvox*. In this organism the cells exhibit a high degree of coordination (Fig. 8.6).

Many groups of green algae are permanently without flagella and are nonmotile. Unicellular types of this sort include *Chlorella*, used extensively in research on photosynthesis, and the large alga *Acetabularia*. This marine organism, up to 2 or 3 inches long, consists of a stalk, an umbrellalike cap at the top, and fine outgrowths at the bottom of the stalk which anchor the organism on the sea floor. The whole is one cell, a single nucleus being situated in the base of the stalk (Fig. 8.7).

Forms like *Chlorella* and *Acetabularia* do not divide except at the time of reproduction, but other algae may divide at any stage of the life cycle. Included in this group is the unicellular, nonmotile type *Protococcus*, which usually grows on moist tree bark and which by division forms loosely aggregated colonies. Somewhat more complexly organized are the filamen-

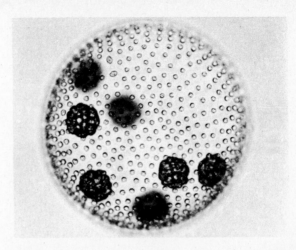

Fig. 8.6.   Volvox, a colonial green alga consisting of many flagellate cells. The cells are arranged as a single-layered sphere, with each cell in direct contact with the water environment. In the interior of the sphere are several offspring colonies, which develop there and eventually burst through the parent. (Courtesy of Dr. M. S. Fuller, University of California, Berkeley.)

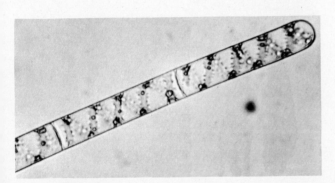

Fig. 8.7.   Green algae. Top left, *Spirogyra*; bottom left, *Acetabularia*; right, *Ulva*. (Top left, courtesy of Dr. M. S. Fuller, University of California, Berkeley; bottom left, General Biological Supply House, Inc.)

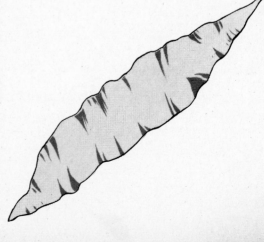

tous green algae, of which *Spirogyra* is a good example. Cell division extends such filaments in length. The most complex green algae are types in which cell division produces extensive sheets of cells, as in the sea lettuce *Ulva*, or elaborate 3-dimensional algal bodies composed of several tissue layers.

PHYLUM CHAROPHYTA
stoneworts (about 250 species)

In many ways these organisms are similar to the most advanced green algae, but they differ enough to be classified as a separate phylum. Stoneworts live in freshwater ponds. They resemble miniature trees, with whorls of leaflike branches attached at more or less regular intervals to a stemlike stalk. This stalk is anchored to the ground by rootlike processes (Fig. 8.8). As a group, the stoneworts may represent an evolutionary experiment which advanced the basic algal organization in a direction actually taken later by terrestrial plants.

PHYLUM EUGLENOPHYTA
euglenoids (about 350 species)

By virtue of its pigments, this phylum belongs to the green-line stock of algae. But the organisms differ in several important respects from other green-line types (see Fig. 8.8). First, euglenoids are almost exclusively unicellular flagellates. Second, there may be a single anterior flagellum, or two flagella of equal length, or one long and one short flagellum, or even three flagella. Third, the cells are naked, without rigid cell walls, and very pliable and deformable. Fourth, the characteristic food storage compound is not starch, but partly fatty material and partly a polysaccharide, called *paramylum*, chemically related to starch.

Paired green and colorless euglenoids are common.

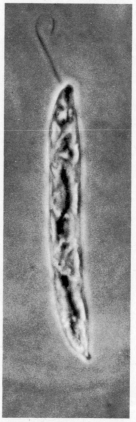

Fig. 8.8. **Left, a specimen of the stonewort** *Nitella;* **right, a specimen of** *Euglena.* (Left, courtesy of Dr. P. Green, University of Pennsylvania; right, courtesy of Dr. M. S. Fuller, University of California, Berkeley.)

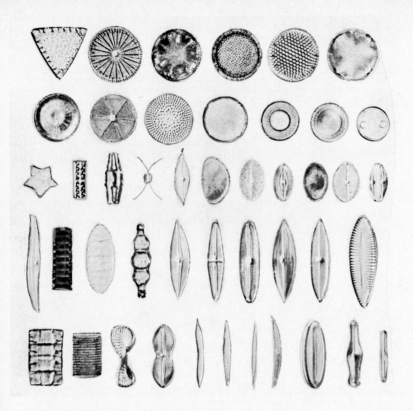

Fig. 8.9.   An array of diatoms. A close-up of a single diatom is shown in Fig. 7.2. (General Biological Supply House, Inc.)

For example, *Euglena* is a green photosynthesizer, interesting also in that it can and probably must occasionally feed as a saprotroph, whether light is present or not. *Astasia*, on the other hand, is a colorless saprotroph otherwise entirely similar to *Euglena*.

The brown line.

PHYLUM CHRYSOPHYTA
golden-brown algae (about 6,000 species)

Class Chrysophyceae: yellow-brown algae

Class Xanthophyceae: yellow-green algae

Class Bacillariophyceae: diatoms

Chrysophytes are identified by chlorophylls *a* and *c* (*e* in some cases), and by various carotene and xanthophyll pigments, the latter including the conspicuous yellow-brown pigment *fucoxanthin*. Foods are **never** stored as starch, but are stored partly as *oils* and **partly** as the polysaccharide *leucosin*. Cell walls may

be absent or present. In the latter case the wall is in two halves, the rim of one half tightly overlapping the rim of the other, like lid and box. Such walls usually contain silicon compounds.

The first two classes listed above are exceedingly diversified groups. Each includes flagellate types, amoeboid types, forms which divide only at reproductive stages, and forms which divide at all stages. Moreover, each such subgroup contains unicellular and multicellular members, and paired photosynthetic and colorless forms are common. Some of these colorless forms may well have contributed to the evolution of other Protista, notably the protozoa and slime molds; a colorless chrysophycean amoeba, for example, is virtually indistinguishable from a protozoan amoeba.

In contrast to the first two classes, the diatoms (Fig. 8.9) are of major economic importance. As already noted in Chap. 7, diatoms are the most abundant single group of plankton organisms, and as such they support much of the flora and fauna of the oceans and the fresh water. The silica shells of dead diatoms make up large tracts of the ocean floor. Geologically uplifted parts of this floor are the source of *diatomaceous earth,* mined for its abrasive and various other properties. For example, it is a common component of toothpaste. Moreover, much of the petroleum used in industry today is probably derived from the oils synthesized and stored by diatoms of past ages.

PHYLUM PYRROPHYTA
fire algae (about 1,000 species)

Class Cryptophyceae: cryptoflagellates

Class Dinophyceae: dinoflagellates

These organisms are almost exclusively unicellular and flagellate. The group possesses chlorophylls *a* and *c* and the pigment *fucoxanthin.* Foods are variously stored in the form of starch, starchlike carbohydrates, and fats and oils. Cell walls are absent in some of the Dinophyceae. In others, as well as in the Cryptophyceae, walls composed of cellulose are present.

The Cryptophyceae are mostly unicellular flagellates. Among them, paired photosynthetic and colorless types are well known. The Dinophyceae (Fig. 8.10) are by far the more important class, for they constitute a major component of plankton. The vast majority of the Dinophyceae are dinoflagellates, that is, unicellular flagellate types. Most of the dinoflagellates possess cellulose walls formed into distinct interlocking "armor" plates (e.g., *Peridinium, Ceratium*). Two flagella are present, one directed backward in swimming, the other undulating within a transverse groove formed by the armor. Different nutritional variants are common. For example, *Ceratium* is photosynthetic, *Blastodinium* is a colorless parasite in animals, and *Noctiluca* either photosynthesizes or feeds like an animal. Paired photosynthetic and colorless types are known as well. Many marine dinoflagellates are bioluminescent (e.g., *Noctiluca*). On occasion, some dinoflagellates proliferate locally in fantastic numbers. For example, the reddish *Gymnodinium* often produces so-called red tides (hence the name of the phylum).

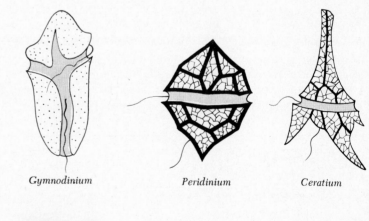

Gymnodinium   *Peridinium*   *Ceratium*

Fig. 8.10.   Dinophyceae, diagrammatic.

Noctiluca

PHYLUM PHAEOPHYTA
brown algae (about 1,000 species)

Among the identifying pigments of these algae are chlorophylls *a* and *c* and the brown fucoxanthin, the latter present in amounts sufficient to mask all other pigments. Foods are stored partly as *laminarin*, a unique polysaccharide, partly as *mannitol*, a complex alcohol. The cell walls are composed of cellulose and *algin*, an organic material unique to the brown algae.

Phaeophytes are exclusively multicellular and sessile; virtually all are marine. Colorless forms are unknown and photosynthesis is the only food-procuring process. The organisms have the form of filaments and more highly advanced organizations of the tissue grade of construction (Fig. 8.11).

Most of the seaweeds are brown algae. They live in shallow water and in the intertidal zone, attached to rocky bottoms by holdfasts. Ebb tides may expose the organisms to air for several hours, but their algin coating retains considerable amounts of water and protects the algae from desiccation. The most familiar of the brown algae is probably the rockweed *Fucus*, found along many shores, and the most spectacular are the giant kelps. For example, the kelp *Macrocystis* sometimes attains lengths of more than 100 yards. *Laminaria*, the commonest of the kelps, is of world-wide distribution. Torn pieces of it, along with other algae, may often be found washed up on beaches, particularly after a storm.

The red line.

PHYLUM RHODOPHYTA
red algae (about 3,000 species)

This phylum is characterized by the possession of chlorophylls *a* and *d* and variants of the pigments *phycocyanin* and *phycoerythrin*. The last two are of unique composition and are chemically not the same as the pigments of like name in the blue-green algae. Red algae store food in the form of *floridean starch*, chemically very much like glycogen. The cell walls are of cellulose.

Red algae are almost exclusively multicellular and marine (Fig. 8.12). They live in somewhat deeper water than the brown algae, and their red pigment

Fig. 8.11. **A portion of *Fucus*, a common brown alga found attached to rocks on the seashore.** Note the air bladders along the leaflike body. The bulbous structures at the ends of the body contain sex organs. (General Biological Supply House, Inc.)

phycoerythrin appears to be an adaptation to their dimmer environment. Phycoerythrin absorbs blue light particularly well, and the "blue" wavelengths of sunlight actually penetrate deeper into water than "red" wavelengths. Indeed, phycoerythrin has been found to play an important auxiliary role in the photosynthesis of these algae. Red algae are lacier and more delicate than the sturdy brown algae. The latter are adapted to withstand pounding surf, but in deeper water the red algae are not so subject to wave action.

Some of the red algae are used commercially. The genus *Gelidium* is the source of agar jelly, and *Porphyra*, *Rhodymenia*, and *Chondrus crispus*, the

Fig. 8.12. Red algae. Left, *Corallina*, a calcium-depositing type. Right, *Polysiphonia*, a highly branched, delicately structured type. (General Biological Supply House, Inc.)

Irish moss, are among several types prized as vegetables in various parts of the world.

Rhodophytes as a whole are a relatively advanced group. They are not obviously related to any of the other algal phyla, and they must have evolved, in ways unknown to us, from early ancestral unicellular stocks.

PROTOZOA

Whereas algae are far more plantlike than animal-like, protozoa are far more animal-like than plantlike. These organisms are entirely without chlorophyll, and their nutrition is accomplished variously by holotrophic bulk feeding, by saprotrophism, and by symbiosis. The unicellular condition is almost universal; only a few protozoan types form colonies.

Two main lines of protozoa are flagellate, and in one of them the flagella are shortened to cilia; these two groups are the *Mastigophora*, or flagellate protozoa, and the *Ciliophora*, or ciliate protozoa. A third line is amoeboid; it comprises the *Rhizopoda*. In a fourth line, the *Sporozoa*, the members are entirely parasitic and their active locomotion is greatly restricted.

In traditional taxonomy, protozoa are ranked as a single phylum and each of the four groups above forms a class. However, the distinctions among the four groups are probably great enough that each should perhaps be accorded independent phylum rank. Protozoa as a whole then become a superphylum, like algae. The number of existing protozoan species has been underestimated fairly consistently. Figures often quoted are in the order of 15,000, but there are known to be more than that many foraminiferan species alone. Moreover, very many animals harbor at least one unique parasitic protozoan species, which means that protozoa could well number in the hundreds of thousands of species. As a conservative figure, at least 100,000 species of protozoa may be presumed to exist.

The protozoan cell is either naked or surrounded by a nonrigid cuticle composed of chitin or chitinlike substances. Cellulose is not present. In many cases, shells of various inorganic compounds are secreted as external skeletons. Foods are stored as glycogen and fats. In free-living flagellate and ciliate types, gullets are usually well developed; rhizopod protozoa use pseudopodia as feeding structures. Contractile vacuoles are present primarily in fresh-water types. Protozoa are largely uninucleate, but all ciliates and some amoeboid types are multinucleate, often highly so.

PHYLUM MASTIGOPHORA
zooflagellates

The ancestors of this group undoubtedly were close kin to the early photosynthesizing flagellates which gave rise to the algae. The most primitive zooflagellates now in existence are largely free-living and holotrophic, and they greatly resemble colorless flagellate algae. For example, the collar flagellate *Proterospongia* resembles certain flagellate chrysophytes. *Proterospongia* feeds on debris and microorganisms. Food is trapped within the collar of these cells, and the flagellum then creates a current which sweeps the food toward the cell body, where it is engulfed. Groups of individual collar flagellates may form loose colonial aggregates of various types (Fig. 8.13). In many of the free-living zooflagellates the flagella may be lost temporarily and the organisms then become amoeboid.

Free-living zooflagellate stocks undoubtedly gave rise to the many symbiotic forms. These are highly specialized and adapted to specific hosts. For example, *Trichonympha* is a mutualistic wood-digesting symbiont in the gut of termites. *Trichomonas* is a commensal in the gut of man and other vertebrates, and different species of *Trypanosoma* live parasitically in the bloods

Fig. 8.13. The colonial zooflagellate *Proterospongia*. The cells are embedded in secreted jelly. Photo of glass model. (American Museum of Natural History.)

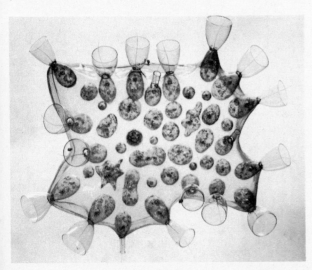

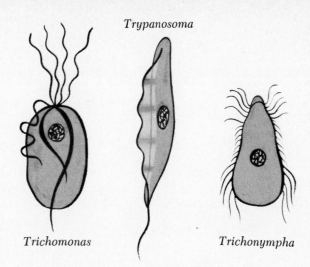

Fig. 8.14. Three types of zooflagellates, diagrammatic.

of various vertebrates. One such species causes sleeping sickness in man (Fig. 8.14).

PHYLUM RHIZOPODA
amoeboid protozoa

Also known as *Sarcodina*, these organisms move and feed by means of pseudopods. Some, like the various species of *Amoeba* (see Fig. 2.4) are naked cells, and they include a good many parasitic forms. For example, *Entamoeba histolytica* causes amoebic dysentery in man.

Other rhizopods enclose their bodies in secreted shells. A chitinous housing is present in *Arcella*, the organism extruding pseudopods through an opening in the shell. *Difflugia* cements tiny sand particles to a chitinous envelope (Fig. 8.15). The *Foraminifera* man-

Fig. 8.15. Two types of sarcodine protozoa.

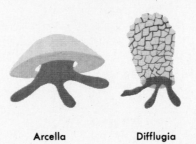

Arcella   Difflugia

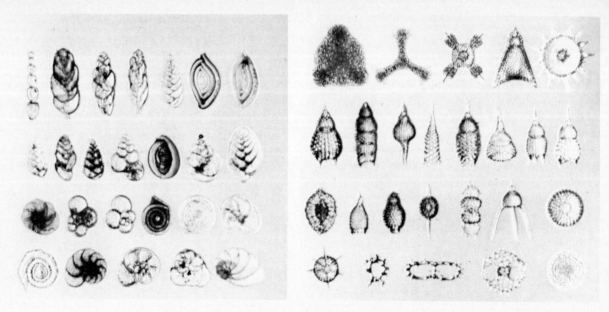

Fig. 8.16.   Sarcodina. Left, foraminifera. Right, radiolaria. The shells of the former are made of calcium salts; those of the latter, of silicon compounds. (General Biological Supply House, Inc.)

Fig. 8.17.   Ciliophora. The photo (third from left) shows the ciliate *Paramecium*, stained to reveal the macronucleus (large dark central body) and the micronucleus (small dark body partly overlapping the macronucleus on the top). At far right is a diagram of a mature suctorian. Note the holdfast and the tentaclelike protrusions with which the organism captures microscopic prey. (Photo, Carolina Biological Supply Co.)

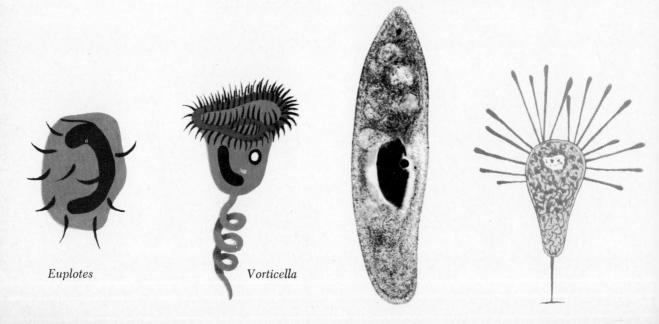

Euplotes   *Vorticella*

ufacture calcareous shells of many different forms, all resembling tiny snail shells (Fig. 8.16). Pseudopods are extruded through holes in these shells, hence the name of the group, which means "hole bearers." Foraminiferan shells may accumulate in given tracts of ocean floor in such numbers that they form the predominant bottom deposit in such regions. This is true also of the silica shells of the *Radiolaria*. Foraminiferan deposits may become transformed into chalk, radiolarian deposits into flint. When either of these is uplifted geologically, they may contribute massively to the formation of land (e.g., the chalk cliffs of Dover).

PHYLUM CILIOPHORA
ciliate protozoa

These organisms (Fig. 8.17) are undoubtedly the most advanced and structurally the most complex protozoa. They include two main groups: *Ciliata*, which are permanently ciliated, and *Suctoria*, which are ciliated only during young stages.

The Ciliata move and feed by means of their cilia, which in most cases are arranged in orderly rows. The phylum is characterized also by the presence of *two* kinds of nuclei in each organism. The so-called *micronucleus* functions principally in sexual processes, and the *macronucleus* controls metabolism, development, and most other cellular processes. Several of both kinds of nuclei may be present in a single organism. This unique nuclear specialization is paralleled by a very high degree of cytoplasmic specialization. For example, ciliates typically possess permanent mouths, excretory vacuoles, contractile fibrils, neural fibrils, holdfasts, and locomotor apparatus.

Some ciliates are sessile, either as solitary or as colonial forms, and very many are symbiotic, particularly parasitic. Suctoria are organized quite like ciliates generally, except that as adults they are sessile and unciliated. They feed by means of tentaclelike protrusions which capture and suck up the contents of other protozoa.

PHYLUM SPOROZOA
spore-forming protozoa

These organisms display evolutionary affinities to both the flagellate and the amoeboid protozoa. In adaptation to their exclusively parasitic ways of life, Sporozoa have exceedingly complex life cycles which often require multiple hosts. As indicated by the name of the group, the life cycles include spore-forming states; that is, a single cell may undergo *multiple fission* and become divided up simultaneously into numerous smaller cells. Such spore cells distribute the species and continue the life cycle. In some Sporozoa the spores are naked and amoeboid; in others, the spores are encapsulated. The most familiar sporozoan type is undoubtedly *Plasmodium*, various species of which cause malaria in mammals and birds. In human malaria, the *Anopheles* mosquito is the specific intermediate host of the sporozoan parasite (Fig. 8.18).

Fig. 8.18.   The life cycle of the sporozoan malarial parasite *Plasmodium*. The organism is injected by an Anopheles mosquito into the human blood stream in the form of flagellate sporozoite cells (1). Sporozoites enter red corpuscles, transform into amoeboid cells, and undergo multiple fission (2) to (4). The corpuscles then rupture and release the amoeboid cells, a process accompanied by a characteristic attack of fever. Amoeboid cells then may reinfect other red corpuscles, undergo fission, and by repeated reinfections bring about repeated fever cycles (5), (6). Some of the amoeboid cells eventually transform into gamete producers (7), (8), and these are sucked up by a mosquito, along with blood. In the gut of the mosquito, gametes form, fertilization occurs, and the amoeboid zygote penetrates through the gut wall into the blood of the insect (9), (10). Here the zygote encysts, undergoes multiple fission, and forms many flagellate sporozoites. These escape from the cyst, find their way into the salivary glands of the mosquito, and are then injected into human blood when the insect bites man.

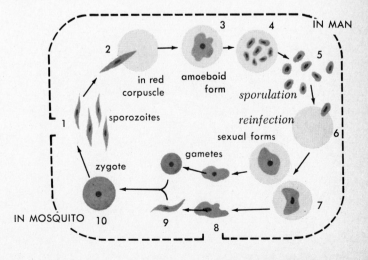

SLIME MOLDS

These interesting organisms, which constitute the phylum *Myxophyta*, share certain characteristics with amoeboid protozoa, others with fungi. In traditional classifications, slime molds are actually grouped sometimes with the "animal kingdom," sometimes with the "plant kingdom." Like protozoa and fungi, slime molds are without chlorophyll, and their exact origin among protistan ancestors is obscure.

Adult slime molds of one group exist in the form of *plasmodia*. These are naked amoeboid sheets, in some cases up to 1 foot in diameter, with irregular, slowly shifting contours (Fig. 8.19). Each such plasmodium contains hundreds or thousands of nuclei, but internal cell boundaries are absent and the whole organism is a continuous living mass. In another group of slime molds, the adult body is a *pseudoplasmodium*, a true cellular colony composed of hundreds or thousands of uninucleate amoeboid cells which do not lose their cell boundaries. Most slime molds live in moist wooded areas, where they creep over fallen leaves and rotting logs like supergiant amoebae.

When such an organism reproduces, its amoeboid life ceases and for a time it becomes rather funguslike. The body flows together into one or more heaped mounds or grows out into one or more upright stalks each of which develops a bulbous upper tip. Such

Fig. 8.19.   Plasmodium of the slime mold *Physarum*. (Carolina Biological Supply Co.)

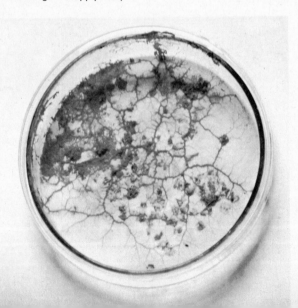

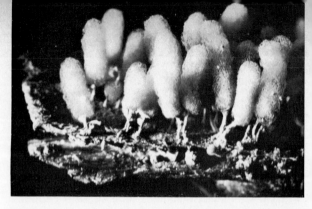

Fig. 8.20.   Fruiting bodies of the slime mold *Arcyria*. (General Biological Supply House, Inc.)

structures are *fruiting bodies* (Fig. 8.20). Within a fruiting body spore cells then form. The spores secrete protective capsules and eventually escape from the fruiting bodies and scatter. In suitable environments they may germinate and produce *swarmers*, that is, single flagellate or amoeboid cells. Swarm cells then undergo repeated cell divisions and they may also fuse pairwise in a sexual process. Eventually the cells collect together into a common amoeboid mass in which the cell boundaries may or may not disappear, depending on the type of slime mold. New generations of plasmodia or pseudoplasmodia are formed in this manner.

FUNGI

PHYLUM MYCOPHYTA
(about 90,000 species)

Class Phycomycetes: tubular fungi
water molds, downy mildews, blights, bread molds

Class Ascomycetes: sac fungi
yeasts, molds, powdery mildews, truffles, cup fungi

Class Basidiomycetes: club fungi
rusts, smuts, bracket fungi, mushrooms, toadstools, puffballs, stinkhorns

Class Fungi Imperfecti: provisional collection of types with incompletely known reproductive patterns, not yet assignable to any of the above groups.

This very large and highly diversified phylum has representatives in almost every available habitat on earth, and many fungi are of major economic or medical significance to man. Fungi are partly free-living saprotrophs, partly symbionts of all possible types. They store foods in the form of glycogen and as lipids.

Primitive fungi are aquatic and produce flagellate reproductive cells. More advanced fungi are terrestrial, with nonmotile reproductive cells dispersed passively by wind, water, and animals.

The body of a fungus is multinucleate, without internal cell boundaries. Phycomycetes are without internal partitions of any kind. In the other classes internal walls do develop, but these partitions are incomplete, leaving pores through which the living substance may flow. Thus the fungus body is always a continuous mass which may grow in size and increase the number of nuclei. True cells, with complete individual boundaries and one nucleus each, are formed only during reproduction.

A fungus is bounded externally by a rigid wall composed in most cases of chitin. The basic unit of the fungus body usually has the form of a tubular, often branched filament. Such a unit is called a *hypha*. As it grows, it may extend in length and branch increasingly. Numerous hyphae may be intermeshed into an irregular network, a so-called *mycelium* (Fig. 8.21). Hyphae may also pack together in more orderly patterns, producing, for example, fruiting bodies like mushrooms.

The class Phycomycetes is probably the most primitive of the phylum. A widely occurring representative is the mold *Rhizopus*, which grows on stale bread. The mycelium of this fungus is on and within the bread, and visible externally are fuzzy growths which are white at first and later turn black. These are the fruiting bodies, tiny spore-forming globes carried on stalks (Fig. 8.22).

The sac fungi are so called because their spores are manufactured in elongated sacs, or *asci*. Such asci are often located in cup-shaped fruiting bodies (Fig. 8.23). The hyphae of Ascomycetes may form thick and fleshy structures, as in truffles. Sac fungi produce many diseases in plants and animals, but some, like *Penicillium*, are sources of antibiotics which will cure disease. Ascomycete molds also produce the characteristic flavor of Roquefort, Camembert, and other kinds of cheeses. Yeasts are unicellular Ascomycetes.

Symbiotic combinations of fungi and algae form

Fig. 8.21. A mycelium of a fungus. Note the fine filamentous hyphae. (Courtesy of Dr. M. S. Fuller, University of California, Berkeley.)

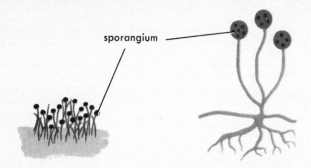

sporangium

Fig. 8.22. Diagram of the spore-producing structures (fruiting bodies, or sporangia) of the bread mold *Rhizopus* (whole view and detail).

Fig. 8.24. A lichen. (Jean Carel, Paris.)

lichens (Fig. 8.24). The fungal members of these grayish and yellowish rock-encrusting combinations in most cases are Ascomycetes, and the photosynthetic members are blue-green and green algae.

The Basidiomycetes, believed to have evolved from the Ascomycetes, are characterized by a specialized spore-producing unit, the *basidium*. This is an enlarged, club-shaped, terminal cell of a hypha. Many basidium-bearing hyphae may be combined into a large, stalked fruiting body, familiarly known as a *mushroom*. In many cases, the cap of a mushroom has radially arranged plates on its underside, called *gills*. On these, the spore-bearing basidia are exposed to the external environment (Fig. 8.25).

Not all Basidiomycetes form mushrooms, however. Among those which do not may be mentioned specially the *puffballs* and *stinkhorns*. In these, the basidia are not exposed to the air, as in mushrooms, but are ini-

Fig. 8.23. Section through the fruiting body of an ascomycete cup fungus. Note the layer of asci just under the inner surface of the cup. (Carolina Biological Supply Co.)

Fig. 8.25. A mushroom with gills on the underside. (Courtesy of Dr. M. S. Fuller, University of California, Berkeley.)

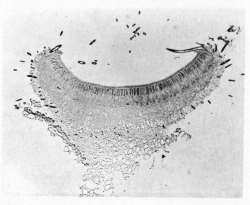

tially embedded within the fruiting body. This body eventually breaks open, and the mass of spores is then extruded. Giant puffballs are known to reach diameters of about 5 yards, and they probably have the distinction of being reproductively the most prolific organisms of all. A single giant puffball may manufacture as many as 100 *trillion* spores. It has been estimated that if each of these were to grow into a mature fungus, a mass of tissue close to 1,000 times the size of the earth would be produced.

The probable evolutionary interrelations of all major protistan groups are outlined in Fig. 8.26.

Fig. 8.26.   The probable interrelations of the various main groups within the Protista. The horizontal line separates photosynthetic forms below from the nonphotosynthetic forms above. Where a phylum contains both photosynthetic and nonphotosynthetic types, the name of the group appears with the more abundant types. The letters in conjunction with the algal groups refer to the variants of chlorophyll present. Note that, in virtually all cases, exact interrelations are not yet known and that the lines of interconnection must be regarded as provisional. Note also that the various algal groups have undoubtedly contributed to the evolution of the other protistan lines, interrelations which are not indicated.

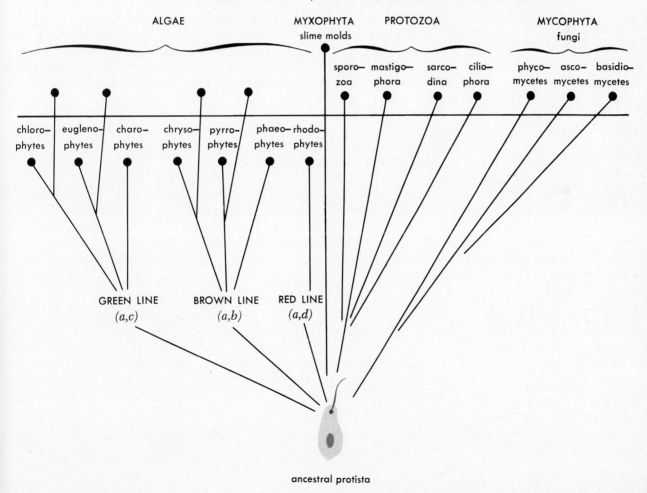

ancestral protista

Review questions

1. Review the hierarchy of taxonomic ranks. What rules are in force in the naming of species? Review the classification of any organism.

2. What are the main categories of organisms in existence today? What distinguishes these categories from one another? What are the major subgroups within each category? How are the main categories probably related evolutionally?

3. Which of the organisms in Question 2 have traditionally been regarded as plants and which as animals? What are customary definitions of "plant" and "animal"? Show how these definitions are inadequate. Why is it incorrect to speak of "higher" and "lower" organisms?

4. Review the identifying characteristics of (*a*) Monera, (*b*) bacteria, and (*c*) blue-green algae. What features distinguish (*b*) and (*c*)?

5. What are the unifying features of the Protista? Describe the probable ancestral type from which Protista are believed to have evolved.

6. What are the group characteristics of the algae? What are the special characteristics of the green-line, brown-line, and red-line algal groups? Review here the (*a*) pigments, (*b*) food-storage compounds, and (*c*) cell-wall compounds of these organisms.

7. What is the probable evolutionary significance of pairs of algae where one is photosynthetic and the other not? Give specific examples of such pairs for three or four algal phyla.

8. Describe the group characteristics of protozoa. What features uniquely distinguish the various protozoan phyla? What are foraminifera? Radiolaria? Describe the structure of a ciliate protozoon.

9. Review the life cycles of slime molds. What justifies the inclusion of slime molds within the Protista?

10. Describe the general characteristics of the various fungal classes. What are Fungi Imperfecti? Lichens? Review the structural characteristics of fungi generally. What are the possible evolutionary relations of this phylum to other Protista?

Suggested collateral readings

Avery, G. S., Jr.: The Dying Oaks, *Sci. Am.*, vol. 196, 1957.

Bonner, J. T.: The Growth of Mushrooms, *Sci. Am.*, vol. 194, 1956.

Bonner, J. T.: A Colony of Cells, *Sci. Am.*, vol. 182, 1950.

Clayton, R. K., and M. Delbruck: Purple Bacteria, *Sci. Am.*, vol. 185, 1951.

Emerson, R.: Molds and Man, *Sci. Am.*, vol. 186, 1952.

Lamb, I. M.: Lichens, *Sci. Am.*, vol. 201, 1959.

Maio, J. J.: Predatory Fungi, *Sci. Am.*, vol. 199, 1958.

Milner, H. W.: Algae as Food, *Sci. Am.*, vol. 189, 1953.

Weiss, F. J.: The Useful Algae, *Sci. Am.*, vol. 187, 1952.

METAPHYTA

Included in the Metaphyta are all the green, terrestrial, multi-cellular plants. As noted earlier, their evolutionary derivation from ancestral green algae is strongly suggested by the presence of chlorophylls *a* and *b*, by cell walls made of cellulose, and by the deposition of food stores in the form of starch. Metaphyta are distinguished from Protista by possessing *organs*, and by the occurrence of more or less distinct *embryonic stages* during the development from egg to adult.

Two major independent lines of Metaphyta have evolved, represented today by two phyla, the *bryophytes*, or moss plants, and the *tracheophytes*, or vascular plants. The latter are far more important, abundant, and spectacular, and they will occupy most of our attention.

Bryophytes

PHYLUM BRYOPHYTA
moss plants (about 25,000 species)

Class Bryopsida: mosses

Class Hepaticopsida: liverworts

Class Anthoceropsida: hornworts

The members of this phylum are distributed all over the world. In general, they occur in more or less shady, perpetually moist places, where the danger of drying out is minimized. Some bryophytes grow in the cold regions of the world, high on mountains and in the tundra; others grow in deserts, near hot springs, and in the tropics. In tropical rain forests, bryophytes occur abundantly on the leaves, branches, and trunks of trees. Several species of bryophytes live in fresh water; none live in the ocean.

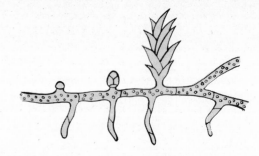

Fig. 9.1. A moss filament, showing rhizoids, buds, and young shoots.

Mosses are believed to be the most primitive members of the phylum. The body of a moss typically consists of fine threadlike strands of green cells, spread flat over the ground. Small nongreen extensions in places project into soil, and such *rhizoids* serve for absorption of water and minerals. Upright, more or

Fig. 9.2. Left, the internal structure of the liverwort *Marchantia*; right, external view of portion of the body, showing also gemma cups. (Photograph courtesy of Dr. M. S. Fuller, University of California, Berkeley.)

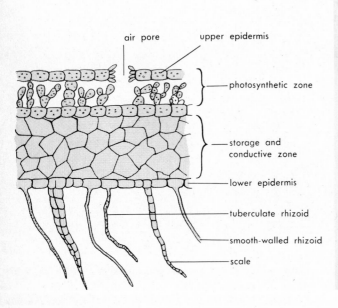

air pore — upper epidermis

photosynthetic zone

storage and conductive zone

lower epidermis

tuberculate rhizoid

smooth-walled rhizoid

scale

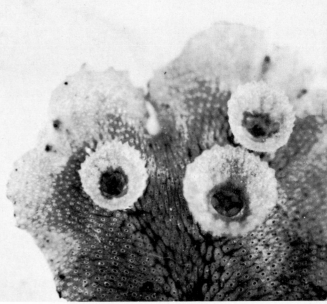

less radially symmetrical outgrowths, or *shoots*, form at different points along the flat mesh of strands. These shoots bear tiny leaflike blades, and at the top of a shoot the sex organs develop (Fig. 9.1).

Whereas mosses are characteristically vertical and radially symmetrical, liverworts are prostrate, horizontal plants. Some are leafy, like moss shoots, and in others the body forms a sheet, or *thallus*, flat on the ground. The thallus of the liverwort *Marchantia* provides a good example (Fig. 9.2). The body here is ribbon-shaped and lobed, with a median furrow along the upper surface. From the underside project numerous rhizoids. At the forward margin of a thallus is a *growing point* consisting of a cluster of a few cells. As these divide off new cells to either side, two lobes are formed. The growing point thus comes to be located in a notch between these lobes. Later the cells of the growing point may become separated into two groups, each of which may initiate the formation of a thallus branch. A growth pattern of this sort thus leads to the formation of two equal branches from one main branch.

Internally, a thallus contains three distinct zones, each composed of one or more tissues. The bottom zone is largely absorptive and consists mainly of nongreen rhizoids. The middle zone is a nongreen tissue which functions in storage and conduction of nutrients. The upper zone is photosynthetic. Its architecture includes elaborate air chambers and air pores. In types like *Marchantia*, the location of the internal air chambers is indicated externally by fine diamond-shaped markings on the surface of the thallus.

In hornworts the body is likewise a thallus, but here there are no surface furrows or midribs. Rhizoids are present on the underside, and internally the thallus is without air spaces or air pores; the whole body is a comparatively simply constructed sheet, composed of a few layers of cells.

Bryophytes as a whole have remarkable powers of regeneration, and many have developed a very specialized method of nonsexual reproduction. This involves *gemmae*, which are small cup-shaped growths on the surface of the plant body. If such a gemma is dislodged from the parent and is deposited on suitable ground, it may develop into a whole new plant (see Fig. 9.2).

Tracheophytes

PHYLUM TRACHEOPHYTA
vascular plants (about 260,000 species)

Subphylum Psilopsida: psilopsids (3 species)

Subphylum Lycopsida: club mosses (about 900 species)

Subphylum Sphenopsida: horsetails (25 species)

Subphylum Pteropsida: large-leafed plants

Class Filicineae: ferns (about 10,000 species)

Class Gymnospermae: coniferous seed plants (about 700 species)

Class Angiospermae: flowering seed plants (about 250,000 species)

Subclass Dicotyledoneae: dicots (200,000 species)

Subclass Monocotyledoneae: monocots (50,000 species)

Vascular plants represent the largest group of photosynthetic organisms and, after the insects, the second largest group of all types of organisms. The phylum is characterized by the presence of two distinct and specialized vascular tissues, the water-conducting *xylem* and the food-conducting *phloem*. Also, the body of virtually all tracheophytes is clearly subdivided into *roots*, *stems*, and *leaves*, each such body part representing a true organ.

The first tracheophytes were ancient psilopsids (see Chap. 25). From them evolved four independent lines of descent, namely, the four subphyla listed above. The first three of these today are little more than evolutionary relics. Only three species of modern psilopsids survive, and their characteristics are remarkably similar to those of their fossil ancestors. The stems are partly underground and horizontal, rhizoids are present instead of true roots, and the upright aerial parts of the stem bear tiny scalelike leaves without veins (Fig. 9.3).

The lycopsids, or club mosses, are more widely represented today, and the ground pine *Lycopodium*

Fig. 9.3.   Left, *Psilotum;* **note bulbous spore sacs.** Middle, *Lycopodium;* note spore-containing cone at top. Right, portion of *Equisetum;* note whorled arrangement of leaves. (Left, middle, courtesy of Dr. M. S. Fuller, University of California, Berkeley; right, Jean Carel and Larousse Publishing Co., Paris.)

in particular is still relatively common (Fig. 9.3). This lycopsid possesses true roots, a partly horizontal and partly aerial stem system, and small, spirally arranged leaves on the aerial stem parts.

The sphenopsids, or horsetails, all belong to the single genus *Equisetum* (Fig. 9.3). This group is characterized by small scalelike leaves, arranged in whorls at the nodes of hollow, aerial stems. Parts of the stem are again underground and horizontal, and roots grow from it in places.

The pteropsids today are the most abundant of the tracheophytes. All pteropsid groups are characterized by large leaves with conspicuous veins, very distinct from the small leaves of the other subphyla (Fig. 9.4). The ferns in part are inhabitants of tropical rain forests, where many reach the dimensions of trees. In the far smaller ferns of temperate regions, the stems are largely horizontal and underground. Roots project downward and the large, complexly shaped leaves grow upward.

The gymnosperms are the more primitive of the two classes of seed plants. Gymnosperms today in-

clude the *cycads*, which form small trees and sometimes resemble ferns superficially. The *ginkgoes* are another living gymnosperm group. Represented today by a single species, they grow as trees up to 100 feet high. The most common gymnosperms are the *conifers*, of which pines, firs, and spruces are familiar examples. Most of the conifers form tall, straight-stemmed trees. The largest are the sequoias, which may be up to 400 feet high and represent the largest living organisms now in existence.

The angiosperms are the most varied and most abundant group of all plants. They differ from other pteropsids principally in the possession of xylem which contains not only tracheids but also true vessels (see Chap. 5), in the possession of flowers and fruits, and in certain other reproductive features to be discussed in Chap. 21. Flowering plants inhabit virtually all environments except the open ocean. They include aquatic types, symbiotic and parasitic types, saprotrophic types, and partly carnivorous types. They enrich the world with color and scent, but they also exude poison and stench. Some survive only a single growing season; others live for centuries. Some complete an entire generation, from seed to seed, within a few days; others require decades. And we may note that terrestrial animals owe their continued existence largely to the angiosperms, for these plants are the essential food producers for all life on land.

Two subclasses of flowering plants are recognized, the Dicotyledoneae and the Monocotyledoneae. A cotyledon is a food-containing leaflike structure within the seed. Monocots possess one such seed leaf; dicots, two (Fig. 9.5). A corn kernel and a peanut seed illustrate this difference. Dicots also possess leaves which are net-veined and flowers in which the petals and other structures occur in fours or fives or in multiples of these. Dicots include both *woody* and nonwoody, or *herbaceous*, types. Monocots have leaves with parallel veins and flower parts in threes or in multiples of three. With one exception (palms), monocots are nonwoody herbaceous plants.

The dicots are the more abundant and probably the more primitive group. They include virtually all

Fig. 9.4.   Left, ferns on tree trunk. Top right, a cycad. Bottom right, a ginkgo, or maidenhair tree. (Left, Paul Popper, Ltd., London; top right, Jean Carel and Larousse Publishing Co., Paris; bottom right, courtesy of New York Botanical Garden.)

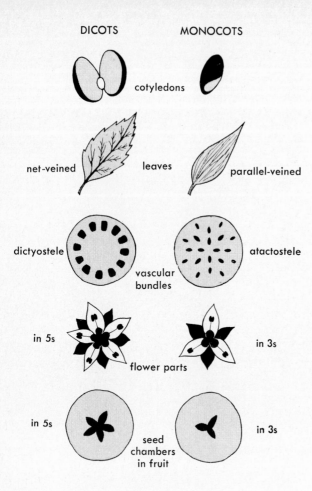

DICOTS   MONOCOTS

cotyledons

net-veined   leaves   parallel-veined

dictyostele   vascular   atactostele
bundles

in 5s   flower parts   in 3s

in 5s   seed   in 3s
chambers
in fruit

Fig. 9.5. Structural differences between dicots and monocots.

the familiar trees and shrubs, as well as roses, straw-berries, peaches, cabbages, cotton, tobacco, cucumbers, dandelions, beans, and innumerable other familiar plants. Monocots have at least equal economic importance, however, for in this subclass are wheat, corn, rice, barley, sugar cane, and all other grasses, as well as date and coconut palms, pineapples, bananas, and orchids.

In the following sections we shall make a more detailed examination of the ways of life and the structure of vascular plants generally and of flowering plants specifically.

Patterns of life

Tracheophytes possess a main axis which is vertical, and the radial symmetry around this axis is conspicuous. Such an organization permits efficient nutrient absorption from all sides around the plant and provides a mechanically balanced body design which anchors the plant safely. Many tracheophytes also taper upward, which allows the greatest weight to rest on the broadest foundation. The comparatively large size of a tracheophyte necessitates long-distance nutrient conduction and a functional subdivision of the subterranean and aerial parts of the plant. The characteristic root-stem-leaf organization of the tracheophyte is a specific adaptation to this requirement. Roots absorb from the ground; leaves photosynthesize; and stems interconnect, conduct, and support.

In a stationary organism in which water is vital and in which food cannot be produced during the night and often also not during the winter, *storage* of water and food is likely to be of major importance. Indeed, water storage is a function of every living tracheophyte cell. Every such cell is *succulent;* it contains a large amount of water, much of it in vacuoles. This condition also makes the cells highly *turgid:* the comparatively large amounts of water are confined by rigid cell walls and this constraint puts the water under considerable pressure. Such cellular turgor gives tissues additional mechanical support and permits even "soft" plant parts like leaves to maintain their shape well. But if water is in insufficient supply, succulence, turgor, and mechanical support may all become reduced and the plant may wilt.

Food storage to some extent also is a function of every living plant cell. Moreover, many tracheophytes possess enlarged body parts often adapted especially for food storage. Stems and roots are modified more frequently for this function than leaves.

Some of the principal types of modified stems are (Fig. 9.6): *rhizomes,* horizontal underground stems common particularly in primitive tracheophytes; *tubers,* expanded portions of underground stems usually adapted for food storage, as in potatoes; *bulbs,* shortened underground stems to which thickened storage leaves are attached, as in onions; *corms,* shortened,

 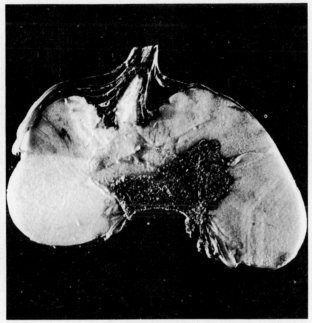 

Fig. 9.6.   Some types of stems. Left, a bulb. The central vertical stem is surrounded by leaves, which form the bulk of the bulb. Middle, a corm. Leaves are borne at the top. Right, a runner. (Courtesy of Dr. M. S. Fuller, University of California, Berkeley.)

bulky, underground storage stems which superficially resemble bulbs but which possess scalelike leaves on the outer surfaces, as in gladioli; *runners,* horizontal stems flat on the ground and supported by the ground, as in strawberries; and *twining stems,* which wind around upright on other objects and obtain support from them, as in beans.

Variant types of roots include (Fig. 9.7): *fibrous roots,* in which numerous branch roots lead off from the stem base into soil in all directions, as in grasses; *taproots,* single, thick, vertical storage roots from which small branch roots may lead off, as in carrots; *adventitious roots,* which sprout from any region of the plant (except a root), even from regions near the tip of the stem; *prop roots,* which are adventitious roots specially adapted to provide mechanical support, as in banyan trees and older corn plants; and *aerial roots,* which are not in contact with the ground at all and

which absorb water from sources available above ground, as in orchids. Such roots have a many-layered epidermis, the cells of which die and become specialized for water storage.

A suitable body design is only one requirement for a successful sessile way of terrestrial life. Another requirement is adaptability to potentially lethal changes in local weather, for a plant rooted to the ground cannot escape extremes of temperature. It can only attempt to protect against them. Water poses the key problem here. In summer heat and in deserts, the plant is in danger of having too little internal water. And in winter or at high latitudes and altitudes there is likely to be too much water, for water freezes and kills.

We already know that, as safeguards against evaporation, plant leaves and other soft tissues exposed to air secrete waxy cuticles over their outer surfaces.

Fig. 9.7.   Some types of roots. Left, fibrous roots; right, prop roots. (Left, U.S. Department of Agriculture; right, Brooklyn Botanical Garden.)

In hot, dry climates such cuticles are greatly thickened, sometimes becoming even thicker than the epidermal cells which secrete them. Leaves and green stems also possess stomata, microscopic surface pores which permit entry of required atmospheric gases but through which a good deal of evaporation may occur. However, plants may minimize such water losses by closing the stomata if conditions of humidity and temperature are not optimal, regardless of whether light is present or not. In hot climates, moreover, stomata are often reduced in number. And they may be located mostly or entirely on the underside of leaves, where shade and somewhat lower temperatures reduce evaporation and where settling dust is not likely to clog them. Or they may be sunk deep into microscopic epidermal pits, which provide shade except when the sun shines straight into them and which again protect against clogging by dust (Fig. 9.8).

Under near-desert conditions, the rate of evaporation may nevertheless be too high. Water vaporization can be held down, however, by reduction of the *area* of exposed parts in proportion to their volume. Thus, plants may possess but a few large leaves (as in ferns), or succulent, water-storing leaves (as in many ornamental house plants). Or, as in cacti, leaves may be reduced to thorny spines and massive stems carry out most of the food manufacture. Exposure may also be reduced by development of underground stems. Through adaptations such as these, tracheophytes are able to survive even in the hottest, driest regions, provided that at least *some* water is available at *some* time.

By contrast, winter frost for even an hour is likely to kill; below the freezing point, water which is not firmly bound in colloidal gels is transformed into ice crystals. Such crystals may tear and disrupt the molecular framework of cells. Therein lies a potentially lethal effect of cold. Probably in response to yearly cold seasons or outright winters, tracheophytes have developed major adaptations which profoundly affect their whole way of life. On the basis of these adaptations, we may distinguish three groups of vascular plants: *perennials, biennials,* and *annuals.*

In perennials, major or all portions of the plant body persist through successive winters. At the approach of winter, such plants may manufacture large quantities of colloidal materials within their cells. This increase in the amount of colloid particles leads to a conversion of much of the living substance of cells into a gel state. As a result, little water remains free inside cells and freezing is successfully forestalled. In evergreen plant groups, such winterproofing, or *winter hardening,* is particularly effective. Even leaves can be retained, and vital processes carry on as in summer though at a slower pace. Conifers like pines are good examples of evergreen perennials.

Other perennials are *deciduous* plants; they cannot protect their foliage against the cold and they shed leaves in the fall. But the rest of the plant lives on. Buds and embryonic leaves have developed during the

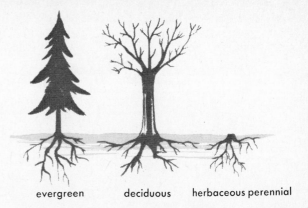

evergreen   deciduous   herbaceous perennial

Fig. 9.9. The perennial patterns of plants. In one pattern, as in conifers (left), the whole plant survives the winter. In another pattern, as in deciduous plants (center), foliage is shed in the cold season but the rest of the plant survives. In a third pattern, as in herbaceous perennials (right), only the roots and a small piece of stem survive the winter.

preceding summer, and these sprout the next spring into new foliage. In the absence of mature leaves during the cold season, little or no food can be produced. However, such plants accumulate food reserves at other seasons and store them in root and stem. Flowering trees living in the temperate zone are familiar examples of deciduous perennials.

Still other perennials are soft-bodied and *herbaceous* (e.g., asparagus, dandelions). In such plants, the leaves as well as the aerial parts of the stem die off in the fall. But the roots and a short underground piece of stem survive. Reserve foods in these underground body parts last through the winter and suffice in spring for the development of a new aerial shoot. Leaves and a mature stem then grow from this shoot. Since the aerial portions of these plants persist only through a relatively short growing season, they never become very extensive; bulky wood is neither required nor formed and the plants remain nonwoody herbs.

The above patterns (Fig. 9.9) give evidence of an adaptive trend in perennials: it is more economical to retrench when life becomes difficult than to maintain elaborate aerial structures against heavy odds. This trend does not halt here, however. Winter retrenchment goes even further in biennial and annual herbaceous plants.

Fig. 9.8. Adaptations to dry conditions. Section of pine leaf showing sunken stoma (top center of photograph) and lobed parenchyma cells in interior. (Courtesy of Dr. M. S. Fuller, University of California, Berkeley.)

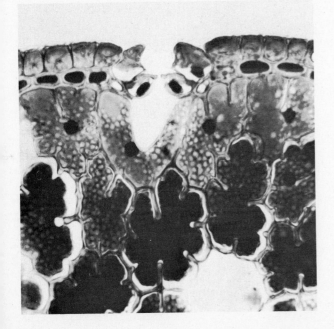

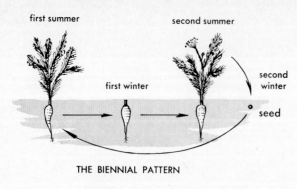

THE BIENNIAL PATTERN

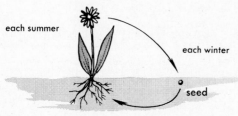

THE ANNUAL PATTERN

Fig. 9.10. The biennial and annual patterns of plants. In a biennial, only the roots and a small piece of stem survive the first winter, and only seeds survive the second winter. In an annual, the whole plant dies every year and is perpetuated only by seeds.

In biennials (e.g., carrots), leaves die off in a first winter, after procuring extensive food reserves which are stored in bulky roots. The roots and portions of the shoot survive that winter, and from them a new plant develops the following spring. This second-year plant flowers and forms seeds. At the approach of the second winter, the entire plant dies, roots included. Only the seeds survive, and these subsequently initiate a new two-year cycle (Fig. 9.10).

The annual plant (e.g., wheat) flowers and produces seeds every year. The whole plant dies in the fall, and its seeds give rise to a new generation the following spring (Fig. 9.10).

Evidently, vascular plants have found several workable solutions to the problem of cold. They may winterproof the whole body or some part of the body, or they may rely entirely and most economically on a handful of hardy cells: seeds. These often contain as little as 5 per cent water and are therefore adapted excellently to withstand the rigors of winter.

We note that tracheophytes have made the most of their difficult terrestrial environment. Actually, there are only two types of land environments to which a tracheophyte cannot adapt: the glacial regions, as at very high altitudes and latitudes, and the permanently arid regions, as in some deserts.

Internal structure

PRIMARY GROWTH: STEM AND ROOT

A tracheophyte may be considered to begin its life history as an embryo. This is an elongated, multicellular structure with a *shoot apex* at one tip and a *root apex* at the other (Fig. 9.11). At these tips, specific cells called *apical meristems* remain permanently

Fig. 9.11. Longitudinal section through a seed, showing the embryo within. (Courtesy of Dr. M. S. Fuller, University of California, Berkeley.)

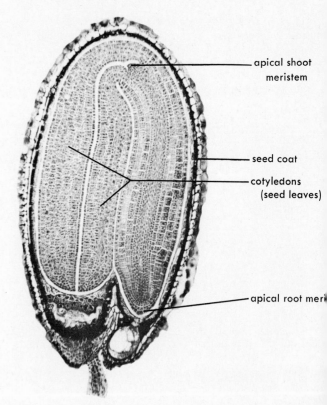

apical shoot meristem

seed coat

cotyledons (seed leaves)

apical root meri

embryonic. They continue to divide, and new cells formed by them are added behind each tip to the embryonic tissues already present. Thus the whole embryo continues to elongate.

New cells produced by the apical meristems soon become organized into the various concentrically arranged adult tissues described in Chap. 5. We recall that these tissues are, from the outside inward, epidermis, cortex, endodermis (in roots), and stele. The latter is a group of tissues consisting of pericycle (in roots), phloem, xylem, and pith (in stems).

In a root, pith is absent. Steles without pith are known as *protosteles*, and they are characteristic of tracheophyte roots generally. The common arrangement of the root tissues is indicated in Fig. 9.12. Recall also from Chap. 5 that root epidermis is without wax cuticles or stomata but does contain root-hair cells. These are usually located in a distinct zone some distance behind the root tip. Root hairs are temporary structures. Ahead of the root-hair zone, hairs have not yet developed; behind it, they have already disappeared. Thus the root-hair zone advances as the root tip advances. Also present in the root is a *root cap*, several layers of cells which envelop the root tip externally (Fig. 9.13). A root cap is formed by the apical root meristem. Such a cap is an important adaptive device, for as the root tip advances, hard soil grains would soon macerate unprotected meristem tissue. In the presence of a root cap, however, cap cells wear off instead and the growing tip is shielded effectively. New cap cells continue to be formed by the root meristem.

In the stem, the epidermis is cutinized and contains paired guard cells which enclose stomata. Endodermis and pericycle are reduced or absent, but generally present is a pith. Steles with pith occur in a large number of variant forms. We need be concerned mainly with two of these, *dictyosteles* and *atactosteles*. Dictyosteles are characteristic of the gymnosperms and of the dicots among angiosperms; atactosteles occur in the monocot group of angiosperms (see Fig. 9.12). In a dictyostele, the xylem and phloem tissues are arranged as distinct and separate *vascular bundles* grouped in more or less circular patterns within the stem. Pith is ringed in by such a circle of bundles and is continuous with the cortex outside the ring of bun-

dles. Vascular bundles also typify an atactostele, but here the bundles are scattered randomly throughout the stem, and it is often difficult to distinguish precisely between pith and cortex.

PRIMARY GROWTH: LEAVES AND BRANCHES

Stem and root growth proceeds indefinitely as a result of the continuing production of new cells at the shoot and root tips. Leaf growth, on the other hand, is usually limited in time, for a leaf does not possess an apical meristem of its own.

A *leaf bud* forms from embryonic tissue just below the shoot apex (Fig. 9.14). Sometimes a single cell but more often several cells give rise to the leaf bud. These embryonic cells divide repeatedly, most divisions occurring along the margins of the expanding and flattening blade. In due course, the embryonic tissues of the leaf become adult. At that time the leaf has attained its final size and it does not grow thereafter.

An *epidermis* covers the outside of the leaf (Fig. 9.15). This layer is continuous with the stem epidermis. As in the stem, leaf epidermis is cutinized and contains green guard cells enclosing stomata. Wrapped in epidermis, *mesophyll* tissue fills the interior of the leaf. This is the chief food-producing tissue of the plant: all mesophyll cells contain chlorophyll. Just underneath the upper epidermis in horizontally placed leaves, and underneath the whole epidermis in most upright and needle-shaped leaves, mesophyll cells are arranged in compact layers, or *palisades*. Elsewhere, mesophyll is *spongy;* that is, it is organized into loose cellular strands and layers. The whole is honeycombed extensively with *air spaces*. These connect with one another and lead to the exterior of the leaf through open passages in the palisade tissue and the stomata. This structural arrangement brings the greater part of every mesophyll cell into direct contact with fresh external air.

Leaf *veins* are bundles of phloem and xylem which ramify extensively throughout the mesophyll and are continuous with the vascular tissues of the stem. Such veins support the tissues of the leaf mechanically and carry nutrients to and from all parts of the leaf. As already noted, the veins are arranged in the form of

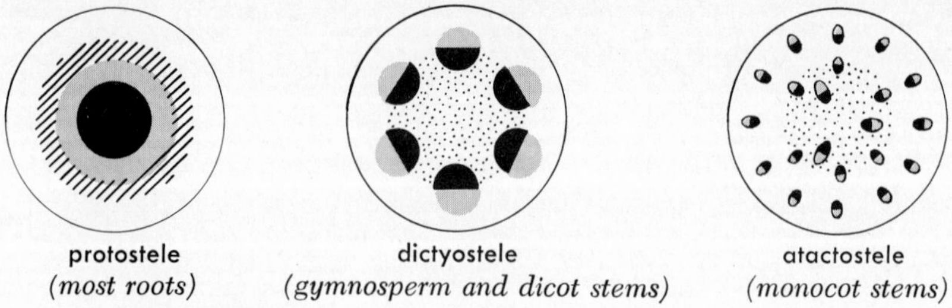

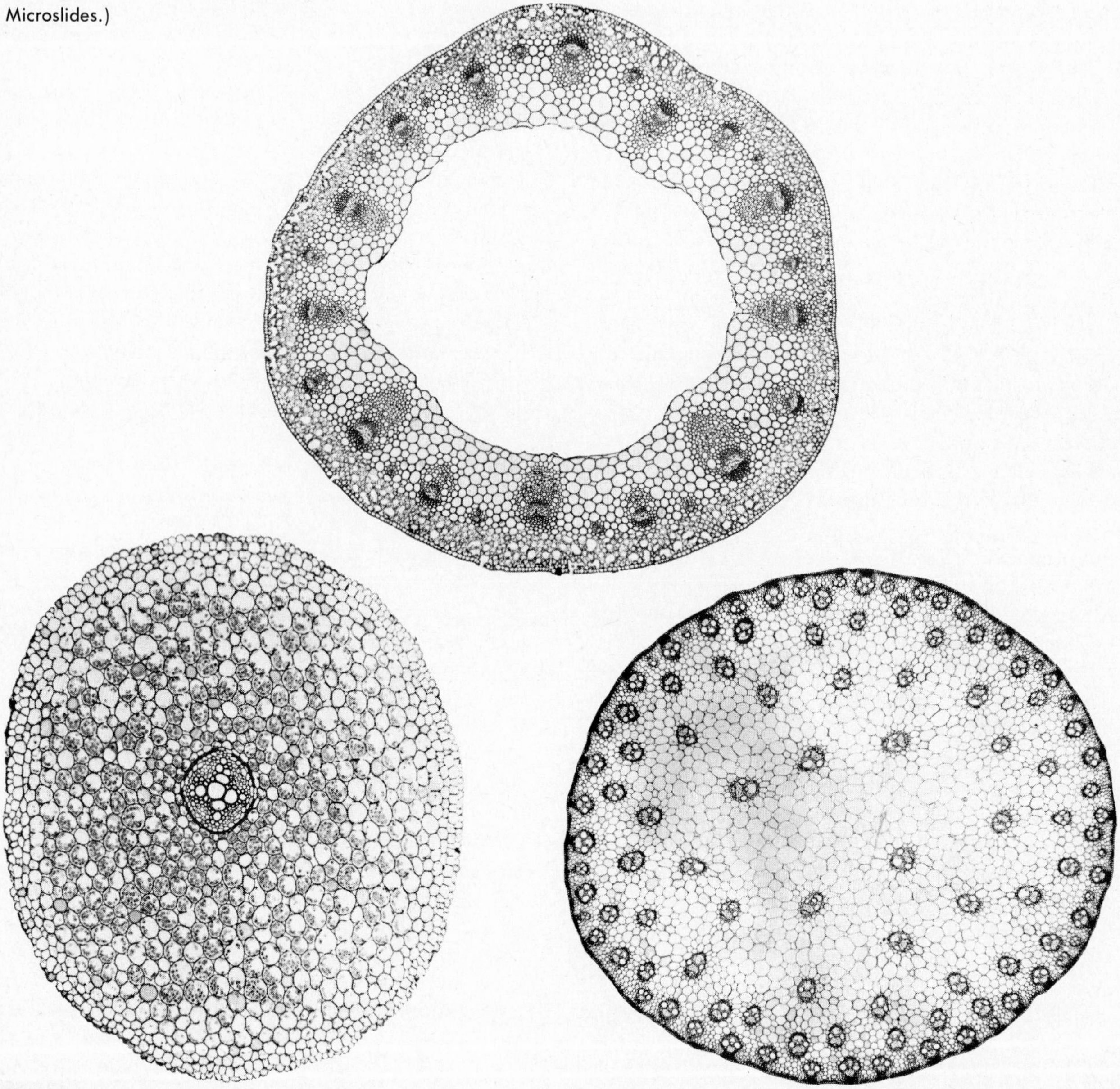

Fig. 9.12. Some types of steles of vascular plants. Top row: white areas, cortex; crosshatched areas, pericycle; gray areas, phloem; black areas, xylem; stippled areas, pith. Bottom row: left, buttercup root; middle, buttercup stem; right, corn stem. (Photographs, left, Carolina Biological Supply Co.; middle, courtesy of G. H. Conant, Triarch Products; right, courtesy of J. Limbach, Ripon Microslides.)

protostele
(most roots)

dictyostele
(gymnosperm and dicot stems)

atactostele
(monocot stems)

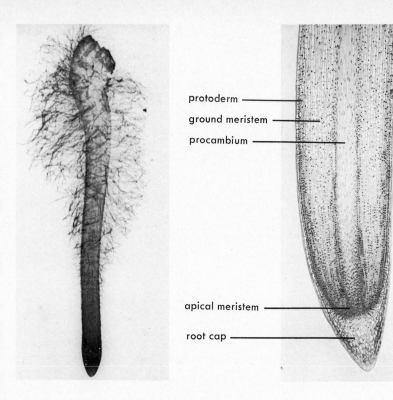

protoderm

ground meristem

procambium

apical meristem

root cap

Fig. 9.13. Left, a root showing root-hair zone; at lower tip, note thickening formed by the rootcap. Right, longitudinal section through a root tip. (Left, General Biological Supply House, Inc.; right, courtesy of Dr. M. S. Fuller, University of California, Berkeley.)

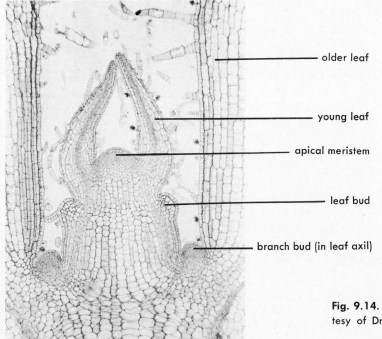

older leaf

young leaf

apical meristem

leaf bud

branch bud (in leaf axil)

Fig. 9.14. Longitudinal section through a shoot tip. (Courtesy of Dr. M. S. Fuller, University of California, Berkeley.)

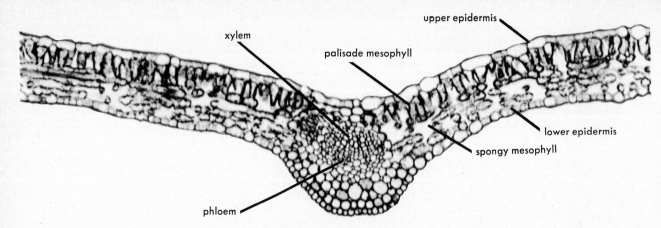

Fig. 9.15. Cross section of a leaf. (Courtesy of Dr. M. S. Fuller, University of California, Berkeley.)

a network in dicots and are parallel in monocots. A whole leaf usually consists of a *petiole*, a thin basal stalk which attaches the leaf to the stem; two *stipules*, small appendages which grow out near the base of the petiole in many species; and a *lamina*, the leaf blade itself (Fig. 9.16).

As pointed out above, deciduous plants shed their leaves at the approach of winter. A fallen leaf leaves a permanent *leaf scar* on the stem. In such plants also, the apical shoot meristems are protected during the winter by *bud scales*. These are modified leaves or leaf parts produced at the approach of winter around an apical meristem. The scales are densely placed and make up a *terminal bud* on a dormant stem in winter condition (Fig. 9.17). When growth resumes the following spring, bud scales fall off and leave densely placed *bud-scale scars* on the stem. By counting the number of stem regions where such scars oc-

cur, it is often possible to determine the age of a plant.

Stems usually produce many *lateral branches*. A lateral branch arises from a *lateral bud*, or *branch bud*, developed in the apical shoot meristem in the so-called *leaf axil*. This is the region where a leaf

Fig. 9.17. Diagram of a dormant stem with buds.

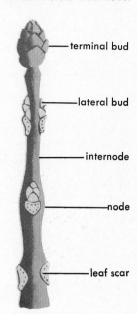

Fig. 9.16. Stem node and leaf base.

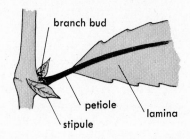

joins the stem, specifically the upper angle between leaf and stem (see Figs. 9.14 and 9.17). Wherever a leaf bud is formed, a branch bud forms in the leaf axil. The areas of branching growth in a stem represent *nodes;* the stem portions between consecutive nodes are *internodes.*

Branch buds often do not mature immediately. Some may remain dormant for many years and some may not develop at all. Accordingly, a leaf may or may not be accompanied by a branch stem. Dormant branch buds are usually clearly visible just above leaf scars in wintering stems. When a branch bud does mature, it develops an apical shoot tip of its own and grows in every respect like the parent stem. We note again that an important difference between a leaf and a branch is that one does not and the other does acquire a growing tip in the bud stage.

Roots may form branches also, but roots do not have nodes, and the process of branch development differs from that of stem branches. At varying distances behind the tip of the main or primary root, *lateral roots* may be formed (Fig. 9.18). Such branch roots originate in the pericycle. Cells in localized regions of the pericycle divide and form a pad of tissue, the so-called *root primordium.* As such a primordium

develops further, it pushes out through the peripheral tissues of the primary root. By the time it emerges through the epidermis, a root cap and the primary meristems have been formed. Later a stele with vascular tissues matures, and these tissues become continuous with the corresponding tissues of the primary root. Thereafter the lateral root is fully established and continues to grow like a primary root.

SECONDARY GROWTH

The whole organization of the plant body described up to this point represents the result of *primary growth:* all body parts are direct derivatives of the apical meristems and the original immature tissue of the embryo. As we have seen, primary growth is essentially growth in *length,* and any increase in the thickness of stems and roots comes about mainly through enlargement of cells in a lateral direction. In many tracheophytes, primary growth is typically the only means of increasing body size. However, large numbers of tracheophytes are capable of growing not only in length but also in thickness, through lateral increase of cell *number.* These plants have evolved processes of *secondary growth,* superimposed on the

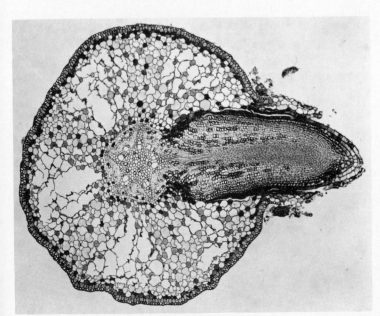

Fig. 9.18. Cross section of a root with outgrowing lateral root. Note that the lateral root originates in the pericycle region of the primary root. (Courtesy of J. Limbach, Ripon Microslides.)

earlier processes of primary growth. Apart from comparatively enormous increases in stem and root girth, the gross result of such secondary growth is the development of *bark* and of bulk *wood.*

Where wood is formed in relatively large quantities, new layers are added each year to those accumulated previously. Such plants develop into shrubs and trees and become recognizably *woody* in character. To be sure, primary growth also produces wood—xylem tissue *is* wood. But primary growth usually produces so little wood, or xylem, that the plant is left in a *herbaceous* condition; and if a distinctly woody external appearance is to develop, secondary growth must form very much more xylem. In short, the term "woody plants" refers largely to plants in which secondary growth occurs.

Plants which actually become woody are the gymnosperms and many of the dicot angiosperms. In these, young shoots and roots first develop as in all other cases through primary growth. Later too, the plant continues to elongate through primary growth at each tip, and the regions immediately behind each tip maintain the characteristic primary organization of nonwoody roots and stems. More specifically, the roots contain protosteles, and the stems, dictyosteles. Transformation of these primary patterns into secondary ones begins only in older regions, well behind each tip; as is well known, even woody plants have early

shoots and later growing tips which remain "green." Since leaves bud off near the shoot apex and do not possess growing tips of their own, they do not participate in secondary development at all.

The transformation of roots and stems from primary to secondary states is brought about by *secondary meristems,* or *cambia.* Two kinds of cambia develop: a *vascular cambium* and a *cork cambium.* Each arises from different primary tissues, and the process of formation differs somewhat in root and stem.

Cambial activity. In a root, the vascular cambium forms between the xylem and phloem in the stele (Fig. 9.19). A layer of cells here remains permanently embryonic and relatively unspecialized. These cells form the vascular root cambium, which ultimately rings in the root xylem completely.

In a stem, part of the vascular cambium again forms from a layer of cells between xylem and phloem. Since the stem is dictyostelic, the vascular tissues are in the form of circularly grouped vascular bundles, with xylem toward the inside and phloem toward the outside. Consequently, the cambium layers between these xylem and phloem bundles are arranged like an incomplete tube, interrupted between neighboring bundles (Fig. 9.20). This discontinuous tube soon becomes continuous, for layers of cells be-

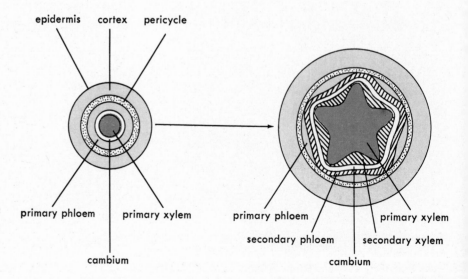

epidermis   cortex   pericycle

Fig. 9.19. The development of cambium-derived tissues in the root.

primary phloem   primary xylem

cambium

primary phloem   primary xylem

secondary phloem   secondary xylem

cambium

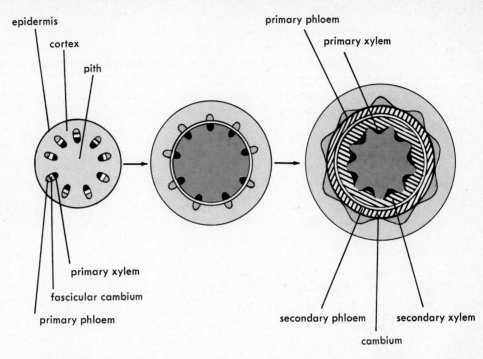

Fig. 9.20. The development of cambium and of cambium-derived tissues in a dictyostelic stem.

tween neighboring bundles acquire the properties of a cambium. As a result, the vascular cambium eventually formed in the stem is a complete tube. It is continuous with the similar tube of the root; and as the stem-root axis continues to elongate through primary growth at the apical tips, the open-ended cambial tube lengthens as progressively more cambium develops behind the shoot and root tips.

The vascular cambium in both root and stem continually buds off new cells toward the inside and outside. In this manner whole *layers* of cells continue to be deposited at both sides of the cambium. Layers produced toward the inside soon mature into all the various cellular components of xylem tissue; layers budded off toward the outside form all the various components of phloem tissue. Vascular tissue so generated by cambium is called *secondary xylem* (or *secondary wood*) and *secondary phloem* (see Figs. 9.19 and 9.20).

As secondary xylem continues to be formed in successive concentric layers within the cambial tube,

the thickness of the stem and the root increases. Also, as secondary phloem develops in concentric tubes from the cambial tube outward, it increases the thickness of stem and root even more and pushes out all the earlier phloem, the cortex, and the epidermis. Since these early tissues are adult and cannot grow in step with the ever-expanding girth of stem and root, they ultimately rupture.

Note that the smallest amounts of secondary tissue are always near the apical tips, where cambial activity is just beginning; the largest amounts are accumulated at the stem-root juncture, the region which has grown for the longest period and is the oldest. This is therefore the region of greatest girth, and from here the stem *tapers* upward and the root tapers downward (Fig. 9.21).

While the vascular cambium produces more and more secondary xylem and phloem, the cork cambium is active also. This cambium develops from the pericycle in roots and from the cortex or the phloem in stems; it is a single layer of embryonic cells. Like the

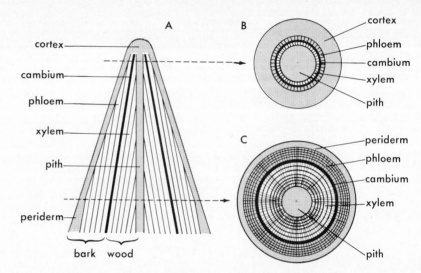

Fig. 9.21.   A, diagrammatic longitudinal view of a shoot, showing the formation of successive tissue layers to the outside and inside of the cambium. A cross section at the level of the upper broken line would appear as in B; at the level of the lower broken line, as in C. (For the components of periderm, see Fig. 9.22.)

vascular cambium, the cork cambium produces new cell layers both toward the inside and outside (Fig. 9.22). The inner layers, called *phelloderm,* become part of the cortex. The outside layers are known as *cork,* and the cells here secrete heavy coats of suberin on their walls. Cork first develops where the epidermis and the cortex have ruptured as a result of the outward expansion of xylem and phloem. Later, after epidermis and cortex have become torn away com-

pletely, a continuous layer of cork comes to surround the entire outside surface of stem and root. Soon, however, further increases in stem and root diameter cause a rupturing and flaking off of the original cork. New cork cambium then develops and new cork is produced. This tissue later ruptures and flakes off in turn, and the cycle of new formation and flaking off repeats indefinitely.

Because of the suberin coating of cork cells, the

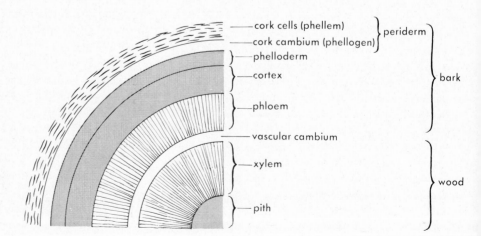

Fig. 9.22.   Diagram of the position of the cork cambium and its products in a woody stem.

Fig. 9.23. Lenticels. (Courtesy of Dr. M. S. Fuller, University of California, Berkeley.)

outer covering of a woody plant is quite impervious to water and air. At various places, however, the cork cambium produces loosely arranged cells separated by intercellular spaces. Such spongy regions are known as *lenticels*. They permit the interior living tissues of the root and the stem to exchange gases with the atmosphere (Fig. 9.23).

The woody condition. It should now be clear that *wood* fills most of the space inside the tube of vascular cambium. All tissues outside the tube of vascular cambium are collectively called *bark*. Thus, in a woody section of a stem, the principal components are, concentrically from the outside inward: cork, the microscopically thin layer of cork cambium, secondary phloem, the microscopic layer of vascular cambium at the line of juncture between bark and wood, secondary xylem (or wood), and a microscopic accumulation of pith in the very center (Figs. 9.24 and 9.25).

Older phloem, toward the surface of a tree trunk, continually flakes off as the trunk thickens. Therefore, only a thin rind of young phloem is present within bark at any given time. Similarly, only young xylem is functional. Older xylem, toward the center of a trunk, in time gradually blocks up with resins and gums, and water conduction through these channels is then no longer possible. Such central regions are called *heartwood*. The core of a tree may therefore be hollowed

out without interfering with xylem conduction. But the outer, young wood of a tree, called the *sapwood*, must remain intact if a tree is to remain alive.

Annual rings are usually fairly conspicuous in an older tree growing in the temperate zone (Figs. 9.24 and 9.25). Xylem vessels laid down during spring generally have a larger diameter than those formed in summer. In spring, melting snow provides the tree with much water. Wider conducting channels are then formed which accommodate the greater flow. The alternation of narrow summer and fall xylem and wider spring xylem is recognizable with the naked eye as concentric dark and light banding—annual rings. The number of rings indicates the age of a tree. Moreover, from the comparative widths of spring and summer rings it is also possible to estimate the amount of rainfall, hence general climatic conditions, during past seasons as far back in time as the tree has lived.

Through the secondary growth processes described, a young, green shoot is slowly transformed into a tall,

Fig. 9.24. Cross section of a three-year-old woody stem. (Courtesy of J. Limbach, Ripon Microslides.)

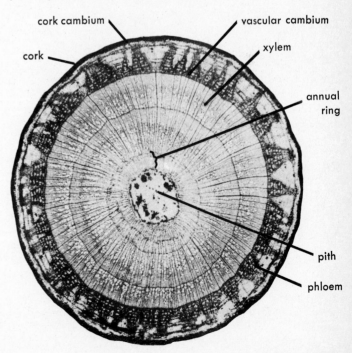

cork cambium · vascular cambium · cork · xylem · annual ring · pith · phloem

Fig. 9.25. Longitudinal section through wood, showing xylem channels. The two dark vertical lines mark out an annual ring. (General Biological Supply House, Inc.)

thick, tapering woody tree. As noted, such events occur in gymnosperms and numerous dicot angiosperms. Other dicots and virtually all monocots remain herbaceous and thus generally much smaller. They are equally successful, however, and indeed they live more economically. As we have seen, many of the tissues produced by secondary growth flake off or block up and so become useless. Yet the woody plant must expend large amounts of energy and materials every year to develop these tissues. A herbaceous plant avoids such waste; the tissues formed by primary growth just suffice

to maintain life and they serve the plant as long as it lives.

To be sure, even a tiny herb is built on a lavish structural scale when compared with a microscopic unicellular alga floating in the ocean. But such lavishness is the price of survival on land; of all photosynthetic organisms, only the tracheophytes really have been completely successful as terrestrial types. In this success the evolution of vascular tissue has been one basic factor. Another has been the evolution of seeds, a topic we shall pursue later.

Review questions

1. Review the identifying characteristics of Metaphyta. How is this category distinguished from Protista? What is a gametophyte? A sporophyte?

2. Describe the group characteristics and the basic structure of all bryophytes. Name the classes of bryophytes.

3. State the identifying characteristics of tracheophytes. How is this phylum classified into subphyla and classes?

4. Review the architectural adaptations of tracheophytes to life on land. How do tracheophytes conserve water? How do they protect against (*a*) heat and (*b*) cold?

5. What different groups of tracheophytes are perennial, biennial, and annual, and what are the life cycles of such plants?

6. Show how the embryo of a tracheophyte develops

into a mature plant by primary growth. Name specific tissues. Describe the organization of different types of steles.

7. Describe the structure of a leaf. How does a leaf develop? In what tissues does photosynthesis occur? What is the structure and distribution of stomata, and how do they function? Would you expect stomata to be open or closed at night?

8. Describe how a stem or a root grows in length. What is secondary growth? Show how a vascular cambium forms secondary xylem and phloem. Describe the activities of a cork cambium.

9. What is the cross-sectional structure of a mature woody tree trunk? Where in such a trunk are xylem and phloem? What are annual rings, and how do they develop?

10. Describe the internal structure of (*a*) a woody, (*b*) a herbaceous angiosperm.

Suggested collateral readings

Biddulph, S. O.: The Circulatory System of Plants, *Sci. Am.*, vol. 200, 1959.

Mangelsdorf, P. C.: The Mystery of Corn, *Sci. Am.*, vol. 183, 1950.

Mangelsdorf, P. C.: Wheat, *Sci. Am.*, vol. 189, 1953.

Salaman, R. N.: The Social Influence of the Potato, *Sci. Am.*, vol. 187, 1952.

Williams, S.: Wood Structure, *Sci. Am.*, vol. 188, 1953.

METAZOA

10

The evolutionary origin of Metazoa is obscure. That they arose from ancestral Protista is hardly in doubt, but it is impossible at present to be sure exactly which protistan group was directly ancestral. Indeed, different metazoan groups may have arisen independently from various different protistan stocks. All we can be reasonably sure of at present is that Metazoa evolved when some ancestral, unicellular, motile protistan group or groups became multicellular and in the process retained and improved powers of locomotion but lost any photosynthetic capacity it or they may have possessed.

Metazoa are distinguished from Protista in that their bodies contain at least organs, and usually several organ systems as well. Metazoan cells typically possess centrioles, and, with the general exception of cells on the body surface, other cells are naked, without walls or cuticles. Metazoan development passes through distinct *embryonic* and typically also *larval* phases.

The metazoan category is subclassified into some 20 to 30 phyla. In some cases universal agreement on phylum designations is lacking, hence the inexactness of the number of phyla.

Patterns of life

NUTRITION AND MOVEMENT

Being nonphotosynthetic, all animals ultimately depend for food on photosynthesizers. Both in space and in time, therefore, animal life waxes and wanes in step with plant life. From the standpoint of food sources, two broad categories of animals may be distinguished: the *symbiotic* and the *free-living* types.

Some of the animal symbionts live in mutualistic or commensalistic associations with individuals of other species. But most are parasites, on or within specific hosts. Free-living animals variously subsist on any usable foods available in the environment: living plants and animals, dead plants and animals, and many different kinds of derivatives of organisms, including in some cases decaying matter. Most of these free-living animals and also most of the symbiotic types are bulk-feeding holotrophs. In other words, they eat, or *ingest*, they *digest* eaten food, and they eliminate, or *egest*, unusable eaten material. Ingestion, digestion, and egestion together constitute the process of *alimentation*.

Animals are usually quite specialized in their eating habits. Thus, *herbivores* are specialized to eat plant foods; *carnivores* subsist on other animals; and *omnivores* eat both animal and plant foods, living or dead.

Directly or indirectly, the whole way of life of an animal is oriented by the requirement of alimentation. One immediate consequence is the necessity of locomotion. Whereas a plant finds raw materials for photosynthesis practically all around it, prefabricated bulk food is in strictly limited supply and its location generally does not coincide with the location of the hungry animal. Therefore, an animal must either move toward food itself or remain stationary and feed on moving organisms which happen to pass by. Actively moving animals constitute the majority of Metazoa. But many Metazoa are specialized as permanently or temporarily sessile forms (e.g., sponges, corals, barnacles). Such animals, all aquatic, generally use their locomotor structures to create water currents which sweep small food organisms toward them.

Locomotion serves not only in food catching but also secondarily in numerous other animal activities. For example, locomotion plays a fundamental role in mate selection and reproduction, functions which the motile animal accomplishes far more readily than the sessile plant. Locomotion also is an important factor in protecting animals against environmental dangers, climatic changes among them. For example, many animals carry out seasonal migrations (Chap. 6).

ANIMAL STRUCTURE

The requirement of locomotion profoundly influences the *external* structure of an animal. Most moving animals have an *elongated, bilaterally symmetrical* shape, which is particularly suited for locomotion. Moreover, the forward end enters new environments first. Sense organs for scouting and the chief nerve centers are therefore placed most advantageously at the front, and mouths should be located close to the sense organs. Thus the leading part of the animal becomes the *head*. Analogously, elimination products of all kinds are best released at the hind end, where they do not impede forward progression. A general build of this sort is actually standard and nearly universal among moving animals.

By contrast, sessile animals and also many of the very slow movers face their environment more or less equally from all sides, like plants, and their architecture reflects this. They are or tend to be *radially symmetrical* and a distinct head is usually not present (e.g., corals, starfish). In many sessile forms also, the intestine is looped into a U, which brings the mouth and the anus close together and both openings away from the region where the animal is attached to the ground.

Locomotion and alimentation also greatly influence the *internal* structure of animals (Fig. 10.1). In certain respects, metazoan structure matches that of Metaphyta. For example, all animals possess *integumentary* and *reproductive* structures, as do all plants. Also, most animals, particularly the larger ones, possess *circulatory* systems and blood, body parts which correspond to the vascular tissues of tracheophytes. However, most other features of animal structure do not have counterparts among plants; because of alimentation and locomotion, the animal organization requires a number of structural systems not needed in plants.

For example, no plant possesses an *alimentary* system, for the obvious reason that the key process in

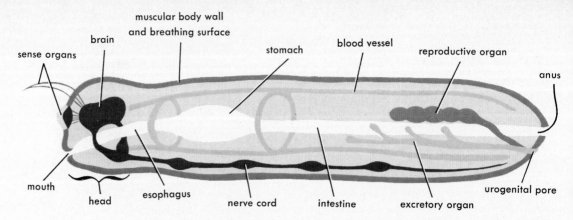

Fig. 10.1. Diagrammatic representation of the basic structure of a moving animal. This is a hypothetical animal, showing the position and function of various body parts and organs usually encountered in many elongated, worm-shaped types.

plant nutrition is intracellular photosynthesis and that complex organ systems for catching and preparing foods are therefore not required. Analogously, no plant possesses structures specialized for the collection of environmental oxygen or for the excretion of metabolic wastes. Yet all but the most simply constructed animals possess both: lungs, gills, moist skins, and other specific body parts for breathing; and kidneys, lungs, gills, sweat glands, and other specific body parts for excretion. Such structures are necessitated by the shape of the animal body and, ultimately, by the requirement of locomotion. The light-requiring, stationary plant is built for maximum surface exposure. Virtually all its cells are in direct contact with the external environment, and each cell may therefore collect oxygen and excrete wastes on its own. By contrast, the moving animal for obvious mechanical reasons cannot be built in the ramified shape of a tree, but must be constructed far more compactly, for minimum surface exposure. Most cells of an animal therefore cannot be in direct contact with the environment, and this necessitates specialized *breathing* and *excretory* systems operating in conjunction with the internal circulatory system.

Above all, animals do not match plants in structures associated directly with the function of locomotion. Apart from *muscular* and *skeletal* systems, animals also possess elaborate equipment for internal coordination. Movement must be readjusted often, in response to rapid changes of external locale brought about by movement. Accordingly, animals possess systems for *chemical coordination*, such as blood, kidneys, and endocrine glands, and systems for *neural coordination*, such as sense organs, nerves, and brains.

In general, therefore, just as the plant body reflects a way of life based on photosynthesis and sessilism, so the animal body reflects the way of life based on alimentation and locomotion.

The various animal organ systems are arranged in a definite structural pattern. Broadly speaking, every animal may be considered to be made up of three groups of layers. Each group forms a "tube" of a sort, and the three tubes are one within the other. The outermost tube is the external body wall, which includes the integumentary system and all derivatives. The innermost tube is the alimentary system and its derivatives. And the middle tube consists of all the other organs and systems between body wall and alimentary tract (see Fig. 10.1). This is more than a rough analogy; the three-layered picture of an animal has biological reality, for at an early stage of embryonic life animal embryos consist of just three single-celled layers. How this stage develops we shall discuss in Chap. 22. Here we may note that the outer embryonic cell layer is called *ectoderm*, the middle one *mesoderm*, and the inner one *endoderm* (Fig. 10.2). These three cell layers, or *germ layers*, later produce the three "tubes" of the

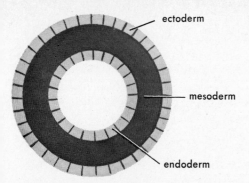

ectoderm

mesoderm

endoderm

Fig. 10.2. Diagram showing the three germ layers of an animal embryo.

adult animal. Ectoderm forms the outer tube of skin, nervous system, and other structures. Mesoderm forms the middle tube of muscles, bones, circulatory system, excretory and reproductive systems, and others. Endoderm forms the inner tube of the alimentary system and associated structures.

In the embryo, the three germ layers do not develop at the same time; the middle layer, mesoderm, forms last. In certain animal embryos this mesoderm arises from cells produced by the ectoderm; in other animals, from cells produced by the endoderm; and in still other animals, from cells produced by both ectoderm and endoderm. Further, once the mesoderm layer is present, it may undergo several later fates. In one series of cases, it develops a large cavity within it. Such a cavity, surrounded entirely by mesoderm cells, is called a *coelom*. Where a coelom forms, it becomes the principal body cavity of the animal. In man, for example, the coelom in part is the cavity inside the abdomen, in which many organs lie (Fig. 10.3).

Animals can be classified into superphyla on the basis of how mesoderm forms, how extensive it becomes, and whether or not a coelom develops in it. Other criteria, particularly structural features of adult animals, are used to distinguish individual phyla within the superphyla. Apart from the separate single phylum of

Fig. 10.3. Diagrammatic representation of the formation of mesoderm and the coelom in the five animal superphyla. In the radiates, jelly fills the space between ectoderm and endoderm, and individual mesoderm cells are embedded in the jelly. In acoelomates, mesoderm accumulates compactly and a coelom does not develop. In pseudocoelomates, mesoderm accumulates regionally and the body cavity is therefore not a true coelom but is bounded by ectoderm and endoderm. In schizocoelomates, the mesoderm splits into outer and inner layers, and in enterocoelomates, the mesoderm grows out as hollow pouches from the endoderm. In both cases, the end result is the same, namely, a mesoderm-lined, true coelomic body cavity.

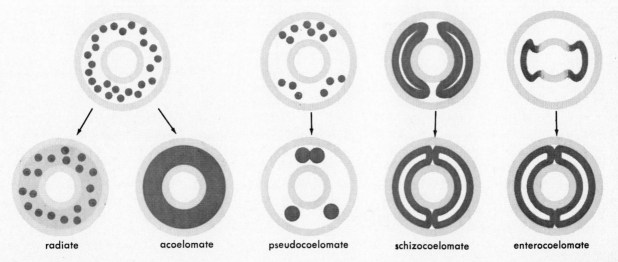

radiate

acoelomate

pseudocoelomate

schizocoelomate

enterocoelomate

sponges, five superphyla may be recognized: the *radiates*, the *acoelomates*, the *pseudocoelomates*, the *schizocoelomates*, and the *enterocoelomates*. These groups will be the broad units of discussion in the following sections.

Sponges and radiates

PHYLUM PORIFERA
sponges (15,000 species)

PHYLUM CNIDARIA
coelenterates (10,000 species)

PHYLUM CTENOPHORA
comb jellies (100 species)

In these groups, the mesoderm is not very well developed; in extreme cases it may even be absent altogether. Where it does exist, it is formed from ectoderm and consists largely of a solid mass of jelly within which are embedded relatively few cells (see Fig. 10.3). An additional characteristic of these animals is a basic

radial body symmetry. This is particularly conspicuous in the radiates, or "Radiata," which are so named because of their symmetry. All other animals, by contrast, are basically bilaterally symmetrical and are often referred to collectively as "Bilateria." A third distinguishing feature of radiates is that they possess an alimentary system with but a *single* opening to the outside. The system is essentially a sac and its one opening serves as both mouth and anus.

Of the three phyla listed above, we shall discuss some of the characteristics of the first two.

SPONGES

Class Calcarea: chalk sponges

Class Hexactinellida: glass sponges

Class Demispongiae: horn sponges

All sponges are sessile as adults, but their embryos are ciliated and free-swimming. The embryos, essentially saclike, are composed of two cell layers, the ectoderm and the endoderm. Jelly often forms a mid-

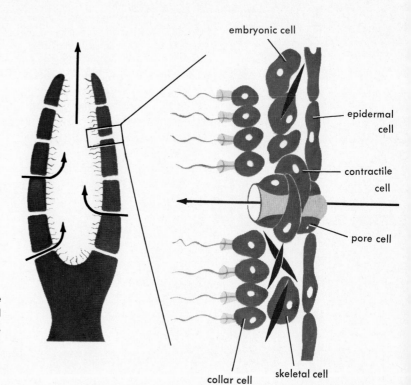

Fig. 10.4. The organization of a simple sponge (diagrammatic). Left, cross-sectional view showing the flow direction of water. Right, detail of a portion of the body wall.

embryonic cell

epidermal cell

contractile cell

pore cell

collar cell

skeletal cell

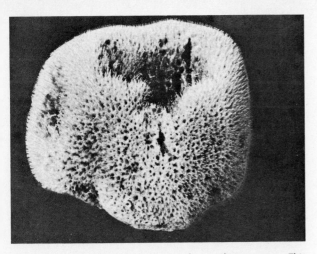

Fig. 10.5. The horny skeleton of a toilet sponge. This quite complex structure was formed by cooperating skeletal cells, each contributing a tiny bit to the mesh of horny fibers. (U.S. Fish and Wildlife Service.)

dle layer. When the embryos settle and become adult sponges, the neat arrangement of the cellular layers becomes greatly obscured. Nevertheless, the adults possess different cell types on the outside, the inside, and the middle (Fig. 10.4).

The outer cells are of several kinds, the most distinctive being those which secrete the intracellular skeletal elements called *spicules*. These have different characteristic shapes in different species and are the basis of sponge classification. In chalk sponges, the spicules consist of calcium salts; in glass sponges, of silica; and in horny sponges, of complex organic materials (Fig. 10.5).

The most characteristic cells on the inside of a sponge are the so-called *collar cells*, which are flagellate and remarkably like the collar flagellates of the protozoan phylum Mastigophora. These cells line a system of interconnecting channels which communicate with the environment through entry and exit pores located on the surface of the sponge body. The collar cells create a water current which flows through the entry pores into the channel system and out through the exit pores. Food present in the current is trapped by the collar cells (see Fig. 10.4).

All sponges are aquatic, and most of them are marine.

COELENTERATES

Class Hydrozoa: *Obelia, Hydra, Physalia*

Class Scyphozoa: jellyfishes

Class Anthozoa: sea anemones, corals

Coelenterates are characterized by a digestive cavity with a single opening, by tentacles which surround this opening, and by *sting cells*, unique to this phylum, located on the tentacles. The body consists of an outer ectodermal cell layer containing sensory cells of various sorts and an inner endodermal layer containing digestive amoeboid cells. Between these two cell layers is a jellylike layer of varying thickness, the *mesogloea*. In this middle layer is embedded a simply constructed nerve net (Fig. 10.6).

The adult coelenterate is either a sessile, saclike *polyp* or a free-swimming, bell-shaped *medusa*. Hydrozoa characteristically pass through alternate polyp and medusa stages. In *Obelia*, for example, the sessile phase is a colony of polyps. Most of these are feeding

Fig. 10.6. The basic structure of coelenterates (diagrammatic). The outer body layer is epidermal, the inner is digestive, and the middle one, the so-called mesogloea, is largely jelly in which is embedded a simple nerve net. A single opening serves as both mouth and anus, and there are usually tentacles around this opening. The sessile phase of a coelenterate (the polyp) is as shown, and if the diagram is viewed upside down, it illustrates the motile phase (the medusa).

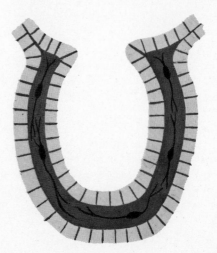

polyps, but some develop as specialized reproductive polyps which produce medusae by budding. These medusae separate away as free-swimming stages. Eventually they develop sex organs, and after fertilization the egg develops into a larva which gives rise to a new polyp colony (Fig. 10.7).

In Scyphozoa, the polyp phase is greatly reduced. For example, in the common jellyfish *Aurelia*, the larva grows directly into a single reproductive polyp which buds off medusae. Such medusae (called *ephyrae* in immature condition) later develop sex organs and give rise to new fertilized eggs (Fig. 10.8).

In Anthozoa, on the contrary, it is the medusa phase which is reduced. Indeed, that phase is absent altogether: the sessile adult is a feeding polyp which develops sex organs. After fertilization, larvae form, and these grow into new adult polyps (see Fig. 10.8).

Whether sessile or free-swimming, coelenterates are efficient carnivores which catch crustacea, small fish, and other prey by means of tentacles and sting cells. Most genera are marine, but some, like the familiar *Hydra*, live in fresh water (Fig. 10.9). Note that *Hydra* is a highly specialized form in which the characteristic hydrozoan life cycle does not occur. In particular, a medusa phase is suppressed. Hydrozoa also include specialized colonial types like *Physalia*, the Portuguese man-of-war, characterized by several different kinds of polyps whose forms and functions are quite distinct (Fig. 10.10). Anthozoa (see Fig. 10.9)

manufacture often very elaborate exoskeletons of calcium salts. The group includes the builders of coral reefs and atolls.

Acoelomates

PHYLUM PLATYHELMINTHES
flatworms (10,000 species)

PHYLUM NEMERTINEA
proboscis worms (600 species)

This superphylum (and all subsequent ones as well) contains bilaterally symmetrical animals. The mesoderm here develops from ectoderm and endoderm, and it remains a solid layer (Fig. 10.3). Therefore, because a coelom cavity does *not* form, the name of the group is *acoelomates*, "without coelom."

Of the two phyla included, the first illustrates the general nature of the whole group.

FLATWORMS

Class Turbellaria: free-living flatworms

Class Trematoda: flukes

Class Cestoda: tapeworms

The body of these animals is flattened top to bottom and the alimentary system resembles that of coelenterates; a single opening (on the underside of the body) serves as both mouth and anus. All other

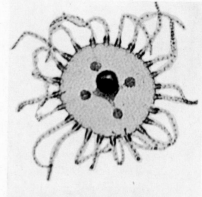

Fig. 10.7. Obelia. Left, a colony of polyps. Note feeding polyps with tentacles, and club-shaped reproductive polyps. The latter produce medusae. Right, a medusa. Dark region in center is the mouth. Note the four sex organs. (Carolina Biological Supply Co.)

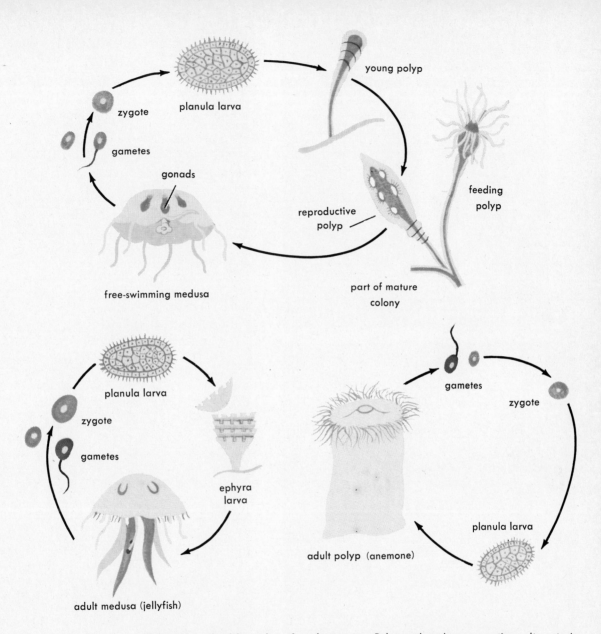

Fig. 10.8.   The life cycles of coelenterates. Polyp and medusa generations alternate in Hydrozoa like *Obelia* (top); polyp phases are suppressed in Scyphozoa like *Aurelia* and other jellyfish; and medusa phases are suppressed in Anthozoa like sea anemones.

acoelomate groups, and indeed all other animals of any kind, possess alimentary tracts with two separate openings, that is, separate mouth and anus.

The most familiar free-living flatworms are the *planarians* (Fig. 10.11). These animals have definite front and rear ends, and the digestive opening is

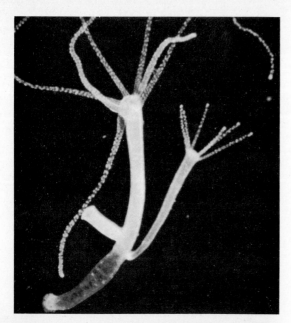

Fig. 10.9. Top, Hydra with buds. Bottom, *Metridium*, a sea anemone. (Top, courtesy of Dr. Roman Vishniac, New York; bottom, Carolina Biological Supply Co.)

Fig. 10.10. Model of *Physalia*, the Portuguese man-of-war. Each tentacle suspended from the gas-filled float represents a portion of a single coelenterate individual. The several different types of tentacles here indicate the high degree of individual variation encountered in such a colony. (American Museum of Natural History.)

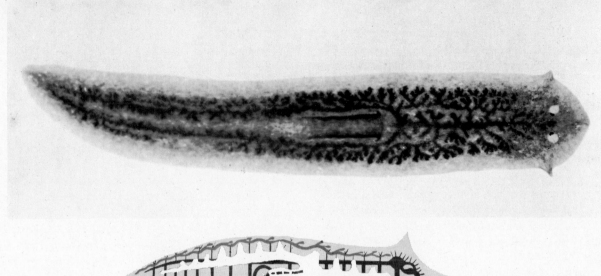

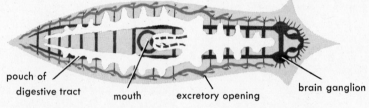

pouch of
digestive tract   mouth   excretory opening   brain ganglion

Fig. 10.11.   Free-living planarian flatworms. Internal structure diagrammatic. (Photo, General Biological Supply House, Inc.)

located in the middle, on the underside. An eversible *pharynx* breaks larger food into particles suitable for ingestion. A pair of *eyes* is present at the head end and the head also contains a concentration of nervous tissue, the *brain ganglion*. From it leads a pair of *ventral nerve cords*, which are interconnected at more or less regular intervals by transverse strands of nerves. The whole has the appearance of a ladder. Circulatory and breathing systems are not present in flatworms, but these animals do possess excretory and elaborate reproductive systems. Locomotion is accomplished by undulating muscular movements, which result in swimming, or by the beat of cilia on the underside of the body, which propel the animal on a solid surface.

The class *Turbellaria*, to which the planarians belong, contains largely free-living scavengers found in both ocean and fresh water. The two remaining classes of flatworms are exclusively parasitic and of considerable general importance to man. We have already discussed the characteristic life cycle in one of these classes (tapeworms) in Chap. 6.

Pseudocoelomates

PHYLUM ROTIFERA
rotifers (1,500 species)

PHYLUM NEMATODA
roundworms (10,000 species)

PHYLUM NEMATOMORPHA
hairworms (80 species)

PHYLUM GASTROTRICHA
(200 species)

PHYLUM KINORHYNCHA
(30 species)

PHYLUM PRIAPULIDA
(3 species)

PHYLUM ENTOPROCTA
(60 species)

PHYLUM ACANTHOCEPHALA
spiny-headed worms (300 species)

In this superphylum, the mesoderm arises largely from ectoderm and it does not become a solid middle layer. Instead, mesodermal tissues collect in limited regions in the space between ectoderm and endoderm. As a result, these animals do possess a body cavity, but this cavity is enclosed by ectoderm on the outside and by endoderm on the inside, not by mesoderm (Fig. 10.3). The cavity is therefore a "false coelom," hence the name *pseudocoelomates*.

Another characteristic of the superphylum is that adult cells in many cases lose their boundary membranes, and the animals so become syncytial. With one exception (Entoprocta), the phyla in the group comprise worm-shaped animals, and most of them exhibit a tendency toward superficial external body segmentation. Pseudocoelomates as a whole include some of the rarest and least known, as well as some of the most abundant, of all animals. Only the first two of the eight phyla listed above will concern us here.

ROTIFERS

These microscopic animals are very largely free-living. They are found predominantly in fresh water, where they are exceedingly common (Fig. 10.12).

Rotifers possess an identifying anterior crown of cilia surrounding the mouth, hence the name "wheel bearers" for the phylum. The cilia are the organs of locomotion, and they also create food currents. The mouth leads into a muscular grinding organ (*mastax*) and then into a straight intestine which terminates at the anus. At the hind end are located *cement organs*, which anchor the animal during feeding and which also make possible a second form of locomotion resembling caterpillarlike creeping. The nervous system consists mainly of a brain ganglion dorsal to the mouth and of a series of nerve cords leading away from the ganglion. Rotifers possess excretory systems, but circulatory and breathing systems are absent.

During spring and summer, female rotifers produce eggs which develop into new females without being fertilized. These females in turn reproduce without fertilization and many generations of females succeed one another in this manner. In the fall, the females lay some eggs which are smaller than the rest. These hatch into small males, degenerate individuals lacking digestive systems but capable of producing sperms. Fertilization may then occur. The resulting eggs possess thick, hard shells and may resist unfavorable environments for very long periods. Under suitably favorable conditions, e.g., in the following spring, the shelled eggs develop into females. In some types of rotifers males are unknown altogether, the species being propagated exclusively by unfertilized eggs. This phenomenon of egg development without fertilization is called *parthenogenesis*. We have already encountered it in the discussion on social insects (Chap. 6).

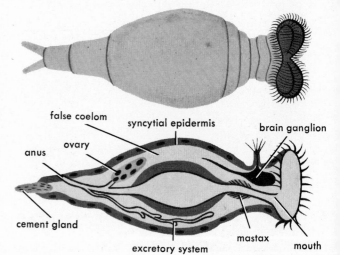

Fig. 10.12. The structure of a rotifer, diagrammatic. Top, dorsal external view. Bottom, sagittal section.

false coelom
syncytial epidermis
brain ganglion
anus
ovary
cement gland
excretory system
mastax
mouth

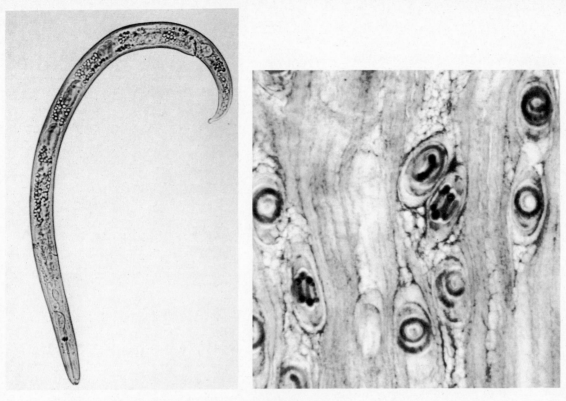

Fig. 10.13. Left, a nematode causing disease in plants. Right, larvae of trichina worms, encapsulated in pig muscle. If infected pork is cooked improperly, the larvae are digested out in the intestine of the host and the worms then invade the host tissues. (Left, courtesy of Dr. W. F. Mai, Cornell University; right, Ward's Natural Science Establishment, Inc.)

ROUNDWORMS

It has been estimated that probably more individual roundworms exist than any other Metazoa except possibly insects. Many nematodes are free-living in water and soil, and they occur in such numbers that a spadeful of garden earth is likely to contain up to a million worms. Many nematodes are parasitic in plants and animals, and they are usually implicated when an animal is said to suffer from "worms." Man alone harbors some 50 species. Most of these are relatively harmless, but some cause serious diseases.

All nematodes are remarkably alike (Fig. 10.13). The body is slender and cylindrical, has tapered ends, and is covered with a tough horny cuticle. As in rotifers, the number of nuclei is constant for each species and cell boundaries are absent in the adult. The worms possess mouth, straight intestine, and anus. Circulatory and breathing systems are not present, and excretory systems are constructed relatively simply. Males are usually smaller than females.

Among the serious nematode pests of man are the *trichina worms*, introduced into the human body via insufficiently cooked pork; the *hookworms*, which live in soil and infect man by boring through his skin; and the *filaria worms*, which are transmitted by mosquitoes and cause blocks in lymph vessels. The disease resulting from filarial infections is characterized by immense swellings and is known as *elephantiasis*.

Schizocoelomates

PHYLUM MOLLUSCA
mollusks (100,000 species)

PHYLUM ANNELIDA
segmented worms (10,000 species)

PHYLUM ARTHROPODA
joint-legged animals (1 million species)

PHYLUM SIPUNCULOIDA
(250 species)

PHYLUM PHORONIDA
(15 species)

PHYLUM ECHIUROIDA
(60 species)

PHYLUM ECTOPROCTA
(2,500 species)

In this important superphylum, the mesoderm has two sources. The mesoderm of the embryo forms from ectoderm but later largely degenerates. New adult mesoderm, developed from endoderm, later splits into two layers, an outer one which comes to lie against the inner surface of the body wall and an inner one which surrounds the alimentary tract (Fig. 10.3). Thus the animals have a true coelom, and since it arises by a splitting of mesoderm, the group is named "schizocoelomates."

MOLLUSKS

Class Amphineura: chitons

Class Scaphopoda: tooth shells

Class Gastropoda: snails, slugs, whelks

Class Pelecypoda: clams, mussels

Class Cephalopoda: squids, octopuses, nautiluses

Among Metazoa, this enormous phylum is second only to the arthropods in numbers of species. Mollusks are mostly marine, but many snails and clams live in fresh water and one group of snails is terrestrial. The phylum includes the largest of all nonvertebrate animals, namely, the giant squids, which may reach lengths of 50 feet.

Despite the external dissimilarities of the mem-

bers of different classes, all mollusks share a common fundamental body organization. The molluscan body consists of a ventral, muscular *foot,* which is the principal organ of locomotion; a *visceral mass,* located dorsal to the foot, which contains most of the internal organs; and a *mantle,* a tissue layer which covers the visceral mass and which in most cases secretes a calcareous *shell* (Fig. 10.14).

The class *Amphineura* includes probably the least specialized mollusks. Chitons occur abundantly on rocks along the seashore, where they creep sluggishly with their broad foot. The dorsal surface of a chiton is protected by a shell of eight overlapping plates, and under the rim of this shell, in the so-called *mantle cavity,* are lateral gills for breathing. Between shell and foot is the visceral mass. The head is greatly reduced, probably a specialized feature of chitons (Fig. 10.15).

In the class *Scaphopoda,* the body is greatly elongated in a dorsoventral direction and the animal is tubular. The shell is a tube open at both ends and the foot of a scaphopod protrudes from the wider ventral end. The mouth is surrounded by delicate sensory and prehensile tentacles. Scaphopods are the least common of the mollusks. They are all marine and they live partly buried in sand or mud bottoms of shallow waters.

Gastropoda like snails have the general architecture of chitons. A distinct head is present, however, which bears retractile tentacles and eyes. Also, the shell is usually coiled and the head and foot of the animal may be withdrawn into the shell. The alimentary tract is U-shaped, and the anus opens to the outside dorsally, under the forward rim of the shell. Aquatic snails breathe by means of gills, located as in chitons in the mantle cavity, under the rim of the shell. In terrestrial snails, parts of the mantle cavity have become adapted to function as lungs. Some land snails have returned secondarily to water, and these must surface periodically for air.

In the class *Pelecypoda,* clams are highly specialized animals, adapted to a burrowing way of life (Fig. 10.16). They are flattened from side to side, the hinge of the two shells, or *valves,* being dorsal.

Lining the valves on the inside are the mantle tissues, which form two openings (siphons) at the

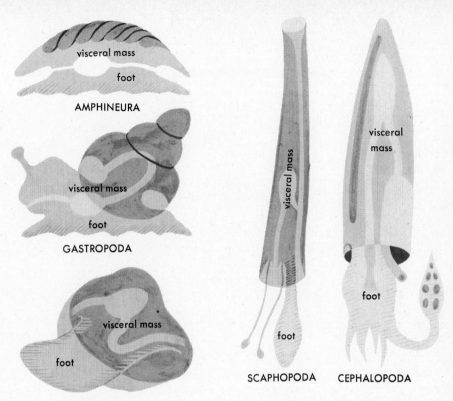

visceral mass

foot

AMPHINEURA

visceral mass

foot

GASTROPODA

visceral mass

visceral mass

foot

SCAPHOPODA

visceral mass

foot

CEPHALOPODA

visceral mass

foot

PELECYPODA

Fig. 10.14. The body plan of the various classes of mollusks. A basic structure is seen to be common to all. Shells are in dark gray; the foot is cross-hatched.

posterior end, one for the entry and one for the exit of water. In many species, these posterior tissues are drawn out into a long retractile tube, which may be pushed out into free water if the clam is embedded in several inches of sand or mud. Hanging freely into the mantle cavity are the gills, folds of ciliated tissue which function both as breathing organs and as food filters. Pelecypods subsist on microscopic food particles brought into the animals by the incoming water current. The gills strain and collect these particles, and the cilia carry them to the mouth. This opening is located anteriorly between the left and right gills, in the visceral mass. The digestive tract is within the visceral mass, and the anus opens posteriorly, discharging into the outgoing water current. The nervous system is highly reduced, a feature undoubtedly correlated with the sluggish way of life of these animals. A head is not present either. The muscular foot, continuous with the visceral mass, may be protruded between the valves. Clams use the foot as a burrow-

ing organ, and by expanding the tip of the foot in sand and pulling the body after it, they may propel themselves forward. Many pelecypods are permanently attached, however. This is true, for example, of oysters and also of the giant clam *Tridacna*, which may be 2 yards long and weigh $\frac{1}{4}$ ton.

The class *Cephalopoda* includes the most highly

Fig. 10.15. A chiton, member of the molluscan class Amphineura. The animal is seen from the dorsal side. Note the eight shell plates and the edge of the foot. (American Museum of Natural History.)

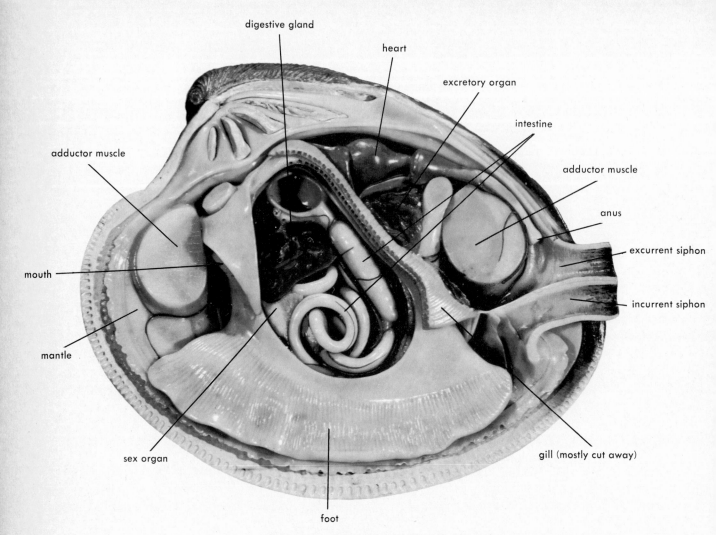

Fig. 10.16. The internal structure of a clam. In this model, most of the gill flap is cut away to expose the organs of the visceral mass. Water enters via the incurrent siphon and passes over the gills, where food particles are strained out and conducted to the mouth, hidden under a flap of tissue. Water and elimination products of all kinds leave the clam via the excurrent siphon. The two adductor muscles control the closing of the valve shells. (American Museum of Natural History.)

organized mollusks (Fig. 10.17). Squids have a greatly reduced horny shell embedded within the mantle. Octopuses are without shells. Cephalopods are elongated dorsoventrally, like scaphopods. In squids and octopuses, the sucker-equipped tentacles represent the foot and the body represents the visceral mass.

Within the wreath of tentacles is a well-developed head, with a large brain and large vertebratelike eyes. The head also bears a mouth equipped with strong horny jaws. The digestive tract is U-shaped, the anus opening into the mantle cavity. Cephalopods are marine, predatory animals.

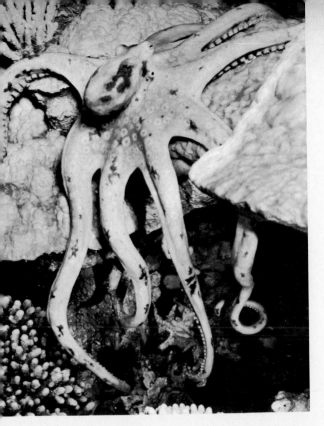

Fig. 10.17. An octopus. Note funnel, here visible under right eye. (American Museum of Natural History.)

SEGMENTED WORMS

Class Polychaeta: clamworms, tube worms

Class Oligochaeta: earthworms

Class Hirudinea: leeches

This phylum comprises animals in which the body is divided internally and externally into numerous *segments,* which are separated from each other by membranous partitions. Except for the segments of the head and the hind end, all others are more or less alike (Fig. 10.18).

The first few segments of an annelid form the head, and the last segment represents the hind end. The mouth, located anteriorly in the head, leads into an alimentary tract which terminates in the last segment. The head also contains the brain ganglia, which form a ring around the pharynx. The rest of the nervous system is essentially of the ladder type, consisting of ventral nerve trunks thickened into ganglia in each segment. The circulatory system is composed principally of a longitudinal dorsal vessel, a longitudinal ventral vessel, and segmental connecting channels between these two. Blood flows forward dorsally and backward ventrally, propelled mainly by contractions

Fig. 10.18. Anterior part of the polychaete *Nereis,* and cross section through the body (diagrammatic).

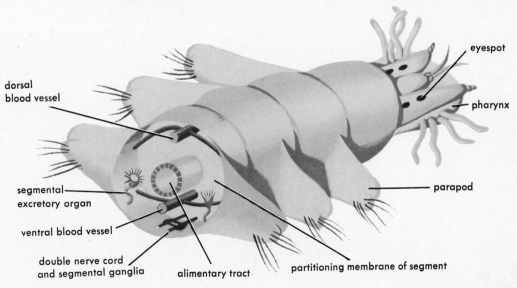

dorsal blood vessel

eyespot

pharynx

segmental excretory organ

ventral blood vessel

double nerve cord and segmental ganglia

alimentary tract

partitioning membrane of segment

parapod

of the dorsal blood vessel. A pair of excretory organs with separate openings is found in each body segment. The cuticle-covered body surface of an annelid serves for breathing.

The *Polychaeta* (Fig. 10.19) are mostly marine. Some are free-swimming. Others manufacture tubes in mud or sand in which they live permanently. And still others are burrowers. All are distinguished by the presence of a pair of fleshy lobes, the *parapodia*, on each body segment. Numerous chitinous bristles grow from these lobes, hence the name *polychaetes*, or "many-bristled" worms. Parapodia provide a large surface for breathing. The beating of the lobes also aids in locomotion or in drawing water in and out of tubes and burrows. Polychaetes are characterized further by

Fig. 10.19. Polychaetes. Section through the tube of the parchment worm *Chaetopterus.* The head of the worm is on the left. Note the greatly elaborated parapodia, used to draw water currents through the tube. Between the arms of the U tube is a sipunculid worm, a member of another phylum. (American Museum of Natural History.)

the presence of eyes and of other specialized sense organs in the head segments.

The *Oligochaeta* include the familiar earthworms. Annelids of this class differ from polychaetes in the absence of eyes and other head appendages, and in the absence of parapodia, each body segment bearing only a few bristles. Oligochaetes live in the ocean, in fresh water, and on land. Some attain remarkable size. For example, the giant earthworms of Australia may reach lengths of over 10 feet.

The *Hirudinea*, or leeches, are without bristles, and unlike other annelids, they possess a fixed number of segments throughout life. Moreover, the external segmentation does not match the internal, external segments being the more numerous. Each end of the body is equipped with a sucker. The most familiar leeches are blood-sucking parasites. They possess digestive tracts equipped with spacious pouches, which may store enough blood to make a single meal suffice for many months. The worms produce *hirudin*, an anticoagulant which prevents blood from clotting during ingestion.

ARTHROPODS

Class Onychophora: *Peripatus*

Class Crustacea: shrimps, lobsters, crabs, barnacles

Class Insecta: insects

Class Chilopoda: centipedes

Class Diplopoda: millipedes

Class Arachnida: spiders, scorpions, mites, ticks

Class Merostomata: horseshoe crabs

By almost any standard, this is today the most successful group of organisms in the whole living world. Arthropods are encountered in all environments in which life occurs at all, and in many tropical environments they maintain supremacy over even man. The insects are by far the most abundant and most diversified of all arthropods, being represented in the phylum by at least three-quarters of a million species.

General characteristics. The body plan of arthropods as a whole is a highly elaborated variant of that of

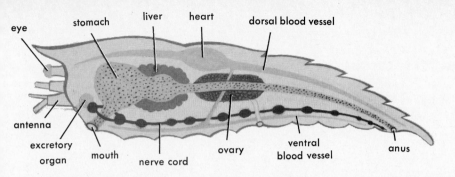

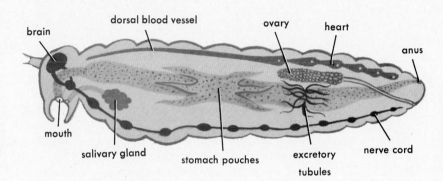

Fig. 10.20. The internal structure of a lobster (top), and a grasshopper (bottom), diagrammatic.

annelid worms (Fig. 10.20). A segmented design is fundamental, and the different segments are specialized in often greatly divergent ways. The body of an arthropod is composed of a *head*, a *thorax*, and an *abdomen*. The whole is covered by an external skeleton which is made of chitin and is molted at intervals. Jointed appendages are present on most or all segments. The head often consists of six segments. Fused together in the adult, each head segment characteristically bears a pair of appendages having either a sensory or an ingestive function. The head also contains either or both of two kinds of eyes. In so-called *simple eyes,* a single lens covers many light-sensitive cells. In *compound eyes,* many complete visual units are grouped together into a large composite eye (as in houseflies). Each visual unit here contains its own lens and light-sensitive cells. Compound eyes are unique to arthropods.

The alimentary tract consists of foregut, midgut, and hindgut. The first and last of these sections are lined with chitin, which is continuous with the external skeleton; hence only the midgut functions digestively.

Nervous structures include dorsal brain ganglia in the head, ventral nerve cords, and paired ganglia either in each segment or grouped together in head and thorax. The circulatory system consists of a single main dorsal vessel. Blood flows out from it anteriorly, circulates freely through the body tissues, and reenters the vessel posteriorly or along the mid-region of the body. The excretory organs either are located in the head appendages, as in crustaceans, or are attached to the midgut and lead to the outside via the anus, as in insects.

Breathing is accomplished in various ways in the different groups. Aquatic arthropods typically possess *gills* of some kind. In lobsters, for example, feathery gills are attached to the upper parts of the walking legs. Terrestrial arthropods like insects breathe by means of *tracheal tubes,* a unique, chitin-lined system of channels which originates on the body surface and ramifies to all interior tissues.

The fertilized eggs of many aquatic arthropods develop into free-swimming larvae. These resemble

Fig. 10.21. Peripatus. This animal
combines annelid and arthropod features.
(Carolina Biological Supply Co.)

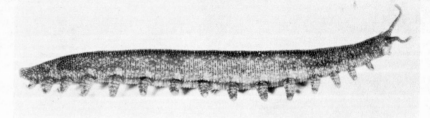

annelid worms to a considerable extent. This also holds
for some terrestrial larvae, for example, the insect
caterpillars. In other arthropods, the annelidlike phase
is greatly abbreviated and when the larvae hatch they
already look like miniature adults. All larval types develop through a series of molting steps, the last of
which produces the adult. Insects do not molt after
adulthood is attained, but crustaceans do molt throughout life.

Class characteristics.   The members of the small class
Onychophora exhibit an interesting and unique mixture of annelid and arthropod traits (Fig. 10.21). It is
believed that annelid ancestors gave rise to an ancestral arthropod stock, and that Onychophora evolved
from this stock very early.

The large class of *Crustacea* is represented by
some 50,000 species. Most crustaceans are aquatic,
and most of these are marine. Many are microscopic
and planktonic, but others, like the giant crabs, may
be some 12 feet across from one leg tip to the other.
Most crustaceans are free-living and free-swimming.
But some are parasitic either as larvae or as adults,
and the barnacles are sessile as adults. In their internal
structure, crustacea display a typically arthropod organization (Fig. 10.20). Externally, they show particularly clearly how different segments may become
specialized for different functions; consider, for example, the pronounced differences among the segmental
appendages of a lobster (Fig. 10.22).

In the class *Insecta*, largest of all animal groups,
the head is marked off clearly from the thorax, and

Fig. 10.22.   **Dorsal view of a crayfish, a freshwater crustacean structurally very much
like the marine lobster.** Note the antennae, eyes, large claws, walking legs, uropods, and
telson. The fused cephalothorax, covered by the carapace, is clearly set off from the abdominal segments. (Carolina Biological Supply Co.)

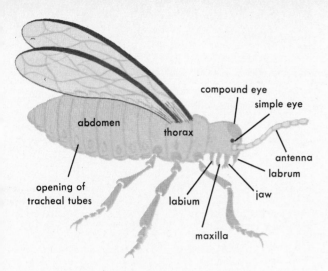

Fig. 10.23.   **The external structure of an insect.**

most primitive insects (which are flightless) and secondarily flightless insects like fleas, each of the last two thoracic segments typically bears a pair of wings. Both pairs may be membranous, as in dragonflies and butterflies. Or the first pair may be heavily chitinized, as in beetles. Or the second pair may be reduced to tiny stalks, as in houseflies and mosquitoes. The abdomen of insects characteristically is without appendages.

Insects become adults by *metamorphosis*, which can be either *incomplete* or *complete*. In the former the larva resembles the adult in general features and reaches adult condition gradually, in the course of five molting steps. Grasshoppers, earwigs, termites, true bugs, aphids, and many other insect types belong to this group. In the second case, the larva is annelid- or caterpillarlike. It eventually transforms into a *pupa*, and the pupa in turn becomes the adult. Butterflies, moths, houseflies, beetles, bees, and ants are in this group. Note that, in either group, only the adult stages fly (Fig. 10.24).

Insects are classified into some 20 orders, each representing a very wide range of ways of life. For example, the order of beetles includes parasites, commensals, carnivores, herbivores, omnivores, aquatic types, subterranean types, arboreal types, diurnal and nocturnal types, and dozens of others, each adapted to

the thorax from the abdomen (Fig. 10.23). The head bears simple and compound eyes, a single pair of antennae, and mouth parts which vary according to how the insect feeds: by *biting* like a grasshopper, by *sucking* like a housefly, or by *piercing and sucking* like a mosquito.

The thorax consists of three segments, each bearing a pair of walking legs. Also, in all except the

Fig. 10.24.   **Complete metamorphosis in insects.** Caterpillar larva (top left), pupa (bottom left), adult (right). Each stage is connected to the preceding and succeeding one through a molt. Larvae pass through several molting stages. In insects with incomplete metamorphosis, the larvae look like miniature adults. (Courtesy of Dr. D. Bodenstein, University of Virginia.)

a particular, often highly specialized mode of living. Analogous diversity is in evidence within most other orders. Incidentally, beetles alone number some 300,000 species. They form the largest of all orders within the largest of all classes within the largest of all phyla.

The classes *Chilopoda* and *Diplopoda* (Fig. 10.25) are exclusively terrestrial. In both groups, the rather wormlike animals are subdivided into numerous segments. In the head, simple eyes are present but compound eyes usually are not. Body segments bear walking legs, *one* pair per segment in centipedes, *two* pairs per segment in millipedes. The first pair in centipedes is modified into poison claws. Centipedes are carnivorous, whereas millipedes are largely herbivorous. Despite the comparatively greater number of legs in millipedes, these arthropods cannot run as fast as centipedes. In their general internal structure, centipedes and millipedes are rather like insects.

The classes *Arachnida* and *Merostomata* are related fairly closely. Arachnids comprise terrestrial arthropods. The head in these animals is without compound eyes and without antennae. In spiders, the head bears sharp-pointed poison-injecting claws. On the thorax are four pairs of walking legs, and this feature readily distinguishes spiders (and arachnids generally) from insects. The abdomen is without segmental appendages, but spiders possess several pairs of posterior

spinnerets, organs which secrete web-forming silk (Fig. 10.26).

The Merostomata are the marine horseshoe crabs, or *king crabs*. They are represented by five living species, all belonging to the genus *Limulus*. The animals are archaic "living fossils," and they probably are survivors of an early stock of arthropods which also gave rise to the modern arachnids.

Enterocoelomates

PHYLUM BRACHIOPODA
lampshells (250 species)

PHYLUM CHAETOGNATHA
arrowworms (30 species)

PHYLUM POGONOPHORA
beard worms (25 species)

PHYLUM HEMICHORDATA
acorn worms (100 species)

PHYLUM ECHINODERMATA
spiny-skinned animals (6,000 species)

PHYLUM CHORDATA
chordates (50,000 species)

Mesoderm in this superphylum arises largely from endoderm. At an early embryonic stage, the endoderm produces hollow pouches which grow into

Fig. 10.25. Left, a centipede. Right, a millipede. Note the two pairs of legs per segment in millipedes, the single pair per segment in centipedes. (Carolina Biological Supply Co.)

Fig. 10.26. **Left, a tarantula.** Note pair of poison claws and, right next to them, a pair of sensory appendages (pedipalps). Right, the horseshoe crab *Limulus*. This arthropod may be regarded as a "living fossil," having persisted more or less unchanged for 200 million years or more. (Left, General Biological Supply House, Inc.; right, Carolina Biological Supply Co.)

the space between ectoderm and endoderm. Eventually, these pouches fill the entire available space, and they also separate off from the endoderm which produced them. The cavities so enclosed completely by the mesodermal pouches are the coelom (Fig. 10.3). Since the mesoderm and coelom here arises from the endoderm, which itself produces the gut (or *enteron*), the group is named "enterocoelomates."

Of the six phyla listed above, the last two are the most familiar. The last is also of very special interest, for man and the other mammals belong to it.

ECHINODERMS

Class Asteroidea: starfishes

Class Ophiuroidea: brittle stars

Class Echinoidea: sea urchins, sand dollars

Class Holothuroidea: sea cucumbers

Class Crinoidea: sea lilies, feather stars

The members of this phylum are exclusively marine, and their unique identifying feature is a so-called *water-vascular system* for locomotion. The embryos and larvae are bilateral, but the adults are radially symmetrical.

A starfish of the familiar genus *Asterias* is composed of a central region from which five *arms* radiate out. In other genera, there may be as many as 20 or more arms. The shell-like skeleton is an endoskeleton made up of small flat *calcareous plates* which are held together by muscles and connective tissue (Fig. 10.27). Short *calcareous spines*, some of them movable, project from the skeletal plates. Covering the skeleton are epidermal tissues, which are studded with many tiny fingerlike protrusions, the *skin gills*. The internal cavities of these gills are parts of the coelom and communicate with the interior body cavity through spaces left among the skeletal plates. Also present on the body surface are numerous very small pincers, the *pedicellaria*. These protect the skin gills from interference by small animals.

The water-vascular system (Fig. 10.28) communicates with the outside through a *madreporite*, a sievelike device located excentrically on the upper surface of the animal. A series of ducts leads from the madreporite into five *radial canals,* one passing into each arm. Short side branches from these canals connect

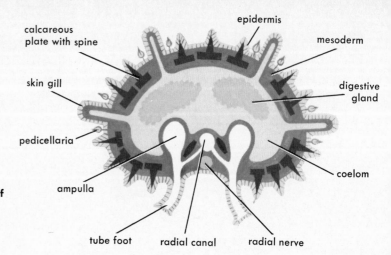

Fig. 10.27.   Cross section through the arm of a starfish; diagrammatic.

with the hollow, muscular *tube feet,* which project from the underside of the arms. At the base of each tube foot is a muscular sac, the *ampulla,* which may force water into the foot and so make it stiff. Tube feet may be used both as walking structures and as suction devices with which a starfish may hold onto rocks or food organisms.

The mouth is on the undersurface in the center of the body, and in the center of the upper surface is a

Fig. 10.28.   The components and the internal arrangement of the water-vascular system in a starfish. Water enters and leaves the system through the sievelike madreporite (sieve plate) at the upper side.

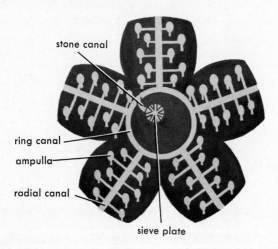

small *anal pore.* Connecting mouth and anus is a *stomach,* into which open five pairs of *digestive glands,* one pair from each arm. Starfishes feed largely on clams. The tube feet, working in relays as suckers, pull on the valves of a clam until the clam is exhausted and opens its housing. The stomach of the starfish then turns inside out through the mouth and digests the soft tissues of the clam. Starfishes are without brain, and the nervous system is not very elaborate. It consists of a ring of nerve tissue around the mouth, from which nerve trunks radiate into each arm. The circulatory system is also greatly reduced. Excretion is accomplished partly by diffusion, partly by migrating amoeboid cells. These are dispersed freely in the body cavity, and they carry wastes to and through the epidermis.

The members of the other echinoderm classes largely resemble starfishes in their general features (Fig. 10.29). Among the brittle stars, the five arms are elongated and slender and their sinuous movements aid materially in locomotion. In some ophiuroids the arms are branched. Echinoids are without arms, but their bodies nevertheless are organized on a plan of five or multiples of five. For example, sea urchins possess five bands of long slender tube feet and a mouth equipped with five radially placed teeth. Long movable spines are characteristic of these animals. The sea cucumbers are elongated along the mouth-anus axis, and they are further distinguished by a highly reduced

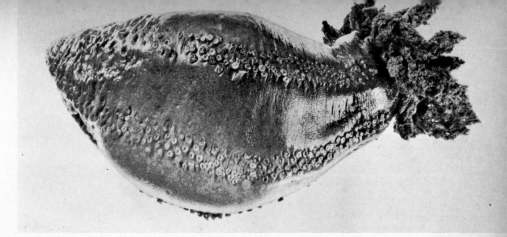

Fig. 10.29. Top left, a sea urchin. Bottom left, a brittle star. Right, a sea cucumber. In right, note the leathery skin, the tentacles surrounding the mouth, and the rows of tube feet. (Top left, right, Carolina Biological Supply Co.; bottom left, American Museum of Natural History.)

skeleton, a leathery body covering, and a circlet of tentacles around the mouth. Five longitudinal bands of tube feet are typical of most members of this class. Crinoids include stalked, sessile, deepwater forms characterized by numerous feathery arms.

The early embryonic development of echinoderms is quite similar to that of chordates, and there is little doubt that echinoderms and chordates are fairly closely related.

CHORDATES

Subphylum Urochordata: tunicates

Subphylum Cephalochordata: lancelets

Subphylum Vertebrata: vertebrates

   Class Agnatha: jawless fishes

   Class Placoderms: armored fishes (extinct)

   Class Chondrichthyes: cartilage fishes

   Class Osteichthyes: bony fishes

   Class Amphibia: amphibians

   Class Reptilia: reptiles

   Class Aves: birds

   Class Mammalia: mammals

Because this phylum includes man and the animals most directly important to man, it is unquestionably the most interesting from almost any standpoint.

Chordates are characterized by the possession of a *notochord*, a hollow *dorsal nerve cord*, and paired *gill slits* (Fig. 10.30). These structures are present either throughout life or only at some stage of development. The notochord (hence the name "chordate") is a dorsal stiffening rod formed from embryonic meso-

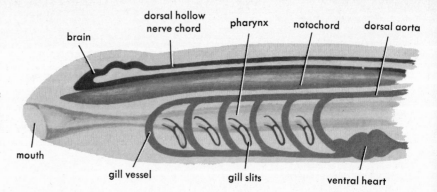

Fig. 10.30. The anterior portion of a hypothetical chordate, to show the basic diagnostic features of the phylum Chordata.

derm. The nerve cord and later nervous system form from the embryonic ectoderm. Gill slits are essentially channels on each side which connect the exterior of the body with the front part of the alimentary tract, specifically the region behind the mouth, called the *pharynx*. Thus a continuous water channel is established from the mouth to the pharynx to the outside through the gill slits. Food present in the water taken in by mouth is collected in the pharynx and is passed on into the esophagus. The water returns to the environment via the gill slits past the gills, where oxygen is absorbed into the circulatory system.

The body is segmented in two of the three chordate subphyla, the lancelets and the vertebrates. This feature is shared in common with the annelid-arthropod group of organisms, but it has here evolved independently. A distinct head is present only in vertebrate chordates.

Subphylum Urochordata. Tunicates, or "sea squirts," are marine. Of the approximately 2,000 known species, most are sessile and many form extensive colonies in the water. The adults are quite unlike typical chordates, but their larvae clearly reveal the chordate characteristics of these animals. A tunicate larva has the general form of a tadpole. It possesses a large muscular tail, a very well-developed notochord, and a dorsal hollow nerve cord, expanded anteriorly into a primitive brain. A complete alimentary system is present, as are pharyngeal gill slits (Fig. 10.31).

After a free-swimming existence of some hours, such a larva attaches with its anterior end to a rock or other solid object and undergoes a remarkable metamorphosis. In the adult (Fig. 10.32), the tail is resorbed, the notochord has disappeared completely, and the nervous system has become reduced to a single ganglion. The pharynx has enlarged, however, and has

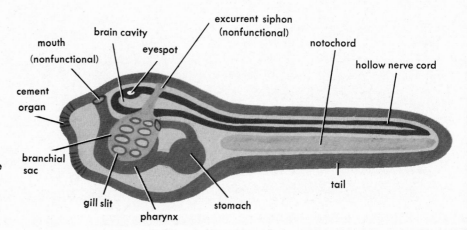

Fig. 10.31. Diagram of a tunicate tadpole.

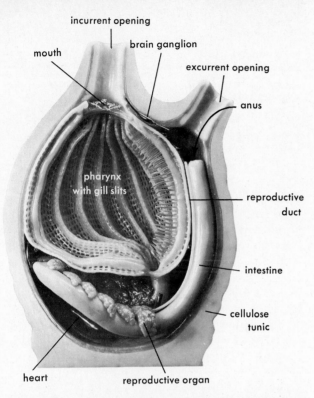

incurrent opening

mouth

brain ganglion

excurrent opening

anus

pharynx
with gill slits

reproductive
duct

intestine

cellulose
tunic

heart

reproductive organ

Fig. 10.32. Cutaway model of an adult tunicate. Food-bearing water is drawn into the pharynx through the incurrent opening. Food passes into the U-shaped alimentary tract, and water emerges through the gill slits and the excurrent opening to the outside. (American Museum of Natural History.)

developed many additional gill slits. Also, the region of the mouth has shifted so that the alimentary tract is roughly U-shaped. A cellulose-containing covering, the *tunic*, has developed around the whole animal, leaving only two openings, the *incurrent* and the *excurrent siphon*. Water and food enter the animal via the incurrent opening. Food is filtered out in the pharynx and is carried over a ciliated groove into the esophagus. Water passes through the gill slits and leaves via the excurrent siphon. This opening also conducts waste products and reproductive cells to the outside.

Ancestral tunicates probably were the first chordates. They "invented" the unique tadpole larva which swims by means of a muscular tail rather than with cilia, as is typical of the larvae of all other animal phyla. Such tadpolelike larval types then probably gave rise to the other chordate subphyla.

Subphylum Cephalochordata. The lancelets, often better known by the group name *amphioxus*, comprise some 30 species of small, marine sand burrowers. These animals are more or less fish-shaped, slender, and compressed laterally (Fig. 10.33). They possess a notochord which persists throughout life and which extends over the whole length of the body. The nerve cord is dorsal and tubular, but there is no brain and a head is not present. The mouth leads into a ciliated pharynx with 60 or more pairs of gill slits. Water passing through these emerges into an *atrium*, an ectodermal chamber which surrounds the pharynx and opens ventrally, anteriorly to the anus.

Amphioxus is a segmented animal. This is shown most obviously by the musculature, which is formed into segmental bundles, or *somites*. The nerves leading to these muscles and the excretory and reproductive organs similarly are arranged on a segmental pattern. Lancelets therefore are clearly and very closely related to vertebrates. They differ from vertebrates principally in the permanence of the notochord and in the absence of a head.

Subphylum Vertebrata. The vast majority of chordates are vertebrates. All other Metazoa are called, contrastingly, "invertebrates." Vertebrates are so named because, in late embryonic stages, a segmented vertebral column develops in addition to or more generally as a replacement of the notochord. The individual vertebrae are made of cartilage or bone. Segmentation

Fig. 10.33. Amphioxus, the lancelet. The many pharyngeal gill slits are very prominent just behind the mouth. Note also the notochord, the very dark rod just above the gill slits, running from front to back. A head is absent. (Carolina Biological Supply Co.)

is a general feature of vertebrate structure, but in many groups the segmental patterns become somewhat obscured in adult stages. Vertebrates possess a well-developed head, with brain, brain case, and paired sense organs. The nerve cord is dorsal and tubular, as in other chordates. Pharyngeal gills are present as well. In most groups an outpouching from the pharynx develops into a lung. Gills and lungs rarely occur at the same time, the gills usually forming first, the lungs thereafter. A distinct adult tail is a virtually unique vertebrate characteristic. The base of the tail is marked ventrally by the anus. Some of the identifying characteristics of the seven living classes are as follows.

Agnatha. These are roughly eel-shaped animals, with smooth, scaleless skin and without paired fins (Fig. 10.34). The anterior end of the body is modified into a funnel-like sucker, in the center of which is the mouth. Jaws are absent. The notochord persists throughout life, and the adult in addition possesses a brain case and segmental vertebral elements made of cartilage. There are seven pairs of gills; lungs do not form. The heart is ventral as in all vertebrates, and as in all fishes it consists of two chambers, one auricle and one ventricle. The sense organs include, apart from lateral eyes, a functional *pineal eye*, located dorsally along the midline of the head. Lampreys comprise freshwater as well as marine species, but even the latter migrate into rivers for spawning.

Chondrichthyes. In this and all subsequent vertebrate classes, the notochord is an embryonic structure only and is replaced completely by a vertebral column. In the chondrichthians, this column and all other skeletal parts consist of cartilage. The class includes sharks, skates, and rays, most of them marine, but some living in fresh water. The skin of these animals is studded with tiny, pointed *denticles*, which in structure and development are quite like the teeth of vertebrates generally. Two pairs of fins are present in addition to several unpaired fins, as are upper and lower jaws, characteristic also of subsequent classes. Breathing is by gills, of which there are five to seven pairs. The cartilage fishes are strongly muscled and most are active, open-water predators. Some are plankton feeders. These include the whale sharks, which sometimes reach lengths of approximately 50 feet and are the largest vertebrates after the true whales.

Osteichthyes. At least half the number of all vertebrate species are bony fishes. As indicated by the name of this class, the adult skeleton is made largely of bone, a feature characteristic also of all four-legged vertebrates. Bony fishes typically have scaly skin, paired fins, and gills on each side of the pharynx covered by a hinged bony plate, the *operculum*. The animals also develop an internal membranous sac, pouched out ventrally from the pharynx. In most species this sac becomes a swim bladder. In the lungfishes, however, the sac functions partly like a lung.

Amphibia. The two main groups of this class are, first, the salamanders and newts, in which a tail is present throughout life, and second, the frogs and toads, which are tailless only as adults. Frogs and toads may be distinguished by their dentition; frogs possess teeth on their upper jaws, toads do not. All amphibia have smooth, moist, glandular skins without scales, and two pairs of legs which are equivalent developmentally and structurally to the paired fins of fishes. Tadpole larvae typically live in fresh water, are fishlike in most respects, and breathe by means of gills and through the skin. The adults of all newts, some salamanders, and some toads are aquatic, and the adults of all others are terrestrial. Virtually all adults have lungs, and the newts and some of the aquatic salamanders in addition retain

Fig. 10.34. Lamprey, lateral view. Note gill slits. (Carolina Biological Supply Co.)

the gills throughout life. The heart of amphibia is three-chambered and consists of two auricles and one ventricle. In most species, fertilization and embryonic development take place in water, regardless of whether the adults are terrestrial or not.

Reptilia. Many people tend to confuse these true land vertebrates with amphibia. But reptiles are easily identified by their dry, scaly skin, by the presence of a fairly well-defined neck, and by their large shelled eggs, which are always laid on land, even when the adults are aquatic. The living representatives of this class are the turtles and tortoises, the snakes and lizards, the alligators and crocodiles, and the tuatara, or *Sphenodon*, a lizardlike evolutionary relic of past ages found today only in New Zealand. The legs of reptiles typically are five-toed and equipped with claws. But in sea turtles they are modified into flippers, and in snakes and some lizards limbs are not present at all. Gills do not mature but develop only partially as nonfunctional structures in the embryo. Breathing is always by lung. This and a four-chambered heart are characteristic of birds and mammals also. Reptiles, birds, and mammals are alike, furthermore, in that fertilization occurs within the body of the female, not in open water.

Aves. In their internal structure, these feathered vertebrates greatly resemble primitive reptiles. Apart from the presence of feathers, birds are characterized by forelimbs which are modified into wings and by the absence of teeth, the mouth armature being a horn-covered beak or bill. Birds maintain a constant body temperature, like mammals. Undoubtedly because of the aerodynamic requirements of flight, birds are more like one another than the members of any other vertebrate class. We may note, however, that many birds have reduced wings and cannot fly. Ostriches, emus, moas, kiwis, and penguins are among the flightless types. Of the 10,000 or so avian species, more than half belong to a single order, the *passerine* or perching birds. These include the songbirds and many other familiar bird types.

Mammalia. The female members of this class possess milk-producing *mammary glands* and nurse their young.

Fig. 10.35. Top, a spiny anteater, an egg-laying mammal of the subclass Prototheria. Bottom, an opossum, a pouched or marsupial mammal of the subclass Metatheria. (Top, American Museum of Natural History; bottom, Carolina Biological Supply Co.)

Three other identifying features are the possession of hair, the transverse division of the body cavity by a diaphragm, and the nonnucleated condition of mature red blood corpuscles. The class comprises some 6,000 species grouped into three subclasses (Fig. 10.35). The subclass *Prototheria* consists of egg-laying types. These are the least progressive mammals, and they still display many of the features of ancestral reptiles from which the class of mammals evolved. Egg-laying mammals today include only the duck-billed platypus and the spiny anteaters. The subclass *Metatheria* comprises the pouched or marsupial mammals. In these, the young are born in a very incompletely developed state and development is completed in an abdominal skin pouch of the female. Opossums and the kangaroos, koala bears, wombats, and other marsupials of Australia belong to this group. The vast majority of mammals is included in the subclass *Eutheria*, the placental mammals. The young of these mammals develop within the body of the female, in a womb or uterus. Among these most familiar of all living creatures, the tiniest are the shrews; the largest are the whales; the most numerous are the rodents; and the brainiest are the primates, which include monkeys, apes, and men.

Review questions

1. What structural and functional features distinguish most Metazoa from most Metaphyta? What are the chief nutritional patterns among animals? How does alimentation influence the general structural and functional organization of animals?

2. How does the requirement of locomotion influence the general architecture of an animal? Contrast the basic design of moving and nonmoving animals.

3. Which phyla are included among the Radiata, and what diagnostic features distinguish these phyla? Describe the characteristics of sponges.

4. Name the classes of coelenterates and describe the life cycles characteristic of each. Distinguish between polyps and medusae. Which phyla are included among acoelomates? Describe the structure of flatworms. Review the life cycles of flukes and tapeworms.

5. Which are the pseudocoelomate phyla and what features characterize the group as a whole? Describe the structure and the life cycle of rotifers. Which are the schizocoelomate phyla?

6. What is the fundamental body plan of mollusks? Describe the internal structure of animals within each of the molluscan classes and show what features distinguish each class from the others.

7. Describe the diagnostic features of annelids. Name the annelid classes and describe the internal structure of polychaetes. How do the other classes differ?

8. Describe the group characteristics and the basic body organization of arthropods. Name the classes and the distinguishing features of each. Show how segmentation is exploited adaptively in (*a*) crustacea, (*b*) insects.

9. Which phyla are included among the enterocoelomates and for what reasons? How do these phyla differ from one another? State the group characteristics of echinoderms and name the various classes. Describe the structure of a starfish.

10. Review the classification of chordates. Contrast the diagnostic features of the three subphyla. Describe the basic structure of the various nonvertebrate chordates. Describe the group characteristics of vertebrates. Name the classes and describe the identifying features of each.

Suggested collateral readings

Griffin, D. R.: The Navigation of Bats, *Sci. Am.*, vol. 183, 1950.

Lyman, C. P., and P. O. Charfield: Hibernation, *Sci. Am.*, vol. 183, 1950.

McLean, F. C.: Bone, *Sci. Am.*, vol. 192, 1955.

Rodbard, S.: Warmbloodedness, *Sci. Monthly*, vol. 77, 1953.

Storer, J. H.: Bird Aerodynamics, *Sci. Am.*, vol. 186, 1952.

part **4**

The Functions of Life: Metabolism

Up to this point, our primary concern has been the "what" of living matter: What are the characteristics of the living world as a whole? What are the structures and functions of the living material, and what kinds of living organisms exist on earth? In the remainder of this book, we shall continue to heed the what, but our primary concern will be the "how": How does the living world come into being and how is it maintained? How are the structures developed and how are the functions carried out? In other words, our preoccupation will be less with the *organizational* and more with the *operational* nature of living material.

The operations of living matter are circumscribed by two words: metabolism and self-perpetuation. In this sequence of chapters, we deal with the first. Metabolism, we recall, may be described roughly as a group of processes which makes the living machinery run, which transforms an otherwise inert system into an active one. Specifically, metabolism includes, first, *nutrition;* second, the production of internal energy, or *respiration*, made possible by some of the nutrients; and third, the *utilization* of raw materials and of energy, always toward chemical activities such as synthesis of new living components, sometimes toward physical activities such as movement.

synthesis reactions, hence energy. Two kinds of autotrophs may be distinguished according to the external energy sources they employ: *chemosynthesizers* and *photosynthesizers*. As noted in Chap. 4, chemosynthesizers are found among bacteria and their external energy sources are various inorganic substances. Far more abundant and far more important generally are the photosynthetic autotrophs. As we already know, they occur abundantly among the Monera and Protista, and the Metaphyta consist entirely of photosynthesizers. Their external energy source for food manufacture is light, and *chlorophyll* is the agent which traps light energy and makes it available internally for food production.

Thus the overall pattern of nutrition in photosynthesizers may be considered to consist of three broad groups of processes:

1. *absorption* of inorganic nutrients from the environment, including CO_2, H_2O, and all other required mineral substances

2. *photosynthesis*, that is, manufacture of organic nutrients out of some of the inorganic ones

3. *transport*, or internal distribution of both inorganic and organic nutrients to all cells of the organism

This chapter is devoted to an examination of these processes, particularly as they occur in tracheophytes.

The inorganic nutrients

ABSORPTION

The raw materials needed by a land plant are obtained from two sources, *air* and *soil*. Air contributes most of the CO_2. As noted in Chap. 9, green cells in leaves are in direct contact with the external air via the stomata, and the interconnected air spaces in the mesophyll permit free circulation of air through a leaf. Carbon dioxide (and also oxygen and water vapor) may therefore be absorbed directly by each leaf cell, right where the gas will eventually be used in photosynthesis.

Soil contributes liquid water and all other mineral nutrients to a plant. Soil water contains dissolved minerals (Chap. 7), and these are present largely in the form of ions. The kinds of mineral ions normally required by plants include, for example, nitrate (NO_3^-), phosphate ($PO_4^=$), chloride (Cl^-), sulfate ($SO_4^=$);

and potassium (K^+), calcium (Ca^{++}), magnesium (Mg^{++}), copper (Cu^{++}), and iron (Fe^{+++}).

Soil nutrients are absorbed by the cells of the root epidermis. Since some 90 per cent of the available root surface is provided by the root hairs, most of the absorption occurs there. As noted earlier, root-hair zones advance continuously as the root grows. Therefore, by the time one region of soil is more or less depleted of raw materials, root-hair zones have already advanced to a new region.

A great deal of water absorption is accomplished through *osmosis*. The cell substance within a root hair normally contains a higher concentration of dissolved particles than soil water. Osmotic pressure therefore moves soil water into the root hair. However, a simple test shows that osmotic force cannot be the only agency responsible for water absorption. If the soil is made to contain a higher concentration of dissolved particles than the root-hair cells (for example, by putting salt into soil), then the plant should lose water to the soil. Yet under such conditions the roots still take up water, though less than before (Fig. 11.1). Clearly, osmotic pull normally contributes some absorptive force, but another agency contributes also. This other agency depends on the *living* condition of the root cell, and it is best described as *active absorptive work* done by the cell. That work is required is known, for water absorption consumes energy and depends on cellular respiration. When the respiratory machinery of the cells is stopped with poison, then biological water absorption is likewise stopped, though purely physical, osmotic absorption still continues. Thus, in ways which actually are understood only poorly as yet, a living root cell actively *pulls* water into itself through the cell surface.

This "living" aspect of absorption is also illustrated clearly in the uptake of soil minerals. If the root-hair membrane were merely passive, like cellophane, then we should expect ions to *diffuse* from higher to lower concentrations; that is, ions should migrate from the more concentrated interior of root cells into the less concentrated soil water, until the concentrations on each side of the membrane were equal. In other words, root cells should lose ions to the soil. This does not happen. On the contrary, ions migrate from the soil *into* the root, *against* the prevail-

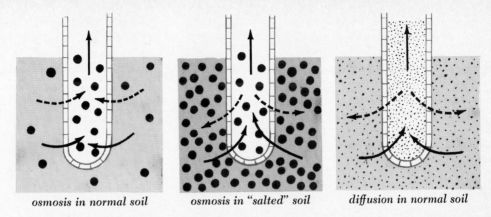

osmosis in normal soil   *osmosis in "salted" soil*   *diffusion in normal soil*

Fig. 11.1. Left, osmosis in roots. Particle concentrations are greater in root cells than in soil; hence more water moves into root cells from soil than in the reverse direction. Middle, the effect of "salting" the soil. Even if the particle concentration in soil is made greater than in the root, water still moves into the root (solid arrows), against the osmotic gradient (broken arrows). This indicates that osmosis is not the only agency in water absorption; active absorption by living root cells is of importance as well. Right, diffusion in roots. Because root cells contain a higher concentration of mineral ions than soil, ions should be expected to diffuse out of roots (broken arrows). Yet ions actually migrate from soil into roots (solid arrows), against the diffusion gradient. This indicates that diffusion cannot be responsible for ion absorption. Active absorption by living root cells is involved instead.

ing diffusion gradient (Fig. 11.1). Here again, energy- and oxygen-consuming work is done by the epidermal cells of the root. Their membranes are selective, moreover. Some ions are passed through readily; others are not. We may conclude that a plant absorbs soil nutrients partly through purely physical processes and partly through active, biological work performed by the root epidermis.

What happens to the water and the minerals absorbed into a root-hair cell? The most immediate effect is that the excess water tends to dilute the substance of the cell. Should we not also expect that cell to swell up? We should indeed, but this does not happen to any appreciable extent, for most of the absorbed water and dissolved materials are removed almost as soon as they enter the cell. The fluid is secreted from the root-hair cell and is absorbed by the cortex cells immediately adjacent to the root epidermis. As a result, water which first has been in the soil and then in the epidermis is now in the outermost layer of the root cortex. *These* cells then tend to swell and their interior tends to become more dilute. However, ex-

cessive swelling is prevented by the cell walls and water is therefore transferred again, into the next inner layer of cortex cells (Fig. 11.2).

In this manner, water and minerals are drawn progressively from cell layer to cell layer, toward the core of the root. Some of these nutritional supplies are re-

Fig. 11.2. The absorption path within a root. Water and dissolved minerals are absorbed by successively deeper layers of cells. In this manner, supplies eventually reach the xylem.

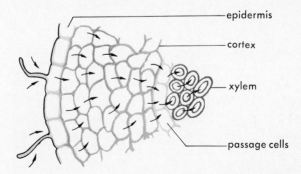

— epidermis

— cortex

— xylem

— passage cells

tained by the cells along the route, but the bulk soon reaches the root endodermis. This tissue, with its *passage cells,* provides a path into the stele of the root. Water and dissolved materials are moved through the endodermis, through the layers of the pericycle, and from there they are pushed into xylem vessels.

"Pushed" is the right word. The water stream from soil to xylem vessel is continuous and uninterrupted and it is not a stream which trickles lazily by its own weight. Rather, the combined osmotic pressure and the combined absorptive force of all root cells are behind the water, and this generates *root pressure.* It is this pressure which drives water forcefully into the xylem tubes at the root core and which also aids in driving sap upward through the xylem vessels (Fig. 11.3).

XYLEM TRANSPORT

In a healthy plant, xylem tubes are never empty of water. Even before a xylem vessel becomes functional, water already fills the interior of the vessel-forming cells. Later, when the living substance of these cells disintegrates, the water remains. As the plant grows in length, each new vessel component joined to the

Fig. 11.3. Xylem tubes contain continuous columns of water. Root pressure adds more water at the bottom, and transpiration removes water at the top through evaporation. Hence a water column in xylem moves upward.

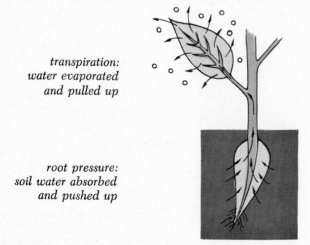

transpiration: water evaporated and pulled up

root pressure: soil water absorbed and pushed up

top of an existing vessel adds a corresponding cylinder of water to the column below. Water thus *grows* up, as the plant grows up. No matter how high the plant, therefore, continuous uninterrupted water columns range from every root-hair membrane, through root cortex, pericycle, and xylem vessels, to every leaf mesophyll membrane.

Upward "transport" consequently becomes a matter of adding water at the bottom of such columns and withdrawing an equivalent amount from the top, minus the fraction which living tissues incorporate into their substance. As we have seen, absorption by the root adds water at the bottom and generates root pressure. This is one force which pushes the water columns up.

But root pressure is not alone responsible for the lifting of water. A second force, and probably a more important one than root pressure, is pull from above. This force is generated by *transpiration,* that is, evaporation of water from the leaves. As water vaporizes from a mesophyll cell, the cell tends to develop a water deficit and so the concentration of cellular particles tends to increase. Osmotic pull therefore draws water in from neighboring cells. These cells now tend to develop a water deficit. Osmotic pull is propagated back in this manner, along cell paths leading to xylem terminals. As in roots, the osmotic pull is accompanied by active cellular absorption. The combined osmotic and absorptive action of leaf cells moves water up through the xylem, in quantities equivalent to the amount evaporated. The effectiveness of this pull from above is familiar to everyone. An isolated leaf or a flower with a stub of stem and a few leaves survives for a considerable time when put into a glass of water; as water transpires from exposed plant tissues, fluid is pulled up from below.

It should be clear that such a mechanism of transport depends on uninterrupted continuity of the water columns. The condition that the transport fluid is water, rather than another medium, greatly facilitates the maintenance of column continuity, for water possesses a high degree of *cohesion.* Individual molecules attract one another rather strongly, and a column of water therefore "hangs together" with appreciable tenacity.

The key point in xylem transport is that the power

source lies in living roots and leaves. The nonliving xylem tubes as such are passive, in the same way that a pipeline between two pumping stations is passive. Conduction through phloem is different in this respect. In this system the power source appears to be spread out all along the transportation route.

PHLOEM TRANSPORT

Whereas xylem transports inorganic nutrients upward, phloem distributes organic nutrients both upward and downward. Downward conduction in phloem has long been known to occur: many roots store carbohydrates, which are photosynthesized only in leaf or stem. The occurrence of upward conduction has come to light through grafting experiments. For example a stem of a tobacco plant grafted to a root of a tomato plant develops normal tobacco leaves, but these are entirely free of nicotine. Conversely, a tomato-plant stem transplanted to a tobacco-plant root produces tomato leaves, but these are full of nicotine. The first graft indicates that only the roots of a tobacco plant synthesize nicotine; the second graft, that the drug is transported upward. And since xylem channels are virtually free of nicotine, upward conduction must occur largely in phloem (Fig. 11.4). We may conclude generally that upward transport in phloem involves organic storage products and materials manufactured from them which travel from roots and stems to the leaves.

We recall the composition of a phloem unit (Chap. 5). A living companion cell is adjacent to and presumably controls the functioning of a sieve tube cell. Such a cell contains cytoplasm but not a nucleus. Transport through phloem units depends largely on *diffusion*. For example, mesophyll cells in a leaf photosynthesize and so they acquire relatively high carbohydrate concentrations. Terminal phloem units in the vicinity do not photosynthesize and their carbohydrate content is therefore lower. Consequently, diffusion tends to equalize the concentrations and the terminal phloem units absorb some of the mesophyll-produced carbohydrate. Their own carbohydrate content increases as a result, relative to that of lower phloem units next in line along the conduction path. These lower sieve-tube cells absorb from units above them, and in this fashion nutrient conduction continues

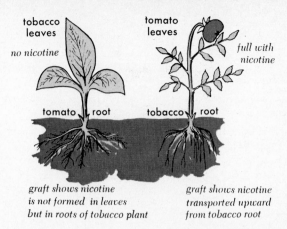

tobacco leaves — no nicotine

tomato leaves — full with nicotine

tomato root

tobacco root

graft shows nicotine is not formed in leaves but in roots of tobacco plant

graft shows nicotine transported upward from tobacco root

Fig. 11.4. If tobacco leaves are grafted onto tomato roots (left), nicotine will be absent from the tobacco leaves. If tomato leaves are grafted onto tobacco roots (right), the tomato leaves will eventually contain nicotine. Experiments of this sort show that only tobacco roots manufacture nicotine and that this substance is transported upward by the phloem.

downward (Fig. 11.5). Cells along the way may retain greater or lesser amounts of the carbohydrate. But the bulk will be carried into the roots, step by step from one section of sieve tube to the next, under the influence of the diffusion gradient pointing from the leaves toward the roots.

Alternatively, organic materials may be carried upward if the concentrations of such materials are high in the roots and lower above. This is the case, for example, in winter and early spring, when leaves are absent and photosynthesis does not take place. Organic nutrients stored in the roots during the preceding summer then travel upward into the food-requiring regions of the stem and the crown.

Phloem conduction, up or down, is slow compared with xylem conduction. In phloem, also, we do not find a distinct flowing sap as in xylem vessels. The transportation medium, namely, sieve-tube cytoplasm, flows and shifts within its cellulose confines only but does not itself flow up or down bodily. Nutrient molecules alone are handed from one unit to the next. Such conduction in phloem is often spoken of as *translocation*.

Xylem conduction to the leaves prepares the way for photosynthesis, and phloem conduction from the

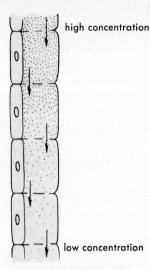

high concentration

low concentration

Fig. 11.5. The role of nutrient concentrations in phloem conduction. If a given nutrient is highly concentrated at one end of a phloem channel and less highly concentrated at the other, as shown, then a diffusion gradient will point from the high to the low concentration. The nutrient thus will be translocated in that direction.

leaves distributes the results of photosynthesis. We now proceed to examine this crucial process of food manufacture.

Photosynthesis

The fundamental importance of the set of reactions in which CO_2 and H_2O are transformed into carbohydrates and oxygen cannot be overestimated. Carbohydrates produced through photosynthesis constitute the basic raw materials which, directly or indirectly, give rise to all organic components of virtually all plants and animals and to virtually all living energy. The only organisms not dependent on photosynthesis are the chemosynthetic bacteria, which together amount to probably less than 0.0001 per cent of all the living matter on earth.

The knowledge that CO_2 and water are among the raw materials and carbohydrates among the end-products makes it tempting to write, as a descriptive "reaction" for photosynthesis,

$$6 H_2O + 6 CO_2 \longrightarrow C_6H_{12}O_6 + 6 O_2$$

This chemical statement, often regarded in earlier days as a correct representation of photosynthesis, is in fact quite incorrect. In actual photosynthesis, CO_2 does *not* react with water. If it did, such a reaction would produce nothing but carbonated water. As already noted earlier, CO_2 reacts only with the *hydrogen* of water, and the oxygen of water becomes a byproduct. Indeed, research in recent years has shown that photosynthesis consists of two series of processes. First, water is decomposed and its hydrogen is removed from the oxygen. Because light and chlorophyll play a major role here, these reactions are collectively called *photolysis*, that is, light-dependent decomposition of water. Subsequently, the hydrogen made available by photolysis is combined with CO_2, resulting in the formation of a carbohydrate. The latter is *not* sugar, as we shall see; but it does consist of C, H, and O atoms, the chemical elements supplied by CO_2 and H_2. This second phase of photosynthesis is light-independent; it is called *CO₂ fixation* (Fig. 11.6).

Both photolysis and CO_2 fixation take place within the chloroplasts of green cells. Into these cytoplasmic organelles must come light and all the raw materials, and from them emerge the finished products and byproducts.

Fig. 11.6. The general pattern of the two phases of photosynthesis: photolysis and CO₂ fixation. Both phases take place within the grana of chloroplasts.

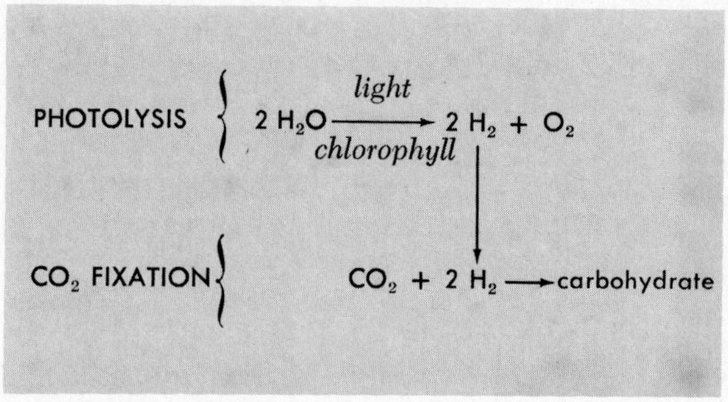

PHOTOLYSIS $\left\{ \begin{array}{c} \end{array} \right.$ $2 H_2O \xrightarrow[chlorophyll]{light} 2 H_2 + O_2$

CO₂ FIXATION $\left\{ \begin{array}{c} \end{array} \right.$ $CO_2 + 2 H_2 \longrightarrow$ carbohydrate

CHLOROPLASTS AND CHLOROPHYLL

A chloroplast is one of three kinds of *plastids* in plants (see Chap. 5). One kind, called *leucoplasts*, does not contain any pigments. Leucoplasts store starch and they are found in roots and in the colorless tissues of stems and leaves. A second type of plastid, known as *chromoplasts*, contains so-called *carotenoid* pigments. These colored substances are of two kinds: the *carotenes*, which vary in color from cream white to turnip yellow, carrot orange, and tomato red; and the *xanthophylls*, which produce the bright yellows and browns of plants. In different plant species, chromoplasts variously occur in roots, stems, leaves, flowers, and fruits. Plastids containing both carotenoids and chlorophyll are called *chloroplasts*. Only they are green, and only they function in photosynthesis.

The electron microscope shows that a chloroplast is composed of numerous *grana* (Fig. 11.7). These

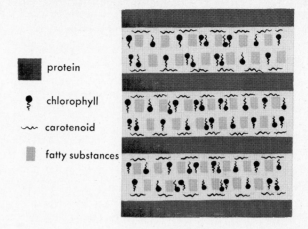

protein

chlorophyll

carotenoid

fatty substances

Fig. 11.8. Diagram of the internal structure of a single granum. Note the layered arrangement of the components.

small granular bodies are the functional units in photosynthesis and the real "factories" for food production. Each granum consists of a series of protein layers, arranged like coins in a stack. Sandwiched in between the layers are molecules of lipids, chlorophyll, carotenoids, and other compounds (Fig. 11.8). The fairly orderly arrangement of these materials in the diagram may depict actual conditions; the compounds are believed to be positioned with a regularity approaching that of a crystal.

The green of chlorophyll largely hides the red-yellow colors of the carotenoids present. Different plant types contain different proportions of these pigment groups, hence the various lighter and deeper shades of green in a landscape. In the fall, when the chlorophyll of flowering plants disintegrates, the more stable carotenoid pigments become unmasked. These are mainly responsible for the brilliant autumn colors of plants. Many leaves at that season also display the colors of *anthocyanin* pigments, substances which are dissolved in the cytoplasm of cells and which produce the deep reds, purples, and blues of various plant parts (including, for example, beet roots and the petals of numerous flowers).

A green cell may possess from a few up to about 80 chloroplasts. In a mature tree, all the chloroplasts together may provide a surface area for light absorp-

Fig. 11.7. Electron micrograph of a single chloroplast, showing the grana. (Courtesy of R. W. G. Wyckoff, "Electron Microscopy," Interscience Publishers, Inc., New York, 1949.)

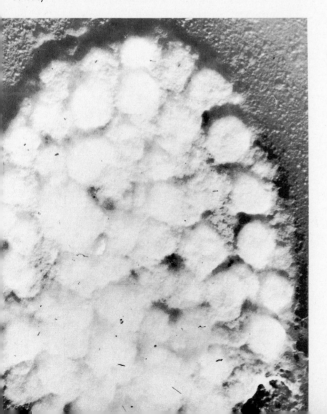

tion totaling some 150 square miles. Chloroplasts reproduce within cells. Thus the chloroplast population of a cell may keep pace with the multiplication of the cell itself.

Chlorophyll itself exists in several chemical varieties, and we already know that photosynthetic Protista and Metaphyta typically possess chlorophyll *a* plus one other variety (Chap. 8). Chlorophyll *a* plays the main role; this variety is particularly required in photosynthesis. Other varieties serve auxiliary functions. A molecule of chlorophyll consists of a "head" and a "tail" (Fig. 11.9). The head contains four carbon-nitrogen rings (known as *pyrrols*), which are joined in turn to form a larger ring (called a *tetrapyrrol* ring). At the center of this ring is a single atom of magnesium. The tail is a chain of linked carbons, attached to one of the pyrrols of the head.

PHOTOLYSIS

What happens when light enters a chloroplast and strikes a chlorophyll molecule? The important event is that the molecule *absorbs* a portion of the light energy. As is well known, visible sunlight consists of a

Fig. 11.9. The chemical structure of a molecule of chlorophyll.

"head"

"tail"

(C₂₀H₃₉)

chlorophyll *a*
(C₅₅H₇₂O₅N₄Mg)

series of light waves, each producing a characteristic "rainbow" color—red, orange, yellow, green, blue, or violet. Each of these light waves contains energy; red waves have the least energy, violet waves the most. When a mixture of these waves, as in sunlight, falls on a chlorophyll molecule, the molecule absorbs much of the red, orange, and yellow waves and much of the blue and violet waves. It is so constructed that it does *not* absorb the green waves but lets these go right on without change. That is why, when we look at a leaf illuminated by sunlight, it appears green to us. The chlorophyll in the leaf has absorbed all but the green waves in sunlight.

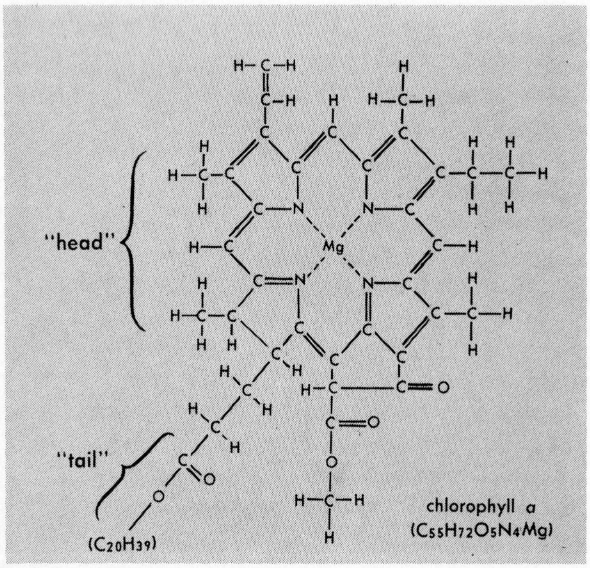

Because it absorbs certain light waves, chlorophyll also absorbs a certain amount of energy; the molecule contains more energy after illumination than before. Research in recent years has shown that the effect of this extra energy is to *ionize* the chlorophyll molecule. An electron (e^-) is dislodged out of the molecule, and in a sense this electron carries most of the extra energy; we may regard it as a "high-energy" electron. Since the electron is negatively charged, the chlorophyll molecule which loses it becomes positively charged, that is, it becomes an ion. For convenience of symbolization in this section, we may assume that all reactions occur twice. Thus if two chlorophyll molecules become ionized, we may write:

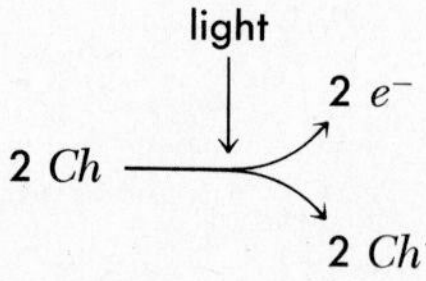

$$2\ Ch \xrightarrow{\text{light}} \begin{array}{l} 2\ e^- \\ 2\ Ch^+ \end{array}$$

We may say, therefore, that the principal photosynthetic function of chlorophyll is to trap light energy and to make it available in the form of electron energy.

Two series of events occur next: the high-energy electrons are transferred to another chemical; and the ionized chlorophylls regain electrons in compensation for the ones lost. Both events ultimately involve water, one of the key participants in photosynthesis. We know that water contains H and OH, and we may now add that H in turn consists of two parts: a single proton which forms a positively charged atomic nucleus (H^+), and a single electron (e^-) which orbits around the nucleus. A whole water molecule may thus be considered to consist of three parts, namely, H^+, e^-, and OH; and two water molecules may be symbolized as:

$$2\ H_2O \rightleftarrows \begin{array}{l} 2\ [H^+] \\ 2\ [OH] \\ 2\ [e^-] \end{array}$$

Each of these three parts of water plays a role in photosynthesis. First, the $2\ [H^+]$ do not remain "loose" in a chloroplast but become attached to a particular chemical which serves as a *hydrogen acceptor*. This acceptor is called *triphosphopyridine nucleotide*, or *TPN* for short. All cells possess it; it is a normal constituent of living matter. One molecule of TPN combines with $2\ [H^+]$, and a $TPN \cdot [H^+]_2$ complex results. This complex in turn now combines with the two high-energy electrons dislodged from chlorophyll originally. The electrons, being negatively charged, neutralize the positive charges on the complex, and the final result therefore is $TPN \cdot [H_2]$:

$$\begin{array}{l} \qquad\qquad TPN \\ (\text{water}) \dashrightarrow 2\ [H^+] \longrightarrow TPN \cdot [H^+]_2 \\ (\text{Ch}) \dashrightarrow 2\ [e^-] \longrightarrow\qquad TPN \cdot [H_2] \end{array}$$

Inasmuch as $TPN \cdot [H_2]$ now incorporates the high-energy electrons from chlorophyll, it contains within it the original energy of light. $TPN \cdot [H_2]$ *is the hydrogen source for the later manufacture of carbohydrates.*

The above accounts for one of the three components of water. The second component, $2\ [OH]$, is the source of photosynthetic byproducts; the $2\ [OH]$ eventually appear in the form of one molecule of water and one atom of free oxygen:

$$2\ [OH] \longrightarrow H_2O + O$$

The water molecule becomes part of the liquid content of the cell and the oxygen may escape as a gas, in the form of oxygen molecules, O_2. This is the source of the free oxygen which has long been known to be liberated in photosynthesis.

The third component of water, $2\ [e^-]$, becomes attached to chemicals which serve as *electron acceptors*. These chemicals are known as the *cytochrome system*. All are variants of the compound *cytochrome*, present in all cells as a normal constituent of living matter. Like chlorophyll, cytochrome has a tetrapyrrol structure but instead of magnesium an atom of iron is in the center of the tetrapyrrol ring. The iron gives cytochrome a red color. When the cytochrome system accepts $2\ [e^-]$ from water, a complex is formed which we may symbolize as:

$$\begin{array}{l} 2\ [e^-] \\ \qquad\qquad\qquad \longrightarrow \text{cytochromes} \cdot 2\ [e^-] \\ \text{cytochromes} \end{array}$$

This complex is the source from which ionized chlorophyll regains electrons to compensate for the ones it lost. We may diagram this electron transfer as:

$$\begin{array}{l} \text{cytochromes} \cdot 2\ [e^-] \longrightarrow \text{cytochromes} \\ \qquad\qquad\qquad 2\ [e^-] \\ 2\ \text{Ch}^+ \longrightarrow 2\ \text{Ch} \end{array}$$

Chlorophyll so becomes electrically neutral again and may now be ionized once more by light.

We may note here in passing that the electrons which are transferred from the cytochromes to chlorophyll carry a certain amount of energy. This energy is removed during the transfer and is used in the formation of ATP molecules. We recall from Chap. 5 that ATP is an important energy carrier in cells and that it is created when ADP and a phosphate group are joined with the aid of energy. The electrons from the cytochromes actually provide such energy, and two molecules of ATP can be formed for every $2\ [e^-]$ transferred to chlorophyll. Therefore, after their energy has contributed to ATP formation, the electrons which eventually combine with ionized chlorophyll are comparatively energy-poor; we may consider them to be "low-energy" electrons.

The whole sequence of reactions is summarized in Fig. 11.10. Note that, for every high-energy electron transmitted *from* chlorophyll to $TPN \cdot [H_2]$, a low-energy electron is returned *to* chlorophyll from water. The energy input via light appears in the form of $TPN \cdot [H_2]$ and in a sense also in the form of ATP, as just indicated above. The net input of materials into the whole reaction sequence is (apart from ADP), one molecule of TPN and two molecules of water; and the net output (apart from ATP) is $TPN \cdot [H_2]$, one molecule of water, and one atom of free oxygen.

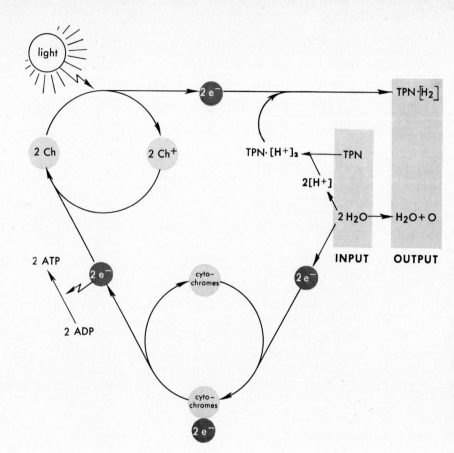

Fig. 11.10.   The pattern of electron transfer in photolysis.

Hence the entire process may also be summarized by the following balanced input-output statement:

$$2\ H_2O\ +\ TPN\ \xrightarrow[+\ chlorophyll]{+\ light}\ TPN\cdot[H_2]\ +\ O\ +\ H_2O$$

or, reduced to the arithmetical minimum,

$$H_2O\ +\ TPN\ \xrightarrow[+\ chlorophyll]{+\ light}\ TPN\cdot[H_2]\ +\ O$$

This in effect is an abbreviated statement of photolysis. Water is supplied as raw material and, in conjunction with the action of light, chlorophyll, and TPN, is transformed into H_2 and free O.

The next phase of photosynthesis is *CO_2 fixation,* the production of carbohydrate out of CO_2 and the H_2 portion of $TPN\cdot[H_2]$.

CO_2 FIXATION

The combining of CO_2 and H_2 is not a simple, single reaction. Rather, CO_2 fixation has been shown to occur through a *cycle* of many reactions. Such a cycle operates somewhat like an endless belt of an assembly line in a factory. As such a belt moves along, a steady stream of raw materials is funneled to it at one point and these materials are processed by various workers or machines along the way. A stream of finished products then emerges at another point, and the empty portions of the belt return to the starting point, where they pick up new batches of raw materials. Many vital metabolic transformations, in plants as well as animals, are known to occur through such cyclical sequences.

The particular cycle of CO_2 fixation may be generalized as in Fig. 11.11. Note here that *A*, *B*, and *C* in the diagram are specific molecules known to be present in chloroplasts. These molecules may be regarded as the "endless belt." In the cycle segment *AB*, which consists of many reactions, CO_2 enters as a raw material. In the segment *BC*, which again consists of many reactions, H_2 obtained from $TPN \cdot [H_2]$ enters as a second raw material. And the segment *CA*, similarly including many reactions, yields the final carbohydrate product and it also "regenerates" the starting condition.

It can be shown that this CO_2-fixing cycle must "go around" three times before one molecule of finished carbohydrate is obtained. In other words, three CO_2 molecules must enter the cycle, one molecule in each turn. Each turn also requires two molecules of $TPN \cdot [H_2]$, hence $6\ TPN \cdot [H_2]$ are needed in three turns. This means that $6\ H_2O$ must have gone through photolysis earlier (which will have yielded 6 O, or $3\ O_2$, as byproduct). When $6\ TPN \cdot [H_2]$ participate in the CO_2-fixing cycle, only the $6\ H_2$ are retained in the reactions; after having "unloaded" their hydrogen, the 6 TPN leave as free molecules, ready to be used again in later photolysis. The net yield of three turns of the cycle then becomes one molecule of finished carbohydrate and three molecules of water, formed as byproduct. These quantitative aspects of the cycle are summarized in Fig. 11.12.

Note that water is both a raw material and a

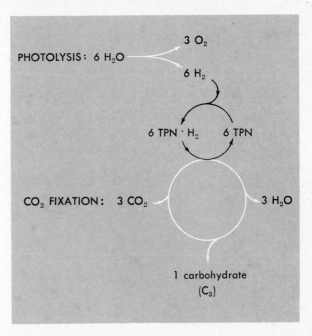

Fig. 11.12. The unit process in photosynthesis. An input of $6\ H_2O$ and $3\ CO_2$ yields, through photolysis and CO_2 fixation, an output of $3\ O_2$, $3\ H_2O$ and one molecule of carbohydrate. The latter, in its C_3 skeleton, joins the three single carbons put in as CO_2.

byproduct: six molecules are used up in photolysis, but three molecules reappear later in CO_2 fixation. Note also that the one resulting carbohydrate molecule is *organic* and that it contains three linked carbon atoms: the three *single* carbon atoms which enter the cycle in the form of inorganic CO_2 emerge as three *linked* carbon atoms in the form of organic carbohydrate. The whole function of photosynthesis is to produce this three-carbon molecule with linked carbons. What is this endproduct and what happens to it?

THE ENDPRODUCT

The name of the carbohydrate product of photosynthesis is *phosphoglyceraldehyde*. It may be called *PGAL* for short, and its atomic formula is $C_3H_5O_3\text{-}\textcircled{P}$, where -$\textcircled{P}$ is a *phosphate* group. In this C_3 compound, the three carbon atoms are linked into a chain. PGAL is

Fig. 11.11. The general pattern of the CO_2-fixing cycle. In segment *AB*, CO_2 enters as raw material, and in segment *BC*, hydrogen enters as raw material. Segment *CA* yields the carbohydrate endproduct and regenerates the starting point *A*.

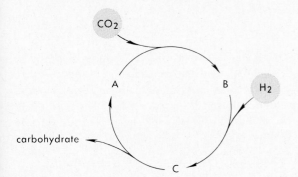

a *food.* A plant nourished artificially with prefabricated PGAL may survive, without photosynthesis and without any other organic supplies.

As PGAL forms in the grana it does not accumulate to any great extent, for it rapidly undergoes one of three main fates: it may be used right away as a *nutrient* in the cell which produced it; it may be "packaged" for *export* to other cells; or it may be packaged for *storage.*

Phosphoglyceraldehyde is usable immediately as a respiratory fuel. It may happen, therefore, that some of the PGAL just manufactured is burned at once to provide the energy for more CO_2 fixation. PGAL is also usable directly as a building material, and it may contribute to the construction of any of the innumerable components of a plant cell. For example, PGAL just produced could be used to build anew, or to repair, some of the chemical machinery required for PGAL production itself.

But a green cell generally manufactures much more PGAL than it requires for its own maintenance. The bulk of the photosynthetic product becomes available for export through the phloem, to root cells, stem cells, and nonphotosynthesizing cells in general. However, PGAL is not exported as such. It is probably too reactive a material. In transit from leaf to root, for example, it would react with other substances long before it could reach its destination. A less reactive, "packaged" form of PGAL would clearly be more advantageous. The green cell actually does package PGAL, by converting it to *glucose.*

In this conversion, two molecules of PGAL are combined into one molecule of glucose. This occurs through a lengthy series of reactions in which the two PGAL molecules are joined, their phosphate groups are removed, and hydrogen atoms are substitued for them. The reaction sequence is of considerable importance in respiratory metabolism as well, and we shall deal with it again in that context. Here a general summary will suffice:

$$2\ C_3H_5O_3\text{-}\textcircled{P} \xrightarrow[+2\ H]{-2\ \textcircled{P}} C_6H_{12}O_6$$
$$\textit{PGAL} \qquad\qquad\qquad \textit{glucose}$$

We may note generally, for animals as well as plants, that if carbohydrates are to be *transported* from cell to cell or from tissue to tissue, the vehicle is primarily *glucose.* This sugar is less reactive than PGAL, hence is not so likely to be altered chemically during transit. Since conversion to glucose and export to other cells is the fate of much of the photosynthesized carbohydrate, glucose is often, though not quite correctly, regarded as the primary endproduct of photosynthesis. Clearly, the green cells of a plant must in daytime manufacture enough PGAL for themselves and must export enough glucose to all other cells to suffice for a 24-hour period.

Actually, green cells normally produce enough PGAL to serve not only for current uses in all plant cells, but also to allow some of it to be stored. Storage occurs largely in roots and stem, but small amounts are generally stored in leaves as well. Like carbohydrate transport, carbohydrate storage does not involve PGAL as such. In any storage problem, two considerations are paramount: first, the stored material should take up as little space as possible, and, second, it should be "out of circulation," relatively unavailable for participation in persisting activities. Since PGAL reacts readily with cellular components in its vicinity, it would not remain out of circulation for long. Even glucose, though less reactive, would enter metabolic processes fairly rapidly. Moreover, both these carbohydrates take up considerable molecular space.

Plants have developed ways to "condense" PGAL molecules into more compact, sufficiently unreactive packets. This may take the form of *dehydration synthesis,* that is, the joining together of two or more molecules accompanied by a simultaneous removal of water. For example, the green cell may first produce glucose from PGAL as above. Two glucose molecules may then be joined, and one water molecule is removed at the same time:

$$C_6H_{12}O_6 + C_6H_{12}O_6 \longrightarrow C_{12}H_{22}O_{11} + H_2O$$

The resulting 12-carbon carbohydrate is *maltose,* or malt sugar, a disaccharide (Chap. 5). Maltose may now be stored as such, or pairs of maltose molecules may be combined and condensed further until up to several hundred glucose units have been joined into single large molecules such as *starch.* For example.

$$500\ C_6H_{12}O_6 \longrightarrow (C_6H_{10}O_5) \times 500 + 500\ H_2O$$

This starch molecule is smaller by 500 water molecules

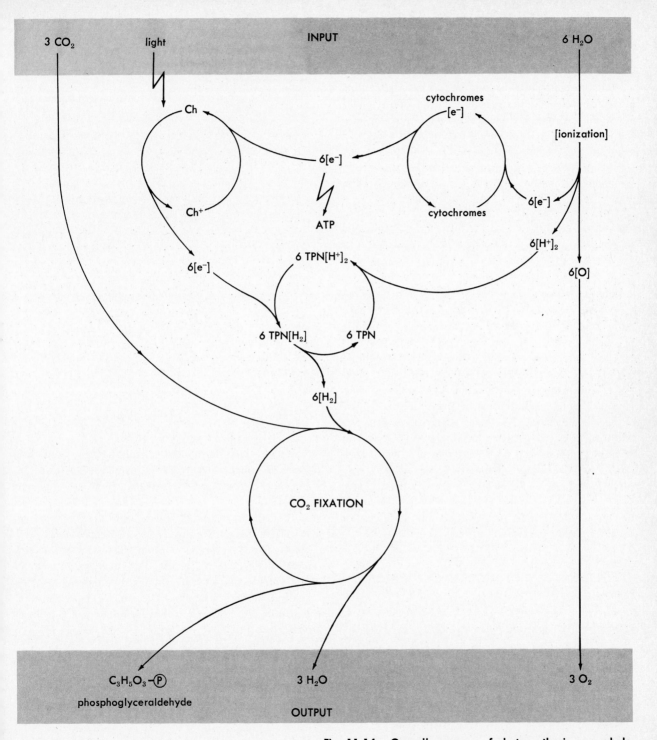

Fig. 11.14.   **Overall summary of photosynthesis as a whole.**

than 500 individual glucose molecules, and it is very much less reactive. It is therefore eminently suitable as a storage form of carbohydrates, and it is actually very common among plants.

Maltose and starch are not the only storage forms of the photosynthetic product. Some plants build PGAL into storage fats (e.g., olive oil, castor oil, peanut oil). Others make a variety of storage sugars. For example, PGAL may be converted partly into glucose, partly into *fructose*. Glucose and fructose may then be combined pairwise into *sucrose*, a disaccharide:

$$C_6H_{12}O_6 + C_6H_{12}O_6 \longrightarrow C_{12}H_{22}O_{11} + H_2O$$
   glucose   *fructose*   *sucrose*

Sugar cane and sugar beets, as well as many kinds of fruits, owe their sweetness to stored fructose and sucrose.

Storage syntheses of this sort occur both in green and in nongreen cells. In the latter, imported glucose is the starting material and nonpigmented leucoplasts often are the sites of storage, as noted earlier in this chapter. Whenever a cell must draw on its stored reserves, the exact reverse of storage synthesis takes place. For example, starch may be converted into glucose by chemical addition of water.

The various possible fates of the photosynthetic endproduct are indicated in Fig. 11.13 and the pattern of photosynthesis as a whole is outlined in Fig. 11.14. Since two PGAL molecules are required for the manufacture of one glucose molecule, the CO_2-fixing cycle must go around six times before one glucose molecule can be obtained. The requirements and yields under such conditions then are:

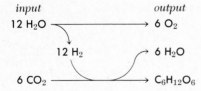

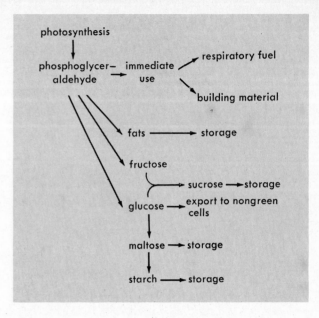

Fig. 11.13. The possible fates of PGAL.

or

$$12\ H_2O + 6\ CO_2 \longrightarrow 6\ H_2O + 6\ O_2 + C_6H_{12}O_6$$

Note here that input and output balance, and that twice as much water must be supplied as is used up. And note again that CO_2 actually reacts with H_2, not with H_2O.

Inorganic nutrients, plus foods in the form of PGAL or its derivatives, now are available to each plant cell. Nutrition is completed at this point and it becomes the task of the individual plant cell to utilize these nutrients in cellular metabolism, namely, respiration and synthesis. The animal equivalent of nutrition in plants will be examined in the next chapter.

Review questions

1. Describe the mechanism of xylem conduction. What kinds of nutrients are transported in xylem and in which direction?

2. What is (*a*) root pressure, (*b*) transpiration? How are these forces generated? What roles do they play in xylem conduction? What is the importance of cohesion of water in xylem conduction?

3. What forces bring about phloem conduction? What kinds of nutrients are carried in phloem and in which direction? Describe in detail the processes which would bring about the upward translocation of a given nutrient.

4. What is the general chemical structure of chlorophyll? What are plastids and what kinds are there? What is the internal architecture of chloroplasts?

5. State the general chemical nature and function of photosynthesis as a whole. Review the sources of the carbon, the hydrogen, and the oxygen atoms which compose photosynthesized carbohydrates.

6. What are the functions of light and chlorophyll in photosynthesis? What are the general events in photolysis and CO_2 fixation?

7. Review the detailed sequence of events in photolysis. How is light energy trapped by chlorophyll and transferred into chemical processes? How is photolytically produced hydrogen transferred into CO_2-fixing reactions? What are the net input and the net output of photolysis?

8. Review the general pattern of CO_2 fixation. What are the major steps? What roles do phosphorylated carbohydrates play?

9. What are the starting materials and the endproducts of each of the three main phases of the CO_2-fixing cycle? What are the net input and output of CO_2 fixation as a whole?

10. What is the principal net endproduct of photosynthesis as a whole? Review the possible fates of this endproduct. What are the main transportation and storage forms of carbohydrates in plants and how is the photosynthetic endproduct converted into these?

Suggested collateral readings

Arnon, D. I.: The Role of Light in Photosynthesis, *Sci. Am.*, vol. 203, 1960.

Bassham, J. A.: The Path of Carbon in Photosynthesis, *Sci. Am.*, vol. 206, 1962.

Evans, R. M.: Seeing Light and Color, *Sci. Am.*, vol. 181, 1949.

Frank, S.: Carotenoids, *Sci. Am.*, vol. 194, 1956.

Greulach, V. A.: The Rise of Water in Plants, *Sci. Am.*, vol. 187, 1952.

Thimann, K. B.: Autumn Colors, *Sci. Am.*, vol. 183, 1950.

ANIMAL NUTRITION

12

Being a heterotroph, an animal requires inorganic as well as prefabricated organic nutrients from its environment. We shall be particularly concerned in this chapter with complexly structured holotrophic animals, in which nutrient procurement is accomplished by *alimentation,* and nutrient transport by *circulatory systems.* As shown in Chap. 10, alimentation in most cases takes place in a tubular alimentary tract which contains a mouth for ingestion, an intestine and often also other structures for digestion, and an anus for egestion. Usable nutrients obtained by digestion are absorbed through the wall of the intestine into the circulatory system. Nutrient transport in this system may occur indirectly via a *liver,* as in vertebrates and some other metazoan groups; or, where a liver is absent, transport may be direct from intestine to other tissues. These various processes are controlled and coordinated by nerves, by muscles, and in vertebrates also by hormones.

The nutrients

We have found in the preceding chapter that a plant cell may survive if it is given water and minerals and if it is supplied with, or is allowed to photosynthesize, organic carbon.

From these three categories of nutrients, a plant cell is able to construct all the other components of its substance. But if an animal cell is given only these three types of nutrients, it soon dies; for it requires four additional types of nutrients which, unlike the plant cell, it cannot manufacture on its own.

First, water, minerals, and photosynthesized organic carbon do not provide usable organic nitrogen required for the construction of proteins and nucleic acids, for example. Organic nitrogen may be in the form of amino groups, —NH_2, and plants are able to make —NH_2 out of mineral nitrates (Chap. 7). But even though nitrates are available to them, animals cannot convert these ions into —NH_2. Their cells therefore must be supplied with prefabricated —NH_2 or other forms of usable organic nitrogen. Plants or other animals which have eaten plants must be the source of supply.

Second, plants can convert phosphoglyceraldehyde (PGAL) or glucose or other forms of organic carbon into all the vitamins they require. Animals cannot do likewise. Most animals do manufacture at least some of the vitamins, although in many cases only in inadequate quantities. Specific abilities here vary with the species, but no species is as self-sufficient in this regard as a green plant. Missing vitamins consequently must be supplied in prefabricated form and plants are again the ultimate source of supply.

Third, unlike plants, animals are unable to convert organic carbon into all two dozen or so kinds of amino acids needed for protein manufacture. Depending on the species, eight or ten kinds, so-called "essential" amino acids, must be supplied in prefabricated form, and plants are the ultimate suppliers here as well.

Fourth, again unlike plants, many animals are unable to convert organic carbon into all necessary kinds of fatty acids. Accordingly, various "essential" fatty acids must be obtained ready-made from plants.

The minimum nutrient supplies to an animal cell must therefore include at least seven types of materials: *water, minerals, organic carbon, organic nitrogen, vitamins, essential amino acids,* and *essential fatty acids.* Evidently, animals cannot survive without plants, which provide five of these seven items (Fig. 12.1).

If an animal could obtain all the nutrients it requires in the form of pure, immediately usable ions and molecules, it would not need an alimentary system. It could then simply acquire such nutrients from the environment by direct absorption through its cell surfaces. This is actually the nutritional pattern in many saprotrophic and symbiotic heterotrophs. But, apart from water and minerals dissolved in water, directly usable nutrients in ionic and molecular form are largely unavailable to free-living holotrophic animals. What a holotroph requires is plant or animal matter in *bulk,* living or dead. And it is the principal function of an alimentary system, first, to provide such bulk nutrients through *ingestion,* and second, to separate the bulk nutrients into individual ions and molecules directly usable by cells.

This second function is accomplished through *digestion. Mechanical digestion* first subdivides ingested materials into fine particles suspended in water, and *chemical digestion* then reduces these particles to molecular dimensions. In the process, usable ions and molecules become separated out and more complex molecules are broken up into smaller, usable ones. In this chemical dissolution of bulk foods, *digestive en-*

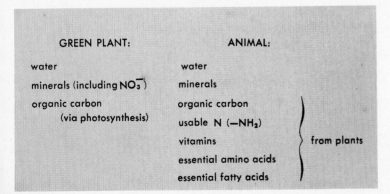

GREEN PLANT: ANIMAL:

water   water

minerals (including NO_3^-)   minerals

organic carbon   organic carbon
   (via photosynthesis)   usable N (—NH_2)

                               vitamins   } from plants

                               essential amino acids

                               essential fatty acids

Fig. 12.1.   A comparison of minimum nutrient requirements of plants and animals.

zymes secreted by *digestive glands* play important roles.

Digestion produces a food solution in which three groups of substances may be found. First, it includes nutrients which animal cells require but cannot manufacture on their own. These comprise water, minerals, and the five categories of plant-derived substances listed above. Second, it includes nutrients which *can* be manufactured by animal cells but, since eaten food generally supplies them, need not be manufactured. For example, animal cells may manufacture various carbohydrates and fats from organic carbon, but they may not need to do so if carbohydrates and fats are included in eaten food. And third, the food solution usually contains indigestible or otherwise unusable materials. Plant cellulose, for example, is a common indigestible component of bulk foods. Substances in this last category are eliminated or *egested* (Fig. 12.2).

Ingestion and digestion

INGESTION: HUNGER

What prompts us to eat *what* we eat? What makes us decide *how much* to eat? As yet, neither question can be answered fully. The first focuses attention on the nature and control of *appetite* and is much more difficult to answer than the second, which raises the problem of the nature and control of *hunger*.

The brain unquestionably plays an important role in appetite control, just as, in mammals, this organ is now known to control the *amount* of food eaten. According to an early popular hypothesis, the stomach was believed to regulate the quantities of food consumed. Muscular contractions of an empty stomach were thought to give rise to sensations of hunger, and a hungry animal was assumed to eat until its stomach was filled. Such filling then was believed to stop the hunger pangs, hence also food intake. But this hypothesis, still widely quoted among nonbiologists, turned out to be untenable long ago; even after surgical removal of the entire stomach, hunger sensations nevertheless continue to come and go as before. Moreover, a "stomach hypothesis" of hunger control does not account for chronic overeating or undereating.

A better explanation has emerged from experiments which have revealed the existence of special eating-control centers in the mammalian brain. In a brain region known as the *hypothalamus* (Chap. 19), two such centers have been identified. One is a *hunger center*. When it is stimulated, it sends out nerve impulses to various parts of the body, which cause the animal to eat. The other is a *satiety center* which, when stimulated, makes the animal refuse food. In test rats, tiny electrodes have been used to stimulate one or the other of these centers continuously. The result of such tests has been that the treated animals either overeat and become extremely obese or undereat and starve amidst a plentiful food supply. Evidently, the amount of food a mammal normally eats is determined by the commands the hunger and satiety centers send to the body.

But how do these centers decide whether to send a command "eat" or a command "do not eat"? Experiments have shown that *blood glucose* is the critical agent which stimulates one or the other of the eating-control centers. As we shall soon see, glucose circulating in the blood is a very sensitive indicator of the hour-by-hour nutritional state of the body. Shortly after a meal, the glucose concentration in the blood tends to rise. Long after a meal, blood-glucose levels tend to fall. If blood reaching the brain contains too much glucose, then the satiety center probably becomes selectively sensitive to this high glucose level and issues the command "do not eat." Conversely, low glucose levels probably stimulate the hunger center selectively, resulting in the command "eat" (Fig. 12.3).

It should be clear that any condition which directly or indirectly influences glucose delivery to the brain, or affects the operation of the brain centers as such, is bound to affect food intake. Dozens of such conditions may actually do so. Proper glucose delivery depends, for example, on normal digestive processes, normal liver function, normal blood circulation, and normal hormone balances. As we shall see, all of these factors affect glucose metabolism profoundly. If, through disturbances in any of these functions, the brain receives consistently false information about the actual glucose supplies in the body, then consistent overeating or undereating may result.

Moreover, the brain centers are themselves subject to faulty operation. And they are influenced by a large variety of psychological factors, by reflexes, and

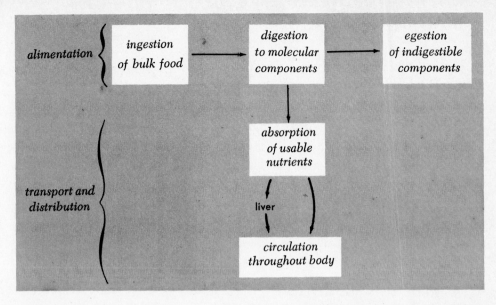

Fig. 12.2. The general pattern of animal nutrition.

by habits of long standing. They are also influenced by inherited genetic constitution, which in the final analysis governs the detailed operation of the body in all its aspects. Clearly, if the brain centers receive correct information but interpret it incorrectly, or interpret correctly but send out faulty commands, then abnormal food intake may again be the result.

We note that whether or not to eat, a seemingly simple decision, actually is determined by a multitude of interdependent, interacting internal processes. It is therefore not surprising that, as is well known, practically *any* disturbance of *any* body function has an effect on food intake.

Granting that desired kinds and appropriate amounts of food are being ingested, what happens to such food in its passage through the alimentary canal?

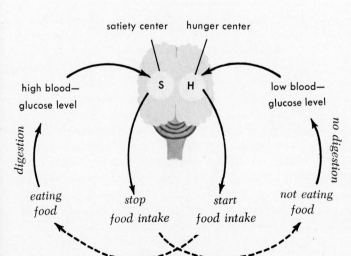

Fig. 12.3. The control of food intake. Desire or lack of desire for food is governed by the satiety (S) and hunger (H) centers of the brain, which in turn respond differentially to the glucose concentration in blood.

DIGESTION: ENZYMES

Digestion in different parts of the alimentary tract is achieved either by *mechanical* means or by *chemical* means or by both. Mechanical digestion, carried out mainly by teeth, tongue, and the muscular grinding action of the stomach, achieves a progressive physical breakdown of bulk food. In parallel with this, chemical digestion occurs.

No matter where they occur or what foods are involved, all instances of chemical digestion are reactions of the same common type: *enzymatic hydrolysis.* "Enzymatic" implies that the reaction is accelerated by an enzyme, and "hydrolysis," that the reaction is one of dissolution or decomposition, *water* being the dissolving agent. A generalized digestive reaction may be written

$$\text{food} + H_2O \xrightarrow{\textit{enzyme}} \text{food components}$$

In most animals, digestive enzymes are *extracellular* enzymes; i.e., they are produced within cells but they are secreted and function outside cells. This puts them into a special category, for virtually all other enzymes in an organism are intracellular and function within cells. Moreover, digestive enzymes are relatively unusual also in that many of them may act on entire categories of chemicals. For example, digestive *lipase*

promotes the decomposition of fat into fatty acids and glycerin:

$$\text{fat} + H_2O \xrightarrow{\textit{lipase}} \text{fatty acids} + \text{glycerin}$$

Here the lipase may be effective with any kind of fat, regardless of which specific types of fatty acids a fat is composed of. Analogously, certain protein- and carbohydrate-digesting enzymes decompose many *different* kinds of proteins and carbohydrates, respectively. By contrast, most other, intracellular enzymes are highly specific and each is effective only in reactions involving one particular type of molecule.

Note, finally, that digestive breakdown of a food molecule often is the exact reverse of the synthesis of that molecule. For example, the digestion of fat yields fatty acids and glycerin; the synthesis of fat requires the joining of fatty acids and glycerin. In general,

$$X + H_2O \underset{\substack{\textit{(enzymatic dehydration)} \\ synthesis}}{\overset{\substack{decomposition \\ \textit{(enzymatic hydrolysis)}}}{\rightleftharpoons}} \text{parts of X}$$

The same enzyme promotes the reaction in either direction; we already know that an enzyme does not determine the direction of a chemical process (Chap. 3).

The principal places where enzymatic digestion occurs are *mouth*, *stomach*, and *small intestine*. At each of these sites, one or more *digestive juices* are secreted by specialized *digestive glands*. The salivary glands produce *saliva*, which acts in the mouth and, carried along by food, also in the stomach. The stomach wall secretes *gastric juice*, the pancreas produces *pancreatic juice*, and the liver manufactures *bile.* Pancreatic juice and bile flow through ducts into the small intestine, where they act in conjunction with *intestinal juice* (Fig. 12.4).

The digestive enzymes present in these various juices are of three general kinds, namely, *carbohydrases, lipases,* and *proteinases.* In other words, digestive juices may decompose complex carbohydrates, fats, and proteins. Note that a given digestive juice may contain not only enzymes, but also other chemicals which serve various digestive functions. For example, gastric juice contains strong *hydrochloric acid,* which macerates food and so aids in mechanical diges-

Fig. 12.4.   The duodenal region, diagrammatic.

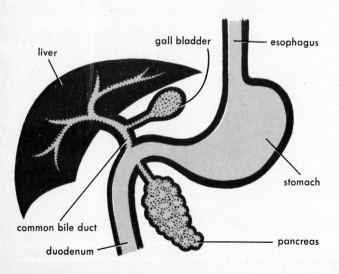

liver

gall bladder

esophagus

stomach

pancreas

common bile duct

duodenum

TABLE 6
The composition of various digestive juices*

	saliva	*gastric juice*	*intestinal juice*	*bile*	*pancreatic juice*
pH	slightly acid or basic	strongly acid	basic	basic	basic
carbohydrases	amylase, maltase		amylase, disaccharases		amylase
proteinases		pepsinogen, rennin	peptidases		trypsinogen, chymotrypsinogen, peptidases
lipases		lipase	lipase		lipase
other components		HCl (H⁺, Cl⁻)	enterokinase	bile salts, bile pigments	

*Note that pepsinogen, trypsinogen, and chymotrypsinogen are inactive proteinases. They are converted into active enzymes when they reach the cavity of the alimentary tract. Hydrochloric acid converts pepsinogen into active pepsin; the catalytic substance enterokinase converts trypsinogen into active trypsin; and trypsin itself converts chymotrypsinogen into active chymotrypsin. Carbohydrases and lipases are immediately active as secreted. For the specific action of digestive enzymes, see Fig. 12.5. Rennin curdles milk; that is, it converts the milk protein caseinogen into the coagulated form casein.

tion. Which digestive juices contain what enzymes and other constituents is shown in Table 6.

In the process of chemical digestion, carbohydrates present in bulk food are gradually decomposed into monosaccharides, e.g., glucose and fructose. Proteins are broken up into individual amino acids. And fats are subdivided physically into colloidal fat droplets through the emulsifying action of bile salts. Some, but not all, of these droplets are also decomposed chemically into fatty acids and glycerin (Fig. 12.5).

Thus, at the completion of digestion, the intestine contains water in which are dissolved mineral ions and monosaccharides, amino acids, fatty acids, glycerin, and vitamins (which have not been affected by diges-

Fig. 12.5. Summary of enzymatic digestion. Polypeptides are partial breakdown products of protein. If they are allowed to act long enough, proteinases and also amylases may digest foods completely; proteinases may yield individual amino acids, and amylases, individual monosaccharides. Bile salts act physically, not chemically: they emulsify fats, i.e., they reduce large fat droplets into tiny droplets of colloidal dimensions.

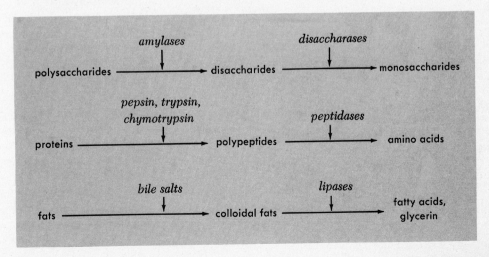

tion). Also present are colloidal fat droplets, plus undigested or indigestible material. The last will be egested, and all other materials will be absorbed.

Absorption and egestion

INTESTINAL PROCESSES

As a food solution begins to be formed during digestion in the intestine, this solution is kept constantly

Fig. 12.6. Abdominal dissection, man. A few of the coils of the small intestine are shown in the right portion of the photo; parts of the thicker large intestine are on the left side and just above the small intestine. The rounded termination of the large intestine, near left bottom, is the caecum, a blind pouch. Attached to it is the appendix (white arrow). Note that what appears on the left in the photo is on the right of the body. (Photographic Department, Rhode Island Hospital.)

moving and churning. The muscles of the intestinal wall (Fig. 12.6) tend to constrict behind a given volume of food and to relax in front of it. Waves of such muscular activity may sweep along whole sections of intestine, and these waves, called *peristalsis*, move food along and keep it agitated. A peristaltic wave may sweep forward for a short distance at some section of the small intestine, then may stop, and another wave may traverse the same or an even longer section. Stationary contractions may occur. Whole loops of the intestine may contract and shift and slide over other loops. Then forward peristalsis may again take place. As these movements proceed all along the gut, they bring food thoroughly into contact with the interior surface of the gut.

This surface is greatly folded and is studded with millions of near-microscopic *villi*, fingerlike protrusions which produce a velvety, carpetlike texture. Covering this whole inner surface of the gut is the intestinal *mucosa* (Chap. 5). By virtue of the folds and the villi, the surface area of the mucosa is exceedingly large. And the villi move continuously from side to side, stirring the food solution additionally and circulating it thoroughly about the mucosal lining.

Such churning of food by peristalsis and the action of the villi is advantageous for two reasons. First, churning mixes and remixes food with the digestive juices, allowing the chemical breakdown of virtually all potential food substances present. Second, agitation brings food into contact with different regions of the intestinal lining, a necessary condition if thorough absorption of food is to occur. The large area of the lining clearly facilitates this.

Absorption brings about a transfer of usable nutrients into the circulating fluids of the body, namely, the blood and lymph. A few substances, alcohol, for example, can be absorbed through the stomach wall, but most foods are absorbed through the intestine. Here nutrients must first be transferred from the gut cavity into the cells of the mucosa, and these lining cells then must release the food molecules into the deeper parts of the gut wall, where blood and lymph vessels are situated.

Nutrient absorption into mucosal cells is brought about by osmosis of water, by diffusion of materials dissolved in water, and by selective, energy-consuming work done by mucosal cells. The selective action of the mucosa is illustrated well by the different rates with which foodstuffs are absorbed. For example, glucose, galactose, and fructose all have the same molecular size and composition, namely, $C_6H_{12}O_6$; yet of these three 6-carbon sugars, galactose is absorbed most rapidly, fructose least rapidly. Moreover, sugar molecules containing only three, four, or five carbon atoms, though smaller than the 6-carbon molecules, are generally absorbed much more slowly, if at all. Mucosal cells evidently "recognize" and select among the substances present in digested food.

In many instances, furthermore, specific chemical reactions occur when given nutrients pass through the gut wall. For example, 6-carbon sugars like glucose cannot be absorbed as such. They are first combined with phosphate groups (-Ⓟ), and only such *phosphorylated* sugars may pass through the mucosa. On the other side, the phosphate groups are removed again and free sugar then enters the blood stream. Similarly, the absorption of fatty acids appears to involve a chemical combination of fatty acids with bile salts, and such fatty acid–bile salt complexes then pass through the gut wall (Fig. 12.7).

During the 4- to 8-hour stay of food in the small intestine, this organ absorbs most of the minerals and the usable organic nutrients—monosaccharides, amino acids, fatty acids, glycerin, colloidal whole fat, and vitamins. The small intestine removes relatively little water from the food solution. On the contrary, by pouring digestive juices into the gut cavity, it actually adds water to food. Water is absorbed primarily in the large intestine.

The large intestine (see Fig. 12.6), so called because of its wider diameter, is both an *absorbing* and an *excreting* organ. During the 10- to 12-hour stay of materials in the large intestine, the bulk of the water and the remaining inorganic nutrients are absorbed. At the same time, many metabolic wastes and inorganic substances present in the body to excess are excreted from the blood into the large intestine. This organ so aids in maintaining a properly balanced internal composition of the body. That the large intestine actually does regulate the internal water balance, for example, is indicated by the familiar upset conditions of diarrhea and constipation.

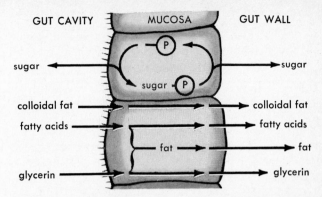

Fig. 12.7. The pattern of absorption of sugars and lipids through the intestinal mucosa. Note that absorption of sugars involves chemical reaction. This is also true for fatty acids, which combine chemically with bile salts during absorption.

The large intestine also initiates *decay* of indigestible and unabsorbable materials. This is brought about by dense, permanent populations of bacteria, which live in the gut as symbionts. These microorganisms obtain food from many of the materials the host cannot digest or absorb. As a result of the nutritional activities of the bacteria, the substances in the colon undergo rapid decay. Frequently, the bacteria release byproducts of their own metabolism, and some of these byproducts may be nutrients usable by the host. Vitamins are among them. Mammals actually obtain an appreciable fraction of their vitamin supply from the intestinal bacteria.

After passing through the large intestine, what is left of the original eaten food is largely *roughage:* tough fibers, gristle, pieces of cellulose, and unmacerated plant tissue, all suspended in more or less reduced quantities of water. Mixed with this are bile pigments, colon excretions, bacteria and bacterial products, and whatever else may have been added or left over in the passage of food through the gut. These *feces* ("dregs") are in a more or less advanced state of decay, and they are ultimately egested as semisolid masses.

The first phase of nutrition, alimentation, is now completed. Water, minerals, and the necessary organic nutrients have been absorbed, have been moved through the intestinal mucosa, and are ready to be transported throughout the body.

TRANSPORT PATHWAYS

In each villus of the intestinal wall are small branches of the two parts of the transport system of the body: capillaries of the blood-carrying *circulatory* channels and capillaries of the *lymph* channels (Fig. 12.8). Blood is pumped to the intestine through a few large arteries, which then branch out in the gut wall into extensive networks of microscopic capillary vessels. The gut wall thus contains a rich supply of circulatory channels and blood reaches into all intestinal villi, where it comes close to the mucosal cells.

Here blood picks up most of the nutrient compounds already absorbed through the intestinal mucosa: water, minerals, vitamins, monosaccharides, amino acids, and fatty acids and glycerin. Colloidal droplets of whole fat, being enormously larger than molecules, cannot enter the blood capillaries in the villi. Food-laden blood then leaves the intestine. The capillaries in the gut collect into larger vessels, these join and rejoin, and a single very large channel eventually emerges from the whole intestine: the *hepatic portal vein*. This vessel leads directly into the liver.

Whatever nutrients are not or cannot be transported to the liver in this fashion are collected by the lymph system. Among such nutrients are mainly the colloidal whole fats, but also water, minerals, and variable quantities of other substances which may have escaped transport by blood.

The lymph system compensates for the "leakiness" of the blood circulation. As blood flows in its closed network of vessels, it loses a certain amount of fluid through the thin walls of the capillaries. This escaped fluid, consisting principally of water, mineral ions, and molecular organic nutrients, is *lymph*. It is responsible for the moist condition of all body tissues. Note here that a leaky blood circulation is not an instance of faulty engineering. On the contrary, fluid escape from

Fig. 12.8. Left, the pattern of the lymph circulation of the body, diagrammatic. Fluid (lymph) escapes from the blood capillaries into the tissues of the body (large arrow at bottom of figure) and returns via lymph vessels into the blood circulation. Right, summary of the pathways of nutrient transport.

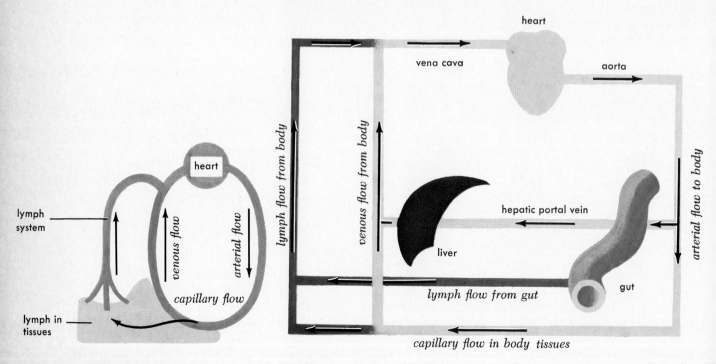

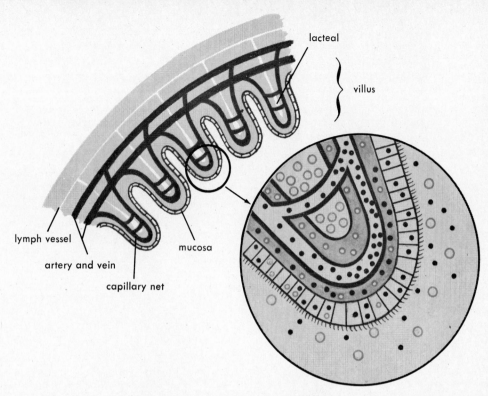

Fig. 12.9. The villi of the intestine and a detailed diagrammatic representation of a single villus. Of the nutrients absorbed through the layer of mucosal cells, whole fats (open circles) collect in the lacteal of a villus and are transported from there through the lymph system. Other nutrients (black dots) are picked up by the blood stream.

capillaries is an adaptive necessity, for this is how the blood ultimately provides the cells of the body with water and all other necessary supplies.

But blood vessels would soon run dry if fluid losses were not made up. This is where the lymph system comes into play. Tiny lymph capillaries originate in all parts of the body, intestine included, and they pick up any free fluid in the tissues. Lymph capillaries then join into progressively larger, progressively fewer ducts until a single large channel is formed. This channel empties into a vein in the left shoulder region, and so it returns to the blood all the fluid lost originally. The lymph capillaries which originate in the intestine are called *lacteals*. One lacteal is situated in each villus (Fig. 12.9).

Thus the transport system is so arranged that col-

loidal fats from the gut bypass the liver and reach the general blood circulation of the body indirectly, via lymph. Most other absorbed foods must travel from gut to liver via blood.

In those animals which possess a liver, this organ is an important food-processing and food-distributing station (Fig. 12.10). Foods received from the gut are transformed chemically or stored or sent out to all cells of the body via the blood. Regardless of when or how often the animal eats, the liver in effect ensures that all cells receive an adequate mixture of all necessary foods in adequate quantities. Such warehousing and traffic-controlling activities make possession of a liver highly advantageous. In animals without livers, as in plants, internal food transport is direct from places of procurement to all other cells of the body.

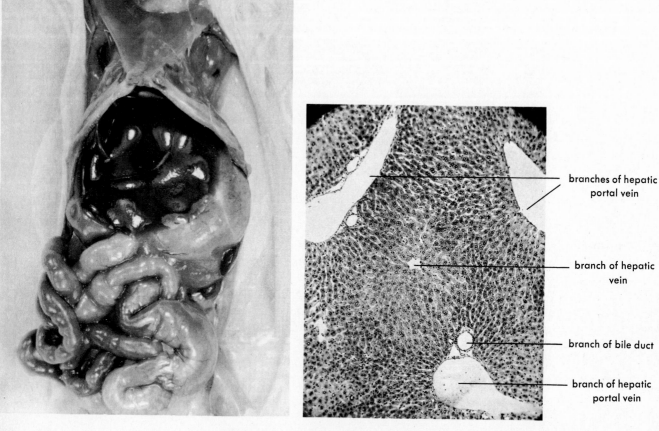

Fig. 12.10.   Left, abdominal dissection, mouse. Note the liver just underneath the diaphragm. The stomach may be seen next to the liver on the left side of the body. The small tongue of tissue on the outer curvature of the stomach is a portion of the spleen. Right, section through mouse liver, showing a functional unit of the organ. Blood from the intestine arrives through the branches of the hepatic portal vein, passes through the canal-like spaces between liver cells, and collects in branches of the hepatic vein, from where it is distributed through the body. As blood flows past the liver cells, many vital metabolic exchanges occur. Bile secreted by liver cells collects in the branches of the bile duct. (Courtesy of Dr. Elizabeth Leduc, Brown University.)

Hence if there is little or no procurement for a given period of time, the cells of the body must go without food. Where a liver is present, on the other hand, foods can be doled out to cells a little at a time and at a steady pace.

Liver function

As noted, *carbohydrates* reach the liver from the gut in the form of various monosaccharides. The liver transforms these into *glycogen*. This polysaccharide is the principal form in which carbohydrates are stored in animals. As in plants, *glucose* is the principal form in which carbohydrates are transported and distributed. All animal cells, liver cells included, can convert glucose into glycogen and vice versa. Normally, then, intestinal monosaccharides coming into the liver are converted to glycogen. From this store the liver subsequently produces glucose, and this glucose is sent in steady amounts to all cells of the body via the blood circulation (Fig. 12.11).

The blood glucose level is kept very constant by the liver. If that level should drop for any reason (e.g., too much is used by body cells), then the liver converts more stored glycogen into blood glucose. Conversely, if the blood glucose level should rise (e.g., too much glucose comes from the gut), then the liver stores the excess as more glycogen.

How does the liver carry out this regulating function? As noted, liver cells contain stored glycogen and blood flowing by these cells contains glucose. Normally, the glycogen and the glucose are in chemical equilibrium; that is, glycogen is converted into glucose just as fast as glucose is converted into glycogen: glucose $\rightleftharpoons$ glycogen. Under such conditions, no net change in the concentrations of either substance occurs. But if the glucose concentration in blood changes, then the chemical equilibrium will be disturbed. For example, if the blood glucose concentration should rise, then the conversion of glucose into glycogen will occur faster than the reverse conversion. As a result, glucose will be withdrawn from blood and liver glycogen stores will be increased. Conversely for a fall in blood glucose levels. These unequal rates of conversion will continue until a chemical equilibrium is reattained. We note that the regulating action of the liver is largely a matter of maintaining and reattaining chemical equilibria.

The amount of glycogen the liver can store is not particularly large. Suppose more carbohydrates are eaten than are immediately needed by the body, and suppose also that the liver already stores glycogen to capacity. What happens to the excess carbohydrates? These are converted into *fats*, the liver also being an important fat store. Conversely, if so few carbohydrates are eaten that liver glycogen stores are reduced to zero (which may happen readily in carbohydrate-free diets), then some of the accumulated liver fat is converted to carbohydrates. Through this source the liver may maintain normal blood glucose levels (Fig. 12.11).

The conversion of excess carbohydrates into fats is one source of stored liver fat. Another is the fatty acids and glycerin which reach the liver from the gut; the liver recombines fatty acids and glycerin into fats. Whatever the source, liver fats may then be sent via the blood to all cells of the body. Apart from the liver, there are numerous other places in the body where fats may be stored, e.g., in the adipose connective tissues under the skin, along membranes in the abdomen, and around the heart, kidneys, and other organs. These *fat depots* receive the colloidal whole fat which travels from the gut via the lymph. The liver and the fat depots communicate via the blood, and fats may be sent from any storage place to any other. Thus if the liver holds fats to capacity, any additional incoming supplies will be sent to some other fat depot. Conversely, these fat depots may replenish reduced liver stores. The cells of the body generally may be supplied with fatty nutrients either from the liver or from other fat depots, or from both sources (Fig. 12.12). Note here that health can be maintained only if the fat stores of the body include the *essential* fatty acids, that is, those which animals are unable to manufacture on their own and which therefore must be supplied in food as prefabricated compounds.

What happens to *amino acids* coming to the liver from the gut? In healthy adults, a normal diet usually yields more amino acids than the body needs. Amino acids are the foods from which tissue proteins are built up, and if an animal no longer grows and is not

Fig. 12.11.   The carbohydrate balance of the body.

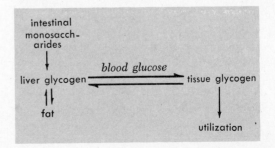

intestinal monosacch-
arides

liver glycogen

blood glucose

tissue glycogen

fat

utilization

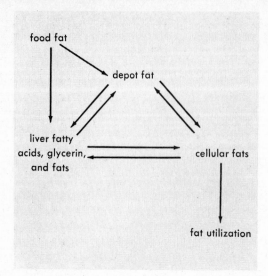

Fig. 12.12. The fat balance of the body.

cal called *urea*, which is a waste material. It is carried away from the liver by the blood, and when it reaches the kidneys it is excreted by these organs in urine (Fig. 12.13).

The other products of deamination,

$$-RCH-COOH$$

that is, amino acids from which the —NH₂ groups have been split away, are not waste materials. On the contrary, these remnants are usable organic nutrients. They are converted by liver cells in some instances into carbohydrates, in others into fatty acids. Carbohydrates so formed then join the glycogen stores of the liver and fatty acids so formed join the fat stores. Since glycogen can be converted to fats, we may note that an animal may "get fat" not just by eating too many fats; too many eaten carbohydrates or too many eaten proteins eventually end up as fats also.

Food does not always provide an amino acid excess; the protein content of eaten food may be so low that an amino acid deficiency develops. Under such circumstances, the liver may counteract this deficiency to a certain extent through the reverse of

Fig. 12.13. The amino acid balance of the body. The splitting of amino acids into —NH₂ and —RCH—COOH fractions is called deamination. The reverse of deamination (dashed arrows) may lead to manufacture of certain amino acids, i.e., the "nonessential" kinds.

diseased, more tissue proteins than are already present are not required. However, the existing proteins all are destroyed sooner or later by normal wear and tear. For example, respiratory decomposition occurs all the time, even in a healthy animal, and proteins are not exempted from such breakdown. It is this normal chemical destruction of proteins which must be counteracted daily, by synthesis of new proteins to replace those decomposed. Therefore, a certain small quantity of amino acids must be supplied daily through food. But eaten food generally supplies far more than this vital minimum quantity and, unlike carbohydrates or fats, amino acids are not stored. The usual situation, consequently, will be one of amino acid excess. The liver processes this excess in the following manner.

We recall that amino acids, NH₂—RCH—COOH, contain amino groups, —NH₂. In the liver, any amino acids which are not passed along directly to body cells via blood are split apart chemically, such that the —NH₂ groups become separated from the rest of the amino acid molecules. This splitting process is called, appropriately, *deamination*. The resulting free —NH₂ groups are then converted to ammonia, NH₃, and this toxic substance is combined immediately with CO_2, amply available in liver cells as a byproduct of respiration. Combination of NH₃ and CO_2 yields a chemi-

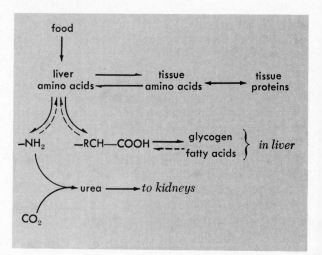

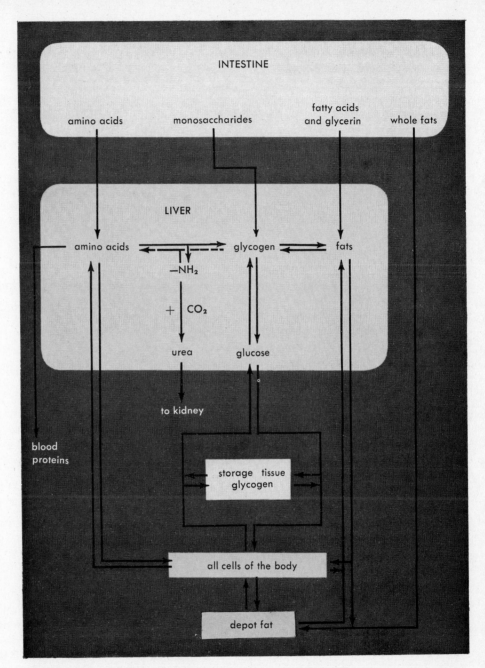

Fig. 12.14.   The overall pattern of liver function, food distribution, and nutrient balances with respect to carbohydrates, fats, and proteins.

deamination. Some available compounds containing organic nitrogen may be the source of —NH₂ groups, and stored carbohydrates or fats may be the source material for the production of —RCH—COOH groups. Amino acids may then be formed from such sources (see Fig. 12.13). But note that animals are not capable of manufacturing all the 23 kinds of amino acids in this way. The "essential" amino acids—or, more specifically, the —RCH portions of the essential amino acids—must be supplied in fully prefabricated form via eaten food. Unless they actually are supplied regularly, an animal will be unable to form complete proteins, regardless of how many other amino acids are available; such an animal will die of malnutrition.

The liver is not involved in any special manner in the distribution of water and inorganic ions absorbed by the gut. Like all other cells of the body, liver cells merely draw portions of these substances from the blood and use them for their own maintenance. But the liver *is* involved specially in the distribution of several vitamins. Some vitamins absorbed from the gut are transported directly to tissue cells. However, others are taken up and collected by the liver and are released as the tissues require them. Vitamins A and D are in this category. The livers of fish store particularly large quantities of these vitamins, hence the nutritive value of, for example, cod liver oil. In certain instances, the liver also manufactures vitamins from nonvitamin sources. The pigment carotene, present in many foods, is not a vitamin. But when carotene reaches the liver, it may be transformed into active vitamin A.

In addition to these many storing and food-processing activities, the liver also performs numerous other, not necessarily nutritional, functions. For example, the liver destroys red blood corpuscles and in the embryo it manufactures them. Other manufacturing processes include bile production and the synthesis of special liver products which, like hormones, are vital for the maintenance of tissue cells but which are not available in food. It may be noted in this connection that the occasional inclusion of liver in the diet has long been known to be beneficial generally and indeed necessary in certain diseases. The main activities of the liver are summarized in Fig. 12.14.

Thus, among the nutrients delivered to individual animal cells are glucose; all different kinds of amino acids; fats, fatty acids, and glycerin; water and mineral ions; vitamins; and various special organic compounds. Being so supplied through the digestive and absorptive agency of the intestine, the regulative agency of the liver, and the transportive agency of blood, the animal cell, like the plant cell, may now see to the main business at hand: utilization of nutrients for survival. This, we already know, means *respiration* on the one hand and *synthesis* of new living matter on the other.

Review questions

1. Review the general nutritional pattern of animals and contrast the nutrient requirements of plants and animals. For which materials are animals dependent on plants and why? What is the basic function of an alimentary system?

2. Review what is known about appetite and hunger control. What role does the brain play in such control? Discuss the chemical aspects of digestion generally. What roles do enzymes play in digestion and how are digestive enzymes distinct from others? What is the relation between digestion and synthesis?

3. Review the specific course of protein, carbohydrate, and fat digestion. What enzymes are involved in each case? What are the results of these digestive processes? What are intestinal villi and what are their functions? How and in what form are different categories of food absorbed into the intestinal wall? What tissue accomplishes absorption?

4. What are the functions of the large intestine? What is the role of the intestinal bacteria? If pure glucose were eaten, where would it be digested? Why are eaten vitamins, or orally administered medicines, not digested in the alimentary tract?

5. Describe the blood and lymph circulation through the intestine. Which food materials are carried away from the intestine by blood? By lymph?

6. What is the function of the liver and what is the adaptive advantage of this organ? What happens to carbohydrates reaching the liver? What happens if carbohydrate supplies are excessive?

7. By what process is the constancy of the blood-glucose concentration maintained? Discuss several specific situations in which the blood-glucose level tends to change, and show how such tendencies are counteracted by the liver.

8. What is deamination? When and where does it occur, and what are the results of this process?

9. Can the liver manufacture carbohydrates and fats from derivatives of amino acids? Conversely, can the liver manufacture amino acids from carbohydrates or fats? Can the liver manufacture essential amino acids?

10. Describe the interplay between liver, fat depots, and body tissues in fat metabolism. Can an animal survive if fats are substituted for carbohydrates in its diet? Can an animal similarly survive in the converse situation?

Suggested collateral readings

Boyd-Orr, I.: The Food Problem, *Sci. Am.,* vol. 183, 1950.

Mayer, J.: Appetite and Obesity, *Sci. Am.,* vol. 195, 1956.

Quisenberry, K. S.: The World's Principal Food Plants, *Sci. Monthly,* vol. 79, 1954.

Remington, R. E.: The Social Origins of Dietary Habits, *Sci. Monthly,* vol. 43, 1936.

Weaver, W.: People, Energy, and Food, *Sci. Monthly,* vol. 78, 1954.

GAS EXCHANGE

13

Most organisms are *aerobes;* that is, their cells require oxygen for respiration. Also, respiration yields the byproduct carbon dioxide and this gas must be eliminated from the organism. Therefore, if a cell is to respire, it must not only be nourished with foods. It must in addition be provided with oxygen and it must be rid of carbon dioxide. The ways in which organisms exchange O_2 and CO_2 form the subject of this chapter.

Patterns of exchange

A first component of gas exchange is *breathing*, which may be defined as an exchange of respiratory gases between a whole organism and the physical environment. A second component in multicellular organisms often is *gas transport*, into and away from all cells. Note, therefore, that breathing and gas transport are *aids* to respiration, the latter being a chemical process of energy liberation *within* a cell. Breathing evidently is not the same as respiration. A whole *organism* breathes; in addition, the individual *cells* of an organism also respire.

In the entire living world there are only five different patterns of gas exchange (Fig. 13.1). All five are governed

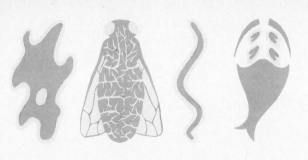 

Fig. 13.1. The five principal patterns of gas exchange. From left to right: direct diffusion of gases through the cell surface (e.g., Monera, Protista, Metaphyta); tracheal tubes (e.g., insects); skin breathing (e.g., earthworms); gill breathing (e.g., fishes); and lung breathing (e.g., mammals). The surface for gas exchange in all but the insects is indicated in light gray.

by purely physical *diffusion*, such that O_2 and CO_2 always move from regions of higher concentration to regions of lower concentration.

By far the most widespread pattern is that of *direct exchange:* each cell of an organism, unicellular or multicellular, individually picks up O_2 from the environment and releases CO_2 into the environment. This individual direct process occurs in all Monera, all Protista, all Metaphyta, and some Metazoa (e.g., sponges, coelenterates, flatworms). All these organisms are so built that every cell, or virtually every cell, is in immediate contact with environmental water or air. Specialized breathing and gas transport systems are therefore not needed and indeed do not occur.

Such systems do occur, however, in the majority of Metazoa, which are built so compactly that interior cells are *not* in direct contact with the environment. Of the four different patterns of gas exchange here encountered, one occurs in insects and some other arthropods. These animals possess hollow *tracheal tubes*, which begin at the body surface and lead into the interior. There they branch extensively, microscopic branch terminals reaching into all tissues. In effect, air is piped from the outside to all interior cells and cellular gas exchange then can take place even deeply within the animal.

In all other compactly built animals, gas exchange occurs across thin membranes. These are usually one cell layer thick. They are exposed on one side to external air or water and on the other to blood vessels. Oxygen is absorbed into blood and carbon dioxide is released from it. Thus the breathing membrane collects and releases gases, and the blood circulation represents the transport system which delivers the gases to and from all cells.

The three principal variants of this pattern are *skin breathing*, *gill breathing*, and *lung breathing*. Earthworms, for example, breathe exclusively through their thin, moist skins. Frogs use their skins too, but in addition, frog tadpoles possess gills and frog adults, lungs. In fish, crustacea, and many other aquatic animals, external water flows past gills and the gill membranes exchange gases. Many differently constructed gills are found in different aquatic animals, but the principle of operation is the same in all.

Lungs occur chiefly in terrestrial vertebrates. These breathing organs operate like gills, except that they are adapted to function in air instead of water. We shall examine the pattern of lung breathing in some detail and the specific pattern in man may serve as an illustrative example.

Breathing

THE BREATHING SYSTEM

Several familiar organs form the air channels of the breathing apparatus: *nose* and *nasal passages, pharynx, larynx* (or Adam's apple), *trachea* (or windpipe), and *lungs.*

The nasal passages are narrow, winding pathways leading past intricately grooved and ridged walls (Fig. 13.2). Along the walls are found a number of paired openings. Some of these connect with the head *sinuses*, hollow air-filled cavities within some of the skull bones. For example, one large sinus is present in each of the two frontal bones which form the forehead.

Another pair of openings admits the contents of the *tear ducts* into the nasal passages. Tears are secreted continuously by glands in the outer corners of the eyes. The lymphlike fluid flows over, and so moistens, the surface of the cornea, then collects in the

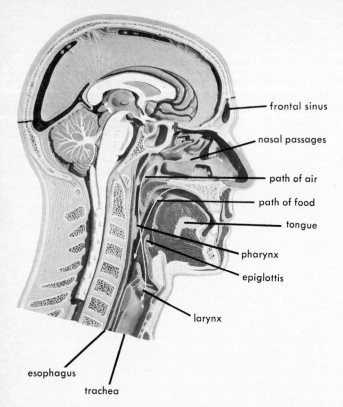

frontal sinus

nasal passages

path of air

path of food

tongue

pharynx

epiglottis

larynx

esophagus

trachea

Fig. 13.2. The nasal passages and the upper parts of the breathing system. In the pharynx, the food channel crosses the air channel (white dashed lines). When a person swallows, the larynx is raised up against the epiglottis. This blocks the air channel into the trachea and normally prevents food from going the wrong way. (Model designed by Dr. J. F. Mueller, Ward's Natural Science Establishment, Inc.)

inner corners of the eyes and runs through the tear ducts into the nose. Near the entry of the nasal passages into the pharynx, another two openings, one on the right, the other on the left, lead into the *eustachian tubes.* These pass into the middle-ear cavities. This connection permits the equilibration of air pressure between the external atmosphere and the middle ear, a space which is closed off from the outside by the eardrum.

Nasal passages, head sinuses, tear ducts, and eustachian tubes are lined with a continuous single layer of epithelial cells. Mucus secreted by the cells moistens the exposed surfaces. The epithelial cells in the nasal

passages are ciliated, and some of these cells are specialized as odor receptors. Nerves lead from them to the nearby brain, where impulses are interpreted as smell.

Air passing through the narrow spaces of the nasal pathways is warmed and moistened, is freed of dust by the ciliated cells which act as a filtering screen, and is smelled. As everyone is uncomfortably aware, inflammation of the passages as in a cold or in hay fever blocks air transmission to a greater or lesser degree. Breathing by mouth under such conditions introduces relatively unwarmed, dust-laden, and unsmelled air.

The air and the food channel cross in the pharynx. The esophagus is more or less collapsed in the absence of food, but some air may pass into it nevertheless. Most of the air enters the larynx through the *glottis,* a slit which can be closed or opened to varying degrees. The larynx consists of a number of cartilages. Held together by membranes and movable relative to one another by muscles, these cartilages enclose a hollow, cylindrical chamber. Attached to the inner surfaces of this chamber is a pair of horizontally placed fibroelastic ligaments, the *vocal cords.* These run from front to back in the laryngeal cavity, leaving an air passage in the midplane. Sound is produced when air is expelled past the vocal cords through the glottis (Fig. 13.3).

The larynx is continuous with the trachea. This tube is prevented from collapsing by C-shaped rings of cartilage set horizontally into its wall. As in the larynx, the inner lining of the trachea is a ciliated, mucus-secreting layer of cells. The cilia beat upward, carrying mucus, dust, and occasional bits of food which "went the wrong way" into the pharynx. Air forced out as a cough facilitates the process.

At its lower end, the trachea divides into two *bronchi,* tubes having a smaller diameter than the trachea but the same structure otherwise (Fig. 13.4). Each bronchus subdivides after a distance into *bronchioles* and each of the latter in turn branches repeatedly. Cartilage supports are not present in these smaller ducts. Also, their walls become thinner as they branch. Only the inner ciliated lining layer and some connective tissue containing elastic fibers are carried forward into the microscopic terminations of the branch system. Each such terminus is a raspberry-shaped sac made of a single layer of thin flat cells. This is an

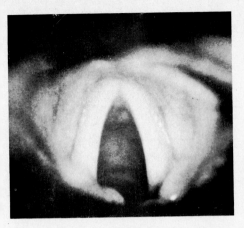
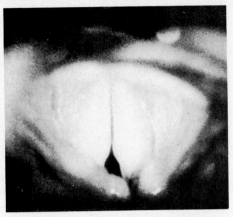

Fig. 13.3.   The vocal cords of man. The view is from above, looking into larynx and trachea. Photos show vocal-cord positions during the transition from quiet breathing (left) to voicing (right). (Bell Telephone Laboratories, Inc.)

alveolus (Fig. 13.5). The sum of all alveoli constitutes the lung. The alveoli are held together by connective tissue, which carries nerves and a dense network of blood capillaries.

The lung on each side is situated in an *intrathoracic space*, which is bounded by a double membrane. Except for openings which admit the bronchi and the blood vessels to the lungs, the intrathoracic cavities are sealed off by the double membrane from the rest of the body. This feature is essential in breathing.

Fig. 13.5.   An alveolus of the lung, surrounded by capillaries and connective tissue.

Fig. 13.4.   The lower parts of the breathing system. Note that the intrathoracic cavity is sealed.

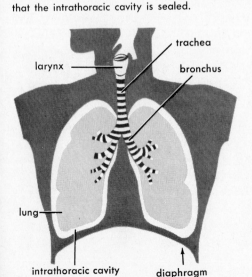

larynx — trachea

bronchus

lung

intrathoracic cavity   diaphragm

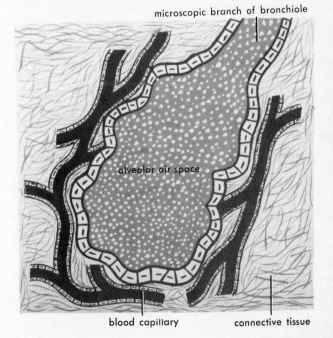

microscopic branch of bronchiole

alveolar air space

blood capillary   connective tissue

THE BREATHING PROCESS

Air is moved through the breathing system by action of the *diaphragm*, the *rib muscles*, or both. The diaphragm participates in *abdominal breathing;* the rib muscles, in *chest breathing.*

The diaphragm separates the chest cavity from the abdominal cavity; stomach and liver lie directly underneath it. In relaxed condition, this thin muscular partition is dome-shaped. When it is contracted, the upward curvature of the dome disappears and the diaphragm flattens out. Such contraction pushes liver, stomach, and intestine downward and outward and so forces the belly out. Hence the designation "abdominal breathing." A flattening out of the diaphragm also enlarges the chest cavity and this is the effective event in *inhalation* (Fig. 13.6). As a result of the enlargement, the pressure in the sealed intrathoracic space falls. This lowered pressure sucks the lung alveoli wide open. Air pressure within the alveoli consequently falls also, but this decrease is rebalanced instantly by air rushing in through the nose or mouth.

When the diaphragm relaxes, it resumes its original dome shape. The belly is pulled back and the chest cavity, together with the intrathoracic space, reattains its former volume. Pressure within the intrathoracic space is then no longer lowered, and further suction is therefore not exerted on the alveoli. As a result, the elastic fibers which cover the alveoli recoil and air is pressed out from the lungs in an *exhalation.*

Breathing movements carried out by the rib cage have the same effect on the lungs as the above. Ribs are hinged to the vertebral column along the back and to the breastbone, or *sternum*, along the front. Attached between successive ribs are two layers of muscles, which raise or lower the rib cage. When the chest is raised, the thoracic cavity expands and, through suction on the alveoli, inhalation occurs. A lowering of the chest results in exhalation. Chest breathing may enlarge the intrathoracic spaces much more than abdominal breathing; as a result, the former may produce deeper breaths than the latter.

Evidently, the mammalian method of breathing is a pressure mechanism. This knowledge has made possible procedures of "artificial respiration," often employed when injury or disease has incapacitated the automatic internal controls which maintain breathing normally. In artificial respiration by hand or in "iron lungs," the chest is subjected to intermittent external pressure, which forces air into and out of the lungs just as does normal breathing.

THE CONTROL OF BREATHING

What maintains the bellowslike breathing movements year after year, without interruption? And what ad-

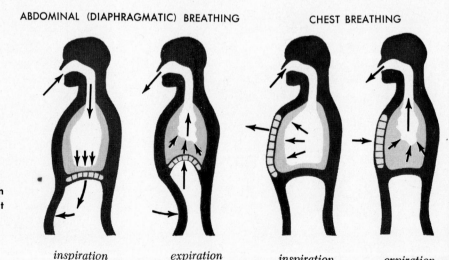

ABDOMINAL (DIAPHRAGMATIC) BREATHING   CHEST BREATHING

Fig. 13.6.   The essential events in abdominal breathing and chest breathing.

inspiration   *expiration*   *inspiration*   *expiration*

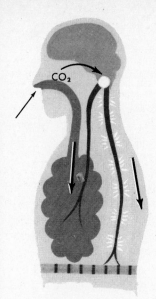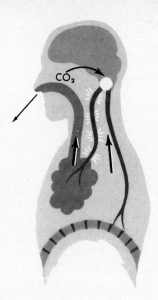

Fig. 13.7. The control of inhalation (left) and of exhalation (right). Left, CO_2 in blood stimulates the breathing center to send impulses to the diaphragm, leading to inhalation. Right, impulses from the inflated lung inhibit the breathing center, leading to exhalation.

justs these movements in rate and depth to changing requirements? Breathing is maintained and regulated by a *breathing center* in the brain. This center is located in the *medulla oblongata,* the hind portion of the brain near the juncture of skull and neck.

The breathing center responds to two kinds of incoming stimuli, one nervous, the other nonnervous. The nonnervous stimulus is *carbon dioxide,* present in blood at all times as a byproduct of cellular respiration. Blood-borne CO_2 accelerates the activity of the breathing center. The higher the CO_2 concentration, the greater the activity, and vice versa. This activity consists in sending nerve impulses to the breathing muscles, i.e., the diaphragm or the rib muscles. Special nerves conduct such impulses. For example, a pair of large *phrenic nerves* innervates the diaphragm. When impulses from the breathing center reach the breathing muscles, these contract, the chest cavity enlarges as a result, and the lung alveoli are sucked open. Air is then inhaled (Fig. 13.7).

The very stretching of the alveoli now stimulates special sets of nerves which originate in the alveolar walls. These nerves conduct impulses from the inflated lung to the breathing center. When such impulses arrive there, the center is *inhibited.* That is, the impulses override and suppress the stimulating effect of blood-borne CO_2. Consequently, the center ceases to send signals to the breathing muscles. This prevents inhalation from going too far, for in the absence of signals from the brain, the breathing muscles relax. As they do so, the chest cavity becomes smaller, the lung alveoli recoil to their original state, and air is exhaled.

After the alveoli have recoiled, they are no longer stretched and the nerve endings in their walls therefore are no longer stimulated. Impulses then cease to be sent to the breathing center and the center consequently ceases to be inhibited. In the absence of inhibition, blood-borne CO_2 can again exert its effect. The breathing center now resumes its impulse transmission to the breathing muscles and a new inhalation begins.

Blood-borne oxygen also has an effect on the breathing center but this effect is much less powerful than that of CO_2, and it probably plays only a minor role during normal breathing. We may conclude that a basic breathing rhythm is maintained by alternating, automatically self-renewing effects on the breathing center, produced largely by nervous inhibitions and carbon dioxide stimulations.

It should follow that, as the inhibitions and stimulations vary, so should the breathing rhythm. This is the case. As is well known, both the rate and depth of breathing can be altered easily. For example, an exercise of will or powerful sensory and emotional experiences may affect breathing greatly. These are nervous influences, relayed to the breathing center over many different and often indirect nerve paths.

Carbon dioxide also produces modifications of the breathing pattern. When the CO_2 concentration in blood is high, the *rate* of breathing is proportionately high, and vice versa. High CO_2 concentrations build up whenever the rate of CO_2 production through respiration is greater than the rate of CO_2 removal via the lungs. This is the case, for example, at the start of strenuous physical work, when intensified energy production in cells liberates increasing amounts of CO_2. By speeding up breathing under such conditions, CO_2 hastens its own removal through the lungs. Faster breathing at the same time increases the oxygen supply, just when the tissues require more oxygen.

The concentration of CO_2 in blood becomes extremely high when breathing is deliberately stopped altogether. But the accumulating gas then soon stimulates the breathing center so strongly that a resumption of breathing is *forced*, even against the most intense will. An animal cannot commit suicide by holding its breath. Conversely, when the CO_2 concentration in blood is low, the breathing center is stimulated rather weakly and breathing slows down. This is the case during sleep or rest, when respiration and CO_2 production are minimal.

Breathing is a means to an end. The most immediate end is the procurement of additional oxygen and the removal of excess carbon dioxide. Fresh atmospheric air as inhaled contains some 20 per cent oxygen and 0.03 per cent carbon dioxide. Exhaled air includes only 16 per cent oxygen, but some 4 per cent carbon dioxide. Evidently, a fifth of the available oxygen has been retained in the body and more than 100 times the amount of carbon dioxide has been expelled. What happens to the one and where does the other come from?

Gas transport

Inasmuch as blood is the transport medium of the respiratory gases, an intimate association between circulation and breathing may be inferred. Indeed, the heart is virtually embedded in lung and millions of blood capillaries ramify over the lung alveoli. Blood and air here approach each other very closely.

If blood is rich in oxygen, it is called *arterial* blood; if it is rich in CO_2, it is called *venous* blood. An *artery* is a blood vessel leading *away* from the heart; a *vein*, a vessel leading *to* the heart. Note that the designation "artery" or "vein" depends not on the kind of blood carried, but rather on the direction of blood flow within the vessel.

In all body tissues, cellular gas exchange takes place; cells take up oxygen from and add carbon dioxide to the blood. Here, therefore, blood becomes venous. This CO_2-rich blood then travels to the heart, entering this organ via a vessel called the *vena cava* (Fig. 13.8). From the heart, venous blood is pumped through a pair of short *pulmonary arteries* into the nearby lungs. These arteries branch into extensive networks of capillaries spread over the lung alveoli. Pulmonary gas exchange takes place here; CO_2 leaves the blood and O_2 enters. Thus blood becomes arterial. This O_2-rich blood now collects in a pair of *pulmonary veins*, which lead back to the heart. Redistributed from the heart via the *aorta* throughout the body, blood supplies new oxygen to tissue cells and is ready to carry off new carbon dioxide. That is the general pattern. How is it realized in detail?

THE EXCHANGES

The transfer of oxygen from the lung alveoli into the blood and the reverse transfer of carbon dioxide are governed primarily by diffusion. This is one of the very few instances where active cellular absorption and secretion do not appear to play a role. The wall of an alveolus consists of a thin, single layer of cells, and the wall of a blood capillary also consists of such a layer (see Fig. 13.5). Neither of these walls offers resistance to the passage of gaseous O_2 and CO_2. Gas exchange may therefore take place much more rapidly than if absorption and secretion were necessary.

The specific direction in which the gases move is determined by the prevailing pressure gradients, or *tension gradients*, between blood and lung. Specifically, atmospheric air in the lungs contains only a little CO_2, but the venous blood which flows into the lungs from

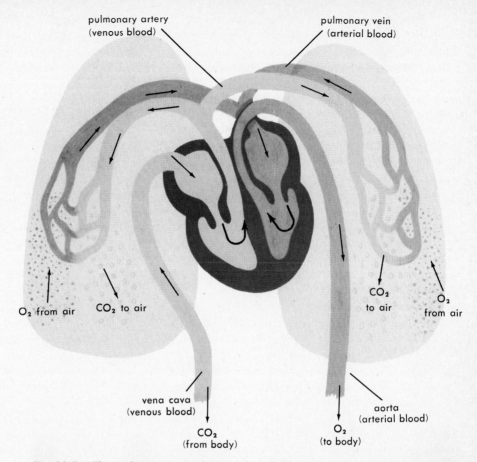

Fig. 13.8. The pulmonary circulation. Arterial blood is shown in dark gray, venous blood in light gray. Note that in this diagram the left side of the body appears on the right and the right side of the body on the left. Anatomical drawings are usually oriented as if observer and subject were face to face.

the body is virtually saturated with the gas. The pressure, or tension, of CO_2 in blood is therefore greater than that in the alveoli and a tension gradient points *out* of the capillaries. Carbon dioxide consequently moves in that direction, or, better, more CO_2 molecules diffuse out of the blood than into it. As a result, blood ceases to be venous (Fig. 13.9).

The pressure pattern is the reverse with respect to oxygen. Blood flowing into the lungs from the body is oxygen-poor, for the tissues have removed much of the gas. But the air in the alveoli contains a maximal amount of O_2. Accordingly, a tension gradient points *into* the blood and more O_2 molecules diffuse

into the capillaries than in the reverse direction. As a result, blood becomes arterial.

These interrelations explain why breathing is inefficient at high altitudes. In rarefied air, the atmospheric oxygen pressure is greatly reduced and the pressure differential between lung and blood is low. Oxygen diffusion consequently does not take place as readily. We may similarly understand why the close atmosphere of an unventilated, overcrowded room makes breathing difficult. The CO_2 tension in the room is high, approaching that in blood. Hence CO_2 cannot easily leave the blood.

Just as in the lungs, cellular gas exchange in the

body tissues is also governed by tension gradients (see Fig. 13.9). Cells continuously use up oxygen in respiration and the tension of this gas in cells is therefore low. The tension in arterial blood is higher, however, and O_2 diffuses from blood into tissue cells. Blood consequently ceases to be arterial. At the same time, since respiratory CO_2 is produced in cells steadily, the CO_2 tension within tissue cells is high. But arterial blood has low CO_2 tensions and the gas therefore diffuses from tissue cells into blood. This makes blood venous.

How are respiratory gases carried in blood?

THE VEHICLE

Transport of respiratory gases requires a medium containing water, a number of inorganic ions, and red blood corpuscles.

The corpuscles owe their red color to *haemoglobin*. This complex pigment, customarily symbolized as Hb, consists of two parts, *haeme* and *globin*. Haeme contains a tetrapyrrol ring and thus resembles chlorophyll chemically. Unlike chlorophyll but like the tetrapyrrol cytochrome, haeme contains iron rather than magnesium. Haeme is the active, functionally significant fraction of haemoglobin. Globin is a protein which probably serves mainly as a carrier of haeme.

Haemoglobin has the capacity of forming a loose chemical combination with oxygen:

$$Hb + O_2 \rightleftharpoons HbO_2$$

By the principle of mass action, this reversible reaction will shift to the right when O_2 is present in excess. As we have seen, this is the case in the lung capillaries, and HbO_2, or *oxyhaemoglobin*, forms there.

Oxygen is carried in blood largely in the form of HbO_2. A little oxygen also *dissolves* in the water of blood, in the same way that all atmospheric gases dissolve in water. Indeed, blood contains dissolved CO_2 and N_2 as well. When the external air pressure suddenly falls, as during rapid ascents into high altitudes or up from great depths, then the dissolved gases may fizz out of the blood in the form of bubbles. Dangerous "bends" may result. The effect here is rather like removing the cap of a bottle of soda; gases then fizz out similarly.

When oxyhaemoglobin reaches the tissues, the reaction above shifts to the left. Cells are oxygen-poor relative to the blood, and the conditions of mass action are therefore such that HbO_2 "unloads" its oxygen. Free Hb forms again and the free O_2 is taken up by the tissues (Fig. 13.10).

It may be noted that haemoglobin may transport not only oxygen but also *carbon monoxide:* $Hb + CO \rightleftharpoons HbCO$. This union is achieved much more easily than the union with oxygen. Accordingly, if carbon monoxide is present in the atmosphere, Hb becomes $HbCO$ in preference to HbO_2. This means that little oxygen can be transported to the tissues, which consequently cannot respire. Therein lies the poisonous effect of carbon monoxide.

Of the CO_2 released from tissue cells, a small fraction dissolves physically in blood water, as already noted. Another small fraction combines with haemo-

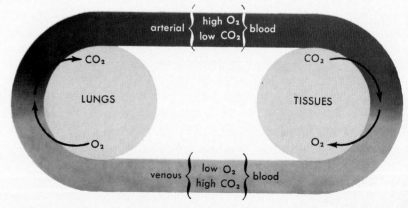

Fig. 13.9. The exchanges of respiratory gases between the lungs and blood and between the body tissues and blood. Oxygen enters the blood in the lungs and leaves in the tissues. Carbon dioxide enters in the tissues and leaves in the lungs.

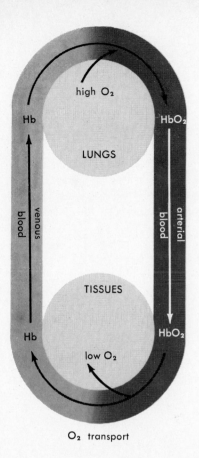

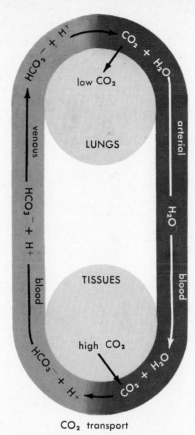

O₂ transport   CO₂ transport

Fig. 13.10. The transport of respiratory gases in blood. Oxygen is carried in the form of oxyhaemoglobin (HbO₂), carbon dioxide in the form of bicarbonate ions (HCO₃⁻).

globin and is transported to the lungs in the form of HbCO₂. But the bulk reacts with water chemically and forms bicarbonate ions (HCO_3^-):

$$CO_2 + H_2O \rightleftharpoons H_2CO_3 \rightleftharpoons H^+ + HCO_3^-$$
$$\text{\textit{carbonic acid}} \qquad \text{\textit{bicarbonate ion}}$$

Inasmuch as tissue cells constantly add CO_2 to blood, this reaction proceeds to the right in the tissues. Most of the CO_2 is therefore transported to the lungs in the form of HCO_3^-. In the lungs, the conditions of mass action are reversed; CO_2 escapes into the alveoli, the reaction consequently shifts to the left, and more free CO_2 is released for exhalation (Fig. 13.10).

The processes auxiliary to cellular metabolism are now completed. Every cell of an organism has been supplied with oxygen, has been rid of carbon dioxide, and has already been provided with nutrients; it is ready to produce energy and to synthesize new living matter.

Review questions

1. Distinguish between breathing and respiration. How does gas exchange occur among plants? What are the principal patterns of gas exchange among animals?

2. Describe the structural organization of the breathing system in man. How is sound produced? What is an alveolus and what is its relation to the lung? What chest structures surround the lungs?

3. Describe the pressure changes in the body associated

with inhalation and exhalation in (*a*) abdominal breathing and (*b*) chest breathing.

4. How are inhalation-exhalation cycles controlled and maintained automatically? Review here the role of CO_2 and that of the brain. Show by what sequence of events inhalation comes to alternate with exhalation.

5. Describe the processes through which breathing rate increases when physical exercise is begun and decreases at the onset of sleep.

6. Describe the pattern of blood circulation through the body. Where, specifically, does venous blood become arterial and arterial blood become venous? In the circulation through the lungs, which blood vessels contain arterial and which contain venous blood?

7. By what processes does arterial blood become venous and vice versa? Show what factors govern these changes and describe the actual changes in lungs and tissues.

8. How is oxygen carried in blood? What reactions occur in the lungs and in the tissues? Why is carbon monoxide a poison?

9. How is CO_2 carried in blood? What reactions occur in the lungs and in the tissues?

10. How are breathing and gas transport affected during ascent to high altitudes? How is nitrogen carried in blood? Why is breathing difficult in an unventilated room? What happens when a person holds his breath for a long time?

Suggested collateral readings

Fox, H. M.: Blood Pigments, *Sci. Am.*, vol. 182, 1950.

Williams, C. B.: Insect Breathing, *Sci. Am.*, vol. 188, 1953.

RESPIRATION

14

Nutrition and gas exchange make cellular metabolism possible. Cellular metabolism in turn makes possible continued nutrition, gas exchange, and indeed life itself.

Whatever the organism and whatever its pattern of nutrition and gas exchange, the pattern of its cellular metabolism is always the same: with or without the aid of oxygen, and with organic nutrients as fuel, cells respire, that is, *produce* metabolically usable energy. Such energy may then be *used* within the cell that produced it, toward cellular maintenance and self-perpetuation. Energy production is the subject of this chapter; energy utilization, that of the next.

The pattern

BONDS AND ENERGY

Respiration may be defined as a conversion of the chemical energy of organic molecules into metabolically usable energy within living cells.

The last part of this definition, "within living cells," means largely *mitochondria*. The main phases of respiration take place in these specialized organelles of the cell cytoplasm. Concerning the remainder of the definition above, we may note that, directly or indirectly, the chemical energy of organic molecules represents *stored solar energy*. It is the sun which, through photosynthesis, makes possible the construction of primary organic molecules. All other organic substances are derived secondarily from these. In a sense, therefore, the bonds of organic molecules incorporate solar energy. And if the bonds are broken under appropriate conditions, the locked-in energy becomes available for metabolic work.

A similar process is very familiar from the nonliving world: burning. Fuels burned in a stove are principally wood, coal, oil, or "gas," all organic materials containing stored solar energy. Energy is obtained here also by breaking bonds. The principle involved is precisely the same as in respiration, and respiration, indeed, may properly be regarded as a burning. If this is so, why does respiration not produce the high temperatures of a fire?

For two reasons. First, a fire is *uncontrolled* combustion, in the sense that all the bonds within a fuel molecule may be broken simultaneously. A maximum amount of energy may then be released all at once. Such sudden, explosive release generates the high temperatures of a fire. Respiration, on the other hand, is *controlled* combustion. Energy is obtained from one bond at a time. If a fuel is respired completely, the total energy yield is the same as if it were burned in a stove; but in respiration the energy is removed bit by bit, bond by bond. Temperatures therefore stay low. Enzymes exercise the necessary control. Respiration is a series of enzymatic reactions, and biological combustion cannot take place any faster than the controlling enzymes will permit.

Second, the energy produced in a fire is dissipated energy—largely heat and to some extent light. But in respiration only very little of the available energy escapes as heat and practically none as light. Instead, most of it is "packaged" directly into new *chemical* energy. As we shall see, fuel energy creates *new* chemical bonds, and it is in this form that metabolic energy is used in cells. Since chemical bonds are not "hot," temperatures stay low during respiration.

OXIDATION

How is chemical energy removed from a bond? As we shall see, there are several ways. One of the most important, in respiration as in a fire, is *withdrawal of hydrogen* from the fuel, or *dehydrogenation*. This process requires the presence of a hydrogen acceptor. If we let *A* stand for such an acceptor, then combustion may be symbolized generally as follows:

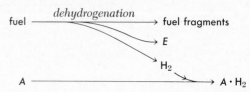

Thus if a hydrogen acceptor is available, hydrogen can be withdrawn from a fuel. The carbon bonds of the fuel may break as a result; bond energy becomes available; and the hydrogen can be collected and held by the acceptor.

Many different substances can and do serve as hydrogen acceptors. One which serves in fires and in a major form of respiration is atmospheric *oxygen*. Combustion in the presence of oxygen thus takes the general form:

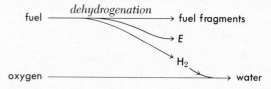

Water is a byproduct.

Note that hydrogen acceptors *do not start* combustion. They merely serve to collect and to remove hydrogen. Note also that dehydrogenation is more or less synonymous with *oxidation*, whether oxygen or any other hydrogen acceptor is involved. In losing hydrogen, a substance is said to become oxidized.

If it is not the hydrogen acceptor that starts combustion, what is? In a fire, the starter is heat. We must supply an initial amount of heat (by friction as in lighting a match, or through an electric spark, for example) to ignite the fuel, that is, to achieve a first dehydrogenation. Enough energy is thereby released in the form of heat to initiate a self-sustaining chain reaction. Adjacent fuel molecules become agitated; *their* hydrogen atoms may be thought to break loose; more energy is thereby released; new fuel molecules become agitated; etc.

In living cells, respiration actually never starts because it never stops. It is always under way, unceasingly. The "fire" of life was lit when life first originated and since then it has been handed down from parent to offspring, without interruption. The continuing dehydrogenations are maintained not by heat but by enzymatic reactions. Special enzymes promote hydrogen removal from fuels and special enzymes also act as primary hydrogen acceptors.

FUELS AND ENERGY

What are the organic fuels in cells? The answer is anything that contains breakable carbon bonds, which means *any* organic constituent of cells: carbohydrates, fats, proteins, their various derivatives, vitamins, other special compounds, and indeed all the innumerable substances which together make up a cell. Like a fire, respiration is no respecter of materials. Anything that can burn will burn, and in cells this is the very substance of cells itself. Respiration does not distinguish between the expendable and the nonexpendable. For example, an amino acid which is an important structural member of the framework of a cell or is part of an enzyme may be burned just as readily as an amino acid which has been absorbed as a food.

However, if a fire is fed much of one fuel but little of another, more of the first is likely to be burned. Indeed, under normal conditions, a cell receives a steady enough supply of foods to make *them* the primary fuels rather than the structural parts of a cell. Also, some kinds of materials burn more easily than others and some are more accessible to the fire than others. On this basis, foods, carbohydrates and fats in particular, are again favored as fuels and the finished components of a cell tend to be spared. Yet the sparing is relative only. The formed parts of a cell *are* burned gradually, including even those which make up the burning apparatus itself, the mitochondria.

But if a cell itself burns away, how can it remain intact and functioning? Only by continuous construction of new living components, offsetting the continuous destruction through respiration. Note that these two processes go on side by side, at all times: destructive energy metabolism and constructive synthesis metabolism. One is in balance with the other, and foods serve both as fuel for the one and as building materials for the other.

What happens to the energy obtained from respiratory fuels? If it were to dissipate freely into the surroundings, it would become more or less useless metabolically. Evidently, an energy-trapping device is required in cells. Such a device exists. We have already referred to it in Chaps. 5 and 11, and it is represented by the reversible reaction which interconverts adenosine diphosphate (ADP) and adenosine triphosphate (ATP):

$$\text{ADP} + \text{phosphate} + \text{energy} \rightleftharpoons \text{ATP}$$

Proceeding to the right, this reaction symbolizes the energy-trapping process of respiration. Energy made available by a fuel molecule becomes incorporated into ADP and phosphate, and ATP is formed. *Hence ATP is the chief endproduct of respiration.*

ATP is also the energy vehicle; i.e., it emerges from the mitochondria and diffuses to all locations within a cell where energy must be utilized. In utilization, the above reaction proceeds to the left: ATP breaks down, energy is released and used, and ADP and phosphate reappear.

In summary, therefore, respiration as a whole consists of three correlated events. First, a fuel molecule is oxidized, which means most often that hydrogen is removed from it. The hydrogen becomes attached to an appropriate acceptor, and if the acceptor is oxygen, water forms. This phase of respiration may be termed *hydrogen transfer.*

Second, as a result of oxidation, the carbon-to-carbon bonds of the fuel molecule may be broken. Smaller fuel fragments then form, and they may be oxidized and broken up in turn until the original fuel has been degraded completely into 1-carbon fragments. These always appear in the form of CO_2. This phase of respiration constitutes *fuel breakdown.*

Third, also as a result of oxidation, energy becomes available. A little of this energy escapes as heat, indicating that respiration is not 100 per cent efficient. However, most of the energy does not become free in this manner but is instead harvested by the ADP/ATP system. ATP then forms the main product of respiration. This phase may be called *energy transfer*. We may symbolize these three events as in Fig. 14.1.

The above outlines the general pattern of respiration sufficiently for a basic understanding of the process. If we wish to carry this understanding one step deeper, we may discuss each of the three phases above in greater detail.

Energy transfer

THE PATTERN

We have just noted that the net result of respiration is a transfer of energy from chemical bonds in fuel into the chemical bonds of ATP. Why, then, respiration to begin with? If fuel energy already exists in the form of chemical bonds, what is the point of respiration if it only creates other chemical bonds?

Some bonds hold more energy than others. We may distinguish between *high-energy bonds* and *low-energy bonds*. To create the former, a relatively large amount of energy must be expended and a correspondingly large amount becomes available when such a bond is broken. However, most bonds in organic fuel molecules are of the *low*-energy type. For example, any of the carbon-to-carbon, carbon-to-hydrogen, carbon-to-nitrogen, or carbon-to-oxygen links we have encountered so far are low-energy bonds. If one of these is broken, only a comparatively small amount of energy becomes available.

A critical dilemma thus arises. On the one hand, organic fuels provide only bond energies of low intensity. But on the other, very concentrated, intense

packets of energy are needed for the synthesis of cellular components, for movement, and for metabolic work in general. Fuels, as it were, provide energy of popgun intensity, but metabolic work requires cannons. What is needed, clearly, is an energy-*intensifying* process, one which would pool the many low-energy packets of a fuel molecule into a smaller number of high-energy packets.

Respiration does just that. It first concentrates the low bond energies of fuel and creates within a fuel molecule one or more high-energy bonds. This is the crucial event in oxidation and in respiration as a whole. Then these high-energy bonds are transferred from fuel into the structure of ATP, a substance which is a high-energy carrier. Clearly, respiration accomplishes more than merely making new bonds out of old ones; it makes high-energy bonds out of low-energy bonds. And through ATP it supplies energy of uniformly high intensity to all points of utilization.

The creation of high-energy from low-energy bonds is achieved essentially by *internal reorganizations* of a fuel molecule. Each such molecule is characterized by a specific pattern of atoms, hence a specific pattern of bonds between the atoms. If a chemical change occurs, some of the atoms may change position, others may be removed, still others may be added. Whatever happens, the arrangement of the atoms will change and the pattern of the bonds will therefore change also. Many changes of this sort do not affect the content or distribution of the bond energies. But some do. And it may then happen that the original bond energies of the molecule become redistributed in such a way that one of the bonds comes to hold a great deal of energy, whereas others hold even less than before. In effect, a

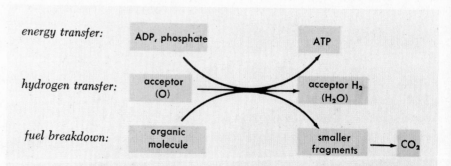

Fig. 14.1.   The three main phases of respiration: breakdown of fuel, hydrogen transfer from fuel, and energy transfer from fuel.

energy transfer: ADP, phosphate   ATP

hydrogen transfer: acceptor (O)   acceptor H$_2$ (H$_2$O)

fuel breakdown: organic molecule   smaller fragments ⟶ CO$_2$

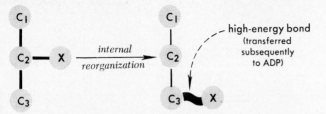

Fig. 14.2. Through internal reorganization of the atoms of a molecule, a high-energy bond may be created. Such a reorganization is an oxidative change.

high-energy bond will have been created at the expense of several low-energy bonds (Fig. 14.2).

If a molecular reorganization occurs which does redistribute the energy so that a high-energy bond is created, then we say that an *oxidation* has taken place. As already noted, one of the important types of oxidative changes is *dehydrogenation*, removal of hydrogen from a fuel. Other chemical changes which can be oxidative include removal of water (*dehydration*), removal of CO_2 (*decarboxylation*), and removal of electrons (a form of *ionization*). The last is particularly significant in respiration and occurs in many instances in conjunction with dehydrogenation, as we shall see. In sum, respiration includes oxidative reactions of the following general type:

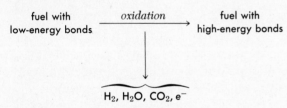

THE PROCESS

The principal high-energy bond in metabolism is the *phosphate bond*, that is, the bond which joins a molecule to a phosphate group (-$\textcircled{P}$). We have already encountered such -$\textcircled{P}$ groups earlier, e.g., in Chap. 11. Not all phosphate bonds are of the high-energy variety. But, put in terms of a crude approximation, the properties of the phosphate bond are such that it can contain a great deal of energy, much more than is needed simply to hold -$\textcircled{P}$ to a molecule. In that case, the phosphate bond in effect stores *extra energy;* it is

a high-energy bond. To distinguish the high-energy bond, we use the symbol $\sim$. Thus, we may have either

$$\text{fuel-}\textcircled{P} \qquad \textit{low-energy phosphate bond}$$

or

$$\text{fuel}\sim\textcircled{P} \qquad \textit{high-energy phosphate bond}$$

A low-energy phosphate bond may be converted into a high-energy phosphate bond if more energy becomes concentrated in it. As noted above, such energy enrichment of a bond may be achieved by oxidation. Hence we may have

$$\text{fuel-}\textcircled{P} \xrightarrow[\substack{\downarrow \\ H_2}]{oxidation} \text{fuel} \sim \textcircled{P} \qquad (1)$$

Clearly, before such a reaction can take place, "fuel-$\textcircled{P}$" must be available as a starting material. In other words, the addition of a low-energy -$\textcircled{P}$ group to a fuel molecule, or *phosphorylation*, will be an important preliminary toward the creation of high-energy bonds. Respiration actually includes such preliminary phosphorylations, and the creation of high-energy bonds proceeds according to the following general sequence of events:

$$\text{fuel} \xrightarrow[\substack{\downarrow \\ \text{-}\textcircled{P}}]{phosphorylation} \text{fuel-}\textcircled{P} \xrightarrow[\substack{\downarrow \\ H_2}]{oxidation} \text{fuel}\sim\textcircled{P} \quad (2)$$

The useful energy of the fuel is now concentrated in the high-energy bond of "fuel$\sim\textcircled{P}$." It is this high-energy phosphate group which can be harvested as a net gain of respiration. As noted earlier, the substance ADP accomplishes the harvesting by transforming into ATP. We already know that this transformation requires a phosphate group and energy, and this is precisely what "fuel$\sim\textcircled{P}$" can supply. The energy transfer may therefore be written:

$$\begin{array}{l} \text{fuel}\sim\textcircled{P} \qquad \text{fuel residue} \\ \\ \text{ADP} \qquad\quad \text{ADP} + \sim\textcircled{P} = \text{ATP} \end{array} \qquad (3)$$

In short, fuel$\sim\textcircled{P}$ hands over its $\sim\textcircled{P}$ to ADP, which becomes ATP as a result. And as a further result, the fuel may have broken up into smaller fragments. ATP now contains the original fuel energy, and

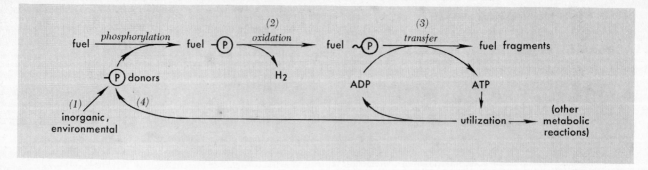

Fig. 14.3.   The general sequence of reactions in respiration.

ATP therefore may serve as an *energy donor* wherever energy is needed in a cell.

The entire energy aspect of respiration may be summarized as in Fig. 14.3. First, a given fuel molecule is phosphorylated. Then it is oxidized, resulting (1) in the liberation of hydrogen and (2) in the creation of a high-energy phosphate bond. Finally, the high-energy phosphate group is harvested by ADP, resulting (1) in the formation of ATP and (2) in the appearance of fuel fragments.

Note here that the chief product, ATP, holds not only energy but also phosphate groups. Hence ATP may serve in a cell not only as an energy donor but also as a *phosphate donor*. This answers a question. For where, we may ask, does the phosphate come from that phosphorylates a fuel to begin with? Ultimately, all phosphates come from the external environment as mineral nutrients. But the immediate phosphate source within cells in many cases is ATP. In other words, a small portion of the product of respiration must be funneled back to the beginning of respiration, to make more respiration possible at all.

What happens to the hydrogen removed from fuel-Ⓟ during oxidation? This question leads to a consideration of the second of the three phases of respiration.

Hydrogen transfer

THE PATTERN

We already know that dehydrogenation of a fuel requires the presence of a *hydrogen acceptor*. Atmospheric oxygen is an excellent acceptor. Yet fuels do not deliver H to oxygen directly. Moreover, oxygen may not always be available.

Fuels release hydrogen only to special organic acceptors of complex construction. Indeed, a whole series of such acceptors exists and, as in a bucket brigade, hydrogen from fuel is passed successively from one acceptor to the next, in fixed sequence. When oxygen is available, this gas functions as the last acceptor in the series; H_2O then forms as a byproduct of respiration. If we let *A*, *B*, *C* stand for different hydrogen acceptors, then the patterns of H transport to oxygen may be symbolized as follows:

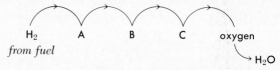

We may ask why such a succession of carriers is required at all. Could not hydrogen be passed on to oxygen directly? Indeed it could, and that this is so can be demonstrated readily in the test tube. When such a test-tube experiment is performed, hydrogen and oxygen are found to combine explosively. We should not conclude, however, that a similarly direct combination in cells would lead to explosion of cells; the quantities of gases involved there at any moment would probably be far too small to cause damage. The important conclusion is, rather, that the combination of hydrogen and oxygen is an *energy-yielding* process. And this undoubtedly explains the adaptive value of the succession of hydrogen carriers in cells. If hydrogen were to combine directly with oxygen, any energy released would appear suddenly, all at once. Most or all of it would then dissipate as heat and would become useless metabolically. But with a succession of carriers, the energy can be freed little by little and can become useful.

What is the source of this energy in hydrogen transfer? The source may be envisaged to be *electron energy;* we may note that "hydrogen transfer" in respiration actually includes *electron transfer*. Approximated crudely, we may picture this process by assuming that, at the start of a transfer sequence, hydrogen *ionizes* into two components, $[H^+]$ and $[e^-]$. The electron here may be thought of as a high-energy electron, and it alone rather than a whole hydrogen atom may be assumed to be passed by a succession of carrier molecules to the end of the transfer sequence. In the process, the energy of the electron may be thought to be "stepped down," as it were, and the energy so made available at each step can become useful. Each time a carrier molecule A "hands off" the electron to the next carrier B in the series, the carrier A is oxidized; as noted earlier, removal of an electron is an oxidative change. The energy obtained in such oxidations is again harvested by the ADP/ATP system. Symbolically:

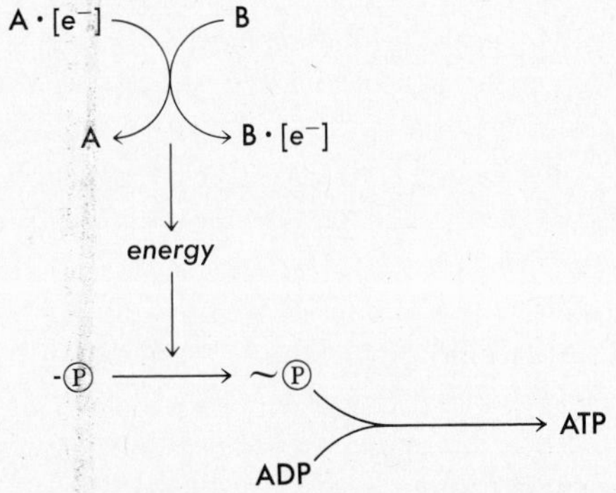

While an electron is carried through the transfer sequence, the hydrogen ion $[H^+]$ formed at the start of the sequence may be thought to remain free in the reaction medium and essentially passive. However, it rejoins its electron when the latter arrives at the end of the transfer sequence and here the hydrogen ion, the electron, and oxygen combine to form water:

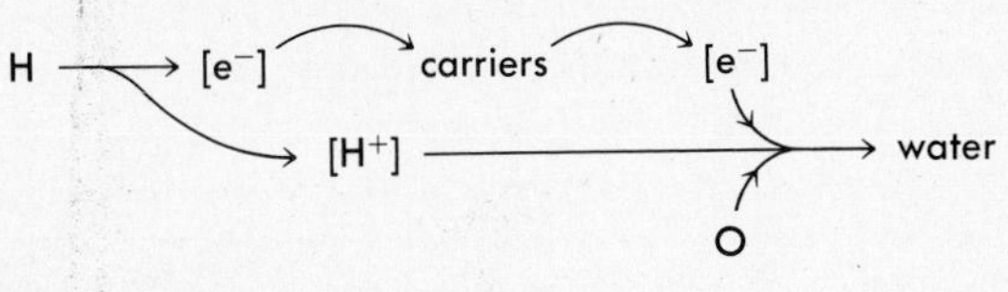

Thus, there are actually *two* sources of $\sim\text{P}$, hence of ATP, in respiration. One is the oxidation of fuel-P into fuel$\sim\text{P}$ by dehydrogenation, as outlined earlier. The other is the creation of $\sim\text{P}$ during electron transfer away from fuel (Fig. 14.4).

Of the two sources of $\sim\text{P}$, the second is the more important. It can be shown that, for every two electrons (derived from 2 H) transferred through the entire carrier series to oxygen, three ATP molecules are usually formed. A given fuel molecule yields numerous hydrogen pairs, hence numerous electron pairs, and the total ATP gained from their transfer to oxygen is usually far greater than the ATP gained from fuel dehydrogenation itself.

The whole pattern of electron and hydrogen transfer in respiration is clearly reminiscent of the analogous transfer in photosynthesis. As we have seen in Chap. 11, photosynthesis resembles respiration in that ATP is created during electron transfers. During photolysis, "low-energy" electrons from water become "high-energy" electrons in chlorophyll, and these electrons then become part of organic molecules. Now we note that respiration yields high-energy electrons which during their transfer to oxygen make energy available. There is a direct continuity in the history of these electrons. They originate in water and are passed successively to chlorophyll, to organic molecules, and finally back to water. Also, there is a direct continuity in the history of the energy. The energy originates in the sun and becomes incorporated into chlorophyll. In conjunction with electron transfers the energy then passes through photosynthesis into organic molecules

Fig. 14.4. **The two sources of ATP in respiration.** One source is oxidation of fuel, and a second is hydrogen transfer from fuel to oxygen.

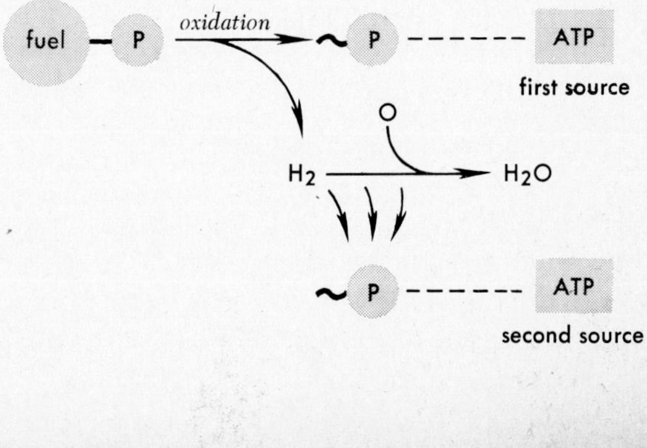

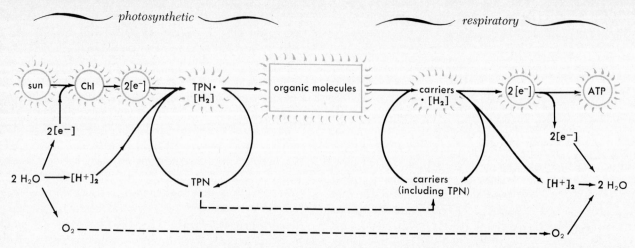

Fig. 14.5. The continuity of energy and electrons in photosynthesis and respiration.
Energy originating in the sun is transferred through photosynthesis into organic molecules
and from there through respiration into ATP. The electrons associated with this energy
transfer originate in water and ultimately again return to water. Note that the hydrogen
carriers in photosynthesis and respiration are partly identical.

and from there eventually into respiratory processes
and finally into ATP. We note once more that the ultimate energy donor of virtually all life is the sun, and
we may now add that the ultimate energy transfer is
associated with electrons which originate in water and
in the end return to water (Fig. 14.5).

AEROBIC TRANSPORT

What substances are the specific carriers in respiratory
electron transfer? To simplify description in the following, we may assume that whole hydrogen atoms, not
just their electrons, are being transferred from fuel
molecules to oxygen. We shall therefore speak of hydrogen carriers or acceptors, realizing, however, that
these substances are fundamentally electron carriers.
Three sets of such carriers play a role.

Two substances serve as the first acceptors when
hydrogen is removed from fuel: *diphosphopyridine
nucleotide,* or *DPN* for short, and *triphosphopyridine
nucleotide,* or *TPN* for short. The TPN here is the very
same that also serves as hydrogen carrier in photosynthesis. (Evidently, the photosynthetic role of TPN
is roughly the reverse of its respiratory role. In photosynthesis, TPN conducts hydrogen from water to food

via CO_2 fixation, and in respiration, it conducts hydrogen from food to water; see Fig. 14.5.)

As their names suggest, both DPN and TPN are
manufactured in part from nucleotides, in part from
pyridine. The latter is a derivative of one of the B
vitamins, namely, *nicotinic acid.* Here is the reason
why this vitamin is essential for life and why it must
be produced by plants and eaten by animals. Each of
their cells requires nicotinic acid as a vital building
material in the construction of DPN and TPN. In
some situations it is DPN, in others TPN, which functions as the first respiratory carrier. Either one accepts
H_2 removed from fuel and passes the hydrogen on to
the second set of carriers in the series to oxygen.

These second carriers are derivatives of another
component of the vitamin B complex, namely, *riboflavin,* or vitamin B_2. Riboflavin is converted in cells
into two types of compounds, either one of which may
function as a hydrogen acceptor. The two compounds
are *flavin adenine dinucleotide,* or *FAD* for short, and
flavin mononucleotide, or *FMN* for short. FAD or
FMN in turn "hands off" hydrogen to the third set of
carriers, which together represent the *cytochrome
system.* We have already encountered the cytochromes
as an electron-carrying system in photosynthesis. After

the cytochromes the last acceptor of hydrogen is oxygen, and water is the final product. Because oxygen is a required acceptor in this form of hydrogen transfer, the whole sequence is known as *aerobic*, or air-requiring, transfer. It is summarized in Fig. 14.6.

ANAEROBIC TRANSPORT

It should be clear that if hydrogen transfer as above is in some way made impossible, then aerobic respiration as a whole will become impossible. Actually, each step of the hydrogen-transfer chain can be blocked readily. For example, dietary deficiency of B vitamins will reduce or stop the availability of DPN/TPN and of FAD/FMN; cyanide poisons the cytochrome system and prevents it from functioning; and choking prevents oxygen from reaching cells altogether. Any one of these conditions prevents hydrogen removal from fuel, hence production of ATP. And as respiration is stopped, death may occur quickly.

But to a greater or lesser extent living organisms have a way out. Some are *anaerobes*, that is, they can subsist without oxygen. For example, certain bacteria today can live only in environments in which oxygen is absent; to them O_2 is actually a poison. (In this connection we may recall that when life first began, atmospheric oxygen probably did not exist at all and all organisms then must have survived without this gas.) Other organisms, notably some bacteria and fungi (e.g., yeast), can use O_2 if it is available, but if not, they can do without it. All remaining organisms are *aerobes* which must have oxygen for survival, yet even a man may get along without the gas for 2 or 3 minutes and can live anaerobically for that length of time.

Whenever oxygen supplies are inadequate or whenever hydrogen transport to oxygen is otherwise blocked, organisms may respire in a way which does not require oxygen. This is *anaerobic respiration*, or *fermentation*, probably the ancient original form of energy production inherited by all organisms. Under conditions of oxygen deficiency, this anaerobic type of respiration may become a substitute or a subsidiary source of energy.

The principle of anaerobic hydrogen transport is relatively simple: when the exhaust pipe of an engine is stopped up, the engine may still continue to operate

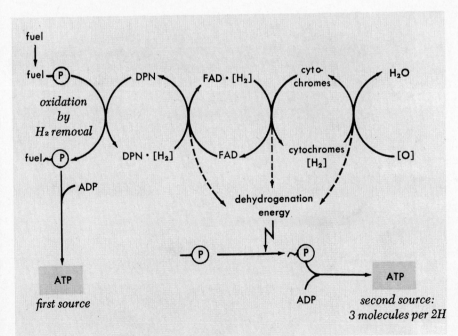

Fig. 14.6. Summary of aerobic hydrogen transfer.

if an alternative outlet for the waste gases is available. Oxygen is the normal outlet for hydrogen. If oxygen is unavailable, another final acceptor is used.

This alternative acceptor functions directly after DPN or TPN accepts hydrogen from fuel. The name of this alternative acceptor is *pyruvic acid* $(C_3H_4O_3)$. As we shall see shortly, this acid is produced normally during the respiratory breakdown of carbohydrate fuels. If oxygen is amply available, pyruvic acid is merely one of the intermediate steps in the combustion of carbohydrates. In other words, it is a fuel which in the presence of oxygen may be burned further. But pyruvic acid has the property of reacting readily with hydrogen. And if DPN or TPN cannot use its normal hydrogen outlet to FAD/FMN, pyruvic acid is used instead. The acid then ceases to be a fuel and becomes a hydrogen carrier.

When pyruvic acid combines with hydrogen, the result is the formation of *lactic acid* in animals and some bacteria and of *alcohol* and CO_2 in plants and some Protista. Different enzymes promote these reactions in plants and animals, hence the difference in the endproducts. The whole process is outlined in Fig. 14.7.

With these reactions, anaerobic respiration is com-

pleted. It should be clear that anaerobic respiration is precisely the same as aerobic respiration up to the point where DPN/TPN accepts hydrogen from fuel. Since only carbohydrates normally yield pyruvic acid directly, fermentation will be most efficient when carbohydrates are available as fuels.

The energy gained anaerobically is far less than that gained aerobically. First, with the path of oxygen blocked, the ATP normally created by H transfer to oxygen cannot be realized. Second, since pyruvic acid now functions as a hydrogen acceptor instead of a burnable fuel, all the potential energy still contained in pyruvic acid must remain unused. For these reasons, fermentation yields only about 5 per cent of the energy which could be obtained through aerobic respiration.

This small amount of energy nevertheless suffices to sustain anaerobic organisms. In most aerobes, however, the energy gained by fermentation alone is inadequate to sustain life for any length of time. If hydrogen transport to oxygen is blocked completely, cell death will occur quickly even though fermentation is under way. Yet fermentation may suffice to *supplement* aerobic respiration when energy demands are high. For example, during intensive physical activity among

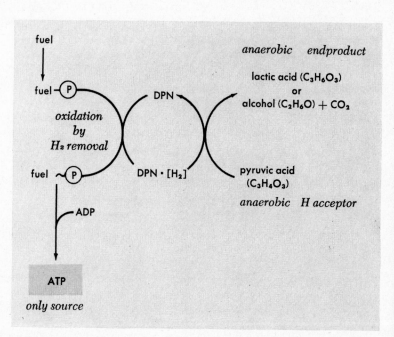

Fig. 14.7. Summary of anaerobic hydrogen transfer.

animals, the oxygen supply to the cells may be insufficient despite faster breathing and an *oxygen debt* will be incurred. Fermentation then proceeds in parallel with aerobic respiration and a little more energy so becomes available. Lactic acid will accumulate as a result, particularly in the muscles, which bear the burden of physical work. But note that the energy content of lactic acid, or of alcohol in plants, need not be lost permanently to an organism. Both lactic acid and alcohol are potential fuels which may be burned completely later, when oxygen supplies are again fully adequate.

These accounts of energy transfer and hydrogen transfer set the stage for a discussion of the third aspect of respiration, namely, the actual combustion of fuels.

Fuel combustion

THE PATTERN

In the course of reorganizing internally and thereby acquiring high-energy bonds, a fuel molecule becomes changed chemically. Sometimes the change is not great and the basic structure of the molecule is not affected. But sometimes the oxidative change may bring about a splitting of the carbon skeleton of the molecule. High-energy bonds may form regardless of whether a molecule splits or not, but when a split does occur, fragments with shorter carbon chains result. These are still energy-yielding fuels. Sooner or later they in turn may be split into still shorter chains. Eventually, fragments will arise which contain but a single carbon atom each.

This final 1-carbon breakdown product emerges from respiration in the form of CO_2. Carbon dioxide represents the end condition of all metabolic fuels. When a fuel has been degraded this far, all extractable energy has already been extracted. Complete degradation of a fuel to CO_2 can occur only in the presence of oxygen.

If we follow the sequence of fuel breakdown backward, then the next-to-last fuel fragment should consist of *two* linked carbons. This is the case. As we shall see shortly, the fundamental molecule representing the 2-carbon stage in respiration is a chemical relative of acetic acid called *acetyl*. This atomic grouping does not normally exist by itself but is combined with a carrier molecule, namely *coenzyme A* or *CoA* for short. We shall discuss the significance of CoA below; for the present we need note only that the 2-carbon stage in fuel breakdown is represented by the acetyl portion of the complex *acetyl CoA*. In other words, progressive breakdown eventually transforms all fuels to acetyl CoA, and this compound then yields 1-carbon CO_2.

The manner in which the stage of acetyl CoA is reached differs for different types of fuels. For example, many carbohydrates are first broken up into 3-carbon compounds. Carbohydrates often contain whole multiples of 3 carbons. As noted, photosynthesis yields a 3-carbon endproduct, and more complex carbohydrates are built up from such units. This holds for glucose and all other 6-carbon sugars, for 12-carbon disaccharides, and for polysaccharides such as starch and glycogen. When any of these are used as respiratory fuels, the original 3-carbon units reappear in the course of breakdown. Many other organic substances, glycerin, for example, are 3-carbon molecules to begin with. All such C_3 compounds are eventually converted to *pyruvic acid* ($C_3H_4O_3$). This acid is the common representative of the 3-carbon stage in respiration. Pyruvic acid subsequently loses one carbon in the form of CO_2 and becomes acetyl CoA.

Fatty acids and related molecules consist of long, even-numbered carbon chains. These do not break up into 3-carbon units, but become 2-carbon units directly. Other fuels are 2-carbon molecules to begin with, and all such C_2 compounds eventually appear as acetyl CoA. Amino acids break down partly to pyruvic acid (which subsequently becomes acetyl CoA), partly to acetyl CoA directly. This holds also for many other organic substances which may happen to be used as fuel.

Thus, the overall pattern of aerobic fuel combustion may be likened to a tree with branches or to a river with tributaries (Fig. 14.8). A broad main channel is represented by the sequence pyruvic acid → acetyl CoA → carbon dioxide. Numerous side channels lead into this sequence, some funneling into the 3-carbon pyruvic acid step, others into the 2-carbon acetyl CoA step. The side channels themselves may be long or short, and each may have smaller side chan-

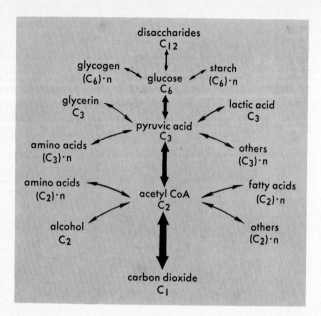

Fig. 14.8. Some of the main pathways in the aerobic combustion of fuels. Pyruvic acid, acetyl CoA, and carbon dioxide form a main sequence which other pathways join, like branches of a tree.

nels of its own. In the end, the flow from the entire system drains out as 1-carbon carbon dioxide.

In any of these breakdown sequences, the reaction pattern is essentially as discussed earlier. A fuel molecule is first phosphorylated, then oxidized, and then ATP is harvested. The resulting fuel fragments still are fuels, which are again phosphorylated, then oxidized, and then de-energized by formation of ATP. These processes occur repeatedly, until only CO_2 is left. During such reaction sequences, also, hydrogen is removed at several points, and all this hydrogen is transferred by the carriers to oxygen.

The actual chemical details of fuel breakdown are exceedingly complex. However, a highly simplified and abbreviated account suffices to provide an understanding of the basic sequence of events.

CARBOHYDRATE BREAKDOWN

As noted above, if carbohydrates are used as fuels they are burned first to 3-carbon pyruvic acid. In this process, polysaccharides and monosaccharides of all kinds

are first converted into phosphorylated six-carbon units; that is, carbohydrate fuels with long carbon chains are split up into C_6 fragments and to each such fragment a phosphate group is attached. We may symbolize the result as C_6-Ⓟ. If glucose is a fuel, it is similarly phosphorylated to C_6-Ⓟ. The subsequent transformations of such C_6-Ⓟ units are outlined in Fig. 14.9.

This figure shows that the reaction sequence consists, first, of successive further phosphorylations; that is, -Ⓟ groups become attached at *each* end of a C_6 chain. Then the chain splits into two C_3 chains, and more -Ⓟ groups are attached to the free ends of these C_3 chains. Second, in successive oxidations, all -Ⓟ groups now present are transformed into ~Ⓟ groups. And third, these high-energy phosphates are transferred to ADP. What is then left of the original fuel is a C_3 compound, namely, pyruvic acid, or $C_3H_4O_3$.

Note here that one of the intermediate steps in breakdown is PGAL, which is also the principal end-product of photosynthesis. Thus, when a plant cell creates photosynthetic PGAL, this molecule may be respired immediately to pyruvic acid, through the reactions to the right in Fig. 14.9. Alternatively, photosynthetic PGAL may be transformed to glucose or starch, and this occurs through the reactions to the left in Fig. 14.9, the sequence proceeding in reverse.

If we assume that the starting fuel is one molecule of glucose, $C_6H_{12}O_6$, then we note that it is broken up into 2 $C_3H_4O_3$, pyruvic acid. In the process also, 2 H_2 are released and 4 ATP are produced. In summary,

$$C_6H_{12}O_6 \xrightarrow[\text{4 ADP}]{} \begin{array}{c} \text{2 H}_2 \\ \rightarrow \text{2 C}_3\text{H}_4\text{O}_3 \\ \text{4 ATP} \end{array}$$

If respiration is *anaerobic,* the 2 H_2 will be accepted by the two pyruvic acid molecules formed and respiration will be completed. Four ATP molecules will then represent the gross energy gain. The net gain is smaller, for as outlined earlier, some of this ATP must be used in the phosphorylations at the start of the whole breakdown sequence.

On the other hand, if respiration is *aerobic,* the 2 H_2 will be transferred to oxygen, more ATP will be formed by this transfer, and the pyruvic acid remains free to be burned further.

This further breakdown of pyruvic acid is not unique to carbohydrates, for other fuels become pyruvic acid also. Certain amino acids, for example, or glycerin, each converts to pyruvic acid through its own special breakdown sequence. Thus, with the formation of pyruvic acid, from any original fuel source, we have reached the "mainstream" of respiratory breakdown from C_3 to C_2 to C_1.

C_3 TO C_1

The C_3 pyruvic acid stage becomes the C_2 acetyl CoA stage through a series of reactions in which both hydrogen and CO_2 are removed from pyruvic acid. In these reactions, DPN must be present as a hydrogen acceptor. Another required participant, playing a role in CO_2 removal, is a derivative of *thiamine*, vitamin B_1. This is the fundamental reason why every cell must possess thiamine for survival. A third vital participant is *coenzyme A*, or CoA, a compound which is likewise a derivative of one of the B vitamins, namely, *pantothenic acid*. Coenzymes are substances which

function like enzymes, that is, they speed up given reactions; but they are not proteins like true enzymes. Moreover, coenzymes appear to function only in conjunction with true enzymes. As noted earlier, CoA serves as a carrier molecule. More specifically, after CO_2 and H_2 have been removed from pyruvic acid, CoA combines with what is then left of the acid. The name of this remnant is *acetyl*, and acetyl CoA so results. In greatly abbreviated and simplified form:

$$\begin{array}{ccc} C_3H_4O_3 & & CO_2 \\ \textit{pyruvic acid} & \nearrow & \\ DPN \longrightarrow & \longrightarrow & DPN \cdot [H_2] \\ & \searrow & \\ CoA & & [C_2H_2O] \cdot CoA \\ & & \textit{acetyl CoA} \end{array}$$

The acetyl CoA stage is a main collecting point in respiration into which funnel many separate breakdown sequences. For example, fatty acids and certain amino acids are converted to acetyl CoA directly. Indeed, by one reaction pathway or another, directly or indirectly, *any* original fuel is eventually degraded to the 2-carbon acetyl of acetyl CoA, the next-to-last stage in fuel breakdown.

The final phase is the degradation of acetyl to

Fig. 14.9. Abbreviated summary of the respiratory degradation of carbohydrates to pyruvic acid. The formulas for chemicals are incomplete, showing only numbers of carbon atoms and phosphate groups.

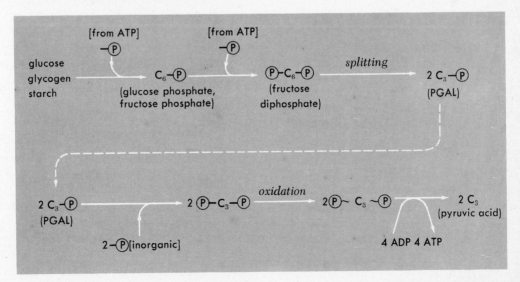

1-carbon CO_2. Note that, in this last segment of breakdown, different fuels no longer exist; the only fuel now is the single common compound acetyl CoA, regardless of what the original starting fuel may have been. Note also that this final phase of breakdown occurs specifically in the mitochondria. Carbohydrate breakdown, for example, can occur in other parts of a cell, but breakdown of acetyl CoA takes place only in the mitochondria.

This degradation has the form of a *cycle* of reactions. Acetyl CoA is funneled in at one point of the cycle; two carbons emerge at other points as CO_2; and the starting condition is eventually regenerated. The whole sequence is known as the *citric acid cycle*, a name taken from one of the substances which form the "endless belt" of the cycle. As we shall see, the energy harvested through this cycle is far greater than that gained in all previous reactions together. The citric acid cycle actually represents the most important phase of fuel breakdown as a whole.

We may depict this cycle as in Fig. 14.10. The figure shows that acetyl CoA first reacts with a C_4 compound normally present in cells. As a result, free CoA

Fig. 14.10.   Abbreviated summary of the citric acid cycle.

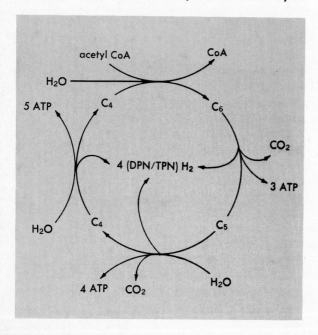

reappears and the acetyl portion together with the C_4 compound gives rise to a C_6 compound. This 6-carbon substance is *citric acid*. The latter subsequently loses two carbons in the form of CO_2, one at a time, and the starting condition is then regenerated. Apart from acetyl CoA, the only other raw material in the cycle is 3 H_2O. The products are 2 CO_2 and 4 H_2. These hydrogen pairs are accepted by DPN and TPN and are transferred to oxygen. In summary:

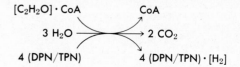

THE ENDPRODUCT

With the complete conversion of fuel to CO_2, combustion has reached its endpoint. What is the overall tally? We may illustrate by considering glucose as the starting fuel and by tracing the fate of its carbons, hydrogens, and oxygens.

As we have seen, the net conversion of one molecule of free glucose to pyruvic acid is described by the equation

$$C_6H_{12}O_6 \longrightarrow 2\ C_3H_4O_3 + 2\ H_2$$

Four ATP is obtained from glucose breakdown as such (if we disregard the amount of ATP needed for the initial phosphorylations). Moreover, each H_2 transferred via carriers to oxygen yields 3 ATP. Hence the transfer of the 2 H_2 above will yield 6 ATP, and the total aerobic energy gain up to the pyruvic acid stage is therefore 10 ATP.

Next, *two* pyruvic acid molecules are transformed into acetyl CoA, according to the equation

$$2\ C_3H_4O_3 + 2\ CoA \longrightarrow 2\ H_2 + 2\ CO_2 + 2\ C_2H_2O \cdot CoA$$

The energy yield here is 6 ATP, from the transport of 2 H_2 to oxygen.

Finally, in *two* turns of the citric acid cycle, one for each of the two acetyl CoA molecules,

$$2\ C_2H_2O \cdot CoA + 6\ H_2O \longrightarrow 8\ H_2 + 4\ CO_2 + 2\ CoA$$

Here the transport of the 8 H_2 to oxygen will yield 24 ATP.

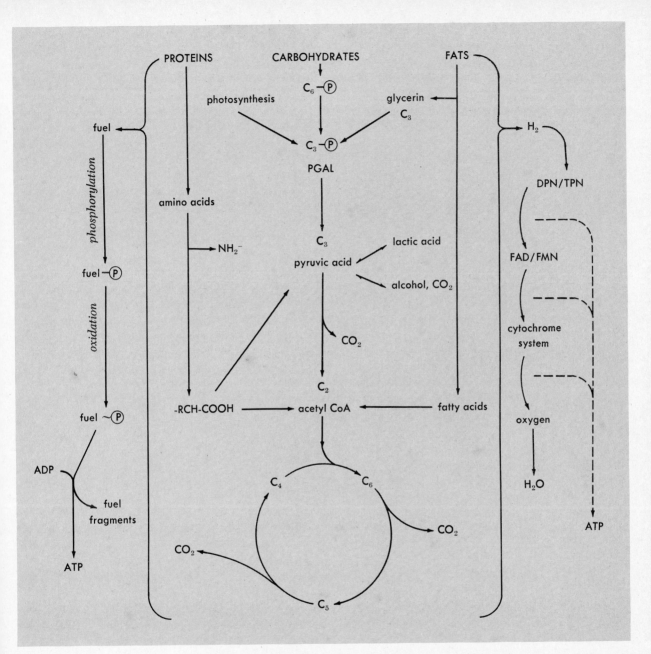

Fig. 14.11. Overall summary of respiration. The center panel outlines the main pathways of the respiratory breakdown of carbohydrates, fats, and proteins. Note here that all reactions shown are reversible and that if they are read in reverse, they may in some cases indicate pathways of synthesis. The left-hand panel summarizes the general nature of any of the respiratory reaction sequences which occur in the center panel, and the right-hand panel, similarly, summarizes the process of hydrogen transport. The two sources of ATP gain are indicated also.

If we now add the three equations above, we obtain

$$C_6H_{12}O_6 + 6\,H_2O \longrightarrow 6\,CO_2 + 12\,H_2$$

The 12 H_2 has been transferred to atmospheric oxygen, yielding water. Twelve oxygen atoms, or 6 O_2, are required to accept 12 H_2, and 12 H_2O then forms. Hence we have, overall,

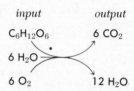

Moreover, the *major* endproduct is an energy yield of 40 molecules of ATP gross, for each molecule of glucose burned aerobically. This contrasts sharply with the gross yield of only 4 ATP when glucose is burned anaerobically. (The *net* gain can be shown to be about 38 ATP aerobically and 2 ATP anaerobically.)

If a fuel other than glucose is used, different quantities of oxygen are likely to be required and different amounts of CO_2, water, and ATP will be produced. Whatever the fuel, more ATP is always gained than is expended in phosphorylations, and it is this net gain which makes the long reaction sequences of vital adaptive value. The entire pattern of respiration is outlined in Fig. 14.11.

In cells, these metabolic processes take place exceedingly fast. For example, a glucose molecule is estimated to be burned completely within a single second. Considering the number of reactions, reactants, enzymes, carriers, and the like, such speed is truly impressive. In mammals, moreover, respiratory rates are greatly influenced by the thyroid hormone *thyroxin*. This hormone accelerates respiration in proportion to its concentration. How this effect is achieved and what particular reactions are influenced is still more or less completely unknown. Most organisms are not mammals, and their respiration is not under thyroxin control. Nevertheless, respiratory breakdowns still occur extremely rapidly. Very efficient enzyme action provides part of the answer. The remaining part of the answer undoubtedly lies in the close, ordered proximity of all required ingredients in the submicroscopic recesses of mitochondria. Just as a well-arranged industrial assembly line turns out products at a great rate, so do the even better arranged mitochondria.

The fate and function of their chief product, ATP, is our next subject.

Review questions

1. Contrast a fire with respiration. What is common? What is different? Which materials are fuels in respiration? What three general types of events occur in respiration?

2. What is oxidation? What happens to the atomic pattern of a molecule during oxidation? What is the result of oxidation in terms of bond energies?

3. Describe the role of phosphates in respiration. What is the ADP-ATP system, and how does it function?

4. What is dehydrogenation? Where does it occur, and what role does it play in respiration? In what general way is hydrogen transferred to oxygen? Review the pattern of ATP formation during this transfer. To which specific carriers is hydrogen first transferred from fuel?

5. Distinguish between aerobic and anaerobic respiration. In which organisms, and under what conditions, does either occur? Review the specific sequence of carriers in (a) aerobic H transfer and (b) anaerobic H transfer. How and where may transfer in (a) become blocked, and what happens then? What endproducts are formed in (b), and what are the subsequent fates of these?

6. What is the general significance of pyruvic acid, and CO_2 in the respiratory breakdown of fuels? Review the chief steps in the breakdown of carbohydrates to pyruvic acid.

7. Which classes of foods break down to pyruvic acid during respiration, and which to acetyl CoA? Describe the steps of these breakdowns.

8. Review the steps of the citric acid cycle. What is the total input and output of this cycle?

9. Review and summarize the overall fate of one mole-

cule of glucose during complete respiratory combustion. What is the total net input and what is the total net output? What happens to the individual atoms of glucose? What is the total ATP gain and how much is gained during each of the main steps of breakdown?

10. Review the general and the specific interrelations of respiration and photosynthesis. In what sense, if any, are the two processes the reverse of each other?

Suggested collateral readings

Green, D. E.: Enzymes in Teams, *Sci. Am.*, vol. 181, 1949.

———: The Metabolism of Fats, *Sci. Am.*, vol. 190, 1954.

———: Biological Oxidation, *Sci. Am.*, vol. 199, 1958.

Lehninger, A. L.: Energy Transformation in the Cell, *Sci. Am.*, vol. 202, 1960.

———: How Cells Transform Energy, *Sci. Am.*, vol. 205, 1961.

Levine, R., and M. S. Goldstein: The Action of Insulin, *Sci. Am.*, vol. 198, 1958.

Siekevitz, P.: Powerhouse of the Cell, *Sci. Am.*, vol. 197, 1957.

Stumpf, P. K.: ATP, *Sci. Am.*, vol. 188, 1953.

Zamecnik, P. C.: The Microsome, *Sci. Am.*, vol. 198, 1958.

ENERGY UTILIZATION

15

In what cellular processes must energy be expended? The answer is, in all processes which contribute to the maintenance and self-perpetuation of a cell.

Such processes include physical as well as chemical ones. The most important physical roles of energy are to produce *heat*, to some extent also to produce *light* and *electricity*, and above all, to produce *movement* of cells and cell parts. The chief chemical roles of energy are maintenance of respiration itself and, most particularly, maintenance of activities associated with the *synthesis* of new cellular components. Such components must be manufactured to offset the combustion and the wear and tear of existing ones, to make possible cellular repairs after injury, to maintain growth, and to permit reproduction. In all these processes of synthesis, energy is one requirement, structural building blocks in the form of nutrients are another. Under the heading of energy utilization, therefore, the two major subtopics are the *physical uses* and *chemical uses* of energy.

Physical uses of energy

MOVEMENT

Probably the most widespread physical use of ATP is made in production of movement, that is, either external locomotion of whole organisms or internal motion of parts of organisms. Among animals, *muscular* movement plays a particularly vital role in virtually all activities. For example, it is the muscular system which maintains breathing, heartbeat, blood pressure, posture, and shape, even during "inactive" periods like sleep. Moreover, muscles are quantitatively the most abundant tissues of animals, and a proportionately large fraction of all available energy must be expended to keep muscles contracting.

The functional units of a muscle cell are elongated organelles called contractile fibrils, or *myofibrils* (Fig. 15.1). They contain two proteins, *actin* and *myosin*, which form the basic contraction apparatus.

That this is so has been demonstrated dramatically by experiment. With appropriate procedures, actin and myosin can be extracted from muscle, and it can be shown that neither actin nor myosin alone is able to contract. But by mixing actin and myosin together, artificial fibers of *actomyosin* can be made. To these fibers may be added ATP. When this is done, it is found that as soon as ATP reaches an actomyosin fiber the latter contracts violently. Such contracting fibers may lift up to 1,000 times their own weight, just as a living muscle may do. And it is also found that, in a contracted fiber, ATP is no longer present but ADP is present instead.

Experiments of this sort provide clues to how contraction might be brought about in a living muscle. The process is far from being fully understood, but some of the main events are known. Muscle activity is at least a two-step cycle involving alternate *contraction* and *extension*. Energy is used up at some point or points in such a cycle. According to one view,

Fig. 15.1. The structure of skeletal muscle. A whole muscle fiber is shown at left. Note here the cross striations, the internal longitudinal myofibrils, and the many nuclei, which appear as dark patches. At right is an electron micrograph of a few individual myofibrils. Note that each myofibril in turn consists of bundles of still finer filaments, composed of the proteins actin and myosin. These latter are the functional units of the contraction apparatus. Note again the prominent cross striations. (Left, General Biological Supply House, Inc.; right, courtesy of Dr. K. R. Porter, Rockefeller Institute.)

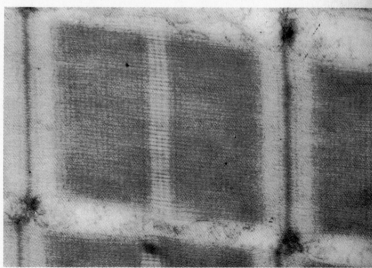

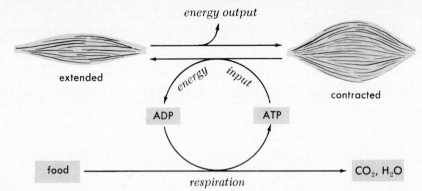

Fig. 15.2. The energy relations in muscle action. Food, via respiration, supplies energy for muscle contraction. Read the diagram from the bottom up.

energy must be expended to extend a muscle, as in stretching a rubber band. Contraction would then be automatic, like releasing an extended rubber band. A good deal of evidence appears to favor this hypothesis.

It is known in any event that the energy donor in muscle is ATP. To make the actomyosin fibrils of a muscle cell ready for contraction, respiratory ATP must be supplied to them. A muscle cell then stays in this energized condition until a nerve impulse arrives. Such an impulse triggers the contraction, just as letting go of a stretched rubber band initiates contraction. By the end of a contraction cycle ATP has been converted to ADP, and new respiratory energy must then be supplied to the actomyosin units to make a subsequent cycle possible (Fig. 15.2).

Muscular motion is not the only form of movement among organisms; *flagellary, ciliary,* and *amoeboid* movements are widespread as well. In all these, ATP again appears to be the common energy source. The action cycles here are understood even less well than

those of muscular contraction. Some evidence suggests that the beat of cilia and of flagella is produced by alternate contraction and relaxation of ultrafine protein filaments. If so, a machinery essentially like that of muscle may conceivably be involved. Contractile protein fibrils energized by ATP also may play a role in the movements of chromosomes during cell division.

HEAT, LIGHT, AND ELECTRICITY

Cellular heat has a number of sources (Fig. 15.3). One source is the external environment, which supplies heat in varying amounts. Another source is the heat generated within cells by the friction of moving parts. A third and major source is food and ATP. Within cells, neither food nor ATP are used with 100 per cent efficiency. Not all food energy is trapped as ATP, and in ATP utilization some of its energy escapes without doing useful metabolic work. This energy dissipates in the form of heat. Moreover, when

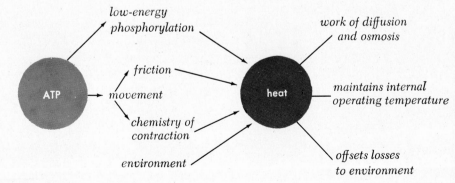

Fig. 15.3. The principal sources and functions of heat in organisms.

ATP phosphorylates a fuel in respiration, ATP loses a high-energy $\sim$ⓟ group, but the fuel only gains a low-energy -ⓟ group. The energy difference between $\sim$ⓟ and -ⓟ again dissipates in the form of heat.

Within organisms, heat maintains body temperature and offsets heat lost to the environment by evaporation and radiation; creates tiny convection currents within cells and so assists in diffusion and osmosis in and among cells; and provides adequate operating temperatures for enzymes and all other functional parts of cells. Heat production in birds and mammals is balanced dynamically against heat loss, and a constant body temperature is thereby maintained. But constant or not, heat is an essential requirement of every organism; and if ATP served no other function than heat production, it would still be among the most vitally necessary components of living matter.

"Living" light is emitted by virtually all major groups of organisms. Monera, Protista, and virtually all animal phyla include marine or terrestrial representatives which are bioluminescent. Evidently, the capacity to produce light has developed independently several times during evolution. Yet the essentials of the light-generation mechanism appear to be alike in all cases. The main parts of this mechanism are two substances, *luciferin* and *luciferase*, present in light-producing cells. When oxygen and ATP are added to these proteins, a flash of light is produced. If more O_2 and ATP are added, a new flash is generated. That this is so can be shown by experiments with extracts of bioluminescent cells.

Bioluminescent organisms may stay lit up for appreciable periods or may produce brief flashes (Fig. 15.4). In bioluminescent animals, light emission depends on nervous stimulation of specialized cells in light-producing organs. The light emitted by different organisms may be of any wavelength in the visible spectrum; to the human eye it may be red, yellow, green, or blue. The actual wave length of the emission is probably determined by the particular chemical makeup of luciferin. In some cases, two or more kinds of luciferin may occur in a single organism, and such an organism then may light up in several colors. In all cases, the available energy is spent very efficiently, for little heat is lost during light production. Hence the frequent designation of living light as "cold" light. Also,

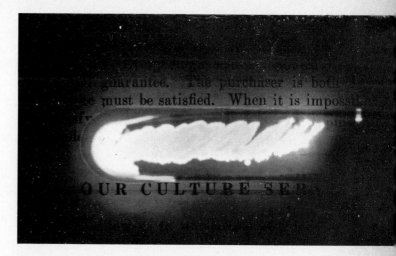

Fig. 15.4. Test-tube culture of bioluminescent bacteria. The continuous light they emit is strong enough to illuminate a portion of a printed page. (Carolina Biological Supply Co.)

the unit intensity of the light is remarkably great. It compares favorably with that of modern fluorescent lamps.

Bioelectricity is a byproduct of all cellular processes in which ions play a part. In other words, electricity is as common throughout the living world as table salt. However, certain eels and rays are highly specialized in their capacity to produce electricity. These fish possess *electric organs* composed mainly of modified muscles. The cells here are disk-shaped and noncontractile, and they are piled into stacks. Assemblies of this sort function somewhat like storage batteries connected in series.

The details of operation here are understood less well than those of light production. However, it is known that the generation of electricity depends on ATP and a substance called *acetylcholine*. Electricity is produced when acetylcholine splits into separate acetyl and choline fractions. The two are then recombined into acetylcholine, with energy from ATP. As in light production, the efficiency of energy utilization is remarkably great. So also is the intensity of the electricity generated. An electric eel may deliver a shock of up to 400 volts, enough to kill another fish or to jolt a man severely or to light up a row of electric bulbs wired to a tank into which such an eel is put. Nervous

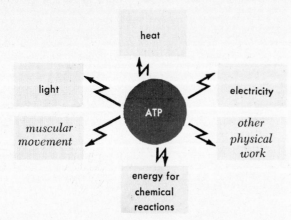

Fig. 15.5.   General summary of the functions of ATP.

stimulation of the electric organ triggers the production of electricity.

It is still unknown just how the chemical energy of ATP is actually converted into light energy or electric energy. But that ATP is the key is clearly established, and this versatile compound emerges as the source of all forms of living physical energy, usual or unusual (Fig. 15.5). Indeed, ATP is even more versatile, for it is also the source of all living *chemical* energy.

Chemical uses of energy

The energizing of *synthesis* reactions represent the chief chemical role of ATP. A cyclical interrelation is therefore in evidence. On the one hand, breakdown of organic compounds leads to a net buildup of ATP through respiration. On the other hand, breakdown of ATP leads either to physical activity as discussed above or to a net buildup of organic compounds through chemical synthesis. Figure 15.6 outlines this basic cycle of energy and materials which governs the overall metabolism of all cells.

Synthesis of cellular components and breakdown occur simultaneously, all the time. As already noted in the last chapter, breakdown may affect any cellular constituent regardless of composition or age. A protein just synthesized through long reaction sequences and at great expense of energy is as likely to be destroyed

as a glucose molecule already present for days. A certain *percentage* of all cellular constituents is decomposed every second. Which constituents actually make up this percentage is largely a matter of chance.

Such randomness applies also to synthesis. Regardless of the source of materials, a certain percentage of available molecular components is synthesized every second into finished cell substance. If synthesis and breakdown are exactly balanced, the net characteristics of a cell may remain unchanged. But continuous *turnover* of energy and materials occurs nevertheless, and every brick in the building is sooner or later replaced by a new one. Thus the house always remains "fresh."

Synthesis and breakdown cannot sustain each other in a self-contained, self-sufficient cycle, even when the two processes are exactly balanced. Energy dissipates irretrievably through physical activities and through heat losses in chemical reactions; and materials dissipate through elimination, evaporation, and friction. Just to maintain a steady state, therefore, a cell must be supplied continuously with energy and raw materials: solar energy, CO_2, and water in the case of photosynthesizing cells, and in the case of all other cells, condensed packages of these three, namely, organic nutrients. Very often, moreover, the rate of supply of such materials must exceed the rate required for mere maintenance, for net synthesis may exceed net breakdown. This is the case, for example, in growth, in repair after injury, and in cells which manufacture secretion products.

Two broad classes of synthesis reactions may be distinguished: *maintenance synthesis*, in which the reaction products stay within the producing cell and

Fig. 15.6.   The fundamental metabolic balance of cellular energy and materials.

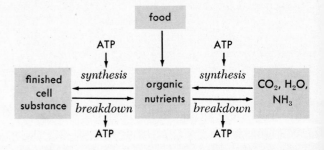

usually contribute to the survival of that cell; and *export synthesis*, in which the reaction products leave the producing cell and often contribute to the survival of other cells.

MAINTENANCE SYNTHESIS

The overall function of maintenance synthesis is the manufacture of all those cellular constituents which a cell does not obtain directly as prefabricated nutrients or secretions from other cells. Such missing constituents include most of the critically necessary compounds for cellular survival: nucleic acids, structural and enzymatic proteins, polysaccharides, fats, and numerous other groups of complex organic substances.

Many of these compounds are manufactured by reactions which are nearly the reverse of breakdown reactions. For example, the synthesis of many polysaccharides and fats in effect has already been discussed: read in reverse, the respiratory and digestive reactions outlined in preceding chapters describe such syntheses adequately. Moreover, similar enzymes, vitamins, and other reaction aids function at the same steps in the reversed sequences. Acetyl CoA often represents a fundamental starting compound, and from it may be produced fatty acids as well as pyruvic acid, glycerin, and glucose. Combination of numerous 6-carbon units, accompanied by removal of water, then may yield polysaccharides. Combination of fatty acids and glycerin, similarly accompanied by dehydration, may yield fats.

The purely chemical aspects of the synthesis of nucleic acids and proteins in many instances are likewise the reverse of breakdown reactions. In the case of proteins, a cell first obtains or manufactures $-NH_2$ and $-RCH-COOH$ groups. These are then combined into amino acids, and the latter are subsequently joined enzymatically to form proteins. Analogously, nitrogen bases, C_5 sugars, and phosphates are joined to form nucleotides, and these are subsequently combined into nucleic acids.

However, the synthesis of nucleic acids and proteins also has vital biological aspects which make it not simply the reverse of chemical breakdown. First, unlike most other compounds, nucleic acids and proteins are synthesized only in special "factory" locations.

Nucleic acids originate in the *chromosomes* of the nucleus; proteins, in the *ribosomes* of the cytoplasm. Second, again unlike other compounds, both nucleic acids and proteins are specific; that is, each cell must manufacture very particular, unique sets of each of these compounds. If a cell contains glycogen, for example, all such glycogen molecules are alike. But all nucleic acid molecules and all protein molecules are decidedly not alike. We have already discussed this condition of specificity in Chap. 5. Because of the specificity requirement, more is needed for nucleic acid and protein synthesis than simply appropriate raw materials, enzymes, and ATP. What is needed in addition is *specificity control*, that is, regulation of the particular sequence in which given nucleotides are linked into a nucleic acid and in which given amino acids are linked into a protein.

The crucial specificity control is exercised by the nucleic acids themselves, notably by the chromosomal deoxyribose nucleic acids (DNA) which form the genes. As already pointed out in Chap. 4, genes carry chemically coded building instructions, and these specify the exact makeup of all the DNA and all the proteins to be synthesized in a cell. We shall see in the next chapter just how the genetic code is believed to influence actual synthesis. It is this immediate genetic control which makes nucleic acid and protein synthesis critically different from all other syntheses. Direct gene control is not essential in carbohydrate synthesis, for example. Starting molecules such as glucose are all alike, and regardless of which two glucose molecules are joined by synthesis, the result will always be the same maltose. All nucleotides or all amino acids are not alike, however, and it makes a great difference which particular two nucleotides or which particular two amino acids are joined. Hence the requirement of direct genetic control in such cases (Fig. 15.7). Note, incidentally, that *breakdown* of any compound, nucleic acids and proteins included, can occur without the immediate participation of genes; for the precise pattern of breakdown is relatively unimportant so long as breakdown is accomplished in *some* way. Pattern becomes important only in building.

Newly synthesized compounds of all kinds contribute to the maintenance of a cell according to patterns already outlined in Chap. 5. For example,

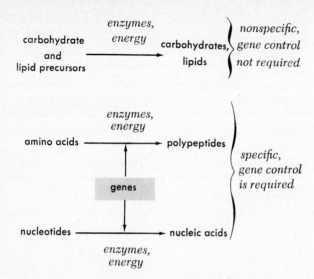

Fig. 15.7. The requirement of specificity control in protein and nucleic acid synthesis. Without gene control, the structural pattern of new proteins and nucleic acids would not match the pattern of preexisting proteins and nucleic acids.

new nucleic acids become part of chromosomes. Newly formed proteins might become incorporated into various fibrils, membranes, mitochondria, chloroplasts, or indeed any other cellular organelle. Alternatively, the properties of a newly manufactured protein might be such that it may come to function as a specific enzyme. Like proteins, fats and carbohydrates become part of the structural and functional makeup of cells. In addition, as we have seen, they serve importantly as storage materials.

Apart from these main categories of chemicals, cells also contain large numbers of other compounds, many of them derivatives of the main categories. Manufactured through special reaction sequences, such substances include, for example, ATP, DPN, cytochrome, and others we have already encountered in various contexts. Some types of synthesis reactions are restricted to specific, variously specialized cell types. A good example of this is the production of chlorophyll and of pigments generally in particular cell types only. Characteristic synthesis products of certain tissues, plant tissues especially, have often proved to be useful to man—rubber, quinine, caffeine, nicotine, to mention only a few. It is still largely unknown what func-

tions, if any, such substances might have in the very cells in which they are manufactured. Inasmuch as such compounds are not formed universally in all cells, they cannot be of general significance in metabolism. In some cases at least, constituents of this type probably represent unique waste products, permanently retained in the cells of organisms which do not possess specialized excretory systems.

EXPORT SYNTHESIS

Every cell is an exporting cell to some extent; for at the very least it exports metabolic wastes such as CO_2 and often water. The term *excretion* is generally used to refer to exported wastes, although what is waste in one cell may often be an essential material in another cell (e.g., H_2O). Specifically synthesized product which are exported from cells and are clearly not wastes are given the general designation *secretion*.

Secretions may have a variety of roles: *nutritive* (e.g., glucose secreted by photosynthesizing cells); *digestive* (e.g., enzymes poured into the gut); *excretory* (e.g., urea formation by liver cells); *regulative*

Fig. 15.8. Glandular hair from the stem of a geranium plant. (Courtesy of Dr. M. S. Fuller, University of California, Berkeley.)

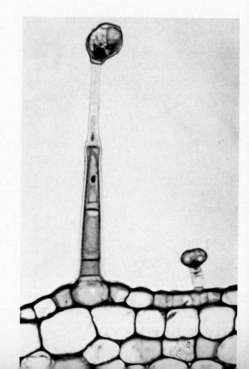

(e.g., hormones secreted by given plant and animal cells); *supportive* (e.g., secretion of cellulose in plants, bone substance in animals); *reproductive* (e.g., aromatic scents secreted by plants and animals); or variously *protective* (e.g., secretion of irritants and poisons by plant and animal cells, including the secretions of antibiotics by soil organisms). Indeed, there are few functions in any organism that do not require cellular secretions of some sort.

In multicellular organisms, cell groups which are specialized for the manufacture of given secretions are known as *glands*. Among plants, for example, the digestive juices produced by leaves of carnivorous species are manufactured in glands. Many vascular plants of saline soils possess root glands which secrete salt.

Young leaves in the buds of many woody plants develop temporary glandular hairs which secrete a gummy substance covering the entire bud and protecting the bud during the winter (Fig. 15.8).

Among animals, glands are broadly of two types. So-called *endocrine* glands are ductless, and they secrete into the blood. *Hormones* are the characteristic products of endocrine glands. Other secretions are manufactured in *exocrine* glands, which empty their products into free spaces or into ducts. Among glands of this type are digestive glands (e.g., liver, pancreas, salivary glands), skin glands (e.g., sweat glands, various oil- and wax-secreting glands), and numerous glands associated with the reproductive, circulatory, and other systems (Fig. 15.9).

Fig. 15.9. Sections through skin showing exocrine glandular structures. Left, the meandering duct of a sweat gland; right, the secreting pouches of a sebaceous gland. These glands produce an oily secretion, which keeps hair soft and pliable. (Courtesy of Dr. William Montagna, University of Oregon.)

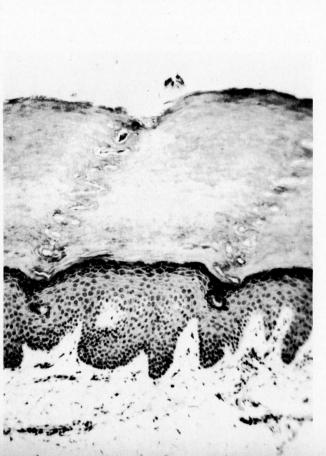
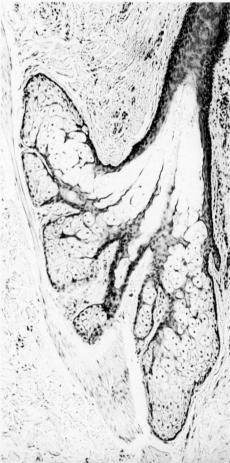

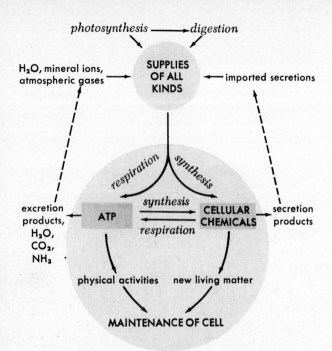

Fig. 15.10. The overall pattern of metabolism and its chief component processes.

Added to materials synthesized and used *within* a given cell, secretions received from *other* cells complete the list of ingredients required for the formation of new cellular substance. This total multitude of chemicals, built up at the expense of ATP, then maintains and perpetuates the body of a cell (Fig. 15.10). But it must not be imagined that newly constructed compounds just happen to arrange themselves into new living material. If the proteins, fats, and other components were merely mixed together in water, the result would be a complex but lifeless soup. New cellular constituents become living matter only if older living matter provides the framework; the house may be added to and its parts may be replaced or modified, but an altogether new house cannot be built. That apparently occurred only once during the history of the earth.

Review questions

1. Describe the internal structure of a muscle. What and where is actomyosin? What are the roles of ATP in muscle? In what specific ways is the ATP supply maintained? Describe the energetic aspects of a unit cycle of muscle activity.

2. What different kinds of movements occur in organisms and their cells? What is known about the role of energy in these movements?

3. In what ways does an organism obtain and produce heat? What are the functions of heat in metabolism?

4. Describe the ways in which organisms produce light and electricity. What are the properties of bioluminescence and bioelectricity as compared with nonliving forms of these energies?

5. Describe the basic balance of synthesis and break-down in living organisms. How does protein specificity influence the ingredients required for protein synthesis? What are the ingredients? By what general sequence of processes does protein synthesis occur, and where?

6. Describe the specific sequence of reactions through which acetyl CoA in cells could be synthesized into (*a*) fats and (*b*) glycogen or starch. If necessary, consult Chap. 14. What are the various possible functions of proteins, fats, and carbohydrates synthesized in cells?

7. What are export syntheses? What are some of their metabolic and self-perpetuative functions? What is a gland? Describe the function of various glands in animals.

8. Review and summarize the broad components of metabolism as a whole, and review the general relation between metabolism and self-perpetuation.

Suggested collateral readings

Gale, E. F.: Experiments in Protein Synthesis, *Sci. Am.*, vol. 194, 1956.

Green, D. E.: The Synthesis of Fat, *Sci. Am.*, vol. 202, 1960.

Hayashi, T.: How Cells Move, *Sci. Am.*, vol. 205, 1961.

Hayashi, T., and G. A. W. Boehm: Artificial Muscle, *Sci. Am.*, vol. 187, 1952.

Huxley, H. E.: The Contraction of Muscle, *Sci. Am.*, vol. 199, 1958.

Johnson, F. H.: Heat and Life, *Sci. Am.*, vol. 180, 1949.

Katchalsky, A., and S. Lifson: Muscle as a Machine, *Sci. Am.*, vol. 190, 1954.

McElroy, W. D., and H. H. Seliger: Biological Luminescence, *Sci. Am.*, vol. 207, 1962.

part 5

The Functions of Life: *Steady States*

Metabolism is one half of life; self-perpetuation is the other. The system which only metabolizes is but an inanimate machine and an uncoordinated machine at that. To ensure internal coordination, to allow it to meet the impact of the external environment, and therefore to make it a *living* system, it must perform the processes of self-perpetuation.

We recall that self-perpetuation comprises three groups of activities: first, processes which control the *steady state* of living units and so prolong individual life as long as inherently possible; second, processes of *reproduction*, which extend the operations of living units in space and in time; and third, processes of *adaptation*, which mold and fit the long-term characteristics of living units to the characteristics of specific environments.

In this set of chapters we deal with control functions, on which all other forms of self-perpetuation are based. First we examine the nature of *control systems* generally and the role of *genes* specifically, the ultimate controllers of steady states. Subsequently we inquire into the action of *growth factors* such as vitamins and hormones and into their controlling influence on cells and whole plants and animals. Lastly we direct our attention to specialized animal control functions without counterparts in plants, namely, various functions of the *circulatory*, the *excretory*, and the *nervous systems*.

CONTROL: GENES

16

The built-in control systems of organisms adjust living processes in such a way that operating conditions tend to be maintained in an optimal, *steady* state, despite changes in the environment. Different control systems accomplish this in different ways, yet in all cases the underlying principles of control action are the same. This common *pattern of control* will be the subject of the first part of this chapter. The second part will be concerned with *genetic control*. Genes are the most fundamental regulating agents in living matter, and on their action depends the operation of all other control devices. Genes so form the foundation of all steady-state maintenance and indeed of all self-perpetuation.

The pattern of control

To define "control," we first define *stress:* any external or internal condition which tends to upset the normal, smooth operations of a system may be regarded as a stress. In a living organism, *external* stresses are often produced by the environment: by enemies, injurious agents, lack of food, change of temperature, and innumerable other physical, chemical, and biological conditions. *Internal* stresses arise continuously as a result of the very processes of life: fuels are used up, concentrations change, parts age and wear out, waste products accumulate, etc. In so far as any external or internal change, usual or unusual, affects living matter, it also becomes a more or less significant stress. Actually, the living system is under stress all the time.

The problem of maintaining a steady state, therefore, is to counteract or to relieve stress. The requirement for this is, first, ability to *recognize* stress when and where it exists, and second, ability to *react* to such stress in self-preserving fashion. What is needed, in other words, is ability to recognize a *stimulus* and ability to carry out an appropriate *response* to that stimulus. So long as a system recognizes stimuli and reacts to them with fitting responses, it exercises *control*. And it may then remain intact and functioning, despite stresses which would otherwise upset its internal coordination. Thus the net result of control in living matter is steady state, and the net result of steady state is maintenance of life for the longest possible time.

CONTROL SYSTEMS

In a system composed of many parts acting cooperatively, as in living matter, steady state will be preserved if the parts may continue to act in harmony despite stress. If a stimulus should change the action of one part, then, in response, the action of all other parts should change correspondingly in such a way that the total action of the system still remains integrated and coordinated.

To achieve such persisting internal coordination, a first fundamental requirement is continuous and rapid *flow of information* among the parts of the system. Each part must be kept informed of what other parts are doing, so that, if a stimulus affects one part, other parts may receive notice of it. Moreover, if the system is capable of responding to a stimulus in more than one way, a second fundamental requirement is ability to make *selections*. A simple system designed to give always the same response is not required to select. But where several response possibilities exist, ability to decide among them clearly is crucial; choice of inap-

propriate responses leads to unsteady, not steady, states (Fig. 16.1).

Thus "control" ultimately becomes a matter of information and of selection. These terms imply messages or signals of some sort, message carriers, senders, receivers, transmission pathways, relays, switches, channel selectors—in short, all the components of a communications system. Indeed, in one form or another, communications systems are found wherever steady states are maintained. In living matter we find them within cells and between cells, within organisms and between organisms, on all levels of organization. Such systems are control systems.

System organization. All living control systems operate on a common pattern. An initial stimulus irritates, or *excites*, a receiving device, called a *receptor*. Excitation of this receptor causes the emission of a signal, which is transmitted over a *sensory pathway* to an interpreting and response-selecting device. The latter may be referred to generally as the *modulator*. This component sends out an appropriately chosen command signal over an appropriately chosen *motor pathway*. The signal leads to an *effector*, a device which

Fig. 16.1.   The general pattern of maintenance and control of steady state.

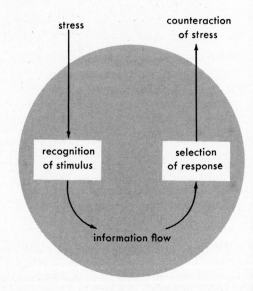

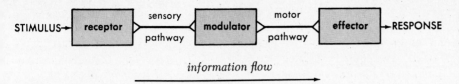

Fig. 16.2. **The pattern of the control components in living matter.**

executes the commands. This is the response which counteracts the original stimulus (Fig. 16.2).

We may illustrate the operation of such a system by means of a mechanical model. Suppose that the water level of a flow tank, as in Fig. 16.3 is to be maintained in steady state. That is, despite possible variations of inflow or outflow (e.g., if an obstruction develops in one of the pipes, or if someone resets the speed of inflow or outflow), the water level is to stay at a predetermined height. Such a system is an *open system,* since materials are continuously entering and leaving; and the problem is to maintain a *dynamic equilibrium.* In these respects the model corresponds closely to living entities, which also are open systems maintained in dynamic balance. By contrast, in a closed system nothing enters or leaves, and balance is a static equilibrium.

To establish a dynamic equilibrium in our model, we must install an automatic control device. Without help from external agencies, such a mechanism ought to be able to "sense" any change in water flow, and, by means of valves, it should so readjust the inflow and the outflow that the water level in the tank remains relatively constant.

We have equipped our tank with automatic controls in Fig. 16.4. An air-filled float R functions as receptor. Inasmuch as it moves up or down with the water, it senses changes of water level. Any up or down motion of R is communicated via a rod sp, the sensory pathway, to the modulator M. Here the sensory message—up or down motion of sp—is interpreted and appropriate commands for response are sent out. Imagine M to be a simple electrical trigger mechanism. It might be so built that any upward motion of sp trips a switch which makes an electric current of certain strength and duration flow through the wires mp. Similarly, any downward motion of sp would reverse the switch position and another electrical impulse, of different strength and duration, would be produced. Indeed, possible switch positions might be

Fig. 16.4. **Model of a steady-state–maintaining device.** R, receptor; M, modulator; E, effector; sp, sensory pathway; mp, motor pathway. If the system is adjusted as described in the text, then any change of inflow or outflow will bring about signals through $R \rightarrow sp \rightarrow M \rightarrow mp \rightarrow E$. Valve positions will then be adjusted in such a way that the change of inflow or outflow will be counteracted and an original water level in the tank will be reestablished.

Fig. 16.3. **The difference between an open and a closed system.** Continuous flow characterizes the open system, and if a balanced condition is attained, the equilibrium is dynamic. Nothing enters or leaves the closed system, and if an equilibrium is attained, it is static.

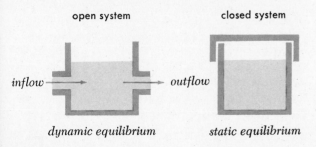

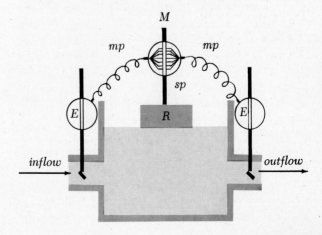

more numerous and each might cause the flow of a current of unique characteristics. These electrical impulses are the command signals, transmitted over the motor pathways *mp* to the two effectors *E*. The effectors are engines which operate the valves at the inflow and the outflow. They are so built that each different command signal received makes them move the valves into different positions.

Imagine now that for some external reason the inflow decreases. The outflow is still as before; hence the water level will begin to drop. But at once the modulator *M* will be informed of this change via *R* and *sp*. Appropriate electric signals will now go to the effectors and the inflow valve will open more, the outflow valve close more. As a result, before the water level can drop very far, the net inflow will increase and the water will rise back to normal. This new change of level will again be communicated to the modulator; new signals will go out to the effectors; and the valves will be returned to their original position.

If at this point the inflow is still reduced, the control device will go into action once more, precisely as above. Clearly, by readjusting as often as necessary, the device is capable of maintaining a steady state despite changes in the "environment."

System properties.   Our model illustrates a number of features common to control systems, living ones included.

First, internal *operating energy* is needed to make the system work. In the model, energy is required for the transmission of electric signals and for the motors which move the valves. In living control systems, similarly, small amounts of energy are needed for the transmission of information and comparatively large amounts of energy are required to operate the effectors. All these energy requirements are supplied by ATP.

A second common feature of control devices is that response to a stimulus is not a sudden, single event, but a stepwise, repeated one. In our model, a small initial change in valve position will produce a small initial change in water level. The receptor immediately signals to the modulator that a certain adjustment has been carried out. Accordingly, the modulator then cues the effectors to continue, to stop, or

to reverse operations. The resulting effector action is essentially a new stimulus, which is again communicated back via the receptor to the modulator. Continuous information thus passes from sensory to motor component and from motor back to sensory component. Many such cyclical passages of information, each contributing a small effector action, are usually required before a total response to a stimulus can be achieved. Indeed, the control device is not at rest even then. For in the absence of environmental stimuli, the receptor in effect signals "no change" to the modulator, the modulator sends "no adjustment required" to the effector, and the effector then informs the receptor of "no operation."

In such unceasing cyclical passages of information, we note that a response is "fed back" into the sensory end of the regulating device as a new stimulus, informing of the degree of counteraction already accomplished. The new stimulus in turn, fed into the modulator, informs of the degree of counteraction yet to be carried out. *Feedback* is to the motor-sensory segment of the cycle what modulation is to the sensory-motor segment. Both feedback and modulation control the direction, the amount, and the duration of adjustment. In living matter, as elsewhere, control activity becomes *effective* control only if appropriate feedbacks are operative. Without feedback, the modulator would never become aware of what the effector has been doing; hence it would never be able to send out "correct" new commands (Fig. 16.5).

Feedbacks and continuous cycles of information account for a third common property of control systems: they function essentially by *trial and error*, by "hunting" for the correct equilibrium condition. Refer again to our model in Fig. 16.4. Suppose that the inflow changes so as to cause an initial drop in water level. Depending on the sensitivity of the apparatus, a given number of seconds may elapse before the valves are brought into corrective positions. By that time, the water level may be down 1 inch, say. Now the water begins to rise, but again there will be a time lag of some seconds before the effectors receive the new command to return the valves to normal. By that time the water may already have risen somewhat *above* the correct level. Fresh signals to reverse valve positions a bit will now be forthcoming, and by the time that

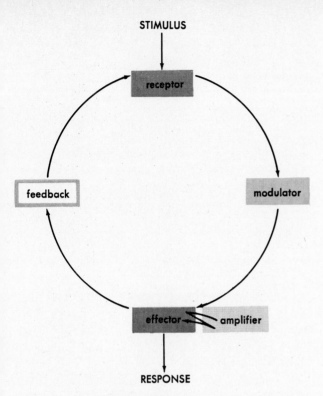

STIMULUS

RESPONSE

Fig. 16.5. The general pattern of a control cycle and the role of feedback in such a cycle.

action is executed, the water may again be down *below* the appropriate level.

Most controls *overshoot* in this fashion, and they undergo hunting oscillations to either side of the equilibrium state. Clearly, it will be important that such oscillations either become smaller and smaller till they subside or else continue at constant amplitude. Poorly adjusted control devices often produce ever-increasing hunting oscillations, in which case "steady" state of course will not be maintained. The zigzagging locomotion of a drunk walking toward a stated object is a familiar example of this. Under the influence of alcohol, nervous control over locomotion becomes loose and imprecise and increased hunting oscillations occur. Normally, such oscillations are so small and subside so rapidly that straight-line locomotion is possible.

A fourth common property of control systems is that they have inherited limits of efficiency. If they are overloaded, i.e., if they must work too fast or too hard,

they may become "neurotic." They may make *errors* in sensing stimuli or in interpreting signals or in selecting and executing responses. Extreme overloading may cause internal structural breakdowns, which may make the device inoperative altogether. In living organisms, functional or structural failures of control systems result in *disease*. Disease itself is a stress stimulus to other, still intact regulating devices, and repair or circumvention of the diseased condition may ensue.

CONTROL LEVELS

The regulating devices of living matter are organized into a hierarchy which parallels the hierarchy of structural levels. Cells contain complete internal control systems made up of molecules. Tissues contain control systems made up of cells. Organs contain control systems made up of tissues. In such an order, the functioning of lower-level controls is essential for the functioning of any higher-level controls. It follows that controls among cellular molecules are the foundations of all other controls (Fig. 16.6).

Molecular control. Regardless of how a cell is stressed, the stress stimulus usually affects one or more metabolic processes. For example, changes in nutrient supplies, waste accumulation, injury, pH change, temperature change, sol-gel transformations, or indeed any other physical or chemical stimuli are likely to influence a cell either by *accelerating* or by *decelerating* particular metabolic reactions. Also, regardless of how a cell responds, the response ultimately is pro-

Fig. 16.6. The hierarchy of control systems in living matter. R, receptor; M, modulator; E, effector. The entire control apparatus of one level (within a rectangular box) is a component of the control apparatus on the next higher level.

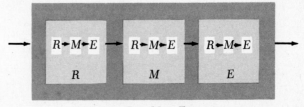

R or M or E

duced by metabolic processes. For whatever the effector action of a cell may be, acceleration or deceleration of respiration or of chemical activities such as synthesis or of physical activities such as movement is likely to be involved. Steady-state maintenance in a cell therefore becomes largely a matter of controlling cellular metabolism. The duration, speed, and amount of every reaction must be suitably geared to the duration, speed, and amount of every other reaction.

Actually, a metabolic reaction is itself the simplest and most basic kind of control system. Molecules function as receptors, modulators, and effectors. The water in which a reaction takes place serves as sensory and motor pathway. For example, consider the reaction

$$\text{glucose} \xrightleftharpoons{\textit{enzymes}} \text{polysaccharide}$$

When this reversible reaction is in chemical equilibrium, it is also in dynamic equilibrium or steady state; a net change does not occur. The totality of glucose molecules in a cell, called a *glucose pool*, may now function as receptor. For example, if additional glucose arrives in the cell as food, this will be a stimulus "sensed" by the glucose pool as an increase in concentration. By mass action, the reaction to the right will now outbalance that to the left and more polysaccharide will be formed. The polysaccharide pool is then the effector, and increase of polysaccharide concentration is the response. For as polysaccharide accumulates at the expense of glucose, the glucose pool decreases back to normal; and the original stimulus is thereby removed. The extra polysaccharide in turn may represent a new stimulus in the cell, initiating other reactions and new responses.

Note that the designations "receptor" and "effector" are not fixed. If a cell were to acquire additional polysaccharide rather than glucose, then the *polysaccharide pool* would be the receptor and the glucose pool the effector. Note further that, in either case, the function of the modulator is performed by the *enzymes*. Mass action notwithstanding, it takes a specific enzyme to "interpret" a specific stimulus and to direct the specific response. Because it is specific for a particular reaction, an enzyme cannot interpret various different stimuli, but only one. And it cannot select among several possible responses, but must promote

the same response every time. Yet inasmuch as it functions like a "clearing center" for incoming and outgoing chemical information, every enzyme is a fundamental modulator in reaction control.

Several other kinds of reaction modulators occur in cells, the most essential of all being the nucleic acids, particularly the genes. Through their control over enzyme synthesis, nucleic acids are the *ultimate* modulators of metabolic reactions. Enzymes may be regarded as the *immediate* modulators. Thus the molecular control system governing the glucose-polysaccharide reaction above may be symbolized as:

$$\left.\begin{array}{c}\textit{genes} \\ \downarrow \\ \textit{enzymes}\end{array}\right\} \text{(\textit{modulators})}$$

$$\underset{\substack{(\textit{receptor or} \\ \textit{effector})}}{\text{glucose}} \xrightleftharpoons{\hspace{2cm}} \underset{\substack{(\textit{effector or} \\ \textit{receptor})}}{\text{polysaccharide}}$$

In addition to genes and enzymes, molecular modulators in cells include various *growth factors*, among them hormones, mineral substances, vitamins, and other classes of compounds. These too control metabolic reactions. For example, we have seen in Chap. 14 that the conversion sequence from polysaccharide to acetyl CoA or vice versa requires, apart from numerous enzymes, several derivatives of B vitamins and, in vertebrates, also hormones such as thyroxin. This is by no means an unusual circumstance, for virtually all metabolic reactions analyzed closely have been found to depend on a whole battery of modulators, including enzymes, vitamin derivatives, often also hormones and inorganic ions, and, ultimately, genes.

All these agents are functionally similar: they are essentially enzyme*like* in action. They are specifically necessary for specific reactions; small quantities of them suffice; and they do not become part of the end-product but are recoverable intact and unchanged after the reaction. In short, they all function more or less like *catalysts*. And in the language of control systems, they function as information relays, or as modulators. They share with enzymes the property of being differentially sensitive to single sensory messages only and of promoting the same reaction responses every time, without freedom of choice (Fig. 16.7).

We may ask here why multiple controls for each reaction are required to begin with. Would not a

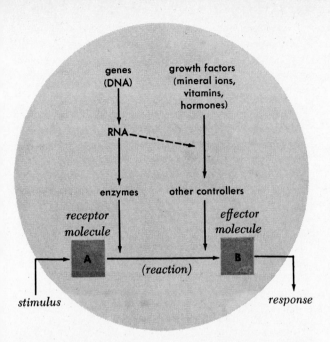

Fig. 16.7. The molecular modulators within cells and the pattern of their control over steady-state–maintaining metabolic reactions.

single modulator suffice? Possibly it might, but there is safety in numbers. Multiple controls reduce the chance of error, and if one modulator becomes inoperative, the reaction may not be stopped completely. Multiple controls provide desirable *redundancy,* or repetition. If one wishes to make sure that information is received exactly as sent, then one repeats the message several times. Just so, chemical messages in metabolism are highly redundant, as are most control messages in living matter generally.

Supramolecular control. All other living controls are based on the molecular controls of metabolism. In the cell, molecules are variously aggregated into organelles and, by virtue of the control functions of their component molecules, the organelles carry out specific higher-level control functions of their own.

Many organelles serve as receptors. For example, pigmented granules absorb light and form excellent photoreceptors (e.g., chloroplasts). Long filaments are sensitive to displacement, to pressure, to touch,

and they may therefore serve as receptors of mechanical stimuli (e.g., sensory hairs, fibrils). Other organelles may be sensitive to particular classes of chemicals, and they may function as chemoreceptors (e.g., mitochondria, storage granules).

Organelles also function as modulators. Of these, the cell nucleus with its chromosomes and genes is the most complex. Analogously complex cellular modulators also include, for example, the ribosomes, the basal granules, the chloroplasts, and other bodies. Their specific control functions have already been discussed. Complex cellular effectors are equally varied. Many contribute to the numerous physical and chemical responses necessary in the internal maintenance of a cell. Others link a cell to its external environment. For example, some bring about cell movement (e.g., flagella) and some absorb or secrete various substances through the cell surface (e.g., Golgi bodies).

A given cell part may have multiple control functions. It may serve as receptor in one instance, as modulator in another, as effector in yet a third. For example, the cell membrane is a receptor when it "recognizes" a glucose molecule, but it is an effector when it allows that molecule to pass through. The cell nucleus has been referred to above as a modulator, which indeed it often is. But it may also serve as receptor—it receives many stimuli from the cytoplasm; or it may be an effector—it executes many responses. Clearly, functional labels are not fixed.

The cellular level is the lowest on which we encounter modulators capable of distinguishing between various sensory messages and of *selecting* among various responses possibilities. For example, the cell surface is *selectively* permeable. Functioning as a modulator, it may interpret the chemical nature of different kinds of molecules in contact with it and it may "decide" how fast and to what extent each such molecule is to be passed through. Similar selectivity is displayed by other complex control components within a cell and also by all supracellular control systems.

How does this crucial capacity of making decisions arise? The answer is not yet clear. But note that a complex cellular modulator contains within it many and different molecular control systems, each capable of a single response. It is therefore likely that the number of decisions a complex modulator may make is correlated with the number of different molecular unit systems of which it is composed.

Superimposed on the controls within cells, most multicellular organisms, particularly the complexly constructed animals, possess regulating devices above the cellular level. Whole specialized tissues, organs, and organ systems serve here specifically as receptors, modulators, or effectors. As above, a given structure may function in more than one of these capacities.

Among animals, an important supracellular mechanism involves the blood as sensory and motor pathway. Change in any one part of the body is signaled to all other parts via the blood. A battery of modulators and effectors may be called into action as a result: heart, blood vessels, skin, kidneys, liver, endocrine and other glands, muscles, to mention a few. Their specific operation counteracts the original change. For example, see Fig. 16.8.

Fig. 16.8. Examples of organismic steady-state controls in animals. Left, sugar balance controlled via blood and hormones; right, two correlated control sequences modulated by the brain, one voluntary, the other involuntary and likely to accompany this particular voluntary sequence.

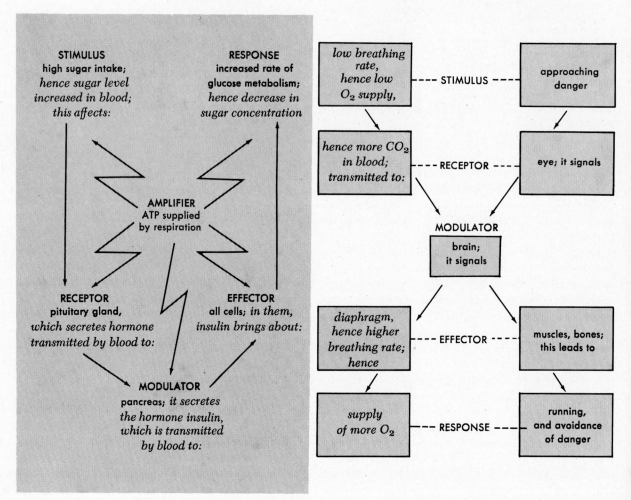

Probably the most familiar and the most complex control device is the nervous system. Sense organs, in the skin and within the body, are receptors. The brain is the chief modulator. Muscle-bone systems and glands function as effectors. Nerves serve as sensory and motor connecting paths. Transmission of information through such a sequence of specialized neural structures, energized along its length by ATP, constitutes a *reflex*. An example is given in Fig. 16.8.

Reflexes are the basis of nervous steady-state control. They may, and often do, act in concert with other control mechanisms, for example, the hormone-producing endocrine system, the circulatory system, the digestive system, and many others. Most situations requiring control actually are regulated by a multiplicity of devices, and the nervous system often is one of them.

The general conclusion emerges that every part of living matter is controlled *by* all other parts and at the same time contributes *to* the control of all other parts. As a result, "controlling" becomes a very major component of "living." Recognizing the stimuli of the environment and actively responding to them is even more characteristic of "being alive" than metabolizing. Without control, life becomes nonlife. Conversely, nonlife became life when the first control mechanism came into existence. That, as we have seen, was the nucleic acid molecule, the gene. The following section will show how this fundamental controller operates.

Genetic control

We already know that, in most organisms, genes are located in the chromosomes within cell nuclei. A chromosome (Fig. 16.9) consists of DNA, RNA, and several types of proteins, all these components forming so-called *nucleoprotein* complexes. It is clearly established that the material of the genes is the DNA fraction of nucleoprotein. That this is so is shown most convincingly by evidence obtained through work on bacteria.

For example, it is possible to extract nucleoproteins from one strain of bacteria and to separate this extract chemically into DNA and protein. If then the DNA is put into a medium in which another strain of

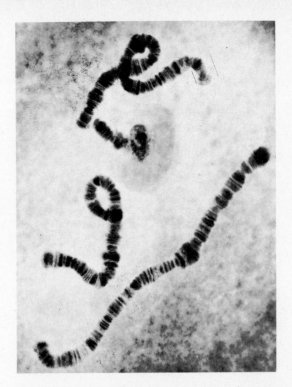

Fig. 16.9. Chromosomes. In this stained preparation of insect chromosomes, characteristic crossbands are clearly visible. Such banding is often found in many chromosomes studied. (From D. F. Poulson and C. W. Metz, *J. Morphol.*, vol. 63, 1938.)

bacteria is present, these organisms will absorb some of the foreign DNA. As a result, the recipient bacteria acquire some of the genetic traits of the original DNA donors. However, if similar experiments are performed with the protein fraction of the original nucleoprotein, genetic changes do not occur in the recipient organisms. Evidently, the *bacterial transformation* is brought about specifically by DNA, and DNA therefore must be the substance of genes (Fig. 16.10).

Gene function therefore must be interpreted on the basis of DNA structure. This structure has already been outlined in Chap. 5 and we know that it is symbolized by the Watson-Crick model. DNA thus may be regarded as a spiraled double chain, each chain being made up of nucleotides containing deoxyribose sugars. Two such chains are held together by pairs of nitrogen bases, four different types of such pairs being present: adenine-thymine and the reverse ($A \cdot T$,

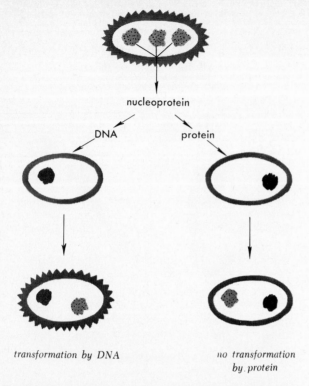

transformation by DNA   *no transformation by protein*

Fig. 16.10. Bacterial transformation. The nucleoprotein of a rough-coated bacterial type is extracted and separate DNA and protein fractions are prepared. If a smooth-coated bacterial type is allowed to absorb the DNA fraction, it will change into a rough-coated type. But it will remain smooth-coated if it absorbs only the protein fraction. Experiments of this sort show that the nucleic acid part, not the protein part, of nucleoproteins is of genetic importance.

$T \cdot A$), and guanine-cytosine and the reverse ($G \cdot C$, $C \cdot G$). These four pairs may occur any number of times and in any sequence, establishing the particular specificity of a given type of DNA (Fig. 16.11).

How can the genetic activity of DNA be explained in terms of this molecular structure?

THE GENETIC CODE

It appears that genes perform their crucial controlling functions by, surprisingly, doing virtually nothing. As is characteristic of controlling agents generally, genes turn out to be, essentially, stable and more or less pas-

sive containers of information. The information in each case consists of a particular, specific sequence of purine-pyrimidine pairs. And all that genes appear to do, or allow to be done to them, is to have their specific information *copied* by other kinds of information carriers. We are led to regard genes somewhat as important original "texts," carefully protected and preserved in the "library" of the nucleus. They are available as permanent, authoritative "master documents" from which expendable duplicates may be prepared.

The specific information contained within genes represents a set of building instructions, like the instructions given by a blueprint. The genetic instructions supply the chemical machinery of a cell with "orders" for just two kinds of building jobs: how to make *new genes* exactly like the originals and how to join amino acids together to make *specific proteins*. In other words, each gene is a guardian of a specific chemical code and gene function consists of transfers of such codes. How are code transfers accomplished and how does this actually lead to control of cellular activities?

Code transfer: DNA to DNA. The first of the two construction activities referred to above, namely, the synthesis of new genes exactly like original genes, occurs in the nucleus every time a cell or a nucleus divides. Just before cell division, the entire set of genes present in a cell is duplicated precisely. One set is subsequently incorporated into each of the two new cells formed by the division of the original mother cell (see Chap. 20). The production of two gene sets out of one requires manufacture of new DNA; and since the two resulting gene sets are identical, an exact code

Fig. 16.11. A portion of a sample DNA molecule based on the Watson-Crick model. P, phosphate; D, deoxyribose; A, adenine; T, thymine; G, guanine; C, cytosine.

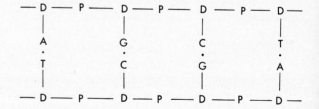

transfer from original DNA to newly manufactured DNA must occur. The Watson-Crick model suggests how new specific DNA may be made from old. For example, consider the DNA model illustrated in Fig. 16.11. The specific coded information contained in this model is represented by the particular sequence of the purine-pyrimidine pairs. Duplication of such a sequence with simultaneous preservation of code specificity is envisaged to occur in three steps (Fig. 16.12).

First, the purine-pyrimidine pairs which hold an original DNA double chain together somehow become disengaged and the double chain so "unzips" into two separate single chains. Second, each single chain now builds on to itself appropriate new nucleotides, present as raw materials. For example, every A (adenine) sticking out from the single chain may attach to itself a new T-D-P; or every C (cytosine) of the single chain may join to itself a new G-D-P. In this way, all the free purines and pyrimidines of the single chain may eventually combine with "right" nucleotides,

Fig. 16.12. Simplified representation of how DNA duplication may occur. Top left, the double DNA chain "unzips" into two single chains. Top right, each single chain attaches appropriate purines and pyrimidines to itself, drawn from the available supply of raw materials. Bottom left, each chain ultimately has attached complete and appropriate nucleotides. Bottom right, final pair of double chains.

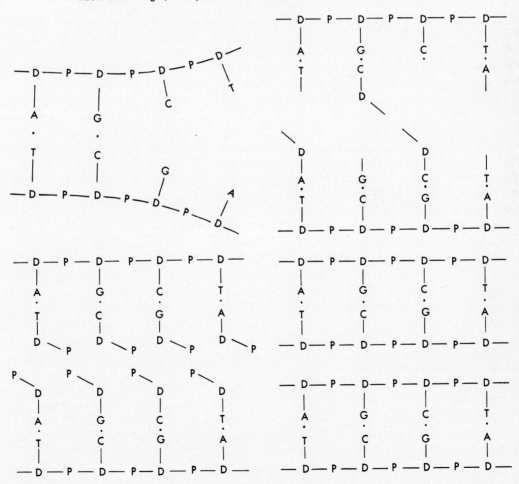

drawn from the pool of nutrient raw materials. The third and final step then requires only a linking together of the newly attached nucleotides.

The overall result is that *one* DNA double chain has given rise to *two* double chains. These are identical to each other as well as to the original "mother" chain. DNA thus has reproduced and the specific information code has been preserved. Note that all DNA always incorporates the old and the new. One of its two nucleotide chains preexists; the other is newly manufactured. It should be remembered here that, according to Watson and Crick, DNA is normally spiraled. Therefore, duplication of a spiral would produce two intertwined spirals, and these would have to unwind before they could separate. This may or may not happen in actuality.

The basic idea underlying this duplication process is often referred to as the *template hypothesis*. Each single nucleotide chain of DNA serves as a *template* or blueprint or master pattern according to which a new, *matching* nucleotide chain is manufactured. It is in this sense that genetic DNA may be regarded as passive, simply permitting its particular information to be copied and to be transferred to new DNA.

Code transfer: DNA to protein.   Granting that the specific information of DNA is preserved through successive cell generations, what is the functional value of this information in the life of a cell? The value lies in the second kind of copying process referred to earlier: the genetic information of DNA instructs the cell how to build specific proteins. In this, a template principle is probably involved again. Through code transfer from DNA to protein, genes ensure that any new proteins manufactured in a cell contain particular, specific sequences of amino acids and so have particular, specific architectural configurations.

Protein synthesis takes place on the cytoplasmic granules called *ribosomes*. But genes are in the nucleus. Clearly, some kind of functional connecting link between nucleus and cytoplasm must exist. Research has shown that this link is almost certainly *RNA*, the second kind of nucleic acid present in cells.

RNA occurs particularly in three places: in the chromosomes, in the nucleoli, and in the ribosomes. And there is now ample evidence indicating that genes control protein synthesis according to the following general scheme. First, RNA appears to be manufactured in the chromosomes. In this process, the DNA of the genes probably serves as a template and the specific information of the different DNA molecules is copied and incorporated into RNA molecules under construction. These RNAs are therefore specific and they now carry the exact code information of the DNAs. Second, variously specific RNA molecules then accumulate in the nucleoli. And third, specific RNAs from the nucleoli eventually reach the ribosomes in the cytoplasm. Here the RNA molecules function as templates in their own turn, that is, they are ready to serve as blueprints in the construction of specific proteins.

Because such RNA molecules carry the genetic code from the nucleus to the ribosomes, they are referred to as *messenger RNA*. This is to distinguish them from another kind of RNA present in cells, called *transfer RNA*. Molecules of transfer RNA are comparatively short chains of nucleotides, and their function is to carry amino acids to the ribosomes. When an amino acid enters a cell as a nutrient raw material for synthesis, the acid becomes attached to one end of a molecule of transfer RNA. This reaction requires ATP and an enzyme. Also, the transfer RNA is specific for the particular amino acid; there are as many different kinds of transfer RNAs as there are different kinds of amino acids. Carrying the amino acids with them, the transfer RNAs subsequently diffuse to the ribosomes, where messenger RNA is already present. The transfer RNAs then "deposit" the amino acids along the chain of messenger RNA. Apparently, the nucleotides in a transfer RNA molecule match the nucleotides in a given section of messenger RNA, and a transfer RNA so "recognizes" the exact place along the chain of messenger RNA where the amino acid is to be deposited. In this manner, different amino acids become lined up in a sequence determined by the genetic code in messenger RNA. And when the appropriately positioned amino acids then are joined to one another, a specific protein is formed (Fig. 16.13).

Ingenious experiments have shown how code recognition between transfer and messenger RNA may be achieved. It has become possible in recent years to construct artificial RNA chains in which the se-

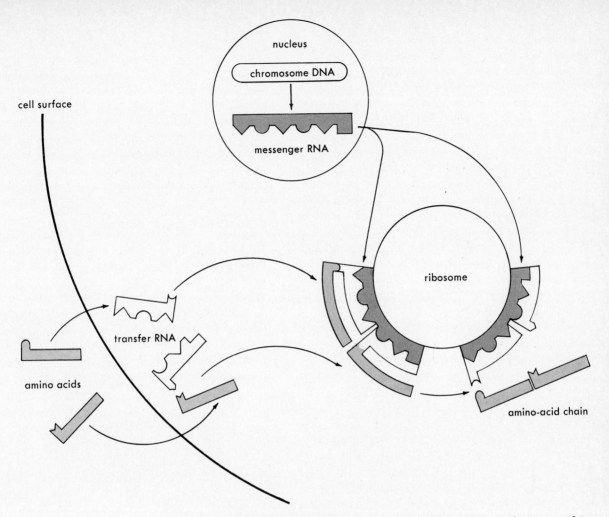

Fig. 16.13.   Gene-controlled protein synthesis. Chromosomal DNA confers its specificity to messenger RNA, which becomes deposited on ribosomes (top and right). Amino acids entering a cell hook on to specific transfer RNA molecules (left) and the latter then become attached to specific places along the messenger RNA. Triplets of adjoining nucleotides form a recognition code for given transfer RNA molecules, as indicated. Amino acids so become lined up in specific sequences, and when the acids finally join to one another (right) the resulting proteins are specific in accordance with the genetic code carried within chromosomal DNA.

quence of nucleotides is known. If, under appropriate conditions, mixtures of known amino acids are added to such chains, proteinlike chains of joined amino acids may be formed in the test tube. The sequence of the amino acids here can be established by chemical analysis, and from this it can be inferred which of the known nucleotides in an artificial RNA chain have determined the position of which amino acid. By such means it has been found that the recognition code for a single amino acid is a unit of three adjoining nucleotides in RNA. For example, wherever an RNA chain contains three adjoining uracil-containing nucleotides, such a triplet of nucleotides represents the specific code for an amino acid called *phenylalanine*. A nucleotide-triplet containing guanine-guanine-uracil analogously represents the code for the amino acid *glycine*. The triplet codes for virtually all others of the 23 different kinds of amino acids are now known as well.

In a ribosome, therefore, the sequence of nucleotides in messenger RNA serves as a linear series of triplet codes. The various amino acids brought in by transfer RNA then become lined up along the messenger RNA in a sequence determined by these triplet codes. Consequently, the finished protein possesses a specificity which matches that of the messenger RNA. And since the different specificities of different messenger RNAs have been determined originally by the genetic DNAs, we may conclude that genes ultimately control the kinds of proteins a cell can manufacture.

Note here that messenger RNA is essentially passive, just as genes are passive. Genes merely allow their specific information to be copied by messenger RNA, which in turn allows that information to be used in protein manufacture. The advantage of such indirect functioning of genes is clear. Genes remain protected within the nucleus as in a vault and are therefore less subject to destruction by the respiratory metabolism of the cytoplasm. Whenever genetic information is required in the cytoplasm, genes do not move to the place of action themselves but send expendable copies of themselves in the form of messenger RNA. In this sense genes may be likened to a policy-making board of directors and messenger RNA to the foremen who actually execute the directives of the managing board.

RESULTS OF GENE ACTION

By governing the synthesis of new genes and of specific proteins, genes play so strategic a role that they ultimately control the whole nature and the very life of every cell in every organism (Fig. 16.14).

First, since proteins make up more of the formed organic framework of cells than any other constituents, genes determine the basic *architecture* of every cell. This means, too, that every normal architectural change during the life cycle of a cell, and every archi-

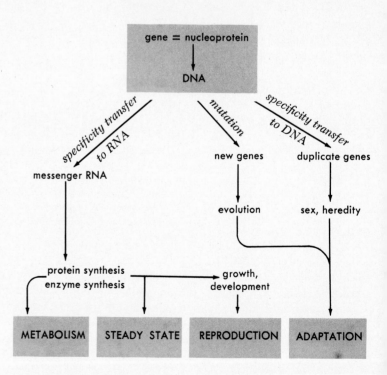

Fig. 16.14. Overall summary of the pattern of gene action. Through their fundamental action of transferring their specificities, genes control cellular metabolism and all phases of cellular self-perpetuation.

tectural difference among the cells of one or of different organisms, is ultimately gene-determined.

Second, by controlling the nature of proteins, genes control the nature of enzymes, all of which are proteins. Since virtually every metabolic reaction in a cell requires at least one enzyme, genes so determine what kinds of *metabolic processes* are possible in a cell. Nutritional reactions, respiratory reactions, motion-producing reactions, synthesis reactions of all kinds, all are enzyme-dependent, hence gene-dependent.

Third, by so governing the metabolism of a cell, genes are the ultimate maintainers of *steady state*. For genes control not only themselves (by governing gene duplication) but also all other control agents within cells. Genes regulate the nature of enzymes, as already noted. Genes also regulate hormone action, first, by determining which cells are to manufacture which hormones, and second, by determining which hormones and what quantities of them are to be admitted into every cell through the plasma membrane. Genes regulate vitamin action by controlling the manufacture of these substances within cells and, again, by regulating surface absorption in cells which do not synthesize vitamins on their own. Control of surface absorption also accounts for gene control over the inorganic constituents of cells.

Fourth, by governing synthesis in general and production of new genes in particular, genes direct growth, development, and the *reproduction* of cells. By being exchanged among cells and pooled within cells, as we shall see, genes become the basis of *sex*. By duplicating and being transmitted to offspring cells, genes become the basis of *heredity*. Moreover, through one final property, genes become the key to *evolution*.

This final property is *mutability*, the capacity to mutate. Genetic nucleic acids are among the most stable of all organic compounds. Indeed, unless an information carrier were relatively stable, it would cease to be useful as a repository of important information. In addition to the inherent chemical stability of genes,

several safeguards exist which ensure that the specific genetic messages are not lost or altered.

One such device is the nucleus itself, which shields genes from the destructive metabolism of the cytoplasm. Another safeguard is *redundancy;* the genetic messages are stored in more than one place. Each cell of most organisms ordinarily contains two complete sets of genes, one set having been inherited originally from the egg-producing parent and the other from the sperm-producing parent. Moreover, each cell type is usually represented by many like cells. Even if some cells die, therefore, the genes of the remaining cells still possess the specific information characteristic of that cell type.

Yet despite inherent stability, protected existence, and redundancy, structural change is bound to occur; genes are no more exempt from the modifying impact of the environment than any other component of the earth. A variety of physical and chemical agents may affect and alter gene structure and therefore gene specificity. Such new specificities will be stable and will be passed on into all subsequent gene duplicates. Protein synthesis will be affected accordingly, and, as a result, cell traits will become changed. *Mutations* of this sort are major factors in evolution, as we shall see.

In summary, therefore, we find that genes serve in just one primary role: they allow their specificities to be copied. Three indirect secondary roles emerge from this: genes control protein specificities; genes control the specificities of duplicate genes; and, to the extent that gene stability is imperfect, genes may change their specificities. Through these three secondary activities, genes indirectly carry out tertiary functions which encompass every aspect of living. For by controlling all metabolism and all self-perpetuation, genes govern cell structure, cell function, and cell development. And by controlling cells, genes govern the life of all organisms, hence the survival of the whole living world. Genes started life, genes still continue it, and, by their failure or absence, genes ultimately end it.

Review questions

1. In general terms, what kinds of processes take place in the execution of control activities? What general function do such controls serve in the maintenance of life? What is the role of information flow in the maintenance of steady states?

2. What are the structural components of every control system in living matter? What specific role does each component play? Review the functional properties of control systems. What is feedback, and what is its significance in control activities?

3. What is the significance of trial and error in control activities? What happens when control systems are overloaded? Interpret the temperature-regulating action of a home thermostat in terms of a control system and indicate the specific roles of feedback and of trial and error.

4. In what sense does a molecular reaction constitute a control system? What kinds of substances may serve as molecular modulators? What functional characteristics do these have in common? What is the relation of genes to control systems?

5. For each microscopic body usually present in cells, describe a cellular activity in which that body functions as (a) receptor, (b) modulator, (c) effector, and (d) sensory or motor pathway.

6. Review the general pattern of steady-state control on supracellular levels. How do plants and animals differ in this respect? Which parts of an organism do not participate in control activities?

7. Where in a cell do (a) DNA and (b) RNA occur? Review the Watson-Crick model of DNA structure. How do DNA and RNA differ chemically?

8. Describe the probable mechanism of code transfer from DNA to DNA, based on the Watson-Crick model. Similarly describe the probable mechanism of code transfer from DNA to RNA. Distinguish between messenger RNA and transfer RNA.

9. Review the pattern of processes by which genes control (a) cellular metabolism, (b) other cellular controllers, including other genes, and (c) all aspects of self-perpetuation.

10. Review the pattern of gene function as a whole. Which function may be regarded as primary? Which indirect secondary functions derive from this and which tertiary functions result in turn from the secondary ones?

Suggested collateral readings

Allfrey, V. G., and A. E. Mirsky: How Cells Make Molecules, *Sci. Am.*, vol. 205, 1961.

Crick, F. H. C.: The Genetic Code, *Sci. Am.*, vol. 207, 1962.

Gamow, G.: Information Transfer in the Living Cell, *Sci. Am.*, vol. 193, 1955.

Hurwitz, J., and J. J. Furth: Messenger RNA, *Sci. Am.*, vol. 206, 1962.

Ingram, V. M.: How Do Genes Act? *Sci. Am.*, vol. 198, 1958.

King, G.: What Is Information? *Sci. Am.*, vol. 187, 1952.

Nagel, E.: Self-regulation, *Sci. Am.*, vol. 187, 1952.

Nirenberg, M. W.: The Genetic Code, *Sci. Am.*, vol. 208, 1963.

Taylor, J. H.: The Duplication of Chromosomes, *Sci. Am.*, vol. 198, 1958.

GROWTH FACTORS

17

Directed by genes and working together with enzymes, other regulators in cells play important roles in steady-state maintenance. Because these control agents often have specific effects on growth, they are frequently referred to as *growth factors* or *growth substances*. To be sure, genes and enzymes qualify as "growth factors" also. However, growth factors are defined customarily as controlling agents which a cell requires for its maintenance but which (unlike genes and enzymes) that cell cannot manufacture on its own. Such agents must therefore be imported into a cell. Depending on where they are imported from, two general categories of growth factors may be distinguished. If a controlling agent is obtained not from within the organism but from the external environment, then the growth factor is referred to as a *growth regulator*. But if a controller is produced in a given body part of an organism and is transported to cells which cannot manufacture it, then that growth factor is a *hormone*.

Through their effects on growth and often also on other cellular processes, growth factors produce various forms of *behavior* in organisms. Such behavioral functions are usually investigated by deliberately making an organism deficient in a given growth factor or by supplying an excess of it. In either case, abnormal *unsteady* states are induced and these may give clues about the normal cellular controlling role of the growth factor. Some of the principal findings of such studies are outlined in this chapter.

Control in plants

In organisms generally, the principal classes of growth regulators are *vitamins* and *minerals*. In animals, both must be obtained in prefabricated form from the environment. But in the autotrophic plants, all vitamins are manufactured within the plant body and in most cases directly within each cell in which these substances must be used. In green plants, therefore, vitamins belong to the same self-manufactured group of compounds as genes and enzymes, and only in heterotrophs are vitamins distinctly identifiable as growth regulators (see below). Green plants do require minerals from the external environment. These substances evidently serve in two general capacities: in part they are nutrients used as structural components of cells, and in part they are growth regulators used in reaction control. In some cases, the same mineral may serve in both capacities. For example, magnesium is both a structural component (e.g., in chlorophyll) and a controlling agent (e.g., in respiratory reactions).

AUXINS

The principal plant hormones are substances called *auxins*. The most important naturally occurring auxin is *indole acetic acid*, IAA for short ($C_{10}H_9O_2N$). Two other auxins are naphthalene acetic acid ($C_{12}H_{10}O_2$) and 2,4-dichlorophenoxyacetic acid, or 2,4-D for short ($C_8H_6O_3Cl_2$). Still other auxins exist and many can be synthesized in the laboratory.

In a plant, IAA is manufactured in various body parts. Actively growing and developing regions usually produce the largest amounts. For example, particularly auxin-rich regions are shoot tips, root tips, cambia, young leaves, developing flower parts, and fruits. How does IAA affect a plant cell? Available data indicate that auxins promote the *elongation* of individual cells by apparently influencing cell-wall metabolism. The effect is such that more wall material is produced and is deposited near the two ends of a cell. The cell lengthens as a result.

This basic action of IAA, and of auxins generally, influences plant behavior in major ways. Two kinds of behavioral effects may be distinguished, namely, *growth* effects and *developmental* effects.

Growth responses. Growth behavior which can be shown to be triggered off specifically by an environmental stimulus is called a *tropism*. Several types of tropisms are recognized on the basis of the various growth-inducing stimuli: light-induced *phototropism*, gravity-induced *geotropism*, contact-induced *thigmotropism*, chemical-induced *chemotropism*, and others. A given tropic response may be either *positive* or *negative*; that is, a plant or plant part may grow toward or away from the stimulus. For example, leaves and stems are positively phototropic and negatively geotropic; they grow toward light and away from the gravitational center of the earth (Fig. 17.1). Roots, on the contrary, are positively geotropic and negatively phototropic. The tendrils of climbing plants are positively thigmotropic, growing along objects on which they can become attached. Most tropic responses are adaptively advantageous in fairly obvious ways.

The phototropic and geotropic growth of plants is known to be under the control of auxins. As noted above, the apical tip of a shoot produces IAA. The hormone then diffuses to cells farther back where it brings about cell elongation. If the cross-sectional distribution of auxin is roughly even, the shoot will elongate straight up. But light is known to reduce in some

Fig. 17.1. **Tropic movements.** Left, the effect of gravity—geotropic response. Right, the effect of light—phototropic response. At right, the plant is illuminated from the left. (Courtesy of Boyce Thompson Institute for Plant Research.)

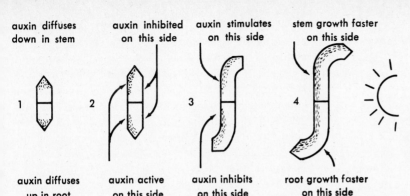

auxin diffuses
down in stem

auxin inhibited
on this side

auxin stimulates
on this side

stem growth faster
on this side

1   2   3   4

auxin diffuses
up in root

auxin active
on this side

auxin inhibits
on this side

root growth faster
on this side

Fig. 17.2. The interaction of light and auxin in the control of stem and root growth. As indicated, light is here assumed to come from the right.

way the growth-promoting effect of auxin. Consequently, if a shoot is illuminated predominantly from one side, auxin will be less effective on that side than on the shaded side. Cells on the shaded side will therefore elongate more extensively and the shoot will then curve toward the light source. In other words, the stem is positively phototropic; the plant behaves as if it were "aware" of the position of the light and grows toward it (Fig. 17.2).

How can the negative phototropism of roots be explained? It has been found that the optimum IAA concentration for elongation of root cells is about 100,000 times less than the optimum for elongation of stem cells. In effect, an IAA concentration which stimulates stem growth *inhibits* root growth. Conversely, an IAA concentration which stimulates root growth is so low that it inhibits stem growth (or at any rate does not promote it). Therefore, if a stem-root system (in water rather than soil) is illuminated from one side, the stem tip will curve toward the light. But any auxin diffusing into the root on the shaded side will be sufficiently concentrated to inhibit root elongation on that side. As a result, the side facing the light will grow faster and the root tip will curve away from the light stimulus; hence the negative phototropism of roots (Fig. 17.2).

The negative geotropism of stems and the positive geotropism of roots can be explained by migration of auxin under the influence of gravity. It is well known that if a plant is placed horizontally, the stem tip grows upward, the root tip downward. These responses take place even in the dark; they are gravity-dependent, not light-dependent. In a horizontal plant, it can

be shown that as much as two-thirds of all the auxin in a shoot tip is present on the lower side of this tip. As auxin moves back to cells capable of elongating, most of the hormone therefore reaches cells located on the lower side of the stem. These cells consequently elongate more than cells on the upper side and the stem tip curves upward as a result. When auxin reaches root cells, the concentration of the hormone is still highest on the lower side, which means that the cells on that side will be inhibited most. Root cells on the upper side then elongate to a comparatively greater extent. The root tip therefore curves downward, in the direction of the center of the earth (Fig. 17.3).

Changes in hormone distribution and concentration may play a role in other tropisms as well. In most of these cases, however, it is still not quite clear how the external stimulus actually brings about particular hormone activities.

Developmental responses. Numerous developmental responses of plants have been shown to be under auxin control. Some of these responses can also be produced artificially, through the use of auxin preparations applied to a plant from the outside.

One action of auxin promotes *bud development.* As noted in Chap. 9, lateral stem buds form at the bases of leaves. Buds near the stem tip usually remain dormant, but those farther back along the stem may break dormancy and develop into branch stems. It can be shown that this evident dominance of the main apical tip is due to auxin. IAA produced by the dominant tip moves back toward the lateral buds. However, the optimum IAA concentration for bud growth is only

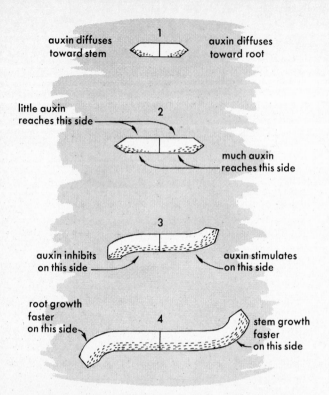

auxin diffuses
toward stem

auxin diffuses
toward root

little auxin
reaches this side

much auxin
reaches this side

auxin inhibits
on this side

auxin stimulates
on this side

root growth
faster
on this side

stem growth
faster
on this side

Fig. 17.3.   The interaction of gravity and auxin in the control of stem and root growth. Responses as shown are obtained in the dark.

about $1/1,000$ of the optimum concentration for cell elongation. Therefore, as high IAA concentrations reach them, buds near the tip are inhibited from breaking dormancy. The apical dominance extends backward for considerable distances until auxin becomes sufficiently dilute to stimulate rather than inhibit bud development. Clearly, these differential sensitivities account for the usual tapering growth pattern of the branch system of a plant (Fig. 17.4). One problem remains to be answered: why is the development of the dominant bud not inhibited by its own very high auxin concentration?

Auxins exert developmental control over embryonic tissues such as *cambia*. It has been suggested that, in woody plants, auxins produced in the spring by actively growing shoots diffuse to the cambia, where they may activate those tissues and stimulate them to form that season's wood and bark.

Another important developmental function of auxins is their control of leaf fall and fruit drop. Leaves and fruits separate from a plant at an *abscission layer*, a region of special cells formed where a leaf or a fruit stalk joins the stem. In such a layer, the cement between adjacent cells dissolves and the cells eventually die. Abscission of the leaf or the fruit is the consequence. It has been shown that such separations are governed by the relative auxin concentrations on either side of the abscission area (Fig. 17.5). So long as IAA concentrations in a leaf or a fruit are higher than in the stem, abscission normally does not occur. This is the case while leaf or fruit growth is under way, that is, while these organs actively produce auxins of their own. But when auxin manufacture ceases, at full ma-

Fig. 17.4.   The effect of auxin on bud development. In this diagram, the assumption is made that auxin released from a terminal bud is concentrated enough to inhibit the development of the first three branch buds behind the terminal bud. Branch buds farther back receive less than an inhibitory concentration of auxin and thus may break dormancy.

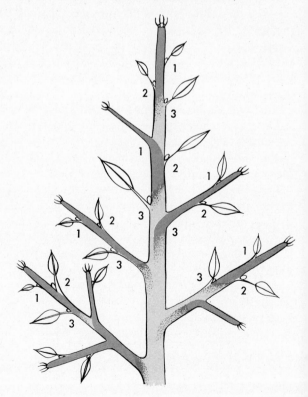

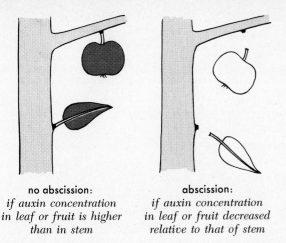

no abscission:
*if auxin concentration
in leaf or fruit is higher
than in stem*

abscission:
*if auxin concentration
in leaf or fruit decreased
relative to that of stem*

Fig. 17.5. The effects of relative auxin concentrations on abscission.

turity, for example, or when cold autumn weather slows growth rates, then IAA concentrations in a leaf or a fruit decrease relative to the concentrations in the stem. Abscission is then likely to take place.

Fruit growers make practical use of these relationships. In spring they may spray stems with auxins, a procedure which raises the hormone concentrations of the stems relative to those of flowers or young fruits. The result will be many premature abscissions and a consequent thinning of the fruits on a tree. The fewer remaining fruits may then become larger and better, since more food will be available to them. Later in the year, auxin spray may be applied to the fruits, which will delay abscission and permit longer tree-ripening of the fruits.

Auxins not only aid in making new plants but also in killing old ones. When auxins are applied externally to certain plants, at much higher concentrations than those which normally promote growth, then the growth factors interfere drastically with the metabolism and development of the plants. Dicot weeds are particularly sensitive to very high auxin levels, and plant death is a frequent consequence. Just how auxins exert this lethal effect is not clearly understood, but the effect itself has become extremely important in weed control. Monocot crop plants such as corn and grain formers are hardly affected by auxin concentrations which kill dicot weeds.

FLOWERING HORMONES

Apart from auxins and hormones like them, at least two other kinds of hormones are known to occur in plants. These hormones have so far not been isolated and identified, but their existence can be inferred from the effect of light and of temperature on the flowering of plants.

Photoperiodism. Responses of plants to varying light durations are described by the term *photoperiodism.* Flower development particularly is affected by different day lengths, or *photoperiods.* On the basis of the photoperiod required for flowering, three groups of plants may be distinguished. In so-called *short-day plants,* flowers develop only if the plants are illuminated for less than 12 hours daily. Violets, asters, cockleburs, strawberries, chrysanthemums, and rice are among many plants in this group. In *long-day plants,* flowers develop only if the daily photoperiod is more than 12 hours. This group includes, for example, corn, wheat, clover, beets, and lettuce. A third group of plants is not limited in its illumination requirements, and such *indeterminate plants* produce flowers regardless of the length of the daily photoperiods. Tomatoes, corn, cucumbers, cotton, sunflowers, and dandelions are representative members of this group.

Short-day plants fail to flower or their flowering is greatly retarded if they are exposed to long photoperiods only. Conversely, long-day plants flower late or not at all if they are grown under short photoperiods. Some of the factors involved in producing photoperiodic responses are known.

First, it has been shown that the receptor organs specifically sensitive to light durations are the leaves. Defoliated plants cannot be made to flower even with proper light treatment. Second, it has been found for short-day plants that the length of the *night* is just as important as the length of the day. If the dark periods are of less than a certain critical length, then flowering will not occur even if the light periods are of appropriate length. Moreover, if an appropriately long dark period is interrupted by even a single brief flash of light, then flowering will again be suppressed. Evidently, short-day plants may justifiably be also called "long-night plants" (Fig. 17.6).

Third, aerial CO_2 is required to induce flowering. The role of the gas here is apparently not nutritional, for even a plant with ample food supplies cannot be induced to flower if CO_2 is not present. It has been suggested that CO_2 may be necessary in leaves as a raw material in the manufacture of a special compound required for flower induction. Such a compound *A* may be synthesized from CO_2 during the light period. During the ensuing dark period, *A* may be converted into another necessary compound *B*. Therefore, if the dark period is too short (or is made too short by a light interruption), there may not be enough time available for the production of sufficient amounts of *B*. Flowering will then not occur.

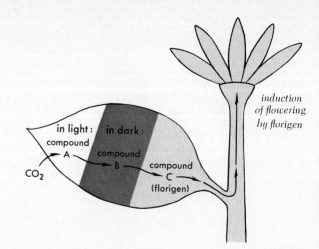

Fig. 17.7. **Hypothetical sequence of events leading to a photoperiodic response.**

Fig. 17.6. **Experiments illustrating the importance of night length and of the continuity of the dark period in photoperiodism in short-day plants.**

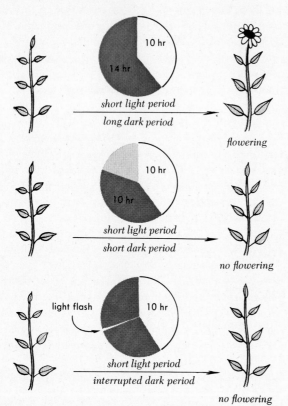

Fourth, compounds *A* and *B* probably cannot be the only substances required for flower induction. *A* and *B* are produced in the leaves, but flowers are formed near the shoot tips. It becomes necessary, therefore, to postulate the existence of a hormone *C*. This hormone must be manufactured in the leaves from compound *B* and must then migrate to a shoot tip where it initiates flowering (Fig. 17.7). The actual existence of such a flowering hormone, or *florigen*, can be demonstrated experimentally. In short-day cocklebur plants, for example, one individual may be grown under short photoperiods, which leads to flowering. Another individual may be kept under long photoperiods, which suppresses flowering. If then the two plants are grafted together and if their earlier photoperiods are maintained, it is found that the previously nonflowering plant now begins to flower too. Evidently, a diffusible florigen has moved from one plant into the other and has induced the latter to flower.

The flower-inducing mechanism suggested by these data accounts for the difference between short-day and long-day plants. In short-day plants, long days would make the nights too short for adequate conversion of compound *A* into *B*. Florigen would then be formed in insufficient quantity and flowering could not occur. In long-day plants, short days would not provide adequate illumination for the formation of enough A, again leading to insufficient amounts of florigen and a suppression of flowering. Indeterminate plants would be able to form enough A, B, and florigen under any naturally occurring photoperiods. Evidently, the photoperiodic differences among plants appear to be quantitative rather than qualitative.

As might be expected, the global distribution of plants reflects their photoperiodic nature. Thus, the days in tropical and subtropical regions are fairly uniformly short (rarely more than 12 or 13 hours), and the plants in these regions are largely short-day species. The temperate zone supports both short-day and long-day plants. The former flower mainly during the short-day seasons of spring and autumn, the latter during the long-day season of summer. In higher latitudes beyond the temperate zone, most plants are long-day species adapted to the long days and short nights which characterize most of the growing season. Indeterminate plants are distributed widely over all climatic zones.

Knowledge of photoperiodic responses has been turned to horticultural advantage. By artificially lengthening or shortening day lengths under controlled conditions, given commercially important plants can be induced to flower at virtually any season of the year or may he inhibited from developing flowers.

Vernalization. We already know that temperature has major effects on metabolic reactions, not only in plants but in organisms generally. Temperature treatment, or *vernalization*, in plants also affects flowering, and this response is probably not due merely to changes in metabolic rates.

Whether or not flowering will occur in mature annual plants can be shown to depend on the temperature to which the germinating seeds of such plants had been exposed. For example, seeds of temperate-zone annuals like winter wheat must be exposed to low temperatures if flowering is to occur later in the mature plants. Such seeds are normally sown in the fall and the ensuing winter provides the required low temperature. If the seeds are not vernalized in this manner, flowers will not be formed later. By contrast, seeds of tropical annuals such as rice must be vernalized at high temperatures (80°F or more) if later flowering is to take place.

The receptor of the temperature stimulus in a seed is the embryo. The suggestion has been made that vernalization may permit manufacture of a special hormone which persists as the plant matures and which eventually induces flowering. The name *vernalin* has been proposed for this hormone but, as in the case of florigen, attempts to extract it have so far not been successful. Experiments do show, however, that a plant must be vernalized first before it will respond to photoperiodic stimuli. Conceivably, vernalin produced early in development may be a prerequisite for the later manufacture of florigen.

In nature, annual plants are normally vernalized in the seed stage, as just described. Biennial and perennial plants usually become vernalized at a later stage, during adult growth. Biennials such as celery, beets, and henbane grow during a first season and the ensuing winter vernalizes the plants. Flowering then occurs during the following season. Perennials such as apples or peaches are normally vernalized in the mature vegetative condition by each successive winter. It follows that if apple or peach trees or temperate-zone perennials in general are grown in tropical or otherwise uniformly warm climates, then they will continue to grow but will not flower. Conversely, if tropical perennials are grown at very high latitudes, then they too will not become vernalized and will not flower.

Whenever vernalization occurs in mature plants, the receptors of the temperature stimulus are the apical buds. That this is so can be demonstrated by grafting experiments. For example, a vernalized apical bud of one plant may induce flower formation in a non-vernalized apical bud of another plant if the two are grafted together. The transmitted signal is apparently quite unspecific, for flower induction occurs even when the graft partners are of different species (Fig. 17.8).

Data such as the foregoing warrant the conclusion that the importance of flowering in the life of plants is fully matched by the complexity of its control. Temperature, light, hormones, and presumably other, still unknown, conditions must all exercise their separate effects toward the total result. In all probability, the adaptive value of such a multiplicity of control factors is that they save energy and materials; a flower is nor-

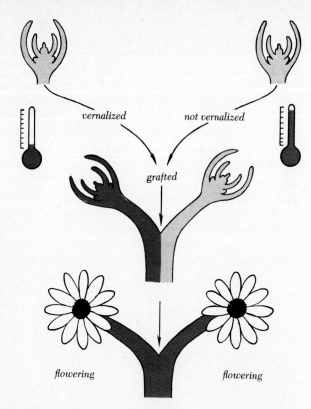

vernalized   not vernalized

grafted

flowering   flowering

Fig. 17.8. Experiment showing that the flowering stimulus resulting from appropriate vernalization may pass from one plant to a grafted unvernalized partner.

mally formed only under the best possible environmental conditions, when the reproductive effort is most likely to succeed. Indeed, by virtue of its hormonal and other controls a plant regulates not only its flowering but also all other aspects of its existence. As a result, the whole plant and all its parts may be maintained in steady state relative to the environment. And as a further result, the plant may attain an actual life span which approaches that potentially inherent in it. We next examine how equivalent control is achieved in animals.

Control in animals

Like plants, animals require growth factors, including growth regulators obtained from the external environment and hormones produced within the body.

Mineral substances represent one group of growth regulators, and animals by and large require virtually the same kinds as plants. Vitamins represent a second group of animal growth regulators. As noted, animals must obtain many of these compounds from the environment. With regard to hormones, most attention has been focused on those which are produced in the specialized endocrine systems of some animals, vertebrates in particular.

VITAMINS

Most animal cell types do synthesize at least some vitamins, but animal cells generally do not manufacture enough or all necessary kinds. Insects, for example, may synthesize all except the B vitamins. A few rodents, apes, and man cannot manufacture their own vitamin C, but other animals can (hence carnivores such as lions may omit orange juice from their diet). Man happens to be a particularly poor vitamin synthesizer, being unable to produce sufficient quantities of any of these growth factors except vitamin D.

These differences between various animal species are undoubtedly a result of mutation and evolution. The earliest animals probably were able to produce all vitamins on their own, as plants still do today. In the course of time, random mutations must have blocked different vitamin-synthesizing reactions in different animals, leading to the present diversity in synthesizing ability. Animals with given genetically determined deficiencies survive nevertheless, for, as heterotrophs, they can obtain the missing vitamins from plant foods. Green plants with such genetic deficiencies could not survive. That mutations may indeed destroy vitamin-synthesizing capacity can be demonstrated experimentally.

More than 30 compounds are known to possess the properties of vitamins. That is, they are required in very small amounts and their prolonged absence from a cell impairs metabolic processes and produces unsteady or diseased states. In this connection, careful distinction should be made between the *biological* and the *clinical* effects of a deficiency. *All* cells of an animal require *all* vitamins; if a vitamin deficiency exists, some metabolic or self-perpetuative process in all cells will be impaired. This is a biological effect. For example, we already know that thiamine is a B vitamin required in all cells for the conversion of pyruvic acid to acetyl CoA. If thiamine is in deficient supply, respiratory reactions in all cells will be affected. Superimposed on such biological effects are clinical ones. That is, the cells of given tissues or organs may be more sensitive to a deficiency than other cells. Such body parts will then exhibit symptoms of disease sooner or more pronouncedly than other body parts. For example, thiamine deficiency in man has long been known to lead to the clinical disease *beriberi*, characterized in severe cases by nervous and muscular paralysis. By themselves, clinical data alone would imply that thiamine is required specifically by nerve and muscle tissues. Actually, however, clinical results represent only the large-scale secondary consequences of the deeper biological effects of deficiency which influence all cells. Thus, clinical results can be a beginning of vitamin studies, but they must not be mistaken for the end (Fig. 17.9).

When they were first investigated, vitamins were given letter designations. Later, virtually every vitamin so labeled was found to consist of not one but of several, often related substances. Letters with subscripts then came into use. Today, the tendency is to refer to a new vitamin by its chemical name only. Many vitamins therefore do not have a letter designation, and some have both letter and chemical labels.

Fig. 17.9. Some effects of riboflavin deficiency. Top: riboflavin-deficient rat. Pronounced loss of hair, sickly appearance. Weight 63 g. Bottom: same rat as above, 6 weeks later, after riboflavin-rich diet. Recovery complete. Weight 169 g. (Bureau of Human Nutrition and Home Economics.)

Vitamins are partly fat-soluble and partly water-soluble. The first group includes vitamins A, D, E, and K; the latter, vitamins B and C. Fat-soluble vitamins require bile for proper absorption from the gut. Therefore, whenever fat digestion is impaired or when fats are rigidly excluded from the diet, vitamin deficiency may develop readily. Water-soluble vitamins frequently pass into cooking water and into the water surrounding canned food. Such juices evidently should not be thrown away.

The names, food sources, and cell functions of the most important vitamins, and the clinical effects of deficiency, are listed in Table 7. To a variable extent among animals, adequate supply of vitamins depends directly on adequate nutrition. The supply of hormones, on the other hand, hinges primarily on internal secretion.

HORMONES

Animal groups known to possess specialized endocrine glands include particularly the insects and the vertebrates. The hormones manufactured and secreted by these glands vary greatly in chemical composition. Some are proteins, a few are amino acids, and the rest are various other simple or complex kinds of compounds. A few can be synthesized in the laboratory, a few have known chemical structure, and the remainder are known only through the effects of hormone deficiency (e.g., undersecretion, excision of the secreting cells) and of hormone excess (e.g., oversecretion, injection of hormone).

Like the auxins of plants, insect hormones are essentially growth promoters. They play particularly important roles during insect development. Produced in special glands located in the brain and the thorax, insect hormones control the development of larvae, the transformation of larvae into pupae, and the final transformation of either larvae or pupae into adults. Beyond these very basic developmental functions, little is known about the cellular, metabolic roles of the hormones. By contrast, the cellular functions of vertebrate hormones may be circumscribed rather well, although the precise reactions in which the hormones participate cannot yet be pinpointed as well as for many vitamins. For example, there is no doubt that the thyroid hormone promotes respiration, but what

TABLE 7
The principal vitamins and their functions

name	food sources	chief cellular functions	effects of deficiency
vitamin A	leaves, yellow foods, liver	chemistry of vision; integrity of membranes	night blindness; infectious diseases; bone, nerve abnormalities
thiamine (B_1)		acetyl CoA production	beriberi
riboflavin (B_2)		FMN and FAD precursor	hair loss; growth failure
nicotinic acid		DPN precursor	pellagra
pantothenic acid		coenzyme A precursor	
folic acid	grain products, yeast, beans, nuts, liver, eggs, meat	nucleic acid metabolism	anemia; growth failure; hemorrhages; bone disorders, nerve, skin disorders; infectious diseases
vitamin B_{12}			
biotin (H)		fat synthesis, CO_2 metabolism	
choline		fat and protein metabolism, amino group transfers	
pyridoxine (B_6)			
vitamin C	citrus fruits, tomatoes, cabbage	aerobic H transfer; synthesis of cell cement	scurvy
vitamin D	liver, fish oils	Ca and P regulation	rickets
vitamin E	most foods	aerobic H transfer	sterility; eye abnormalities; nerve, muscle disorders
vitamin K			failure of blood clotting

specific reaction or reactions are affected are still obscure (Fig. 17.10).

Just as cells probably require all vitamins, so also do all vertebrate cells probably require all hormones. The term "sex hormone," for example, is somewhat misleading. True, sex hormones are manufactured in sex organs and the hormones contribute to the proper functioning of these organs. As we now know, however, sex hormones also contribute to the functioning of virtually every other organ in the body. It happens that the effect of deficiency or excess of a given hormone may reveal itself first or most obviously in a particular body part. For convenience we may then name the hormone according to this body part, but we cannot conclude that the hormone functions only there.

Apart from their other controlling roles in cells, many hormones perform an additional special function: they control the manufacture and secretion of one another. For example, many endocrine glands cannot secrete their hormones unless they are stimulated to do so by other hormones, secreted in other endocrine glands. As a group, such glands in effect function like a board of directors, in which the members hold one another in close mutual check. The output of each gland is controlled wholly or partially by the output of one or more other glands. As a result, the overall output by all glands is carefully balanced. This is essential, for whereas one hormone may accelerate a given cellular process, another hormone may inhibit the same process. Therefore, unless the amounts of hormones are continuously readjusted relative to one another and relative to the requirements of the moment, flexible control over cellular processes would not be possible.

This "checking" action of one endocrine gland by another is illustrated well in the case of the pituitary and thyroid glands. The pituitary (Fig. 17.11)

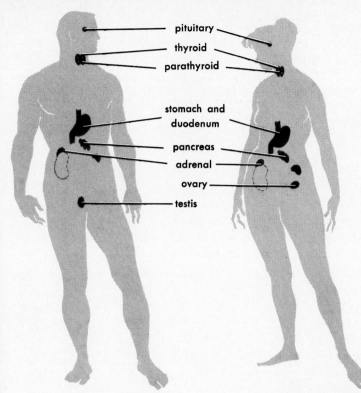

pituitary

thyroid

parathyroid

stomach and
duodenum

pancreas

adrenal

ovary

testis

Fig. 17.10.   The endocrine system.

Fig. 17.11.   **Longitudinal section through a human pituitary gland.** The right side of the photo points in the direction of the face; the left side, in the direction of the back of the head. Note the anterior lobe in the right part of the gland and the intermediate and posterior lobes in the left part. The posterior lobe continues dorsally as a stalk which joins the whole gland to the brain. (Courtesy of Dr. B. J. Serber, College of Medicine, New York University.)

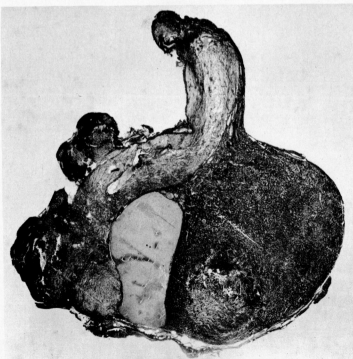

TABLE 8
The principal vertebrate endocrine glands and their hormones

gland	hormones	chief functions	some effects of deficiency or excess
pituitary, anterior lobe	TTH FSH, LH ACTH lactogenic growth	stimulates thyroid stimulate ovaries and testes stimulates adrenal cortex stimulates milk secretion promotes cell metabolism	dwarfism; gigantism
pituitary, mid-lobe	intermedin	controls adjustable skin-pigment cells (e.g., frogs)	
pituitary, posterior lobe	at least five distinct fractions	controls water metabolism, blood pressure, kidney function, smooth-muscle action	increased or reduced water excretion
thyroid	thyroxin	stimulates respiration; inhibits TTH secretion	goiter, cretinism; myxedema
parathyroid	parathormone	controls Ca metabolism	nerve, muscle abnormalities; bone thickening or weakening
adrenal cortex	cortisone, other similar hormones	controls metabolism of water, minerals, carbohydrates; controls kidney functions; inhibits ACTH secretion; duplicates sex-hormone functions	Addison's disease
adrenal medulla	adrenalin	alarm reaction, e.g., raises blood pressure, heart rate, produces "gooseflesh"	inability to cope with stress
pancreas	insulin	promotes blood glucose → tissue glycogen conversion	diabetes
testis	testosterone, other androgens	promote cell respiration, blood circulation; maintain primary and secondary sex characteristics, sex urge; inhibit FSH, LH secretions	atrophy of reproductive system; decline of secondary sex characteristics
ovary	estradiol, other estrogens		

secretes a hormone known as the *thyrotropic hormone, TTH* for short. The only known function of this hormone is to stimulate the thyroid gland. Without TTH, the thyroid is inactive; with TTH, the thyroid is stimulated to secrete its own hormone, *thyroxin*. We already know that thyroxin controls the rate of respiration. But thyroxin also has one other function: it acts on the pituitary and *inhibits* it. Therefore, when thyroxin reaches the pituitary, the output of TTH by that gland will be reduced or even stopped. And since TTH is required for thyroid secretion, reduced TTH output by the pituitary will also reduce the thyroxin output. But less thyroxin will mean that it will inhibit the pituitary less, which in turn means that the pituitary can again produce more TTH. The net effect of these successive stimulations and inhibitions is that the hormone output of both pituitary and thyroid is controlled and is actually kept relatively constant.

Indeed, the two glands and their two hormones form an automatic, self-adjusting control system with built-in feedback. Through such control, the thyroid can secrete neither too little nor too much of its hormone (Fig. 17.12).

We may note here that the pituitary gland also interacts in similar manner with the cortisone-producing adrenal gland (specifically, the adrenal cortex) and with the sex-hormone-producing ovaries and testes. We shall have occasion to discuss these sex-hormone effects in Chap. 22.

The names, glandular sources, and main functions of the chief hormones, as well as some of their clinical effects in deficiency or excess, are listed in Table 8.

As noted in the previous chapter, steady-state regulation in animals is achieved not only by cellular growth factors such as hormones and vitamins, but also by various tissue- and organ-level control systems which do not have counterparts in plants. Of particular significance here are circulatory, excretory, and nervous systems. We shall deal with these uniquely animal controls in the next two chapters.

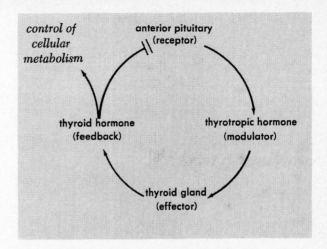

Fig. 17.12. The action of certain pituitary hormones and their feedback control. Pituitary-thyroid interaction is shown as an example. Pointed arrows symbolize stimulation, and the arrow tipped with a transverse double bar symbolizes inhibition. Through this control cycle, the output of thyrotropic hormone is automatically self-adjusting.

Review questions

1. Define growth factor, growth regulator. What is the effect of auxins on cells? Show how these substances contribute to the control of steady-state maintenance in plants.

2. Describe various tropistic responses of plants and review the role of auxins in producing such responses. Show how differential auxin sensitivities are of importance.

3. What is an abscission layer? How can fruit or leaf abscission be promoted or inhibited by artificial means? In what processes other than growth do auxins play a role?

4. Describe the responses of plants to light duration. What is a photoperiod? Define short-day, long-day, and indeterminate plants.

5. What are the roles of (a) florigen, (b) vernalin. Where and when are these substances produced? Show how the photoperiodic characteristics of given plants are reflected in the global distribution of the plants.

6. Review the cellular functions of all vitamins, as far as known. How do autotrophs and heterotrophs differ in their vitamin requirements? How, and why, do different heterotrophs differ in their vitamin requirements?

7. Distinguish between clinical and biological effects of vitamin or hormone deficiencies. Which vitamins are fat-soluble and which are water-soluble? Review the food sources of the principal vitamins. What are the clinical effects of deficiencies of these vitamins?

8. How do given endocrine glands control the activity of other endocrine glands? Show how the activity of the thyroid gland is regulated by the pituitary, and vice versa.

9. Review the general functions of insect and vertebrate hormones. What determines whether a medicinal hormone preparation for man must be injected or may be taken orally?

10. What are the specific hormones produced by the various endocrine glands? As far as is known, what are the functions of each of these hormones?

Suggested collateral readings

Butler, W. L., and R. J. Downs: Light and Plant Development, *Sci. Am.*, vol. 203, 1960.

Funkenstern, D. H.: The Physiology of Fear and Anger, *Sci. Am.*, vol. 192, 1955.

Gray, G. W.: Cortisone and ACTH, *Sci. Am.*, vol. 182, 1950.

Jacobs, W. P.: What Makes Leaves Fall, *Sci. Am.*, vol. 193, 1955.

Levine, R., and M. S. Goldstein: The Action of Insulin, *Sci. Am.*, vol. 198, 1958.

Li, C. H.: The Pituitary, *Sci. Am.*, vol. 183, 1950.

Rasmussen, H.: The Parathyroid Hormone, *Sci. Am.*, vol. 204, 1961.

Salisbury, F. B.: The Flowering Process, *Sci. Am.*, vol. 198, 1958.

————: Plant Growth Substances, *Sci. Am.*, vol. 196, 1957.

Zuckerman, S.: Hormones, *Sci. Am.*, vol. 196, 1957.

THE BODY FLUIDS

18

It was pointed out earlier that, in an animal, each organ system contributes *to* the steady state of every other system and is in turn maintained in steady state *by* every other system. For example, the steady-state function of the digestive system is to provide an adequate supply of nutrients for all other systems. But the digestive system is itself kept in steady state by the nervous system, the circulatory system, and by every other system as well. No one system can therefore be said to be "more important" than any other; each fulfills a necessary role.

However, four particular systems contribute perhaps more continuously to the steady state of the body than most others. The four are the *breathing*, the *circulatory*, the *excretory*, and the *nervous* systems. Other systems may suspend operations temporarily and the organism may yet survive; muscles may become paralyzed, food may be unavailable, reproduction may cease, skin may be burned, bones may be broken. These and similar conditions may well be extremely damaging, but they need not be lethal. By contrast, stop breathing, stop the heart, stop kidney function, stop brain function—any one alone will bring death almost immediately. The four systems evidently exercise controls which the animal cannot do without even briefly. Their constant operation is vitally necessary if immediate and irreversible unsteady state is to be avoided.

The function of breathing has already been discussed in Chap. 13, and the operations of the nervous system will be outlined in the following chapter. Here we deal with the circulatory and the excretory systems. Both control the attributes of the *body fluids*, blood and lymph, which permeate the entire body and constitute the immediate environment of every cell. The *circulatory system* carries the body fluids and governs their *physical* characteristics—pressure, distribution, rate of flow. The *excretory system* governs the *chemical* characteristics of the fluids—which materials are and which are not to be retained in them.

Blood and lymph

Blood is a tissue. It is composed of loose *cells* and of *plasma*, a fluid in which the cells are suspended. Approximately half of the blood of a vertebrate is cellular, the other half plasma.

BLOOD PLASMA

The main constituent of plasma is water. Its source is food and metabolic water excreted by cells into the body fluids. The supply of water is carefully counterbalanced by excretion, through lungs, sweat glands, and kidneys. The total water content of the body, hence blood volume, is thereby maintained constant.

Blood water has many functions. This store supplies all cells with the water they require. Oozing out from capillaries as the main constituent of lymph, blood water envelops all tissues of most animals, in the same way that ocean water enveloped the cells of their primitive ancestors. By its very presence in a certain quantity within a closed channel system, blood water contributes importantly to blood pressure. After extensive blood loss through wounds, one of the foremost requirements is restoration of blood volume, that is, restoration of water.

Blood water functions as the *transport vehicle* for all other plasma components, for respiratory gases, and for blood cells. The cells are suspended; all other constituents are largely dissolved. Apart from the cells, the other components may be grouped into two general classes. One consists of substances normally maintained at *constant* concentrations. In this category are water, many of the mineral ions, plasma proteins, and other compounds which are either nutrients in transit to tissue cells or waste products in transit to the excretory organs.

Constancy of such plasma components is achieved by a balance between supply and removal. Supply of a given component may take the form of absorption from the gut or release by tissue cells or manufacture and release by the liver. Removal may involve liver storage, elimination via the excretory system, or absorption by tissue cells. In each case, too high or too low a concentration of a given substance in the blood is the critical stimulus for its own removal or replenishment. As we have seen, for example, a moderately high blood-glucose level stimulates liver cells to lower it by storing the excess as glycogen. A still higher level stimulates storage not only in liver but also in muscle and skin, for example. And a very high concentration leads to glucose excretion from the kidneys. The sensitivity of these control organs to actual supply and demand of a given compound brings about a steady state in blood.

The second group of plasma constituents consists of substances which fluctuate more or less widely in concentration, depending on body activity. In this category are a number of foods in transit, urea and other waste products in transit, hormones in transit, and many other substances.

Each of the plasma substances serves one or more functions. For example, inorganic ions and blood proteins of all kinds aid in maintaining a constant *blood pH* (normally 7.3) and a constant *osmotic pressure*. Some of the blood proteins also function in *blood clotting* (see below), and others serve as defensive *antibodies*, which destroy infecting bacteria or render them harmless (Fig. 18.1). Certain of the blood proteins are the basis of differences in blood type. Table 9 lists the main components and functions of blood plasma.

Clearly, this fluid plays many roles in steady-state maintenance. It serves as a sensory and motor path interconnecting all cells. It is a modulator contributing

TABLE 9

The principal constituents and functions of blood plasma°

components	functions
1. water	maintains blood volume, pressure; forms lymph; water supply of cells; vehicle for other constituents
2. mineral ions	maintain osmotic balance, pH balance; varied effects on tissue cells
3. plasma proteins	all maintain osmotic and pH balance
fibrinogen	participates in blood clotting
prothrombin	participates in blood clotting
albumins, enzymes	functions obscure
globulins	basis of blood types; act as antibodies
4. glucose, other organic substances	in transit to and from cells
5. urea, CO_2, O_2, various foods, hormones, vitamins, and others	in transit to and from cells

°Categories 1 to 4 are maintained at constant concentrations; materials in category 5 occur in variable concentrations.

to the constancy of chemical and physical conditions in all tissues. And it is a receptor of infectious stimuli and a defensive effector against them. All this is in addition to the purely transportive functions of plasma, namely, delivering nutrients and collecting wastes, and in addition also to the function of plasma as lymph, through which it provides a proper operating environment for all cells.

BLOOD CELLS

Three kinds of cellular components are found in blood: *red corpuscles, white blood cells,* and *blood platelets* (Fig. 18.2).

The major function of the *red corpuscles* is the transporting of oxygen (Chap. 13). In the adult, red corpuscles are manufactured in the red marrow present at the ends of long bones (e.g., ribs, arms, legs). Liver and spleen are the production sites in the embryo, before bones mature. After the skeleton is fully formed and blood-cell production is initiated in it, the spleen becomes principally a blood-storing organ. It may contract like a sponge and squeeze reserve blood into the circulation. The liver becomes the organ where red corpuscles are destroyed.

Production in bone marrow is so geared to destruction in the liver that the number of red corpuscles is

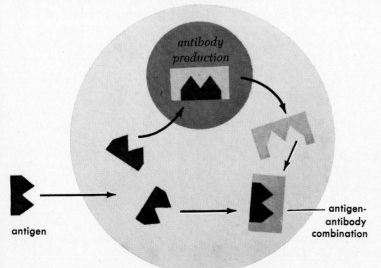

antibody production

antigen

antigen-antibody combination

Fig. 18.1. The action of specific antibodies. A foreign protein introduced into an organism is an antigen. It elicits the formation of antibodies (special proteins in blood plasma), which "fit" precisely the surface configuration of the antigen. These specific antibodies may then combine with the antigens, making the latter harmless.

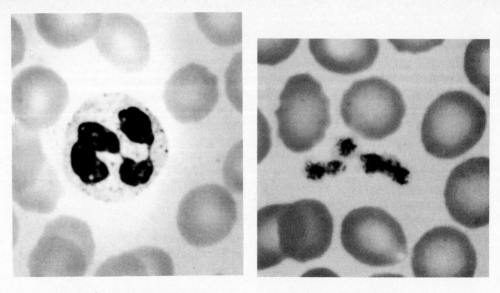

Fig. 18.2.   Human red blood corpuscles are shown in both photos. Note absence of nuclei. A white blood cell (nucleated) is shown in center of left photo and a few blood platelets in center of right photo. (General Biological Supply House, Inc.)

kept fairly constant. The controlling signal is the amount of oxygen carried by blood (Fig. 18.3). Low oxygen content stimulates bone marrow to produce red corpuscles at a faster rate. At the same time, the liver is inhibited from destroying corpuscles at too fast a rate. Accordingly, when inhaled air contains too little oxygen for extended periods, as at high altitudes, then more blood corpuscles are manufactured. An adequate

quantity of gas thus may still be delivered to the tissues by this greater number of corpuscles. A persistently high oxygen concentration in blood has the opposite effect on liver and bone marrow.

In man, each cubic millimeter of blood, roughly the volume of a pinhead, contains over 5 million red corpuscles. It has been estimated that every *second* some 10,000 corpuscles are manufactured and just as

Fig. 18.3.   Control of red corpuscle number. Production in bone marrow and destruction in liver are geared to each other by the oxygen content of blood.

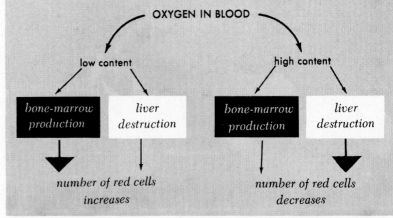

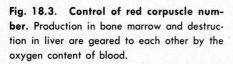

many are destroyed. In mammals, but not in other vertebrates, maturation of a red corpuscle in bone marrow includes the disintegration of the cell nucleus. Corpuscles in the mammalian blood stream consequently are enucleated and not "cells" in the strict sense.

White cells are complete cells with nuclei. They normally do not divide. Whereas red corpuscles are quite uniform in size and appearance, white blood cells are not. Two groups may be distinguished, *leucocytes* and *lymphocytes*, each including a number of subgroups.

Leucocytes are manufactured in red bone marrow, probably by the same generating tissue which gives rise to red corpuscles. Lymphocytes are formed in lymphatic tissue, principally in the lymph nodes found along the path of the lymph vessels. Lymphocytes reach the blood stream via the lymph channels. Altogether, white blood cells are much less abundant than red corpuscles. A cubic millimeter of human blood contains about 8,000 white cells.

To greater or lesser degree all white cells, but leucocytes particularly, are capable of amoeboid locomotion. Like an amoeba, a leucocyte may extend pseudopods into which the rest of the cell then flows. In this way, leucocytes may squeeze in between adjacent cells in the walls of blood capillaries and leave the blood stream (Fig. 18.4). Once they are out in the tissues, the leucocytes migrate toward sites of infection. There they engulf and digest bacteria, in the same way that an amoeba engulfs and digests food. Accumulations of white cells, bacteria, and the debris from infected tissue constitute *pus*. We note that the principal function of white cells is internal body defense.

Platelets are not whole cells but cell fragments, often without nuclei. A plasma membrane covers each platelet. About one-quarter million of these bodies are found in each cubic millimeter of human blood. The origin of platelets is obscure, as is the control system which keeps their number constant. They are probably manufactured predominantly in red bone marrow. A certain fraction is believed to be formed in the connective tissue which binds the lung alveoli together.

Platelets are essential in blood clotting. This self-sealing mechanism of the circulatory system is brought into action whenever platelets encounter obstructions and rupture. In most cases, such obstructions are the rough edges of torn blood vessels. External clotting then occurs. But air bubbles in blood (e.g., when dissolved gases effervesce) or roughness of the inner surfaces of blood vessels (e.g., as produced by solid

Fig. 18.4.   The migration of blood cells through capillary walls. In each photo, a blood-filled capillary is in upper-right portion. In photo at left, two white blood cells have just penetrated through the capillary wall into surrounding tissues. In photo at right, the white cells have migrated farther into the tissues. (Courtesy of Dr. Robert Brenner, Oregon Regional Primate Research Center, Beaverton, Ore.)

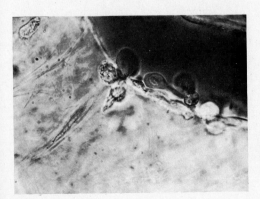
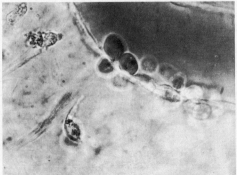

deposits in hardened arteries) may suffice for the rupturing of platelets. An internal blood clot may then form.

The clotting process is exceedingly complex, far more so than the following simplified and abbreviated outline (Fig. 18.5). Among the materials oozing out from ruptured platelets is an enzymatically active substance, *thrombokinase*, also called *thromboplastin*. This substance interacts with two components of blood plasma, namely, calcium ions and the plasma protein prothrombin. This protein is an inactive precursor of the catalyst *thrombin*. In the presence of calcium ions and thrombokinase, prothrombin becomes converted to thrombin. Subsequently, thrombin reacts with fibrinogen, another of the plasma proteins. As a result of the reaction, fibrinogen becomes *fibrin*, an insoluble coagulated protein. Fibrin constitutes the blood clot.

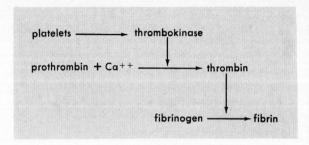

Fig. 18.5.   The main features of the clotting reaction.

It is a yellowish-white meshwork of fibers in which blood corpuscles are trapped, hence the redness of the clot.

Clotting can be prevented when any of the ingredients are missing or are made inoperative. For exam-

Fig. 18.6.   Left, the human heart. The large blood-vessel stump is the aorta. The auricles are partly hidden by the aorta. The size of your fist is very nearly the actual size of your heart. Right, the heart cut open to show the interior of the left ventricle. Note the strands of tissue attached to the two flaps of the bicuspid valve. These strands prevent the valve from opening into the auricle (white area above the ventricle). (Photographic Department, Rhode Island Hospital.)

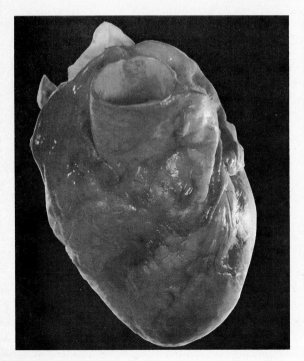

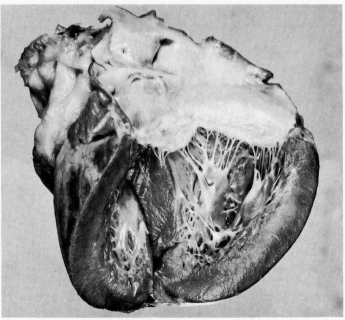

ple, fibrinogen can be withdrawn fairly easily from whole blood or plasma. This procedure is often used in storing blood or plasma for transfusion. Plasma minus fibrinogen is called *blood serum*.

We note that blood as a whole forms the first line of internal defense. However, this control function of blood and its other functions in transport and tissue maintenance can be exercised only if blood *circulates*.

Circulation

The component organs of the circulatory system are the heart, the blood vessels, and the lymph vessels. Together they represent more than a pumping station and a system of pipes, for they also regulate the speed and force of motion and the internal distribution of the moving fluids.

From the standpoint of individual tissue cells, the important parts of the circulatory system are the microscopic *capillary vessels*. It is through them and only through them that circulating body fluids and tissue cells exchange life-sustaining materials and information. But to make such capillary exchanges possible, structures like heart and large blood vessels become necessary prerequisites.

THE PATHWAY

In mammals, the heart lies in the midplane of the chest, directly underneath the breastbone. But it is tilted somewhat, the lower tip projecting over to the left. This is where the beat of the heart is most readily discernible (Fig. 18.6).

The mammalian heart consists of four chambers, the right and left *auricle* and the right and left *ventricle*. Typically, one large blood vessel is connected to each (Fig. 18.7). The *aorta* leaves the left ventricle and the branches of this vessel supply all parts of the body with arterial (oxygen-rich) blood. Venous (oxygen-poor) blood collects from all body regions and returns through the *vena cava* into the right auricle.

The right auricle connects with the right ventricle through the *tricuspid valve*, an opening equipped with three flaps. This valve lets blood through from auricle to ventricle but not in the reverse direction. Venous

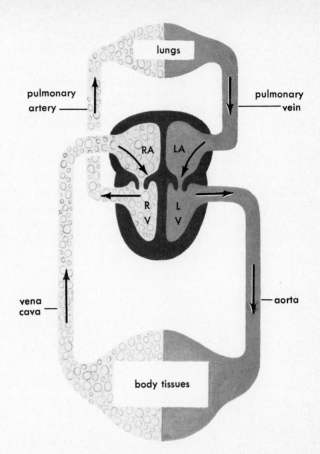

Fig. 18.7. Diagram of the course of blood circulation through the body. Arterial blood is in the left side of the circulatory system (right side of the diagram), venous blood in the right side (left side of the diagram).

blood collected in the right ventricle leaves this chamber via the *pulmonary artery*, a vessel leading to the lungs. Here blood is oxygenated, and arterial blood returns through the *pulmonary vein* into the left auricle (see also Fig. 13.8).

A *bicuspid* or *mitral* valve, equipped with two flaps, separates the left auricle from the left ventricle. Like the tricuspid on the right, the mitral valve also opens into the ventricle only. The flaps of both the bicuspid and tricuspid valves are prevented from letting blood pass in the wrong direction by strands of tissue resembling parachute strings. These are attached to the free edges of the valve flaps on one end and to the ventricle walls on the other (see Fig. 18.6). The bicuspid and tricuspid valves together may be referred to as the auriculo-ventricular valves, or A-V *valves*. Smaller valves are situated where the aorta and the pulmonary artery leave the left and right ventricle, respectively. These valves open away from the heart and close toward it.

Note that the left chambers of the heart are not connected directly with the right chambers. The left carry arterial blood only; the right, venous blood only. Inasmuch as the auricles pump blood only as far as the ventricles, relatively thin muscular walls suffice. But the ventricles, the left one in particular, pump blood into the farthest parts of the body. These chambers possess proportionately thick walls.

THE PROCESS

The heart is a pressure pump. It generates pumping force on contraction, here called *systole*, and it rests during muscular relaxation, or *diastole*. A complete heartbeat consists of one systole and one diastole, the whole beat lasting about 0.8 second in a normal human adult at rest. On an average, therefore, 72 beats take place per minute.

A heartbeat starts with the contraction of the auricles (Fig. 18.8). These chambers gradually distend as blood returns via vena cava and pulmonary vein. When the auricles are fully distended, their muscular walls contract. The ventricles are relaxed at that time. As the auricles contract, blood cannot flow backward

Fig. 18.8. The pumping action of the heart. In the left figure, the auricles are shown contracting, forcing blood into the relaxed ventricles. The A-V valves are open, but the pressure of blood closes all others. In the right figure, the ventricles contract, forcing blood into the pulmonary artery and the aorta. The auricles are relaxed at the same time, filling with blood in preparation for the next beat.

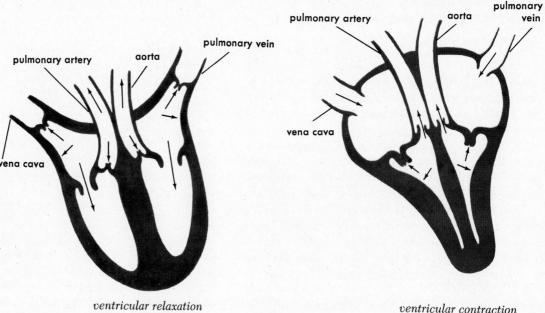

auricular contraction

auricular relaxation

pulmonary artery   aorta   pulmonary vein

pulmonary artery   aorta   pulmonary vein

vena cava

vena cava

ventricular relaxation

ventricular contraction

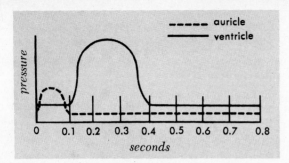

Fig. 18.9. The time relationship between auricular and ventricular beats. Note that the auricles contract and generate pressure when the ventricles are relaxed, and vice versa. Note also that the whole heart is relaxed for half the time of a beat.

because incoming blood presses steadily *into* the auricles. Therefore, the only path open to auricular blood is through the A-V valves, which lead into the ventricles. These chambers now distend as the auricles empty. The auricular phase of the heartbeat lasts about 0.1 second. The auricles then relax for the remaining 0.7 second of the cycle, slowly redistending during this interval in preparation for the next beat (Fig. 18.9).

As soon as the auricles have relaxed, the ventricles, by this time fully distended, contract in their turn. Their thick walls generate much more pressure than the walls of the auricles. Also, ventricular systole lasts longer, namely, some 0.3 second. As the contraction peak is reached, blood is forced against all ventricular openings, including the A-V valves. But as blood slaps against the A-V flaps, these snap shut and prevent backflow into the auricles (see Fig. 18.8). The impact of blood against the valve flaps produces the *first heart sound*, which can be felt or heard as "the" heartbeat.

The only way blood can leave the ventricles is via the aorta on the left and the pulmonary artery on the right. The exit valves into these vessels open as blood presses against them with great force. The sudden quantity of fluid now rushing out dilates portions of the exit arteries adjacent to the heart. But the arterial walls are elastic and snap back into position, thereby adding to the pressure of blood. Most of the blood is

thus forced forward, where the open paths lead to the lungs and to all body tissues. But some blood tends to press back into the ventricles. This back pressure snaps the exit valves shut and blood then cannot flow in this direction (see Fig. 18.8). The impact of blood in closing the exit valves generates the *second heart sound*, fainter than the first.

Note that even the ventricles rest more than half the time. Note also that all heart chambers are always completely full with blood. The quantity of blood in different chambers does vary, however, and such blood is also under greater or lesser pressure. This differential pressure alone determines the position of the heart valves, hence the course in which blood can flow.

Arterial blood "flows" in rhythmic spurts, according to the rhythm of the heart. As each spurt of fluid impinges on the walls of arteries, it gives rise to *pulse* vibrations. With increasing distance from the heart, arterial spurts become less and less forceful. By the time blood is through capillary vessels and has reached veins, it no longer spurts but flows in a continuous, even stream. The heart here produces very little direct push. Venous blood keeps moving slowly by the push of blood from behind and by contraction of skeletal muscles which squeeze the veins. The pressure of lymph is even lower than that of blood. Here again, push of lymph from behind and muscular activity provide the major forces which return lymph to the blood circulation (Fig. 18.10).

How are heartbeat and circulation as a whole maintained?

THE CONTROL

Heart rate. The main nervous regulating center of heart rate is located in the *medulla oblongata*, the same general region of the hindbrain which also houses the breathing center. Two pairs of nerves lead from a *heart-rate center* to the heart (Fig. 18.11). Impulses through one pair accelerate heartbeat; impulses through the other slow it. The accelerator nerves travel through the spinal cord for some distance, emerge in the chest region, and innervate the heart. The inhibitory nerve fibers pass from the heart-rate center into the large *vagus nerves*. One vagus nerve on each side

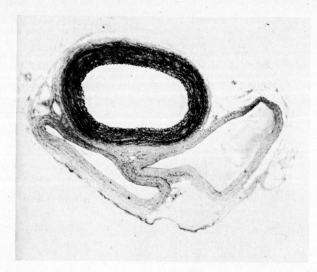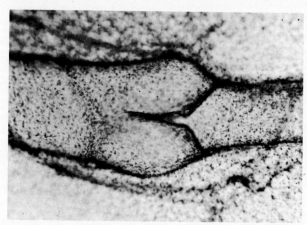

Fig. 18.10.   Left, section through an artery and two veins. Note the thicker wall of the artery and the presence of many elastic fibers (dark wavy lines) in this wall. Right, longitudinal section through a lymph vessel, showing an internal valve. Such valves prevent backflow. Valves very much like this are present also in the larger veins. (Left, courtesy of Dr. B. J. Serber, College of Medicine, New York University; right, General Biological Supply House, Inc.)

leaves the hindbrain and runs through the neck alongside the trachea. Some branches of the vagus then lead to the heart.

Both the accelerator and inhibitor nerves terminate in the wall of the right auricle, at a small patch of specialized tissue called the *pacemaker* or *sinus node.* When the pacemaker is stimulated, a wave of contraction spreads out from it through both auricles. Auricular contraction in turn stimulates a second patch of tissue, the *A-V node,* situated in the partition which divides the left and right sides of the heart. At the A-V node originates a bundle of modified heart muscle, the *bundle of His,* specialized for impulse conduction. The strands of this bundle radiate through the walls of both ventricles. Thus, auricular contraction stimulates the A-V node, and impulses transmitted from there through the conductive strands initiate ventricular contraction. The time required for stimulus transmission from pacemaker to A-V node ensures that the ventricles contract a fraction of a second *after* the auricles.

The pacemaker is the immediate regulator of

heart rate, and the heart-rate center in turn controls the action of the pacemaker. Like other processes, the rate of heartbeat is a restrained compromise between acceleration and deceleration. Experiments show that inhibitory signals via the vagus nerves allow a more flexible adjustment of heart rate than accelerator signals. For example, it can be demonstrated that an acceleration of the heart is brought about specifically by a *decrease* of impulse frequency through the vagus nerves; the heart beats faster primarily because of reduced braking action, not because acceleration has been stepped up. Similarly, a slowing of the heart is primarily a result of increased braking via the vagus nerves.

Pressure and distribution of blood.   If blood pressure became too high, thin blood vessels and the thin-walled auricles of the heart might burst. And if blood pressure became too low, blood would not possess sufficient momentum to circulate.

Even in the absence of a pumping mechanism, a quantity of fluid filling a confined space is under a certain pressure. The larger the volume of fluid and the smaller the available space, the greater will be the pressure. Blood pressure therefore depends on three main factors: blood *volume*, blood *vessel space*, and in addition also the *force* of the heartbeat.

Blood volume is adjusted to some extent through contractions of the spleen, which bring stored blood into circulation, and to a major extent through regulation of fluid intake and fluid loss. Adjustments of blood pressures by such means are comparatively slow. However, virtually instant adjustments may be brought about by alterations in the force of the heartbeat and in the space within blood vessels.

The main determinant of the force of heartbeats is the *amount* of blood received and pumped out in a given span of time. This is a curious but little-understood phenomenon characteristic of all muscle. Within certain limits, the greater the work load of a muscle

and the more it is thereby stretched, the stronger is its contraction. For example, when the heart receives small quantities of blood in each beat and distends only a little (as under conditions of sleep or rest), then its contraction will be weak. But when much blood distends the ventricles fully, as during exercise, then the pumping action will be powerful and blood pressure will increase correspondingly.

The space available within blood vessels is adjusted by contraction and relaxation of the muscles in the vessel walls. *Vasoconstriction* reduces the diameter of blood vessels; *vasodilation* increases it. Vasoconstriction and vasodilation together are referred to as *vasomotion*. These muscular activities are controlled by a *vasomotor center* in the brain, located again in the medulla oblongata, close to the breathing and heart-rate centers. Nerves lead from the vasomotor center to all blood vessels except the capillaries, which do not possess muscles. Impulses through these nerves to given vasomotor muscles bring about a narrowing or a widening of blood vessels.

Vasoconstriction in all parts of the body simultaneously raises overall blood pressure, and vasodilation lowers it. Vasomotion may also occur in limited regions of the body, leading to localized changes in blood pressure. Thus blood pressure can rise in one part of the body and at the same time fall in another part (Fig. 18.12). This also means that less blood will flow through one region and more through another. Evidently, vasomotion adjusts not only blood pressure, but also the *distribution* of blood in the body.

These adjustments are controlled by the vasomotor center, which, like the heart-center, acts in response to nervous and chemical cues. Nervous cues are exceedingly numerous. Virtually any nervous signal reaching the brain is likely to have an effect on both the heart-rate center and the vasomotor center. For example, pain, emotions, and stresses generally all tend to affect heart rate, blood pressure, and vasomotion. When an animal sustains a wound, heart rate and overall blood pressure usually rise but the wounded area swells through local vasodilation. The adaptive advantage of this is clear. A rise of heart rate and overall blood pressure produces a state of readiness, through faster food flow and oxygen flow to the cells. This enables the organism to combat stress more ef-

Fig. 18.11. The motor innervation of the heart. Impulses through both inhibitor and accelerator nerves may affect the pacemaker. Impulses from there then stimulate the auricles, as well as the A-V node, which in turn sends signals to the ventricles through the bundle of His.

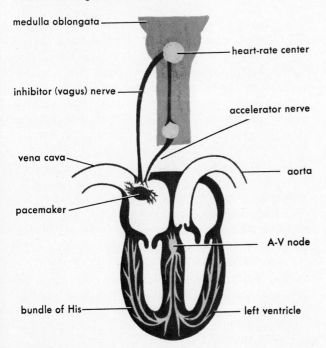

medulla oblongata

heart-rate center

inhibitor (vagus) nerve

accelerator nerve

vena cava

aorta

pacemaker

A-V node

bundle of His

left ventricle

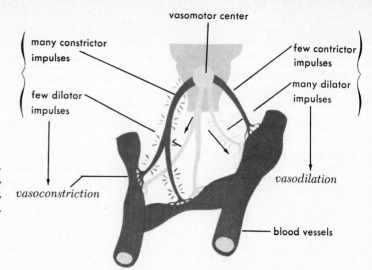

Fig. 18.12. The pattern of vasomotion. Vasoconstriction occurs when a blood vessel receives many constrictor impulses from the vasomotor center and few dilator impulses. Vasodilation occurs when constrictor impulses are few and dilator impulses many.

fectively. And a local vasodilation in the stressed region itself permits more blood to flow into that region. More nutrients and oxygen, as well as more water to dilute any toxic materials, become available there as a result.

The chief chemical cue to which the vasomotor system responds is carbon dioxide in blood. If blood reaching the vasomotor center carries a high concentration of CO_2, then the center transmits constrictor signals throughout the body. Blood pressure therefore rises. Conversely, low CO_2 concentrations bring about a fall of blood pressure. Carbon dioxide also affects the heart-rate center in such a way that high concentrations accelerate heartbeat, low concentrations decelerate it. Moreover, as noted in Chap. 13, high CO_2 concentrations also bring about an increased breathing rate. Therefore, whenever CO_2 needs to be eliminated more rapidly through the lungs, as during strenuous exercise, this waste gas actually controls its own removal; increased breathing, heart rate, and blood pressure permit faster collection of CO_2 from the tissues, faster transport in blood, and faster elimination through the lungs. In this manner, the whole circulatory machinery is geared neatly to the varying activities of the body tissues.

Control of the physical motion of blood is one requirement if blood is to service the tissues adequately. A second requirement is control of proper chemical conditions in blood, despite changes produced continuously by actively metabolizing tissues. This requirement is met by the excretory system.

Excretion

The excretory system is more than an eliminating apparatus. It is made up of many screening stations which continuously check and adjust the composition of the fluids circulating through them. More specifically, the excretory system controls the water content and the blood volume of the body, the pH and the osmotic pressure of blood, and, above all, the chemical composition of blood and the body fluids in general. Moreover, through its water-balancing activities, it is also a major regulator of body temperature.

The organs composing the mammalian excretory system are shown in Fig. 18.13. We have discussed the excretory action of many of these in various earlier contexts. For example, the lungs contribute to the elimination of excess water and carbon dioxide. The sweat glands aid in regulating water balance and also mineral balance. The large intestine makes a further contribution to mineral balance. The liver excretes many diverse materials via bile. And various excretory functions are performed also by the nasal epithelium and by the salivary and the other digestive glands—

in short, by all the organs with access to the exterior of the body either directly or via the alimentary tract.

But the kidneys exercise the major excretory control. When the kidneys are inoperative, all the above organs together are inadequate to prevent death from excretory failure.

KIDNEY STRUCTURE

The structure of the mammalian kidney is complex in detail but relatively simple in principle. Each kidney consists of an outer *renal cortex* and an inner *renal medulla* (Fig. 18.14). Located partly in the cortex

Fig. 18.13.   Some of the component organs of the excretory system.

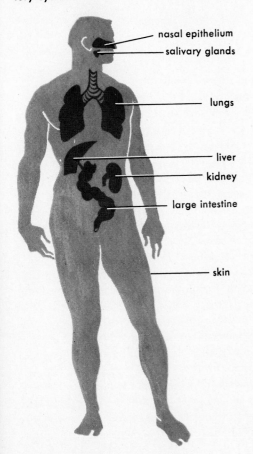

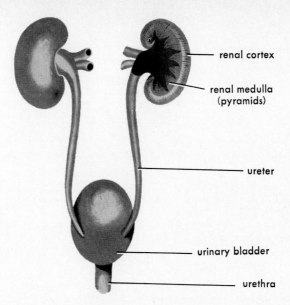

Fig. 18.14.   The renal system. Kidney on right is shown in section.

and partly in the medulla are many thousands of *nephrons*, the operational units of the kidney (Fig. 18.15).

The most conspicuous component of a nephron is a tube, called the *nephric tubule*. At one end this tubule enlarges in a *nephric capsule*, a structure resembling a double-layered cup. At the other end the nephric tubule leads into a *collecting duct*, which receives the output of many neighboring nephric tubules. The numerous collecting ducts in a kidney eventually join and form a wide vessel, the *ureter*. This channel carries urine into the *urinary bladder*. A final duct, the *urethra*, connects the bladder with the outside.

Between the nephric capsule and the entrance into the collecting duct, the nephric tubule is variously coiled and looped. As might be expected, a nephron is in extensive contact with the blood circulation. A large *renal artery* enters the kidney in the region where the ureter leaves, and it branches out repeatedly into many smaller arteries. One of these smaller arteries leads to each nephron. Dipping into the hollow of the nephric capsule, the small artery breaks up into a dense ball of capillaries called a *glomerulus*. The capillaries then rejoin into a single vessel which leaves the capsule and passes into the tubular portion of the nephron. Here this blood vessel

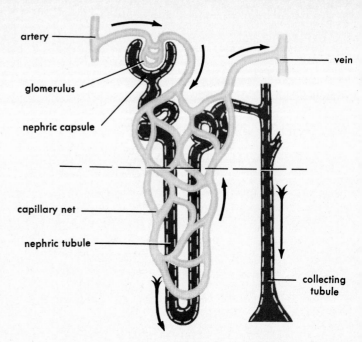

artery

glomerulus

nephric capsule

vein

capillary net

nephric tubule

collecting tubule

Fig. 18.15.   The structure of a nephron and its blood circulation. The portions above the horizontal broken line form part of the renal cortex (see also Fig. 18.14), and the portions below the line, part of the renal medulla. Flow of urine is indicated by feathered arrows; flow of blood, by plain arrows.

branches out once more into a dense capillary net. This net envelops all parts of the nephric tubule. Near the collecting duct, the capillaries lead into a small vein and many such veins from neighboring nephrons join into larger vessels. All these eventually form a single channel, the *renal vein*, which leaves the kidney where the renal artery enters.

KIDNEY FUNCTION

Two basic processes occur in a mammalian kidney (and indeed in any excretory organ of any animal): *filtration* and *reabsorption*. In filtration, all blood constituents which can pass through the walls of capillaries are taken out from the blood stream. In reabsorption, all those constituents which are waste or are present in excess are eliminated as urine; all other constituents are returned into the blood stream. We note that a kidney functions as an "inspector" of blood; it determines which materials should and which should not be retained in the body.

Filtration takes place in the capsule of each nephron. The filters are the walls of the glomerular capil-

laries and the adjacent wall of the capsule (Fig. 18.16). Blood pressure supplies the force necessary for filtration. Pushed by this pressure, every blood component which can go through the glomerular and capsular walls will pass into the upper cavity of the nephric tubule. Only two groups of blood constituents normally can *not* pass through the filters, namely, blood cells and plasma proteins. All other components do pass through without change of concentration. Present within the cavity of the nephric capsule is therefore blood minus cells and proteins—*lymph*, or, as lymph in this space is commonly called, *capsular urine*.

Capsular urine next passes into the tubular portion of the nephron, and here reabsorption takes place. This process is carried out by the cells which compose the nephric tubule. On their inner surfaces such cells absorb from passing capsular urine a picked group of substances. And on their outer surfaces the cells secrete these substances back into the blood stream, through the adjacent walls of blood capillaries (see Fig. 18.16). Whatever is not returned into the blood in this manner constitutes urine, specifically *bladder urine*, since it is carried through the collecting ducts and the ureters into the bladder. The wall of the bladder stretches as urine accumulates, and at a certain stage of stretching, sensory nerve endings in the wall are stimulated. A reflex initiates contraction of the muscles in the bladder wall and the organ then empties to the outside.

Of the substances filtered out from blood and subsequently returned to blood in the kidneys, the most abundant is water. In man, blood contains about 5 to 6 quarts of water and this amount is filtered through the kidneys roughly once every 45 minutes. In a 24-hour period, therefore, the kidneys filter about 150 quarts of liquid. Yet in the same period, only about 1½ quarts of urine, on an average, is actually excreted by the normal adult. This means that tubule cells reabsorb 99 per cent of the water in capsular urine and leave only 1 per cent as urine.

Another substance always reabsorbed by the tubule cells and returned to blood is glucose. Capsular urine contains glucose in the same concentration as in blood. Under normal conditions, all the glucose in capsular urine is reabsorbed into the blood and none escapes into bladder urine. Other materials treated similarly include amino acids, fatty acids, glycerin, vitamins, hormones, in short, all the essential nutrients and other usable supplies in transit to cells.

On the other hand, some substances in capsular urine are always left in urine by the tubule cells. Among such substances are urea, pigmented blood-breakdown products, and other outright wastes. They become highly concentrated as water is withdrawn from capsular urine. For example, bladder urine contains some seventy times more urea than an equal volume of capsular urine. Note that, as urine becomes more concentrated by withdrawal of water back to blood, the osmotic pull of urine becomes greater. But despite this force, which tends to draw water *from* blood *into* urine, tubule cells nevertheless continue to transport more water from *urine* to *blood*.

Tubule cells evidently possess exquisite discriminatory powers. They are not only capable of distinguishing one type of compound from another but they are also sensitive to concentrations of materials in blood and are able to readjust these concentrations. By now rejecting, now reabsorbing given substances, they are the final arbiters of the chemical composition, the pH, and the osmotic properties of the body fluids. The overall result is that the excretory system is much more than an expeller of waste. Indeed, what is or is not "waste" is determined from moment to moment principally by the excretory system. In such determi-

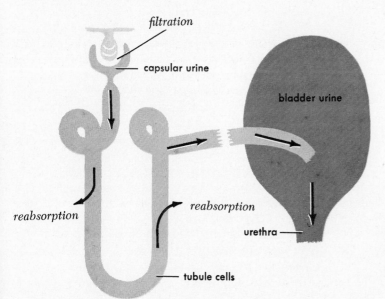

filtration

— capsular urine

bladder urine

reabsorption

reabsorption

urethra —

— tubule cells

Fig. 18.16.   The operation of a nephron. Through filtration of blood, capsular urine is formed, and through reabsorption of various components present in capsular urine, bladder urine is formed.

nations, the function of *retention* is at least as significant as that of excretion, and the excretory organs could justifiably be said to constitute a "retention system." Moreover, it may be appreciated why examination of urine will reveal not only how well the kidneys function, but also how well steady state is maintained in the body as a whole.

Review questions

1. Review the composition of blood plasma and the functions of each group of components. What are antibodies? When and where are they produced? How do they act?

2. What cellular components occur in blood, and what are the functions of each? By what processes is the number of red corpuscles in the blood maintained relatively constant?

3. What are the ingredients required for blood clotting, and through what reactions does clotting take place?

4. Name the principal parts of the heart and the principal blood vessels, and review the general course of blood circulation. What structural features distinguish arteries, veins, lymph vessels, and capillaries?

5. Review the events during a complete heartbeat, with attention to durations, pressure patterns, valve positions, direction of blood flow, and heart sounds. How is blood moved through veins and lymph vessels?

6. Describe the nervous controls of the heart. How are control signals transmitted through the heart itself? Through what specific processes is the heart speeded up when physical exercise is begun and slowed down during rest or sleep?

7. What three major factors control blood pressure and what governs each of these factors? Describe the action of the vasomotor center. What nervous and chemical agencies affect this center, and how?

8. What is the interrelation between vasomotion, heart rate, and breathing rate? Suppose that physical exercise is begun; describe the specific processes leading simultaneously to increased heart rate, increased breathing rate, increased blood pressure, and redistribution of blood within the body.

9. What are the overall functions of the excretory system? What organs compose this system and what is the excretory function of each? Describe the general structure of the kidney and its associated ducts and the specific structure of a nephron.

10. Review the process of urine formation. What are the roles of filtration and reabsorption, and where and how does each occur? How does bladder urine differ from capsular urine with respect to the kinds and the concentrations of substances present?

Suggested collateral readings

Burnet, M.: The Mechanism of Immunity, *Sci. Am.*, vol. 204, 1961.

Burnet, M.: The Thymus Gland, *Sci. Am.*, vol. 207, 1962.

Ponder, E.: The Red Blood Cell, *Sci. Am.*, vol. 196, 1957.

Smith, H. W.: The Kidney, *Sci. Am.*, vol. 188, 1953.

Solomon, A. K.: Pumps on the Living Cell, *Sci. Am.*, vol. 207, 1962.

Surgenor, D. M.: Blood, *Sci. Am.*, vol. 190, 1954.

Wiggers, C. J.: The Heart, *Sci. Am.*, vol. 196, 1957.

Wood, W. B.: White Blood Cells vs. Bacteria, *Sci. Am.*, vol. 184, 1951.

Zweifach, B. W.: The Microcirculation of the Blood, *Sci. Am.*, vol. 200, 1959.

NERVOUS COORDINATION

19

Nervous activity is based on *reflexes*, the functional units of the nervous system. A reflex is routed through a *reflex arc*, which, like any other control apparatus, consists of five components: receptor, sensory pathway, modulator, motor pathway, and effector.

The neural receptors are specialized *sensory cells* which may or may not be housed in elaborate organs such as eyes or ears. Receptors translate the energy of incoming stimuli into nerve impulses. These are transmitted over *sensory nerve fibers* to the modulators, namely, *brain* and *spinal cord*. Their activity produces nerve impulses which travel over *motor nerve fibers* to the effectors, that is, *muscles* and *glands*. Such effectors translate the motor impulses they receive into explicit responses.

The effector functions of muscles and glands have already been discussed in various earlier contexts. In this chapter, therefore, we concentrate primarily on the *neural pathways*, the *neural receptors*, and the *neural centers*.

The neural pathways

The mammalian nervous system consists of two subdivisions, the *central nervous system* (*c.n.s.*) and the *autonomic nervous system* (*a.n.s.*). Brain and spinal cord house the neural centers of both. The c.n.s. controls largely voluntary, conscious activities, and the a.n.s., involuntary, unconscious ones. But the c.n.s. and a.n.s. are highly interdependent. As we shall see, they form a unified, intimately coordinated functional complex.

Regardless of whether reflex activity occurs in the c.n.s. or the a.n.s., the internal working material of the entire nervous system is always the same: nerve cells, which produce and transmit nerve impulses. These properly demand our first attention.

NERVE CELLS

A nerve cell, or *neuron*, typically consists of a nucleus-containing cell body, or *cyton*, and of one or more *nerve fibers*, which are filamentous outgrowths extending away from the cyton (Fig. 19.1). Nerve impulses normally originate at the terminal of one of the fibers, travel toward the cyton, traverse it, then lead away from the cyton through another of its fibers. Nerve fibers in which impulses travel toward the cyton are termed *dendrites;* those carrying impulses away from the cyton are called *axons.* A neuron characteristically

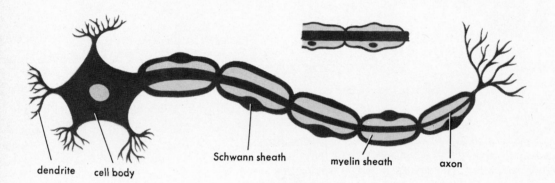

dendrite   cell body   Schwann sheath   myelin sheath   axon

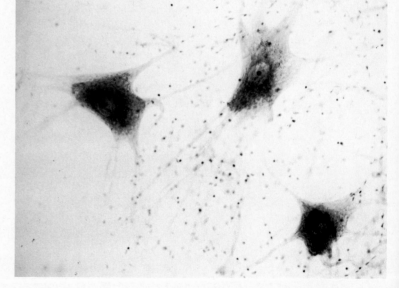

Fig. 19.1. The structure of a neuron. Dendrites may be proportionately longer than shown in the diagram. Upper inset: a length of non-myelinated axon. The photomicrograph shows fixed and stained cell bodies. (Photo, General Biological Supply House, Inc.)

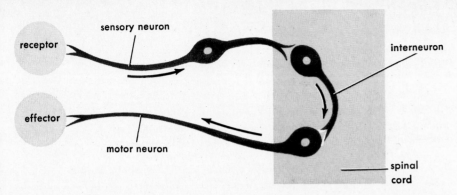

receptor

sensory neuron

interneuron

effector

motor neuron

spinal cord

Fig. 19.2. The pattern and the components of a reflex arc. Note that neurons are not joined anatomically, but make functional connection across microscopic spaces called synapses. Note also that the cell body of the sensory neuron lies outside the spinal cord, in a so-called ganglion; that the entire interneuron lies within the spinal cord; and that the cell body of the motor neuron also lies within the spinal cord. Sensory fibers always enter the spinal cord dorsally; motor fibers always leave the cord ventrally.

possesses only a single axon, but it may have one or several dendrites. By and large, neurons are comparatively huge cells. Dendrites and axons may be as much as a yard or more long, or they may be relatively short.

Long nerve fibers, but not the cytons or the shorter fibers, are enveloped by one or by two sheaths. Most of the long fibers of the central nervous system are surrounded directly by a layer of secreted fatty material, the *myelin sheath*. This sheath in turn is enveloped by the *Schwann sheath*, which is made up of a single layer of thin flat cells. In most nerve fibers of the autonomic nervous system, only a Schwann sheath surrounds the axon; myelin sheaths are absent here.

Myelin sheaths probably increase the speed of nerve-impulse transmission. It can be shown that myelinated fibers of the c.n.s. may conduct impulses at speeds of about 100 yards per second, whereas non-myelinated a.n.s. fibers conduct at about 25 yards per second at most. The suggestion has been made that the accelerating effect of the fatty myelin layer results from an insulating action; a myelin envelope would be to a nerve fiber what a rubber envelope is to an electricity-conducting metal wire.

Individual neurons are placed end to end, forming long neural pathways. The axon fiber of one neuron connects functionally with a dendrite of the next. But there is never a structural connection. Fiber terminals come exceedingly close to one another, yet a microscopic gap, a *synapse*, still separates them. We shall soon see how nerve impulses are transmitted across such synapses.

REFLEX ARCS

The minimum number of neurons in a reflex arc is two: one *sensory neuron*, which transmits impulses from a receptor to either brain or spinal cord, and one *motor neuron*, which relays the impulses sent out by brain or spinal cord to an effector. Most reflex arcs consist of more than two neurons. One or more additional *interneurons* may be located within brain or spinal cord, between the end of the sensory and the beginning of the motor neuron. In the entire nervous system, interneurons are actually the most abundant, for they make up the bulk of the brain and the spinal cord (Fig. 19.2).

Sensory neurons leading to and motor neurons leading from brain and spinal cord are collected into discrete bundles. Traversing the body like the cables of telephone trunk lines, such bundles of neuron fibers are called *nerves*. In a so-called *mixed nerve*, both sensory and motor fibers are present. In certain nerves only sensory fibers are present, and these are called *sensory nerves*. Analogously, some nerves contain motor fibers only, and they are referred to as *motor nerves*. Nerves are also classified as *cranial* or *spinal*, according to whether they connect with the brain or the spinal cord.

The c.n.s. and the a.n.s. possess their own sets of nerves. Each set connects with distinct c.n.s. or a.n.s.

Fig. 19.3. Diagram of the underside of brain and anterior part of spinal cord, showing the origin of the cranial nerves and a few of the spinal nerves. The names and functions of these nerves are given in the accompanying tabulation.

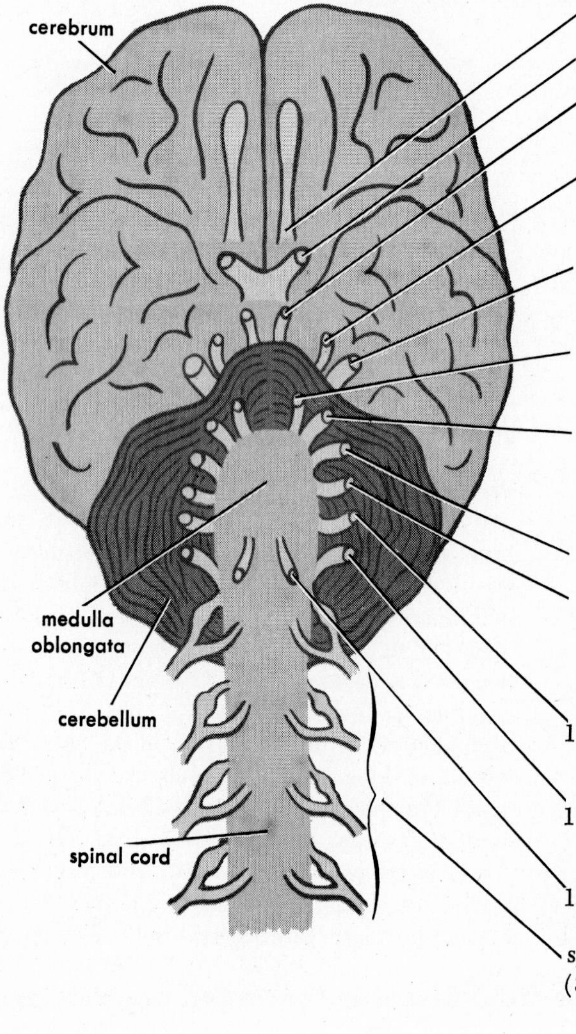

The nerves of the central nervous system

name	type	innervation
1. olfactory	sensory	from nose
2. optic	sensory	from eye
3. oculomotor	motor	to muscles of eyeball
4. trochlear	motor	to muscles of eyeball
5. trigeminal	mixed	from and to face, teeth
6. abducens	motor	to muscles of eyeball
7. facial	mixed	from taste buds to salivary glands and facial muscles
8. auditory	sensory	from ear
9. glossopharyngeal	mixed	from and to pharynx, from taste buds to salivary glands
10. vagus	mixed	from and to chest and abdomen
11. spinal accessory	motor	to shoulder muscles
12. hypoglossal	motor	to tongue
spinal nerves (31 pairs)	mixed	from and to muscles in arms, legs, and trunk

cerebrum

medulla oblongata

cerebellum

spinal cord

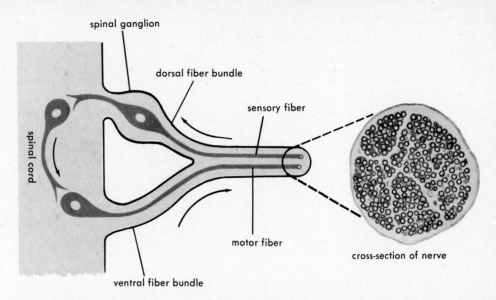

Fig. 19.4. The structure of a spinal nerve. Many fibers, sensory, motor, or both, traveling together constitute a nerve. The photo inset shows what such a nerve looks like in cross section. In this particular section, note that each nerve fiber is enveloped by a myelin sheath (the dark rings). The arrows in the diagram indicate the direction of the nerve impulses. (Photo courtesy of Dr. Mac V. Edds, Brown University.)

centers in brain and spinal cord. Thus each of the two subdivisions of the nervous system possesses its own reflex pathways.

C.N.S. pathways. In the c.n.s. of man, 12 pairs of cranial and 31 pairs of spinal nerves carry information to and from brain and spinal cord. These nerves are named and described in Fig. 19.3.

Note that spinal nerves are all mixed nerves and that each divides into two fiber bundles just outside the spinal cord (Fig. 19.4). One bundle attaches to the cord dorsally; this bundle contains fibers of all the sensory neurons of the nerve. The other bundle attaches ventrally; it contains the fibers of all the motor neurons of the spinal nerve. Along the dorsal bundle, close to its attachment to the spinal cord, is a thickened region. Present within it are the cytons of the sensory neurons which make up the dorsal bundle. Each of these sensory neurons possesses two fibers; a long dendrite carries impulses from a receptor to the cyton in the thickened region, and a shorter axon carries impulses from the cyton into the spinal cord.

Any collected group of cytons found outside the brain or the spinal cord is referred to as a *ganglion*. The thickened region in the dorsal bundle of a spinal nerve is therefore called a *spinal ganglion*. Inasmuch as there are 31 pairs of spinal nerves, each with a dorsal bundle, there are, correspondingly, 31 pairs of spinal ganglia. The ventral bundles of the spinal nerves are without ganglia. The cytons and dendrites of the motor neurons are embedded directly within the spinal cord, and only the long axon fibers project to the outside via the ventral bundles (Figs. 19.4 and 19.5).

The spinal nerves innervate mainly the skeletal muscles in the chest, the abdomen, and the limbs, and they provide the pathways for numerous c.n.s. reflexes. The familiar knee-jerk reflex is a good example (Fig. 19.6). This reflex is one of many *spinal reflexes*, so called because the basic neural path leads through spinal nerves and spinal cord. C.n.s. activity also includes numerous *cranial reflexes*, executed by the brain and the 12 pairs of cranial nerves. Such reflexes likewise control voluntarily movable muscles, particularly in head and neck.

Fig. 19.5.   Cross section through mammalian spinal cord. Note the spinal nerves, each dividing into two fiber bundles. The motor bundle connects with the cord ventrally, and the sensory bundle passes through a spinal ganglion and connects with the cord dorsally. The spinal cord itself is a dense meshwork of neurons, the cell bodies of which are aggregated around the center, forming so-called gray matter. The axons and dendrites of these neurons are collected around the gray matter, forming white matter. The central spinal canal contains lymphlike spinal fluid. (Ward's Natural Science Establishment, Inc.)

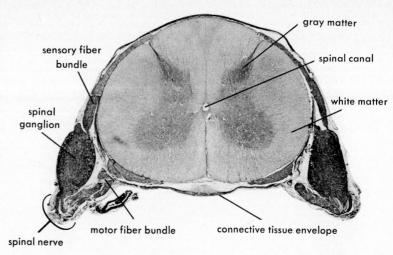

Fig. 19.6.   A reflex arc in the central nervous system. The knee-jerk reflex is illustrated. Impulses from the knee to the hip level of the spinal cord are also relayed to the brain, leading to awareness of the stimulus. However, the kicking response occurs even if such awareness is lacking; the motor impulses leave the spinal cord at hip level.

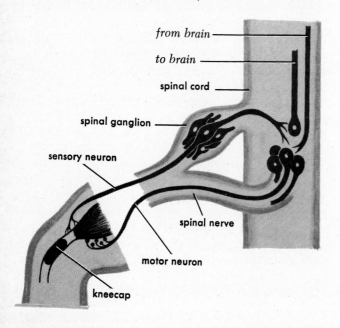

A.N.S. pathways.   Reflexes in the a.n.s. regulate the functioning of body parts which are not under voluntary control: smooth muscles, the heart, and most glands and other internal organs. Like the sensory neurons of the c.n.s., those of the a.n.s. similarly pass through ganglia. Indeed, the cytons of a.n.s. sensory neurons lie in the same 31 pairs of spinal ganglia which also contain the cytons of c.n.s. sensory neurons.

In brain and spinal cord, the centers of the a.n.s. are organized into two separate sets (Fig. 19.7). One set, located in the middle part of the spinal cord, represents the so-called *sympathetic* portion of the a.n.s. The other set, called the *parasympathetic* portion, is located both above and below the sympathetic portion. The upper parasympathetic centers thus reach into the brain, and we may note that all a.n.s. centers present in the brain belong to the parasympathetic system.

A given internal organ controlled by the a.n.s. receives motor fibers from some part of the sympathetic system *and* from some part of the parasympathetic system. Therefore, the *motor pathways* to every a.n.s.-controlled organ are double and come from two parts in brain or spinal cord. One of these two motor fibers stimulates the organ, the other inhibits it. In some cases, the stimulating fiber originates in the sympathetic system; in other cases, it originates in the parasympathetic system. For example, the fibers which accelerate the heart are sympathetic, and the fibers which slow the heart are parasympathetic. Such dual motor innervation of a.n.s.-controlled organs permits efficient adjustment of steady state; the net activity of an organ is a resultant of a given degree of stimulation or acceleration by one set of motor nerves and a given degree of inhibition or deceleration by another set of motor nerves. The a.n.s. motor controls of a number of other organs are illustrated in Fig. 19.8.

Fig. 19.7. Diagram showing the location of sympathetic and parasympathetic a.n.s. centers in brain and spinal cord. Each subdivision receives its own sensory nerves and sends out its own motor nerves. A given a.n.s.-controlled organ therefore is innervated by two sets of motor nerves, one originating in sympathetic centers, the other in parasympathetic centers.

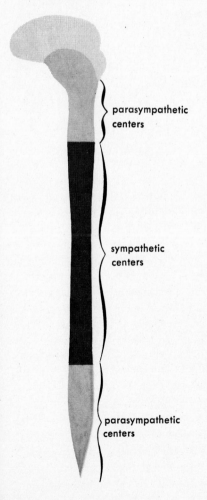

Note also that each motor path in the a.n.s. usually consists of at least two neurons, one following the other. These two neurons synapse in a ganglion located somewhere along the path to a given organ. The first motor neuron, which leads from spinal cord or brain to the ganglion, is called a *preganglionic fiber;* the second motor neuron, from ganglion to the organ, is called a *postganglionic fiber.*

In the *sympathetic* system, preganglionic fibers in many cases terminate just outside the spinal cord in the so-called *sympathetic chain ganglia.* These a.n.s. ganglia form two interconnected chains, one along each side of the spinal cord (see Fig. 19.8). In such chain ganglia, terminating preganglionic fibers synapse with postganglionic fibers. The latter then innervate given organs (e.g., the sympathetic motor path to the heart). In other cases, sympathetic preganglionic fibers do not terminate in the chain ganglia but extend farther, to other a.n.s. ganglia located in various parts of the body. Postganglionic fibers then originate there (e.g., the sympathetic paths to stomach and intestine).

The motor paths of the *parasympathetic* system do not lead through the sympathetic chains. Nevertheless, such paths consist analogously of preganglionic and postganglionic portions, specific ganglia being located along the way to given organs (see Fig. 19.8).

C.N.S.-A.N.S. interrelations. Although the c.n.s. and the a.n.s. each possess their own reflex pathways and centers, these two subdivisions of the nervous system are interrelated both anatomically and functionally. The anatomical interrelation is indicated by the presence of both c.n.s. and a.n.s. centers in the same brain and spinal cord and by the presence of the cytons of both c.n.s. and a.n.s. sensory neurons in the same spinal ganglia. Also, nerve fibers of the c.n.s. and the a.n.s. often travel together within the same nerve trunk. For example, the parasympathetic a.n.s. motor fibers to the heart are situated within the trunk line of the vagus nerve, which otherwise contains nerve fibers of the c.n.s. (and is actually listed as a cranial nerve of the c.n.s.).

The close functional interconnection between c.n.s. and a.n.s. is borne out by many familiar observations. For example, visual experiences, which are

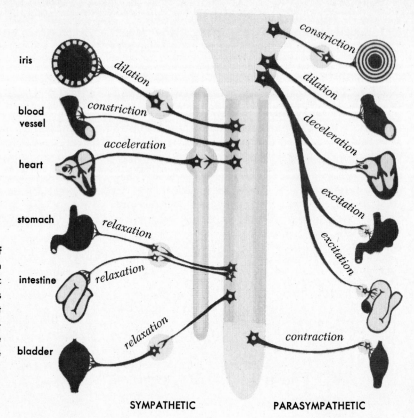

iris

blood
vessel

heart

stomach

intestine

bladder

dilation

constriction

acceleration

relaxation

relaxation

relaxation

constriction

dilation

deceleration

excitation

excitation

contraction

SYMPATHETIC   **PARASYMPATHETIC**

Fig. 19.8. Some of the motor pathways of the autonomic nervous system. Column to the left of spinal cord represents sympathetic chain ganglia. Each neural path shown occurs pairwise, one on the left and one on the right of the body. Similarly, sympathetic chain ganglia occur to both the left and the right of the spinal cord. For simplicity, however, only one side is indicated in each case.

c.n.s.-controlled and voluntary, may affect heart rate, which is a.n.s.-controlled and involuntary. A frightening sight may initiate a c.n.s. reflex from the eyes to the visual center in the brain and from there to the muscles of the legs. This might lead to running and to deliberate, conscious avoidance of the frightening sight. At the same time, heart rate increases and blood pressure rises. Evidently, impulses coming into the visual center from the eyes are relayed also via interneurons to the heart-rate and vasomotor centers. Only such information relays between c.n.s. and a.n.s. can produce an adaptive total response, for voluntary running could not be long sustained without an appropriate involuntary adjustment of the body circulation (Fig. 19.9). We may note generally that a.n.s. and c.n.s. are geared together so intimately that any reflex in one system is likely to initiate one or more concurrent reflexes in the other.

The above outlines the structural arrangements of the neural pathways. How do these pathways function? What is a nerve impulse, and how is it transmitted?

NERVE IMPULSES

The precise nature of a nerve impulse is still unknown. We may say, in general, that an impulse is a sequence of metabolic reactions propagated along a nerve fiber. After an impulse has passed, the reaction balance returns to the original state, readying the fiber for a new impulse. These processes consume oxygen and energy.

Accompanying the chemical changes are electrical phenomena. Indeed, the intriguing resemblance of the nervous system to a meshwork of electrical wires conducting electrical currents has been the basis of many attempts to explain nervous activity. Moreover, just as one can measure currents in wires by galvanometers, voltmeters, ammeters, and the like, so this same electrical equipment can be used on nerves. But nerve impulses are not simply electrical impulses. The latter travel some 100,000 miles per second in a wire, the former about 100 yards per second in a nerve fiber. Nerve impulses are neither purely electrical nor purely chemical, and at present they may best be described as *electrochemical* events.

Whatever else an impulse may be, it is known that it is a *wave of electrical depolarization* sweeping along a nerve fiber. It can be shown that a resting, nonstimulated neuron is electrically positive along the outer side of its surface membrane and electrically negative along the inner side. These electric charges

are carried by mineral ions attached to the two sides of the neuron membrane. As a result, an *electrical potential* is maintained across the cell membrane, and the membrane is said to be *polarized* electrically.

Polarization, as well as the integrity of a neuron membrane, appears to depend on *semipermeability*. The membrane is so constructed that it prevents the positive and negative ions from coming together. If semipermeability were destroyed, the membrane would depolarize; that is, the positive and negative ions *would* join. Conversely, if depolarization were to occur, membrane semipermeability would be abolished.

When a nerve impulse sweeps along a nerve fiber, local depolarization and simultaneous destruction

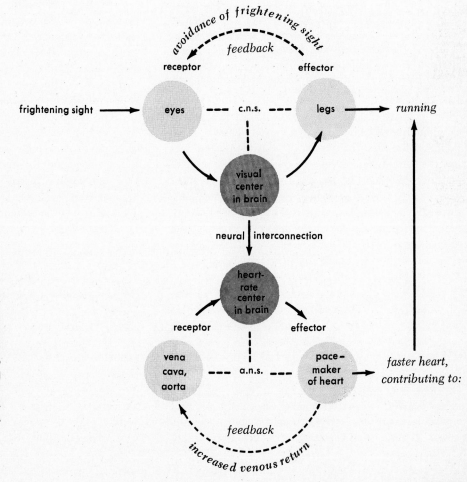

Fig. 19.9. The functional interconnection between the c.n.s. and a.n.s. In the example shown here, a sense perception registered via the c.n.s. leads to coordinated responses controlled by both the c.n.s. and the a.n.s. Note the effect of the a.n.s.-controlled heart on the c.n.s.-controlled running.

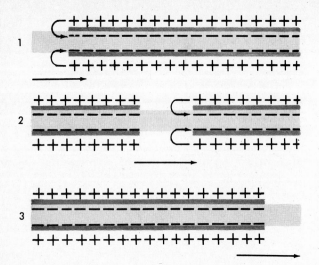

Fig. 19.10. The passage of an impulse through a nerve fiber produces a local depolarization and destruction of the permeability properties of the fiber membrane, propagated in a wavelike manner through successive portions of the fiber. After an impulse has passed a given region, the original polarization and membrane characteristics reappear.

of semipermeability actually do occur at successive points of the fiber membrane. As this happens at any one point, an avenue is created through which positive and negative ions of an adjacent point may meet (Fig. 19.10). In other words, the impulse itself produces the necessary conditions which allow it to advance farther. In this manner, it travels wavelike along

a fiber. Some short time after an impulse has passed a given point, the membrane at that point recovers; both the polarization and the semipermeability are restored.

What happens when an impulse reaches an axon terminal? How does it jump across the gap of the synapse to the dendrite terminal of a neighboring neuron? Synapses appear to be bridged by chemical processes. In certain cases it can be shown that, when an impulse reaches an axon terminal, the terminal acts like a miniature endocrine gland; it secretes minute amounts of a hormone. This hormone diffuses through the synaptic gap; some of it eventually reaches dendrite terminals of adjacent neurons, and the hormone there affects a dendrite in such a way that a new impulse is initiated in it (Fig. 19.11).

Two different hormones are known to play a role in synaptic transmission. One is *adrenalin* or a substance very similar to adrenalin in chemical structure and biological effect. This hormone is secreted by the axon terminals of the postganglionic fibers of the sympathetic a.n.s. Because they produce adrenalin, these fibers are said to be *adrenergic*.

The preganglionic fibers of the sympathetic system, all fibers of the parasympathetic system, and possibly also the nerve fibers of the c.n.s. secrete a second type of hormone, namely, *acetylcholine*. Like adrenalin, acetycholine brings about impulse transmission across neural synapses. Acetylcholine-secreting fibers are said to be *cholinergic*.

The consequences of synaptic impulse transmission

Fig. 19.11. Diagram of a neural synapse, showing the release and local spreading of hormones from the axon terminal of one fiber to the dendrite terminal of another. Impulses are transmitted across synapses by such chemical means.

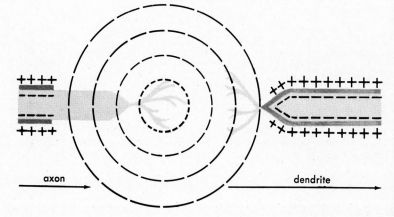

axon   dendrite

by chemicals are far-reaching. For example, diffusion takes much longer than impulse conduction within a fiber. A complete reflex, which usually passes through many synapses, consequently lasts longer than would be expected on the basis of impulse speeds within fibers alone. Being "slow in the uptake" is largely a result of delays at synapses. Moreover, nerve fibers as such rarely fatigue but synapses get "tired" fairly easily. During intensive activity, axon terminals may temporarily exhaust their hormone-secreting capacity, and synaptic transmission then slows even more or stops altogether for the time being.

Note that the synaptic hormones impose a one-way direction on neural pathways. A nerve fiber can be stimulated artificially at either end or in the middle, and impulses then travel backward, forward, or in both directions. But only axon terminals are specialized to secrete hormones and only dendrite terminals are sensitive to these hormones. As a result, the conduction of impulses is unidirectional.

The *first* nerve impulse in a reflex arc is normally produced by a sensory receptor. Such structures start all nervous activity, and on their functioning depend all subsequent neural events. How are receptors constructed and how do they work?

The neural receptors

Mammals possess many more than the familiar five senses of vision, hearing, smell, taste, and touch. They also sense pain, pressure, heat, and cold. They sense the position of their limbs and the mechanical equilibrium and the motion of their bodies, all without looking. They possess a genital sense, and they experience distinct sensations when tickled, when a limb "falls asleep," when the skin "stings" or "burns," and when they are hungry, thirsty, or sleepy. These are only some of the numerous senses which penetrate into the conscious. In at least as many other senses conscious awareness is lacking. For example, when a blood vessel dilates under pressure, sensing occurs even though it is unconscious.

A separate type of receptor structure probably does not exist for each of these senses. Only about a dozen different kinds of receptors are demonstrable.

They mediate different sensations when they are stimulated singly and when a varied group of them is stimulated together. Some types of receptors occur in large numbers throughout the body. Others are few in number and are found in circumscribed body regions only, principally in the head. We shall discuss the abundant receptors first.

DISPERSED RECEPTORS

The simplest type of neural receptor is a free nerve ending (Fig. 19.12). In many cases, the hairlike dendrite terminals of sensory neurons also carry a series of nodular thickenings or are bunched together like balls of twine. Other parts are not present, however. Relatively simply constructed sensory endings of this sort are probably the most widespread, and they relay a.n.s. signals from many internal organs as well as a large variety of c.n.s. signals. For example, plain or variously nodulated and coiled sensory endings mediate the sense of pain and also muscle and tendon sense (which inform about the position of body parts).

Moreover, comparatively simple nerve endings represent one type of receptor for touch stimuli. Each hair in the skin is surrounded at its base by a network of sensory fiber terminals. When a hair is bent, the position of the hair base changes slightly and this stimulates the fiber terminals. The resulting nerve impulses are interpreted as touch sensations.

Touch stimuli are received additionally by true sense *organs* located in the skin. These are tiny structures made up of many specialized cells (not neurons), and they are innervated by sensory fiber terminals (see Fig. 19.12). In these instances it is the organ, not the fiber terminal, which translates stimulus energies into nerve impulses. Touch organs may be clustered together relatively densely, as in fingertips, palms, and lips, or they may occur sparsely, as on the back.

In addition to touch organs, the skin also contains tiny organs sensitive to heat, to cold, and to pressure. Together with the numerous touch organs and pain fibers in the skin, these make up the so-called *cutaneous receptors*. They vary in relative distribution and in number. It is estimated that the human skin contains some 4 million pain receptors, half a million pressure

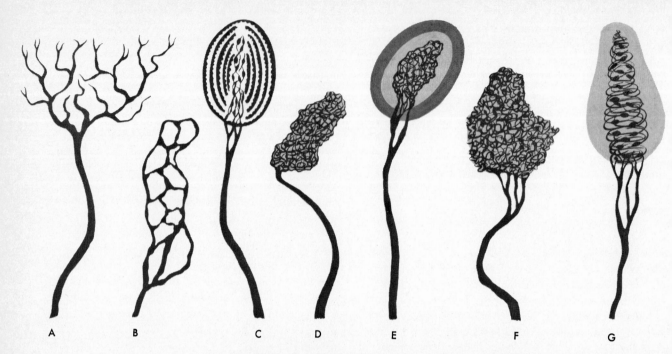

Fig. 19.12.   Some types of neural receptors in the skin. *A,* free nerve ending (pain). *B,* nerve net surrounding hair (touch). *C,* Pacinian corpuscle (pressure). *D,* organ of Ruffini (pressure). *E,* organ of Krause (cold). *F,* end organ of Ruffini (warmth). *G,* Meissner's corpuscle (touch).

receptors, 150,000 cold receptors, and 16,000 heat receptors.

Very little is known about the mechanism by which specific stimuli, affecting either the tiny sense organs or the free sensory nerve endings, actually produce nerve impulses. Environmental change as such is known to be an important factor, for when a given stimulus persists unchanged for a time, a sense dulls or "adapts." For example, we soon become relatively insensitive to the pressure of clothes, to a persistent odor, or to a taste. Ease of adaptation varies considerably. Pain is most difficult to adapt to, but odor perception dulls very easily. We cannot judge our own body odors, for example. We live with them constantly and we are continuously adapted to them.

Sensations depend on stimulation of *appropriate* receptors. Thus, a feeling of pressure can be produced only by impulses from pressure receptors; pressure stimuli cannot register in heat receptors, for example.

However, given stimuli may affect more than one kind of receptor simultaneously, in which case a composite sensation is perceived. For example, simultaneous impulses from heat and pain receptors may give rise to a burning sensation. In a hot shower, both hot and cold receptors may be affected and one may feel hot and cold at the same time. Ice on the skin may produce sensations of burning, through simultaneous stimulation of cold, heat, and pain points.

It can be shown dramatically that the different kinds of sense perceptions depend not so much on impulse differences as on the different *central connections* of nerve fibers. For example, suppose that a fiber from a heat receptor and a fiber from a cold receptor were cut and that the cut ends were allowed to reinnervate the sense organs in switched order. The fiber from the heat receptor would then terminate in the cold center of the brain and the fiber from the cold receptor would terminate in the heat center. Under such conditions, the animal would feel hot every time the cold receptor was stimulated and cold every time the heat receptor was stimulated. Evidently, the sensation depends on which of various centers receives signals.

The receptor types discussed so far agree in that their distribution is body-wide. The most familiar receptors, on the other hand, are confined to specific head regions. In this category of localized receptors are the sense organs of the tongue, the nose, the eye, and the ear.

TONGUE AND NOSE

Our reduced tasting ability when the nose is blocked with a cold reveals that smell is an integral component of "taste." The receptors on the tongue are affected by chemicals in *solution*, whereas the receptors in the nasal epithelium are affected by *vapors* of chemicals. Our sensory judgment about a substance is keenest when impulses from both tongue and nose reach neural centers.

Clusters of elongated ciliated cells, set into depressions in the tongue, form *taste buds* (Fig. 19.13). Sensory fiber terminals from each of the bud cells lead into the brain. Taste buds are distributed all over the upper tongue surface. Structural differences among buds cannot be demonstrated, but well-known functional differences exist; the four primary taste sensations, *sweet, sour, salty,* and *bitter,* arise through stimulation of buds at different regions of the tongue. Bitter substances primarily affect buds located at the back of the tongue; sweet substances, buds in the forward part of the tongue; and sour and salty materials are tasted predominantly along the tongue edges.

Like other sense perceptions, tasting depends on the central connections. Certain chemicals produce a sweet sensation when applied to the tongue tip but a bitter sensation when applied at the back of the tongue. Evidently, chemicals possess not "inherent" taste but only the property of stimulating or not stimulating this or that taste bud. And depending on which of the tongue areas sends impulses to its unique brain connections, a given subjective taste sensation will be registered.

Therefore, to say that "sugar is sweet" errone-ously implies an objective property of sugar. Sweetness is a subjective sensation; the only pertinent objective property of sugar is its capacity to stimulate certain taste buds. Indeed, in individuals with different genetic backgrounds, one and the same sugar may produce qualitatively and quantitatively different sensations of sweetness.

Numerous composite tastes are built up from different combinations and intensities of the four basic tastes, from smell, and from other sense perceptions initiated in the mouth. For example, both a hot meal and a cold meal affect the same taste buds if the two

Fig. 19.13. Portion of a section through the tongue, showing taste buds. The buds are located along a deep narrow channel leading into the tongue from the surface. (General Biological Supply House, Inc.)

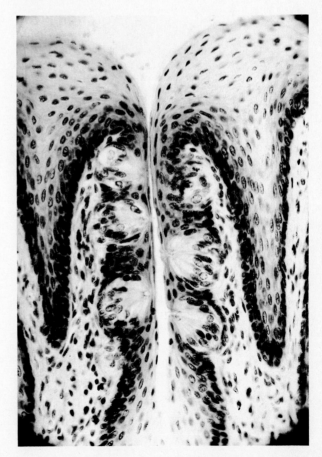

meals are alike chemically. But the hot meal vaporizes more and therefore smells more, and it also stimulates heat receptors in the lining of the mouth and on the tongue. The hot and the cold meals consequently taste differently.

Varied as taste sensations are, odor perceptions are even more diversified. Attempts to establish basic odors from which all others can be derived have met with relatively little success. Part of the ciliated lining in the upper nasal passages is the receptor tissue for the sense of smell in vertebrates. Sensory fibers lead into the *olfactory lobe* of the brain, relatively small in man but large in other vertebrates. Man is a comparatively poor smeller, but in most other vertebrates the sense of smell is as well developed and has the same outstanding importance as vision in man.

As among taste buds, structural differences among the cells of the nasal epithelium cannot be detected. Moreover, it is virtually impossible to determine which receptor cells in the nose mediate perception of what odors. Paradoxically, our understanding of smelling mechanisms is much less satisfactory than that of the more complex visual and auditory mechanisms.

THE EYE

The human eye is among the most efficient light receptors developed during evolution. Insect eyes possibly are better adapted for the detection of motion, and many vertebrates have a larger visual field without moving their heads than man. But the human visual apparatus probably registers color more clearly than that of any other animal, and human eyes are virtually as light-sensitive as eyes can possibly get.

The eye is made up of three coats (Fig. 19.14): an outer *sclera*, fibrous in man, cartilaginous in many other mammals; a middle *choroid*, a layer which is pigmented black and carries blood vessels to and from the eye; and an inner *retina*, the actual light-receptor tissue. In many mammals, a thin film of white-green crystalline material coats the choroid layer. This material reflects light and makes the eyes of these animals shine and glow in the dark.

In the front part of the eye, the three coats are modified structurally. The sclera merges into the transparent *cornea*. The choroid coat continues as the some-times pigmented *iris*, which encloses the *pupil*. Just behind the iris is a ring-shaped muscle, the *ciliary body*, to which the *lens* is attached by ligaments. The spaces between lens and cornea are filled with the fluid, lymphlike *aqueous humor;* and the space between lens and retina contains a glassy, jellylike material, the *vitreous humor*.

Functionally, the eye resembles a photographic camera. But whereas a camera is focused by varying the distance between lens and film, the eye is focused by adjustment of the curvature of the lens; the distance between lens and retina remains fixed. A beam of light passes through the cornea and through the pupil into the lens. The pupillary opening corresponds to the diaphragm of a camera; it enlarges or becomes smaller and so regulates the amount of light admitted into the eye. This control mechanism is set into operation by light itself. Intense light initiates a reflex via retina, the autonomic nervous system, and a set of circularly arranged muscles in the iris. These muscles contract and the pupil becomes smaller. Conversely, low light intensity results in reflex signals to a set of iris muscles arranged like the spokes of a wheel. When these muscles contract, the pupil of the eye enlarges (see Fig. 19.8).

The lens focuses an object onto the retina. When a far-off object is viewed and when the eye is at rest, the lens is fairly flat. As an object moves nearer, the lens curves out increasingly (Fig. 19.15). Lens shape is controlled by the ciliary body. When this muscular ring is relaxed, the ligaments holding the lens are taut and the lens is flat. Conversely, when the ciliary muscle contracts, the lens ligaments relax and the lens, an elastic structure, is then allowed to curve out. The ciliary muscle is under reflex control. A blurred image on the retina elicits reflex impulses to the ciliary body. These impulses produce contraction or relaxation of the ciliary body until the image is no longer blurred. The adjustment reflex then ceases and a focused image so reaches the retina. Note that the image of an object is projected on the retina in an inverted position, just as an image is inverted on the film of a camera.

The retina is made up of several layers of neurons and of one layer of *rods* and *cones*. These are the receptor cells which translate light energy into nerve impulses (Fig. 19.16). The rod and cone layer is ad-

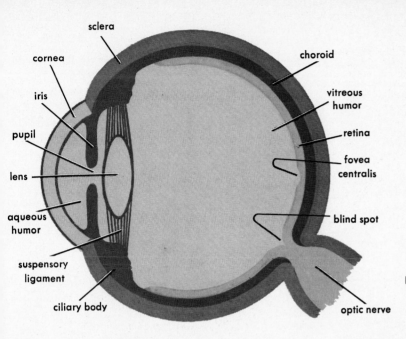

Fig. 19.14. The structure of the eye.

jacent to the choroid coat; light must therefore pass through the neuron layers before it reaches the rods and cones. The light-sensitive cells connect functionally with the neurons of the retina, and the neurons in turn synapse among one another in intricate ways. Nerve fibers from the whole inner surface of the retina eventually collect in one region and form the *optic nerve* to the brain. Where this nerve leaves the eye, somewhat off center, it interrupts the continuity of the rod and cone layer and of the choroid and sclera. This area of discontinuity is the *blind spot*, so called since visual images cannot be formed in it.

Cones are responsible for color vision and for the perception of sharp, bright images. The greatest concentration of cone cells is found in the *fovea centralis*, a tiny depression in the center of the retina. Only cones are present in this area; rods are absent. Also absent are overlying neurons, and the cones are therefore exposed to light directly. By virtue of its dense accumulation of cones, the fovea permits the most acute vision. The concentration of cone cells decreases with increasing distance from the fovea, and at the retinal periphery cones do not occur at all. Rods, on the other hand, are particularly abundant there. Rod cells are sensitive to dim light, and they serve impor-

tantly in black-and-white vision and in the detection of motion, particularly motion along the lateral edges of the visual field. Rods are distributed more sparsely away from the retinal periphery and are absent altogether in the fovea, as noted.

Some of the chemical aspects of light reception

Fig. 19.15. Focusing when object changes distance. Left, far object, flat lens. Right, near object, curved lens. Lens curves out when the muscles of the ciliary body contract.

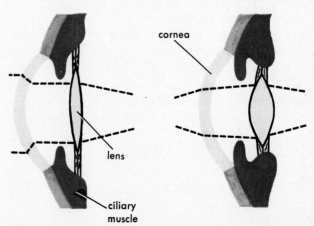

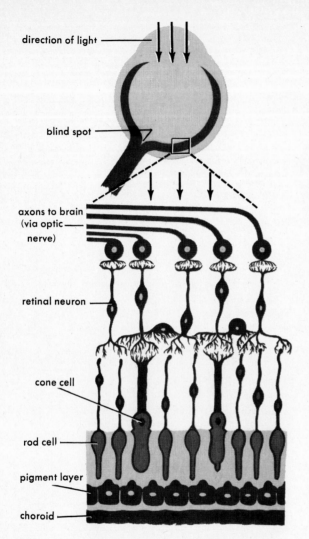

direction of light

blind spot

axons to brain
(via optic
nerve)

retinal neuron

cone cell

rod cell

pigment layer

choroid

Fig. 19.16.   The diagram illustrates the retina in section, greatly simplified. Note that the neuron layers of the retina are toward the inside of the eye and that light must pass through these layers before it reaches the photosensitive rods and cones.

are known for rods. These cells contain *rhodopsin*, a photosensitive pigment also called "visual purple." Rhodopsin consists of two linked fractions, namely, a *retinene* part, which is a derivative of vitamin A, and an *opsin* part, which is a protein. When light strikes rhodopsin, the molecule splits into separate retinene and opsin components and a nerve impulse is pro-

duced at the same time. In the dark and with the aid of respiratory energy, retinene and opsin are recombined and visual purple is regenerated in this manner (Fig. 19.17). In very intense light, visual purple may be split faster than it can be regenerated. Vision may then become impaired (e.g., snow blindness). A similar result would follow if vitamin A were in deficient supply, for retinene could not be synthesized. Light-initiated chemical reactions which produce nerve impulses occur in cone cells also, but the details of these processes are still very poorly known.

An external object is "pictured" on the retina as a series of points, like the points of a newspaper photograph. Each point corresponds to a rod or a cone. Impulses from these points are transmitted into the brain according to the pattern illustrated in Fig. 19.18. In each brain hemisphere the fibers from the eyes lead to an *optic lobe* which contains the visual centers. Impulses to neurons in these lobes register as vision.

Why is an inverted retinal image not also "seen" as an inverted picture? The answer is that the optic centers in the brain have learned to give visual experiences correct orientations. Recognition of up and down and of space orientation generally is based ultimately on sensing the direction of gravitational pull. Muscles and ears play an important role in this, as the next section will show. Therefore, even if retinal images actually arrived in the optic lobes in an inverted position, gravity perception would teach, shortly after birth, to associate the bottom part of a picture with

Fig. 19.17.   The pattern of the chemistry of rod vision. Note that vitamin A may replenish the supply of retinene and thus indirectly the supply of visual purple (rhodopsin).

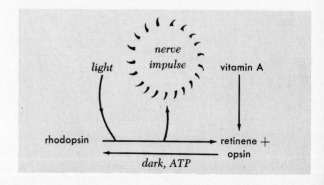

the idea of "up" and the upper part with the idea of "down." Without gravity (as in outer space), the frame of reference for space orientation is lacking and the notion of "right-side-upness" becomes meaningless.

How do impulses coming into the vision centers actually produce a conscious sensation of light? How indeed does any other sense become conscious? Answers to such questions cannot be given as yet. However, it is known that immense numbers of neural paths lead from the vision centers to virtually all other centers in the brain and spinal cord. Consequently, a tremendous number of reflexes can be initiated through the receptor cells in the eyes. It is this which makes the sense of vision so important to most animals.

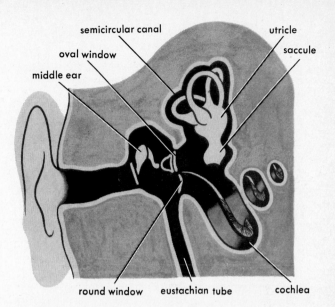

Fig. 19.19. The gross structure of the ear. Note ear bones in the middle-ear cavity and attachment of semicircular canals to utricle.

Fig. 19.18. The nerve fiber tracts from eye to brain. An object in the left field of vision registers on the right halves of both retinas, and impulses are transmitted into the right half of the brain.

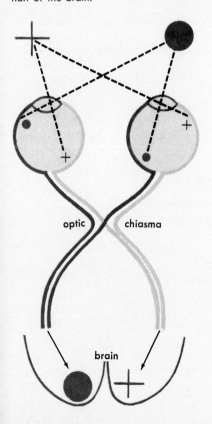

THE EAR

In mammals, this organ houses receptors for three different senses: the sense of *static body balance*, the sense of *dynamic body balance*, and the sense of *hearing*.

The *outer ear* carries sound to the *eardrum*, a membrane which separates the cavity of the *middle ear* from the outside (Fig. 19.19). The connection of this cavity with the mouth, via the eustachian tube, has already been referred to in Chap. 13. Three tiny middle-ear bones, *hammer*, *anvil*, and *stirrup*, moved by the smallest muscles in the body, form an adjustable bridge from the eardrum, across the middle-ear cavity, to the *inner ear*. The latter is closed off from the middle ear by two membranes. One is stretched across a so-called *round window* and the other across an *oval window*. The stirrup bone of the middle ear is anchored to the membrane of the oval window.

The inner ear is an intricate system of interconnected canals and spaces, all surrounded by bone and filled with a lymphlike fluid. Three main subdivisions may be distinguished: a chamber consisting of two parts, the *utricle* and the *saccule;* the *semicircular canals;* and the *cochlea,* a structure coiled like a snail shell. Each of these subdivisions contains the receptor structures for one of the three senses listed above.

Balance. The receptors for *static* body balance are located in the utricle and the saccule. At several places along the walls of these chambers, clusters of specialized cells are found. Sensory nerve fibers lead off from one side of such cells and cilialike hairs project from the other side. The tips of the hairs of a cell cluster attach to a tiny *ear stone,* a calcium-containing body (Fig. 19.20). When the stone is in a certain position, it pulls on some of the hairs more than on others and this stimulates the cells to which the hairs are connected. Nerve impulses from the hair cells to the brain register the particular position of the ear stone. When the head is tilted or when the balance of the body as a whole is changed, then gravity acts on all the ear stones and shifts them in a given manner. Such a change in the position of the stones produces pull on different sets of hair cells. Correspondingly different sets of impulses to the brain then inform of the change in balance. Reflex signals from the brain to appropriate muscles subsequently ensure that equilibrium is not lost. This sense permits recognition of up, down, side, front, and back, even when visual stimuli and sensory impulses from muscles fail to provide such recognition.

The sense of movement and of *dynamic* body balance is mediated by the semicircular canals. Three such canals are present in each ear, and they loop from the utricle back to the utricle. The canals are placed at right angles to one another in the three planes of space (see Fig. 19.19). At one end of each canal is an enlarge portion in which is found a cluster of hair cells, rather similar to those described above. However, an ear stone is not present and the hairs are longer.

When the head is moved, the semicircular canals move with the head. But the fluid in the canals "stays behind" temporarily as a result of its inertia and "catches up" with the head only after the head has stopped moving. This delayed fluid motion bends the hairs of the receptor cells and produces nerve impulses. Different impulse patterns are transmitted to the brain according to the direction and intensity of fluid motion in the three pairs of canals. Every straight-line motion or rotation of the head or of the body as a whole produces a distinct impulse pattern, hence a distinct sense perception (Fig. 19.21).

Mammals pursue a more or less two-dimensional

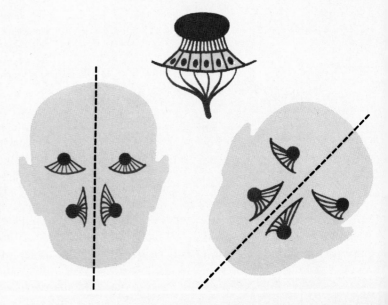

Fig. 19.20. Upper figure, a receptor organ for static balance, showing hair cells and ear stone (diagrammatic). Lower figures, position of the receptor organs in relation to the head, and the effect of tilting the head.

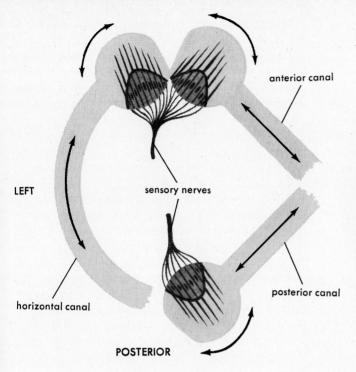

anterior canal

LEFT

sensory nerves

posterior canal

horizontal canal

POSTERIOR

Fig. 19.21.   The semicircular canals of the left ear. The top of the diagram is anterior, and the right side is toward the mid-plane of the head. The three canals are set at right angles to one another, and therefore only the horizontal canal reveals its curvature in such a view. Both ends of each canal open into the utricle. One end of each canal is enlarged into a chamber, and in it are present the hair cells which function as receptors for the sense of dynamic balance. Arrows indicate motion of internal fluid when the head is moved.

way of life and are relatively unaccustomed to up-and-down motion. When such motion occurs in man, it initiates reflexes via the semicircular canals leading to well-known symptoms of dizziness, nausea, and gastric upsets. Seasickness is produced in this way, as is the discomfort experienced when one rides in an elevator.

Hearing. The cochlea is the receptor organ for the sense of hearing (Fig. 19.22). The internal space of the cochlea is partitioned into canals by membranes which run the length of the cochlear coils. One of the membranes, the *basilar membrane,* supports rows of hair cells. These are the actual receptors; nerve fibers lead from them to the brain. The hairs make contact with the *tectorial membrane,* a fold of tissue which overhangs the receptor cells. Basilar membrane, hair cells, and tectorial membrane together constitute the *organ of Corti.*

Sound waves produce vibrations in the eardrum. This motion is communicated via the middle-ear bones to the oval window. As the membrane at this

window now vibrates, it sets the fluid of the inner ear into motion. Since fluid is practically incompressible, the membrane over the round window bulges outward every time the membrane over the oval window bulges inward; and vice versa. In other words, the round window permits the fluid of the inner ear to vibrate in harmony with the oval window and thus in harmony with external sound waves.

Fluid motion in the inner ear next affects the basilar membrane. The membrane contains strands of tough connective tissue fibers stretched transversely across the cochlear tube. These fibers are shortest at the base of the cochlear coil and longest at the tip of the coil. They may vibrate at different rates or frequencies according to their different lengths. In this respect the fibers resemble the tone strings of a piano. Thus, as the cochlear fluid vibrates at a given frequency under the impact of external sound waves, it sets in motion those basilar fibers which can vibrate at the same frequency. This is a selective *resonance* effect. In a similar way, a string of a piano may be set into resonating vibrations if a corresponding sound

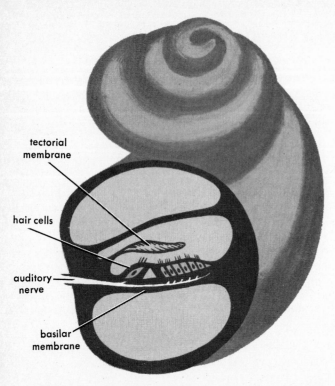

Fig. 19.22.   The cochlea. The diagram shows the coils of the cochlea and a cochlear cross section with the parts of the organ of Corti.

is produced nearby with a tuning fork, for example, or by striking an appropriate key on another piano.

In the ear, therefore, different external sound patterns first produce different vibration patterns in the cochlear fluid. Such vibrations in turn then produce corresponding vibrations in particular sets of basilar fibers. As a result, the hair cells attached to the vibrating basilar fibers move up and down. And as these cells touch against the overhanging tectorial membrane, their hairs are bent and nerve impulses are initiated. Each different sound pattern gives rise in this manner to a different pattern of nerve impulses. Such impulses are transmitted via the auditory nerves into the *temporal lobes* of the brain, where the hearing centers are located. In the centers, a given incoming impulse pattern is interpreted as a sound of a particular pitch.

Although mammals such as dogs hear a wider

range of sounds and are probably more sensitive to sound than man, the ear of man is unsurpassed in distinguishing tones of only slightly different pitch and tones of widely different quality. As an interpretive sense and as in important adjuster of speech, hearing has acquired a human importance second only to vision.

The neural centers

The normal roles of many parts of the brain and the spinal cord have been discovered by observing the effects of accidental or experimental damage to such parts. In a more precise method, selected points in the brain or the spinal cord of a test animal may be stimulated electrically with needle electrodes. The resulting responses of the animal may then provide clues to the control functions of the stimulated areas. By such means, distinct subdivisions have been identified in the brain and the spinal cord and the locations of a large number of neural centers have been pinpointed.

In the brain (Fig. 19.23), the deep central *midbrain* and the posterior *medulla oblongata* contain most of the cranial a.n.s. centers. Situated dorsal to the medulla oblongata is the *cerebellum*, which is the chief motor coordinator. It integrates, for example, the many muscular motions involved in walking, speaking, and other complex activities. The outer portions of the brain, along the top and the sides, constitute the *cerebrum*. This brain part is very large in mammals, and it is divided conspicuously into a right and a left hemisphere. The cerebrum contains c.n.s. control centers; the locations of some of them are indicated in Fig. 19.23.

The highly grooved surface layers of the cerebrum form the *cerebral cortex*. It is composed predominantly of cytons. The axons and dendrites of such neurons project into the deeper portions of the cerebrum. Inasmuch as the cytons do not and the fibers do contain white-colored myelin sheaths, the cerebral cortex is said to consist of *gray matter* and the deeper parts of the cerebrum of *white matter*. The arrangement is reversed in the spinal cord (see Fig. 19.5). Here the gray matter is in the core and the white matter is on the outside.

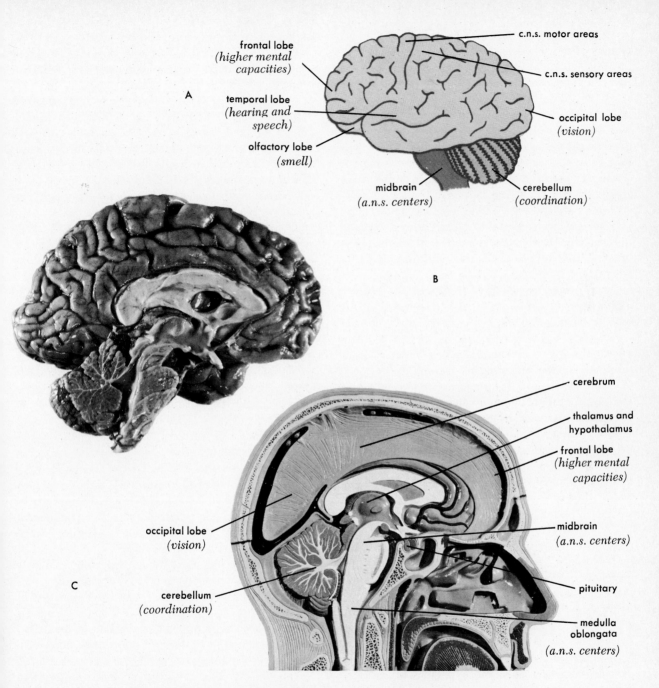

Fig. 19.23. *A, the left half of the brain, viewed from the outside.* The functions of the various labeled parts are indicated in parentheses. *B, the left half of the brain, viewed from the inner cut side.* The various parts and their functions are indicated in the model shown in C. (B, Photographic Department, Rhode Island Hospital; C, Detail of model designed by Dr. J. F. Mueller, Ward's Natural Science Establishment, Inc.)

The functions of the brain and the spinal cord are broadly of four kinds.

First, brain and spinal cord serve in *pathway selection*. Neural centers receive sensory impulses from receptors and then *select* among thousands of possible motor pathways going out to effectors. Signals are sent only to *some* effectors and only to *appropriate* effectors. As a result, the effector response of an animal to a given stimulus can be adaptively useful and can actually aid in steady-state maintenance. In all probability, the spinal cord carries out such "switchboard" activities only and none of the functions below.

Second, in addition to its role as pathway selector, the brain also serves as *reflex modifier*. It may *suppress* or *exaggerate* responses to incoming information, as when we decide not to cry out under pain or to cry out more than is necessary. It may *store* incoming information as memory and may thereby *delay* the completion of a reflex for shorter or longer periods. On occasion its modifying action may be unduly intensified, as in different mental diseases. Variously inappropriate effector responses are then produced.

Third, the brain is the principal *coordinating center*. It integrates into composite, unified sense perceptions the impulses arriving from many different receptors. And it gears together into smoothly coordinated actions the motor responses of many different effectors.

Fourth, the brain is the controller of such *higher mental capacities* as an animal possesses. The significance of these capacities to mammals in general and to man in particular is well appreciated.

Of these control functions, pathway selection probably is the most fundamental, and all others may be based on it. As yet, very little is known about the mechanism of pathway selection. Among several tentative suggestions and speculations, one is the idea of pathway facilitation. This notion emerges from the observation that nerve impulses often may travel more easily over some neural pathways than over others. For example, it is easier to perform a familiar activity than an unfamiliar one. The hypothesis of pathway facilitation suggests that the more frequently impulses travel over given neural circuits, the less resistance this circuit may offer to subsequent impulses. Wherever a choice of circuits exists, therefore, the often used, *facilitated* circuits may be selected in preference to the previously little used, unfacilitated ones. To be sure, it is far from clear just how a circuit in brain or spinal cord might become different structurally or functionally or both when it becomes facilitated.

Nevertheless, a hypothesis of facilitation could account in general terms for phenomena such as *habit* formation and *learning* by repetition and by trial and error. In a young animal, for example, few brain pathways are as yet firmly established by facilitation. Incoming impulses are transmitted more or less in all directions and behavior is relatively uncoordinated and random. But among the random impulse paths, some will bring about advantageous effector results. The same pathway pattern may then be tried time and again, and a facilitated neural route so may be established eventually.

Facilitation may also be at the root of learning by association, as in *conditioned reflexes*. Such reflexes were first studied by the Russian biologist Pavlov in experiments on dogs. When a hungry dog sights food, his saliva and gastric juice begin to flow reflexly. If on many successive occasions a bell is sounded every time food is presented, then the flow of the digestive juices can eventually be initiated by sounding the bell alone, without giving food. Evidently, the dog learns to associate a ringing bell with food. Instead of one facilitated pathway to the digestive glands, two now exist; one is mediated via the eyes as before and another has been newly established via the ears. Either one alone or both together may initiate digestive secretions. Neural conditioning of this sort plays a considerable role in behavior development not only in dogs but in mammals generally, man included.

The net result of neural activities of all kinds is control of *muscular movement* and of *glandular secretion*. But is it not really more than this, particularly for man? Conscious, contemplative thinking, reasoning, reading, aesthetic appreciations, higher mental functions in general—are they not more than mere reflex control of muscles and glands? Actually not. For *all* mental activity aims toward some *action*, potential or actual, present or future. On the one hand, we see, hear, learn, experience, store and correlate information—in short, we *think*. And on the other hand, we speak, walk, build, vote—in short, we *do*. All this doing requires and is directly brought about by muscular and glandular activity. In the final analysis, therefore, thinking sets the stage for moving muscles and better thinking implies more judicious and more diversified use of muscles. Because muscular control contributes powerfully to the maintenance of steady states, nervous systems have become vital components of animals.

Review questions

1. Describe the structure of a neuron. How do neurons in c.n.s. and a.n.s. differ structurally and functionally? Describe the components and the arrangement of a reflex arc. Distinguish between nerve fibers and nerves. What different kinds of each are known?

2. Describe the organization of the c.n.s., its nerves, and its centers. Review the course of a c.n.s. reflex arc. What is a ganglion?

3. Describe the organization of the a.n.s., its nerves, and its centers. What are the (a) structural, (b) functional differences between the sympathetic and the parasympathetic systems? What are sympathetic chain ganglia?

4. What are preganglionic and postganglionic fibers? Describe the course of an a.n.s. reflex arc. Review the innervation of the heart. How are c.n.s. and a.n.s. interconnected (a) structurally and (b) functionally?

5. What is a nerve impulse? How is an impulse transmitted through a nerve fiber? Across a synapse? What electrical phenomena take place during impulse transmission in a fiber?

6. What is the basic function of all sensory receptors? Describe the location and general structure of receptors for pain, touch, pressure, heat, and cold stimuli. Describe the location and structure of the taste and smell receptors. What are the primary taste sensations? Are tastes and smells inherent in given substances?

7. Describe the structure of the eye. What components form the focusing mechanism, and how is the function of focusing carried out? What is the distribution pattern of rods and cones in the retina? Review the chemical changes leading to impulse production in rods. Describe the pattern of the neural pathways between the eyes and the brain.

8. Describe the structure of the ear. What components form the receptors for (a) static body balance and (b) dynamic body balance? How do these receptors function? Describe the internal structure of the cochlea and the organ of Corti. Show how different sounds produce corresponding sensations of hearing.

9. What are the general functions of neural centers? Review the structural organization of the brain. What is the specific function of each major part or region? What is meant by pathway facilitation?

10. What are conditioned reflexes? Show how such reflexes might be established by pathway facilitation. How do conditioned reflexes contribute to learning, habit formation, and behavior development?

Suggested collateral readings

Bekesy, von G.: The Ear, *Sci. Am.*, vol. 197, 1957.

Gerard, R. W.: What is Memory? *Sci. Am.*, vol. 189, 1953.

Haagen-Smit, A. J.: Smell and Taste, *Sci. Am.*, vol. 186, 1952.

Hyden, H.: Satellite Cells in the Nervous System, *Sci. Am.*, vol. 205, 1961.

Katz, B.: The Nerve Impulse, *Sci. Am.*, vol. 187, 1952.

Katz, B.: How Cells Communicate, *Sci. Am.*, vol. 205, 1961.

Snider, R. S.: The Cerebellum, *Sci. Am.*, vol. 199, 1958.

Sperry, R. W.: The Eye and the Brain, *Sci. Am.*, vol. 194, 1956.

Sperry, R. W.: The Growth of Nerve Circuits, *Sci. Am.*, vol. 201, 1959.

Wald, G.: Eye and Camera, *Sci. Am.*, vol. 183, 1950.

part **6**

The Functions of
Life: Reproduction

In time even the best-controlled system goes out of control. As the component parts of a living system age and wear out, irreversible unsteady states and death must be the eventual outcome. But before final disintegration supervenes, the living controls may call into action another self-perpetuating device, one which circumvents even death: *reproduction*.

Of all living functions, reproduction happens to be among the most noticeable and most dramatic to the casual human observer: now there is one, then there are two. To be sure, the deep significance of reproduction lies not in its dramatic nature but in its results. We recall that we have assigned "living" properties to the first of the ancient nucleic acids largely because they possessed *reproductive* properties. These properties have been handed down in an unbroken succession from the first genes to all present genes, and they still form the basis of all reproductive events today.

In this series of chapters, we examine first the *reproductive patterns* among molecules, cells, and whole organisms. Following this, we proceed with a systematic study of specific *reproductive processes* encountered in all main categories of organisms.

REPRODUCTIVE PATTERNS

20

If we define reproduction broadly as extension of living matter in space and in time, then its fundamental importance as a self-perpetuative device is readily apparent: the formation of new living units makes possible *replacement* and *addition* at every level of organization. Among molecules or cells, among organisms or species, replacement offsets death from normal wear and tear and death from accident or disease. *Healing* and *regeneration* are two aspects of replacement. Above and beyond this purely restorative function of reproduction, addition of extra units at any level results in four-dimensional *growth*, i.e., increase in the net amount of existing living matter.

Any new living unit resembles the old, and reproduction therefore implies exact duplication. To create new units, raw materials are required. Indeed, reproduction at any level depends on ample nutrition specifically and on properly controlled metabolism generally. It is also clear that duplication of a large unit implies prior or simultaneous duplication of all constituent smaller ones. Reproduction must therefore occur on the molecular level before it can occur on any higher level.

Cellular reproduction

THE PATTERN

The multiplication of cellular molecules may take four different forms, according to the nature of the molecule to be multiplied. We are already familiar with all four (Fig. 20.1).

If water or another inorganic substance is to be reproduced within a cell, additional molecules or ions of such substances must be supplied ready-made by nutrition. Evidently, *accumulation* is the simplest form of molecular "reproduction."

If a carbohydrate, a fat, or any of their numerous derivatives is to be duplicated, it may have to be synthesized from accumulated simpler raw materials with the aid of appropriate enzymes. So long as the enzymes of a cell remain the same, most newly synthesized organic molecules will automatically be exact duplicates of molecules synthesized earlier. Thus, the second form of molecular reproduction is *enzymatic synthesis.* It includes the first form, accumulation, as a component phase.

If a protein molecule is to be duplicated, we know that enzymes are required to link amino acids into a new protein. We also know that proteins are specific. If, therefore, the new protein is to be an exact copy of a preexisting protein, genes and RNA must provide the specific information, the template, for the joining of particular amino acids in particular sequences. Clearly, the third form of molecular reproduction includes the first two forms, but it is additionally characterized as *template-dependent synthesis.*

Lastly, if a genetic nucleoprotein is to be dupli-cated, it must serve as its own template and control its own replication (see Chap. 16). All three other forms of molecular reproduction play a part here. Phosphate must be accumulated; sugars, purines, pyrimidines must be synthesized enzymatically; and protein must be synthesized with the aid of both enzymes and genetic templates. But in addition, duplication of genes hinges on specific *self-duplication,* and this is the fourth form of molecular reproduction.

In viruses, where the structural organization does not exceed the level of the molecular aggregate, molecular reproduction is equivalent to reproduction of the whole unit. In all truly living systems, accumulation, enzymatic and template-dependent synthesis, and self-duplication contribute either to normal molecular replacement within cells or to molecular additions to cells. The result is *cell growth.*

Such increase in cell *size* may be followed by increase in cell *number,* that is, reproduction of a cell as a whole. This reproductive process is *cell division,* or *fission.* In the vast majority of cases, cells divide by *binary fission;* one "mother" cell becomes two roughly equally large "daughter" cells. After a period of growth, daughter cells may divide in their turn and successive cell generations so may follow one another.

In Protista, Metaphyta, and Metazoa, cell division consists of at least two separate processes: *cleavage of the cytoplasm* into two parts and *duplication of the nucleus.* Nuclear duplication includes a mathematically precise doubling of the chromosomes and their genes. One of the two chromosome sets so formed becomes incorporated into one of the daughter nuclei, and the second chromosome set, into the other daughter nucleus. This form of nuclear duplication is known as

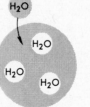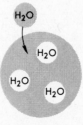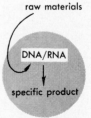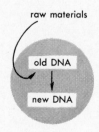

Fig. 20.1.   The four forms of molecular reproduction.

accumulation   enzymatic synthesis   template-dependent synthesis   self-duplication

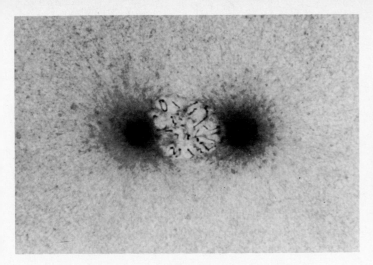

Fig. 20.2. Early prophase in animal mitosis. The nuclear membrane is just dissolving, and chromosomes are already visible. To either side of the nuclear region is a darkly stained centriole area. These areas develop after a single centriole has divided and the two daughter centrioles have migrated to opposite sides of the nucleus. From each centriole area fine fibrils are beginning to radiate out; i.e., asters are beginning to form. (General Biological Supply House, Inc.)

mitosis, and the type of cell division in which it occurs is referred to as *mitotic division.* Note therefore that "mitosis" is not simply another word for cell division, but designates a particular kind of *nuclear* division.

Monera do not possess nuclei or chromosomes like other organisms. Cell division in Monera does include gene duplication but does not include mitosis.

THE PROCESS

The first demonstrable event of mitotic division is a chemical event which occurs well before microscopically visible changes can be detected: the DNA content of the cell nucleus doubles and the genes and chromosomes reproduce. A certain amount of time elapses before the visible phases of cell division begin. These visible phases consists of four successive, arbitrarily defined stages: *prophase, metaphase, anaphase,* and *telophase.* Nuclear division, or mitosis proper, encompasses all four stages; cytoplasmic division takes place in the last stage.

One of the first happenings of prophase (Fig. 20.2) is the division of the *centriole.* It will be recalled that such a granule is found in the cells of Protista and Metazoa and that it is situated just outside the nucleus. As soon as the centriole has divided, the two resulting granules behave as if they repelled each other; they migrate toward opposite sides of the cell nucleus. Concurrently, portions of the cytoplasm transform into fine gel fibrils. Some of these radiate away from each centriole like the spokes of a wheel and form *asters.* Other gel fibrils develop between the two centrioles. Looping from one centriole to the other, these fibrils constitute a *spindle.* The centriole at each end marks a *spindle pole.* As the centrioles move farther and farther apart, the fibrils of the spindle and the asters lengthen and increase in number. Centrioles are not present and asters do not form in the cells of Metaphyta. Spindles do develop, however.

During these stages of prophase, the nuclear membrane dissolves, the nucleoli disintegrate, and nuclear and cytoplasmic substances mix freely. Moreover, distinct chromosomes become visible. Close examination reveals that each chromosome is a *double* filament (Fig. 20.3). As noted, each chromosome has manufactured a mathematically exact duplicate some time before prophase. Such twin chromosomes lie closely parallel and are joined to each other only at a single point, the so-called *centromere.* Two spindle fibrils become anchored to each centromere, one from each pole of the spindle. In this way, the chromosomes become linked to the spindle. At this general period, prophase comes to a close and *metaphase* begins.

Early during metaphase the chromosome pairs are still scattered randomly through the central portion of the cell, but later they begin to migrate. If we draw an imaginary line from one spindle pole to the other, we mark out a spindle axis. Chromosomes mi-

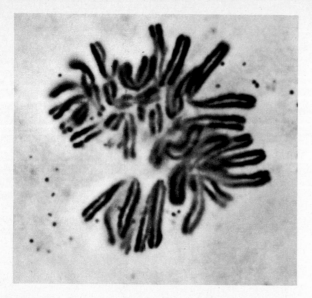

Fig. 20.3.   At the time of prophase, chromosomes have already duplicated, and doubled chromosomes, each known as a chromatid, are therefore present. The members of each pair of chromatids are still held together at one point, the centromere. (General Biological Supply House, Inc.)

grate into a plane set at right angles to the spindle axis, midway along it. Specifically, it is the centromere of each chromosome pair which comes to occupy a station precisely within this plane. During the migration, the chromosomes trail behind their centro-

meres like streamers. Lined up in one plane, the centromeres are said to form a *metaphase plate* (Fig. 20.4).

The lengthwise separation of the chromosome pairs now becomes complete. Each centromere divides and entirely independent chromosomes are produced in this manner. A small gel fibril arises at once between the centromeres of formerly joined chromosomes, and such chromosomes begin to move apart. Once they are completely separated, the members of a pair of chromosomes behave as if they repelled each other. Thus, one set of chromosomes migrates away from the metaphase plate toward one spindle pole and an identical twin set migrates in the opposite direction, toward the other spindle pole. The centromeres again lead and the arms of the chromosomes trail. Also, the gel fibrils between twin centromeres lengthen and fibrils between the centromeres and the spindle poles shorten. This period of poleward migration of chromosomes represents the *anaphase* of mitotic division (Fig. 20.5).

The beginning of telophase is marked by the appearance of a *cleavage furrow* in animal cells and a *division plate* in plant cells. Both furrow and plate form in the plane of the earlier metaphase plate. The cleavage furrow at first is a shallow groove circling the surface of a cell. This groove gradually deepens, cuts through the spindle fibrils, and eventually constricts the cell into two daughter cells. The division plate of plant cells is a partition of cellulose which is

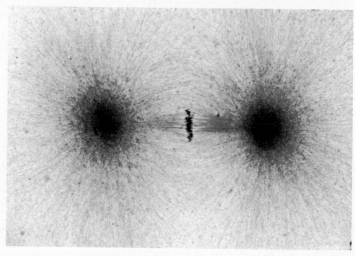

Fig. 20.4.   Metaphase in animal mitosis. Note asters, spindle, and the metaphase plate, halfway along and at right angles to the spindle axis. Note also the fibrils which join the chromosomes lined up in the metaphase plate with the spindle poles. (General Biological Supply House, Inc.)

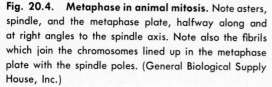

laid down more or less simultaneously at all points of the plane of cleavage.

While cytoplasmic division is in progress, the chromosomes within each prospective daughter cell aggregate near the spindle pole. Spindle fibrils subside and the gel composing them reverts to a sol state. A new nuclear membrane forms at each spindle pole, and this membrane surrounds the chromosomes. Concurrently, the chromosomes in each newly forming nucleus manufacture new nucleoli in numbers characteristic of the particular cell type. These nuclear processes terminate roughly when cytoplasmic cleavage nears completion, and mitotic division then has reached its endpoint. The events of this form of cellular reproduction are summarized in Fig. 20.6.

THE RESULT

The net result of cell division is the cleavage of one cell into two cells containing *precisely* identical gene sets, incorporated in identical chromosome sets, and *approximately* equal quantities of all other cellular constituents. Consequently, the structural and functional potential of both daughter cells is the same as that of the original mother cell.

In unicellular organisms, cell division is equivalent to reproduction of the whole organism. Daughter cells

Fig. 20.5.   Anaphase in plant cell. Note absence of asters and centrioles but presence of spindle. (General Biological Supply House, Inc.)

generally separate, but in some forms they remain sticking together and, as we have seen, form *colonies.* In multicellular organisms, cell division either contributes to *cell replacement,* as in regeneration or wound healing, or adds to *cell number.* This leads to

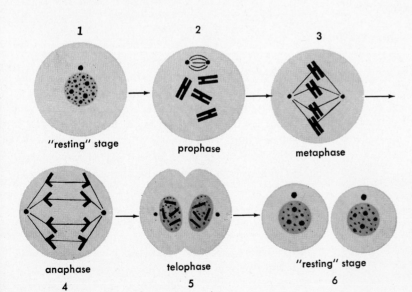

1 "resting" stage

2 prophase

3 metaphase

4 anaphase

5 telophase

6 "resting" stage

Fig. 20.6.   Mitosis summary. The assumption here is that cytoplasmic cleavage accompanies mitosis. Note that a "resting" cell is resting only from the standpoint of reproductive activity. In all other respects it is exceedingly active.

growth of tissues and organs. The growth of an organism, we note, may be a result either of molecular reproduction and increase in cell *size* or of cellular reproduction and increase in cell *number,* or of both.

The rates of cellular reproduction vary greatly. Among multicellular organisms, the highest rates of cell division occur in embryonic stages, the lowest in old age. Cells which form epithelial sheets retain a fairly rapid but steadily decreasing rate of division throughout the life of an organism. By contrast, liver or muscle cells, for example, divide only rarely in the adult. And after being formed in the embryo, nerve cells do not divide at all. Nerve cells may grow, but only by increase in cell size. Destroyed neurons cannot be replaced. In general, the more highly specialized a cell, the less frequently it divides, and vice versa.

Why does tissue and organ growth slow down with increasing age? With few exceptions, cellular reproductive capacity in the adult remains *potentially* as great as in the embryo. This is shown, for example, by the high rates of cell division in wound healing, in regeneration, in cancers and other tumors, and in *tissue cultures.* Such cultures are prepared by separating groups of cells from an organism and growing them in artificial nutrient solutions. Under isolated conditions of this sort, cells are found to reproduce faster than if they had remained within an organism. Moreover, if newly formed cells in a tissue culture are cut away from time to time, the original bit of tissue may live almost indefinitely long, certainly far longer than it would have lived within an organism. Through tissue culture, for example, a piece of the heart muscle of a chicken embryo has been maintained alive for over 30 years, which exceeds the life span of the whole chicken several times.

It is conceivable, therefore, that cell reproduction in intact organisms may slow down mainly because the cells are *not* isolated, as in a tissue culture. Instead, cells are integrated very finely into a larger organization, where their reproductive potential is held in check. Occasionally, given cells escape this check and normal healing processes or abnormal cancer may be the result.

Organismic reproduction

After periods of growth by molecular and cellular reproduction, the whole multicellular organism may reproduce. The general pattern consists of two phases. First, a *reproductive unit* separates from the parent organism. Second, a duplicate organism then forms out of the reproductive unit through *development.*

In many cases, the reproductive unit consists of the whole or a substantial portion of the parent organism. For example, in Monera and unicellular Protista, the whole body of the adult cell is the reproductive unit and reproduction is accomplished by cell division. In branching algae and liverworts, two organisms may arise from one when the main portion of the body dies off, leaving two branch portions as separate individuals. Similarly, certain flatworms, sea anemones, and other animals may on occasion divide into two or more portions. Each portion then grows into a whole adult (Fig. 20.7).

This general type of multiplication is called *vegetative reproduction.* Its characteristics are that the reproductive unit is either the whole organism or a substantial portion of the organism, and that the parent

Fig. 20.7. Vegetative reproduction in sea anemones. This animal is splitting lengthwise into two offspring organisms. (Courtesy of D. P. Wilson, Marine Biological Laboratory, Plymouth, England.)

Fig. 20.8.   Regenerative reproduction. An arm of a starfish regenerates all missing parts and becomes a whole animal. (Courtesy of D. P. Wilson, Marine Biological Laboratory, Plymouth, England.)

cells which form the reproductive unit are not specialized primarily for reproduction. Virtually *any* portion of the parent may cease its adult function and become part of a vegetative reproductive unit.

Closely allied to vegetative reproduction and representing in fact a special form of it is *regenerative reproduction*. Here the reproductive units arise fortuitously, as a result of injury to the parent by external agents. For example, many organisms may be cut into several pieces and each piece may then grow into a new, whole individual. Almost any piece of a plant, a few segments of an earthworm, an arm of a starfish, a chunk of tissue from a hydra or a sponge— each is an effective reproductive unit. The parent organisms which lose such sections of their bodies usually regenerate the missing parts (Fig. 20.8).

On theoretical grounds, a reproductive unit should not have to be a large portion of the parent organism. The smallest unit which possesses the genetic information and the operating equipment representative of an entire organism is a *single cell*. Accordingly, the minimum unit for the construction of such an organism should be one cell. This is actually the universal case. Regardless of whether or not it may also reproduce vegetatively, every multicellular organism is capable of reproducing through single *reproductive cells*. All such cells are more or less specialized for reproduction,

and they are formed in more or less specialized reproductive tissues or organs of the parent.

According to the manner of their formation and their later fate, two general classes of reproductive cells may be distinguished. One includes cells which may develop into adults *directly*. Such cells are very common in Protista and Metaphyta and are called *spores*. Among Metazoa, cells of this type are rarer. They are given a variety of names, the designation *bud* cell probably being the most frequent.

Reproductive cells in the second general class can *not* develop directly. Instead, they must first undergo a *sexual process*, in which two reproductive cells fuse. Such cells are called *sex cells*, or *gametes*. Male gametes are *sperms*, female gametes are *eggs*. A *mating* process makes possible the pairwise fusion of gametes. This fusion is *fertilization*, and the fusion product is called a *zygote*. Development of gametes into adults cannot normally occur until fertilization has taken place.

We conclude that an organism may reproduce in one or more of three general ways:

1. through *vegetative reproduction*, by means of relatively large reproductive units variously produced and not specialized primarily for reproduction

2. through *sporulative reproduction*, by means of spores or similar specialized reproductive cells which develop directly

3. through *gametic reproduction,* by means of gametes, specialized reproductive cells which develop only after a sexual process

Each of these basic methods has an adaptive advantage which the other two methods lack. The chief advantage of vegetative reproduction is speed of propagation. Huge numbers of offspring may be produced by this method within a very short time. Moreover, the method requires little tissue or cell specialization and it also offers obvious advantages to an organism in the form of regenerative reproduction.

The chief advantage of sporulation is that it represents an excellent device for geographic dispersal. In water, a spore cell may be equipped with flagella and may swim to new territories. On land, spores may be protected against drying out by a thick wall, as in plants, and may be distributed widely by wind and animals. In any environment, moreover, spores can be produced in very large numbers. As might be expected, therefore, spores typically are formed by sessile organisms like plants, which cannot disperse by locomotion.

Gametic reproduction entails serious disadvantages. For example, the method depends on chance, for gametes must meet and very often they simply do not. Meeting also requires locomotion, but eggs cannot move, nor can many organisms. Above all, gametic reproduction requires a water medium. In air, gametes would dry out quickly unless they possessed evaporation-resistant walls. But if two cells were so encased, they could then not fuse. However, gametic reproduction offers one advantage which outweighs all the disadvantages so strongly that the method has become virtually universal. This advantage is sex. An organism may or may not reproduce vegetatively or via spores, but in any case its life cycle is likely to include sex. What is the significance of this process?

Sexuality

THE PROCESS

The role of sex is revealed most clearly in those Protista in which sexual processes do not occur together with reproduction. A good example is *Spirogyra,* a filamentous green alga forming dense growths in freshwater ponds. Throughout spring, summer, and early fall, the cells reproduce vegetatively by mitotic division and add to the length of the filament. Pieces of the alga may break off and settle elsewhere, starting new individuals. Later in the fall, two cells from two filaments lying side by side may *conjugate:* a bridge forms which interconnects the two cells. The contents of one cell then pass in amoeboid fashion through the bridge into the other cell and the two cells fuse (Fig. 20.9).

That is a sexual process. What initiates its occurrence, characteristically at that season of the year? Subsequent events provide the clue. All nonconjugated cells soon die as a result of falling autumn temperatures. But the fused double cell, the zygote, is able to secrete a heavy wall around itself. The *zygospore* so formed is then able to live through the winter. In the following spring, the cyst wall breaks open and a new *Spirogyra* filament develops.

A similar sexual process occurs in many other protists. In the ciliate protozoon *Paramecium,* for example, reproduction is achieved as in *Spirogyra* by vegetative cell division. Sex takes place separately

Fig. 20.9. Sexuality of *Spirogyra*. A, colony of cells. B, two filaments side by side prior to conjugation. C, bridge between opposite cells (top); migration of contents of one cell into the other cell (center); formation of cyst or zygospore (bottom). D, growth of new filament from opened zygospore.

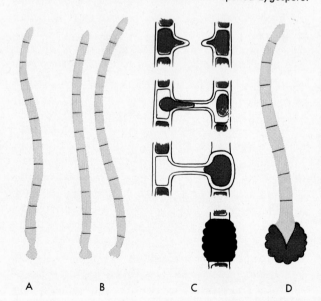

A   B   C   D

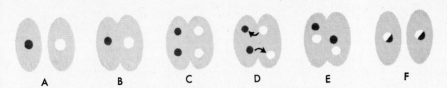

**Fig. 20.10. Sexuality of Parame-
cium.** A, original partners. B, mating.
C, nuclear division. D, gene exchange.
E, result. F, nuclear fusion and separation of partners. Note that sexuality
in *Spirogyra* involves fusion of two
entire cells; in *Paramecium*, only exchanged nuclei fuse.

through conjugation. In *Paramecium*, however, the
sexual process does not involve *fusion* of whole cells,
but only *exchange* of nuclei and thus of *gene sets*
(Fig. 20.10). Evidently, whereas the gametes of *Spirogyra* are whole cells, the gametes of *Paramecium* are
nuclei only.

Note, first, that the sexual process is fundamentally
quite distinct from reproduction. *Spirogyra* and *Paramecium* do not "multiply" by sex—if anything, quite
the contrary. In *Spirogyra*, two cells form one; in *Paramecium*, two cells enter the process and two cells
again emerge. In all other organisms, sex and reproduction are equally distinct, even though in most cases
the two processes do occur together.

Note further that in *Spirogyra*, in *Paramecium*,
and in virtually all other organisms, man not excepted,
sexual activity is particularly evident during periods
of persistent *stress*. Sexuality may be brought out or
intensified by unfavorable climates, by widespread food
shortages, by overpopulation, or by other stress conditions. Indeed, most plants and animals living in
temperate climates manifest sexual activity typically in
the fall or in the spring. Initial unfavorable changes in
the fall environment bring forth sexual responses as
though anticipating the worse conditions of winter, and
sexual activity during spring anticipates the stress conditions of summer heat and dryness.

Just how is sexuality effective against conditions of
stress? Events in *Spirogyra* and *Paramecium* supply the
general answer: every cell resulting from the sexual
process possesses the genes of *both* cells which entered
the process. Accordingly, sex may be defined as the
accumulation, within a single cell, of genes derived
from two relatively unrelated cells.

Sex therefore counteracts stress conditions on the
principle of "two are better than one." If the self-
perpetuating powers of two relatively unrelated parent

organisms are joined, through union of their genes,
then the resulting offspring organism may acquire a
survival potential which is greater than that of either
parent alone. By combining the genes of two parents,
sex introduces *genetic change* into the resulting organisms. And to the extent that such change may be advantageous for survival in new environments or under
new conditions, sex has adaptive value. That is the key
point; *sex is one of the chief processes of adaptation.*
Sex is *not* a process of reproduction (Fig. 20.11).

Since the sexual process involves single cells, it
must be carried out at a stage when an organism
consists of but a single cell. In unicellular organisms,
therefore, sex may occur at any stage of the life cycle
regardless of when reproduction occurs, and it may

Fig. 20.11.   The role of sex in combating stress. *a* and *b*
represent two different environments in which live two genetically different prospective parents; A and B symbolize their
genes. Through sex, the offspring acquires the genes of both
parents, hence also the ability to live in either environment
a or *b*. Sex combines the adaptation potential of the parents
and so endows the offspring with increased adaptation potential.

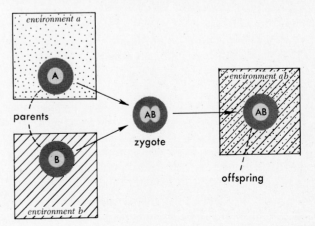

be dissociated completely from reproduction. By contrast, if in the life cycle of a multicellular organism sex is to take place at all, it *must* take place at a unicellular reproductive stage. Hence, "gametic reproduction": sex occurs *after* the formation of reproductive cells and *before* the development of such cells into multicellular adults.

MALE AND FEMALE

In *Spirogyra, Paramecium,* and many other Protista, all parent organisms look exactly alike. There is no structural distinction between males and females, and the gametes are not visibly distinguishable as sperms and eggs. Nevertheless, functional differences do exist. Not any two gametes can conjugate. The cells of a *Spirogyra* filament, for example, have all originated from the same zygospore and may be regarded as being of the same "sex," or better, the same *mating type.* Cells within such a filament cannot unite sexually. Two cells from two different filaments are required (Fig. 20.12). Functionally distinct mating types exist in *Paramecium* as well, and cells from different ones are necessary for sexual union.

In other organisms, the functional sex differences are accompanied by visible, structural ones. True male and female sexes may be distinguished here. Structurally different sperms and eggs are produced in differently constructed sex organs. Among plants, *antheridia* form sperms, *archegonia* form eggs; among animals, *testes* form sperms, *ovaries* form eggs. Moreover, the sex organs of males and females may be components of differently constructed reproductive systems, and numerous secondary sex characteristics may provide additional distinctions. In advanced animals, virtually every part of the organism, not only the reproductive structures, actually exhibit characteristics of maleness or femaleness.

In most cases, a given individual is either a male or a female and the sexes then are said to be *separate.* But in very many species, a given individual may possess *both* male and female reproductive structures within the same body. Known as *hermaphroditism,* this condition is particularly common among sessile organisms and also among sluggish, slowly moving forms. Many Protista are hermaphroditic, as are many, possibly

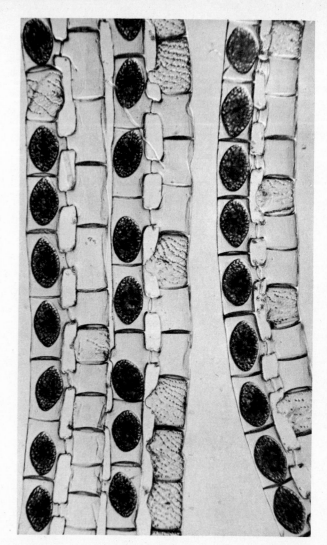

Fig. 20.12. Zygospores of *Spirogyra*. Note that all cells within a given filament have the same sexual properties: they may be either migrating sexual partners or stationary partners which receive cells from a neighboring filament. All cells of a given filament are the same *mating type,* and this accounts for their uniform sexual behavior. (General Biological Supply House, Inc.)

most, Metaphyta. Among Metazoa, the phenomenon occurs in flatworms, clams, earthworms, and many other forms, and it is sometimes encountered as an abnormality in vertebrates, man included.

Hermaphroditism is a direct adaptation to the

slow or sessile way of life. Since a normal hermaphrodite functions both as a "male" and as a "female," its gametes may not need to search each other out: *self-fertilization* may take place. In such cases, the gametes of one sex type are genetically compatible with the gametes of the other sex type produced in the same individual. Most hermaphrodites, like all other organisms, must carry out *cross-fertilization;* that is, the sperms of one individual must fertilize the eggs of another individual (Fig. 20.13). The advantage of hermaphroditism here is that fewer reproductive cells are wasted. For example, if a given plant species is hermaphroditic, sperms from one individual may meet eggs in *any* other individual, for *every* hermaphrodite contains eggs. In sessile nonhermaphrodites, by contrast, many sperms would be wasted through chance misdistribution to the wrong sex. Similarly, if cross-fertilizing hermaphrodites are capable of some locomotion, like earthworms, then fertilization becomes possible whenever *any* two individuals meet (Fig. 20.14). Since sluggish individuals are not likely to meet very frequently to begin with, and since every such meeting may result in fertilization, the adaptive value of hermaphroditism is clear.

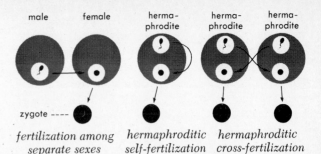

fertilization among separate sexes   *hermaphroditic self-fertilization*   *hermaphroditic cross-fertilization*

Fig. 20.13. Self- and cross-fertilization. Left, the pattern of fertilization among nonhermaphrodites. Center and right, the patterns of self- and cross-fertilization among hermaphrodites.

Meiotic cell division

One consequence of every sexual process is that a zygote formed from two gametes possesses twice the usual number of chromosomes. An adult organism developing from such a zygote would consist of cells which would all have a doubled chromosome number. If the next generation were again produced sexually,

Fig. 20.14. Copulating earthworms. These animals are cross-fertilizing hermaphrodites; hence whenever *any* two of them meet, each may be fertilized by the other. (General Biological Supply House, Inc.)

the chromosome number would then quadruple, and this process of progressive doubling would continue indefinitely through successive sexual generations.

This does not happen in actuality. Chromosome numbers do stay constant from one life cycle to the next, and the constancy is maintained by a series of special nuclear divisions known as *meiosis*. In many cases meiosis is accompanied by cytoplasmic divisions, and both events are then referred to collectively as *meiotic cell divisions*. *It is the function of meiosis to counteract the chromosome-doubling effect of fertilization by reducing a doubled chromosome number to half.* The unreduced doubled chromosome number, before meiosis, is called the *diploid* number, and it is symbolized as *2n*; the reduced number, after meiosis, is the *haploid* number, and it is symbolized as *n* (Fig. 20.15).

Meiosis occurs in every life cycle which includes a sexual process—in other words, more or less universally. Organisms differ according to *when* and *where* meiosis occurs in the life cycle. For purposes of illustration, we may consider the life cycle of the unicellular green alga *Chlamydomonas*. In this organism, meiosis occurs right after fertilization, as a first step in the further development of the zygote. Thus, fertilization produces a zygote with a diploid chromosome number and meiosis then restores the haploid condition immediately. How is this reduction of chromosome numbers achieved?

A zygote does not contain a *2n* collection of mutually different chromosomes, but instead contains a collection of *n* mutually different *pairs* of chromosomes. For a zygote receives one haploid, *n*, set of chromosomes via the male sex cell, and a like haploid set via the female sex cell. Therefore, like shoes, the chromosomes of any diploid cell come in pairs. One of each pair is paternal in origin, the other maternal (Fig. 20.16). During meiosis in such a diploid cell, chromosome reduction occurs in such a way that any resulting haploid cell contains *one of each maternal-paternal pair* of chromosomes. In this haploid cell, it is entirely a matter of chance which and how many chromosomes will be maternal and which and how many will be paternal. For example, a zygote of *Chlamydomonas* contains 16 chromosomes, 8 of them paternal, the other 8 maternal. After meiosis, a haploid cell contains half of 16, or 8, chromosomes. Of these eight, a chance-determined number will now be paternal, the remainder maternal (Fig. 20.17).

The phrase "chromosome reduction" might imply that in a diploid cell one of each pair of chromosomes is destroyed or otherwise lost. This is not the case. Instead, the diploid chromosome number is reduced to half by *two* meiotic cell divisions. The general pattern of these divisions is as follows. A diploid cell undergoes two successive cytoplasmic cleavages, which transform the one original cell into four cells. During or before these cleavages, the chromosomes of the diploid cell duplicate *once*. As a result, *2n* becomes *4n*. And of these 4n chromosomes, one *n* is incorporated into each of the four cells formed. In sum, *one diploid* cell becomes *four haploid* cells (Fig. 20.18).

In *Chlamydomonas*, for example, a zygote contains 16 chromosomes, as noted. During meiosis the number doubles to 32 and at the same time the cytoplasm of the zygote divides twice in succession. Four cells result which share the 32 chromosomes equally. Hence each mature cell of *Chlamydomonas* contains eight chromosomes, a complete haploid set.

The two meiotic divisions have many features in common with mitotic divisions. For example, each

Fig. 20.15. The relation of meiosis to life cycle.

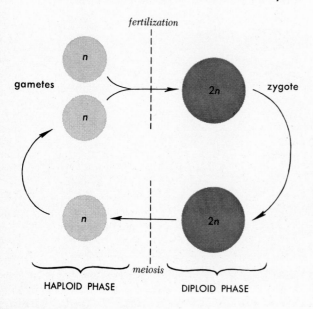

fertilization

gametes

n

n

zygote

2*n*

2*n*

n

n

meiosis

HAPLOID PHASE DIPLOID PHASE

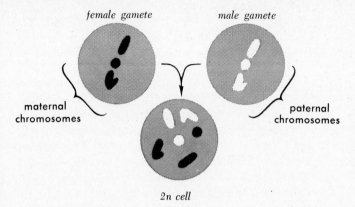

female gamete   male gamete

maternal
chromosomes

paternal
chromosomes

2n cell

Fig. 20.16. Each diploid cell contains two like sets of chromosomes, representing maternal-paternal pairs. The maternal set originated in the female gamete; the paternal set, in the male gamete.

meiotic division passes through prophase, metaphase, anaphase, and telophase, as in mitosis. Moreover, spindles form and other nonchromosomal events are as in mitotic divisions.

The critical difference between mitosis and the *first* meiotic division lies in their metaphases. In mitosis, we recall, all chromosomes, each of them already duplicated, migrate into the metaphase plate, where all the centromeres line up in the same plane. In the first meiotic division, the $2n$ chromosomes similarly duplicate during or before prophase. These $2n$ pairs, the members of each pair again joined at the centro-

mere, also migrate into the metaphase plate. But now only n pairs assemble in one plane. The other n pairs migrate into a plane of their own, a plane which is closely parallel to the first. Moreover, every pair in one plane comes to lie next to the corresponding type of chromosome pair in the other plane. The metaphase plate is therefore made up of *paired chromosome pairs,* or *tetrads* of like chromosomes lying side by side. And there are n of these tetrads in the whole plate (Fig. 20.19).

During the ensuing anaphase, two chromosomes of each tetrad migrate to one spindle pole, two to the

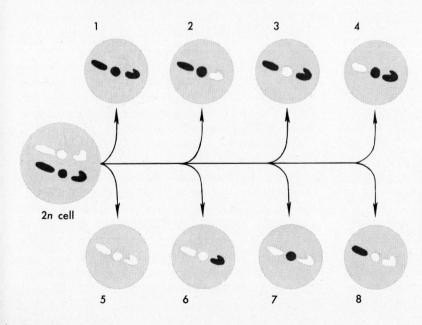

1   2   3   4

2n cell

5   6   7   8

Fig. 20.17. When the chromosome number of a diploid cell is halved by meiosis, a resulting haploid cell contains a single set of chromosomes consisting of a chance-determined number of paternal and maternal chromosomes. The diagram shows the various possible paternal-maternal combinations if $n = 3$.

one diploid (2n) cell

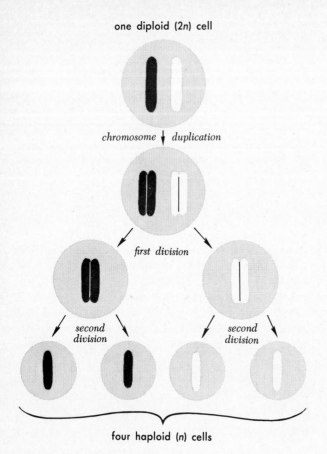

chromosome ↓ duplication

first division

second division   second division

four haploid (n) cells

Fig. 20.18.   The general pattern of events during meiosis, on the assumption that 2n = 2.

other. At the end of the first meiotic division, therefore, there are two cells, each with n pairs of chromosomes. In the metaphase of the subsequent second meiotic division, the n pairs of chromosomes line up in the same plane and n single chromosomes eventually migrate to each of the poles during anaphase. At the termination of meiosis as a whole, therefore, four cells are present, each with n single chromosomes, a complete haploid set.

In unicellular forms such as *Chlamydomonas*, the four haploid cells resulting from meiosis are four new adult organisms. In many other organisms, as noted, meiosis occurs not in the zygote but at different stages of the life cycle. What are these stages and how do they affect the nature of a life cycle?

Life cycles

A life cycle in which the adult is haploid, as in *Chlamydomonas*, probably represents a primitive condition. It is reasonable to suppose that an ancestral moneran or protistan cell possessed only a single complete set of genes, i.e., that it was haploid. When sex occurred, a diploid zygote resulted from fertilization, and immediate meiosis then must have been a likely event. The chromosome-doubling process of fertilization must have been a stimulus to which the chromosome-reducing process of meiosis was the rapidly following response.

A life cycle characterized in this way by zygotic meiosis and haploid adults is known as a *haplontic* life cycle (Fig. 20.20). It occurs in all Monera (insofar as sex is known in this category); in all primitive and many advanced groups among green, yellow-brown, and several other types of algae; and in many fungi. The list suggests clearly that the haplontic life cycle is basic in the Monera and the Protista. Where sporulation occurs in these haplontic groups, spores are produced at some point in the life cycle between one fertilization and the next. The method of spore production is mitotic division and, like the adults which produce them, the spores are haploid.

Haplontic patterns have probably given rise to all other types of life cycles. With regard to the timing of meiosis, we may readily guess at which points the process possibly *could* occur. Like sex, meiosis is a cellular process, and it can therefore take place only at a stage when the life cycle passes through a unicellular phase. The zygote does represent such a phase. But even a multicellular organism may pass through unicellular stages on two other occasions, namely, at the stage of the *gamete* and at the stage of the *spore*. Conceivably, therefore, meiosis could occur at either of these points, and in many organisms it actually does.

In man, for example, meiosis takes place during the formation of gametes. Within the sex organs of the adult, diploid gamete-producing cells mature into sperms and eggs. As part of this maturation, meiosis takes place in these diploid cells. Mature gametes consequently are haploid. The mature haploid gametes

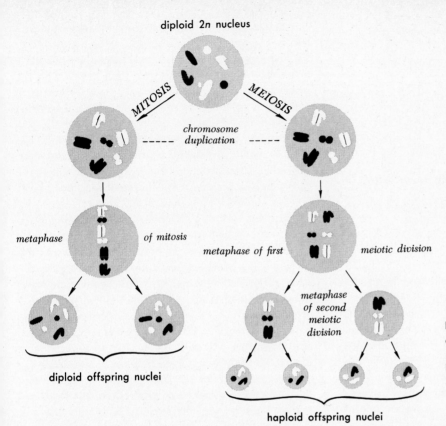

diploid 2n nucleus

MITOSIS   *MEIOSIS*

chromosome
----- *duplication* -----

metaphase   *of mitosis*

metaphase of first   *meiotic division*

*metaphase
of second
meiotic
division*

diploid offspring nuclei

haploid offspring nuclei

Fig. 20.19.   A comparison of mitosis and meiosis, on the assumption that 2n = 6. Note that the key difference between the two processes is the way the chromosomes line up in metaphase.

subsequently participate in fertilization, and the zygote is then diploid. But now, as the zygote divides and develops into a mature human being, the cells *remain* diploid. The whole human adult becomes diploid in this fashion, including the sex organs it eventually forms. Gamete-producing cells consequently are diploid as well. And meiosis occurs again during the maturation of gametes.

Such a life cycle, characterized by meiosis during gamete formation and by diploid adults, is called a *diplontic* life cycle (Fig. 20.21). In it, the only haploid stage is the gamete itself, all other stages being diploid. We note that this is almost completely the reverse of a haplontic cycle. Diplontic cycles are very abundant. They are encountered not only in man but in all Metazoa, and among Protista such cycles occur in various advanced groups of algae, in some fungi, and in most protozoa.

We may readily guess how the evolutionary transition from haplontic to diplontic cycles must have been achieved. In the ancestral haplontic type, meiosis occurs in the zygote, at the very start of the life cycle. In diplontic types, meiosis is *postponed* to the

Fig. 20.20.   The haplontic life-cycle pattern.

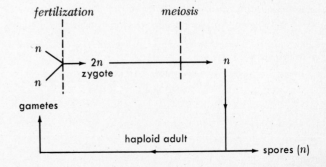

fertilization   *meiosis*

n

$2n$
zygote

n

n

gametes

haploid adult

spores (n)

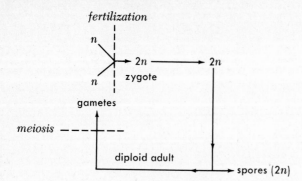

Fig. 20.21.   The diplontic life-cycle pattern.

time of gamete formation, that is, to the very end of the life cycle. Thus, sooner or later during the evolution of Protista, some groups evidently delayed the timing of meiosis as long as it could be delayed.

A powerful adaptive advantage results from postponing meiosis. As noted, one consequence is that the adults, and indeed all stages except the gametes, are diploid. This means that each gene in each adult cell is represented twice rather than just once. Therefore, even if one gene of a pair changes in some way, e.g., by mutation, then the other gene still preserves the original message. In short, the diploid state increases the genetic stability of the individual.

Note that if an organism with a diplontic life cycle produces spores, such cells are manufactured by a diploid adult. The method of spore formation is again mitotic division and the spores consequently are diploid as well.

The third possible time of meiosis is the stage of spore production. In this case, fertilization produces a diploid zygote, and the developing adult remains diploid. In due course the adult produces a spore-forming organ. In it, diploid spore-producing cells give rise to spores. Meiosis occurs during this transformation of spore-producing cells into spores. Such spores therefore are haploid, and since their production includes meiosis, we may refer to them as *meiospores*.

A haploid meiospore subsequently develops into a new, *haploid* adult. This adult later manufactures haploid gametes, and these subsequently participate in fertilization. A new life cycle then begins with the resulting diploid zygote.

We note that, because meiosis occurs during sporulation, such a life cycle is split up into two generations, each represented by a separate adult. The diploid zygote gives rise to a diploid adult; and since this adult later produces meiospores, it is called the *sporophyte generation*. The haploid meiospore gives rise to a haploid adult; and since this adult later produces gametes, it is called the *gametophyte generation*.

Cycles of this sort, characterized by meiosis during spore formation and by an *alternation of generations*, are known as *diplohaplontic* life cycles (Fig. 20.22). They are exceedingly widespread, occurring in numerous algae, many fungi, all slime molds, and in all Metaphyta. Such cycles are again derived from the haplontic type by a postponement of meiosis, in this case from the zygote stage to the spore-producing stage. Diplohaplontic cycles combine the adaptive advantages of both haplontic and diplontic ones.

With this account of general reproductive patterns as a background, we continue next with a discussion of specific reproductive processes encountered in given groups of organisms.

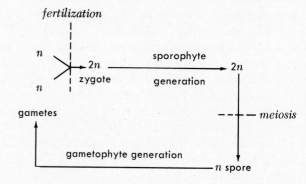

Fig. 20.22.   The diplohaplontic life-cycle pattern.

Review questions

1. How does reproduction contribute to steady-state maintenance? To self-perpetuation in general? Review the forms of molecular reproduction and the nature of each. How does molecular reproduction contribute to organismic reproduction?

2. What basic events occur in all forms of cell division? What is mitosis? Distinguish between mitotic and amitotic division. How does cell division contribute to organismic reproduction? Describe the process of mitotic division.

3. Distinguish between reproduction and development. What is vegetative reproduction? In which organisms, under what circumstances, and in which forms does vegetative reproduction occur?

4. What is sporulation? What is gametic reproduction? In which organisms does each of these occur? What is a spore? How is vegetative reproduction different from sporulation? How is sporulation different from gametic reproduction?

5. What are the most basic events of every sexual process? Under what conditions does sex tend to occur? In what way is sex of adaptive value?

6. Define mating, fertilization, zygote, gamete, mating type. What are the limitations of, and the environmental conditions required for (a) gametic reproduction and (b) sporulation? Contrast in detail.

7. What is hermaphroditism? In which organisms does it occur, generally and specifically? What is its adaptive function? Distinguish between self-fertilization and cross-fertilization.

8. What is the basic function of meiosis and what makes such a process necessary? Where does meiosis occur? Define haploid, diploid. How many *pairs* of chromosomes are found in a diploid cell?

9. How many chromosome duplications and how many cell duplications occur during meiotic division? In what respects are mitosis and meiosis alike? What is the essential difference between the metaphase of mitosis and the metaphase of the first meiotic division?

10. Describe the nature of a haplontic life cycle. Name organisms in which such a cycle occurs. Do similarly for diplontic and diplohaplontic life cycles. Which type of life cycle is probably primitive and how may it have given rise to the other types?

Suggested collateral readings

Biesele, J. J.: Tissue Culture and Cancer, *Sci. Am.*, vol. 195, 1956.

Mazia, D.: Cell Division, *Sci. Am.*, vol. 189, 1953.

———: How Cells Divide, *Sci. Am.*, vol. 205, 1961.

Singer, M.: The Regeneration of Body Parts, *Sci. Am.*, vol. 199, 1958.

Tinbergen, N.: The Courtship of Animals, *Sci. Am.*, vol. 191, 1954.

White, P. R.: Plant Tissue Cultures, *Sci. Am.*, Vol. 182, 1950.

Zahl, P. A.: The Evolution of Sex, *Sci. Am.*, vol. 180, 1949.

REPRODUCTION: MONERA, PROTISTA, METAPHYTA

21

All three basic reproductive methods are encountered in these organisms. Very frequently, notably among Protista, a given organism is capable of reproducing by any of the three methods at different times, specific environmental conditions usually determining the particular method. In aquatic forms, spores and gametes most often are flagellate and swimming. Inasmuch as the water supply is abundant, gametic reproduction can be accomplished readily. In terrestrial forms, spores are usually encapsulated. Gametes cannot be, but despite the absence of abundant free water gametic reproduction is made possible by special evolutionary adaptations.

Monera

Among bacteria and blue-green algae, the main reproductive process is rapid vegetative binary fission (Fig. 21.1). Inasmuch as microscopically identifiable chromosomes are absent, cell division is not mitotic. It is unknown just how the genetic material of a bacteria is duplicated exactly and distributed

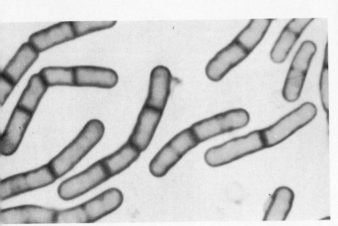
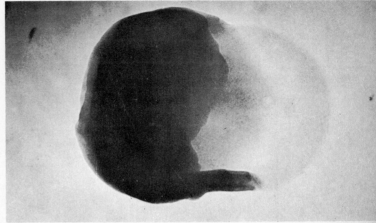

Fig. 21.1.   Left, bacteria named *Bacillus megatherium* stained to show the cell walls. These organisms have grown in length for a period of time and, as the transverse partitions show, are now in various stages of reproduction by subdivision. Right, electron micrograph of a germinating spore of the bacterium *Bacillus mycoides*. Note the bacterial cell emerging from the coat of the resting spore. (Left, courtesy of Dr. C. F. Robinow and the Society of American Bacteriologists; right, courtesy of Dr. G. Knaysi, Dr. R. F. Baker, and Dr. J. Hillier, *J. Bacteriol.*, vol. 53, 1947, and Society of American Bacteriologists.)

equally to the two daughter cells; but that some such process takes place is clear.

Under stress, many bacterial types secrete heavy cyst walls around themselves, which protect the cells and keep them in a relatively inactive, dormant state, often for years. Such cysts are called "resting spores," or *endospores*. Despite the implications of the name, endospores are not reproductive units. The same single cell which encysts in the capsule eventually excysts again, still single.

However, some bacteria and many blue-greens do produce true reproductive spores. In certain cases, series of spore cells may be budded off from the end of a vegetative cell. In other cases, the interior of a vegetative cell may subdivide into numerous spore cells, each with its own nucleus.

It is now known that sex occurs as a fairly rare laboratory phenomenon in certain bacteria and blue-green algae. Whether or not sex also takes place in nature is still undetermined. The sexual process is conjugative, that is, cells join pairwise and exchange portions of their genetic material. The partners then separate. Genetic experiments have also established that conjugating Monera are *haploid* and that some (still unknown) kind of gene-reduction process equivalent to meiosis takes place immediately after conjugation. In other words, insofar as sex occurs in them, moneran life cycles are haplontic.

If sex is at best rare and is perhaps completely absent in many or most Monera, how do these organisms adapt to their changing environments? They may do so without sex, by their extremely rapid vegetative multiplication. Rapid reproduction means rapid evolution, through mutations. Monera are haploid, which means that every mutational gene change will immediately produce a change in a trait. Therefore, even if millions or billions of organisms succumb to one environment, a single survivor with appropriate mutations may within a few hours produce new millions or billions of readapted organisms. Monera evidently rely on safety through numbers, and they generally can do very well without sex.

Protista

ALGAE

Vegetative multiplication by cell division occurs in most algae. The process increases the number of whole organisms in unicellular types, the size of a given organism in multicellular types. Many filamentous algae may break into several multicellular pieces, and each such fragment then grows back into a whole individual.

Virtually all algal groups produce spores. The process is well illustrated in the filamentous green alga *Ulothrix*, which resembles *Spirogyra* superficially. In given cells of *Ulothrix*, the cell substance may divide a number of times within the original cell wall. Each small cell so produced secretes its own wall and matures into a flagellate spore. An opening subsequently forms in the wall of the original cell and the spores escape through it (Fig. 21.2).

In somewhat similar fashion, this alga may also produce gametes. Given cells again divide within their cellulose walls, as in spore production. However, many more successive divisions occur, and many more, smaller cells are produced. These develop flagella, escape through an opening in the original cell wall, and function as gametes. After gametes fuse pairwise, the resulting zygote swims about for a time and then undergoes meiosis. The four haploid cells so formed eventually settle and grow into four haploid multicellular adults.

Evidently, the life cycle of *Ulothrix* is haplontic. This is true also of many other algae, both of unicellular types (e.g., *Chlamydomonas*) and multicellular types (e.g., *Volvox*, *Spirogyra*, *Oedogonium*). Certain other algae are diplontic (e.g., the green alga *Acetabularia*, the brown alga *Fucus*), and still others are diplohaplontic (e.g., the green *Ulva*, many brown and red algae). In the latter group, the spore-producing and gamete-producing generations often are structurally alike. In the sea lettuce *Ulva*, for example, external appearance alone does not reveal whether a

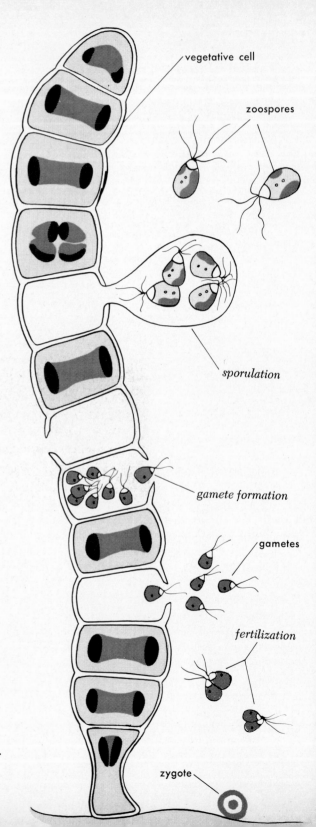

vegetative cell

zoospores

sporulation

gamete formation

gametes

fertilization

zygote

Fig. 21.2.   Reproduction in *Ulothrix*.

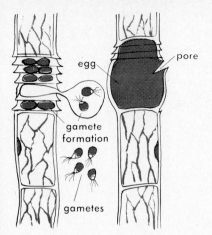

Fig. 21.3. Sperms and eggs in *Oedogonium*.

cell of one filament may enlarge and mature into a true egg and a cell of another filament may subdivide into a number of true, flagellate sperms (Fig. 21.3). If swimming sperms then happen to encounter egg-bearing filaments, fertilization may occur. An even greater degree of sex distinction is in evidence in the rockweed *Fucus*, for example. This organism not only produces sperms and eggs, but the cells which give rise to these gametes also are located within clearly different male and female reproductive structures (Fig. 21.4). Similarly distinct sperm- and egg-producing structures can be identified in the stoneworts. We may conclude that, as a group, algae exhibit the whole range of possible reproductive patterns, including all types of reproductive methods, all types of life cycles, and all basic variations in the degrees of maleness and femaleness.

given individual is a diploid spore-forming sporophyte or a haploid gamete-forming gametophyte.

Many algae are hermaphroditic. In those in which the sexes are separate the degree of sex distinction varies greatly. For example, structurally different sex types cannot be distinguished in *Ulothrix* or *Spirogyra*. But in the fairly closely related form *Oedogonium*, a

SLIME MOLDS, PROTOZOA

The life cycle of slime molds, already outlined in Chap. 8, is fundamentally diplohaplontic. An adult plasmodium or pseudoplasmodium represents the

Fig. 21.4. Conceptacles of *Fucus*. Left, conceptacle with a lining layer bearing sperm-producing branches. Note the sterile hairs, or paraphyses, projecting through the opening of the conceptacle. Right, conceptacle with conspicuous egg-producing structures. (Courtesy of Dr. M. S. Fuller, University of California, Berkeley.)

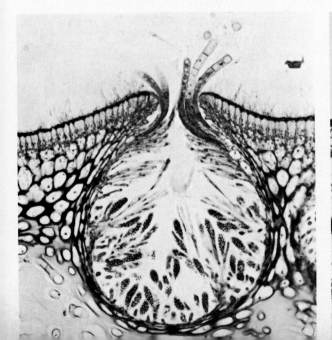
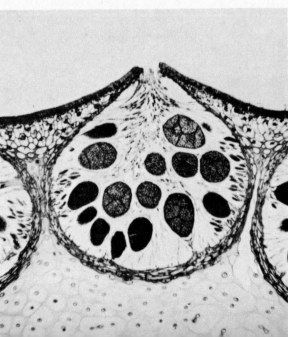

diploid sporophyte generation. From it develops a stalked fruiting body in which spores are formed. Meiosis occurs during spore production. The spores give rise to flagellate or amoeboid swarm cells which are haploid. Successive vegetative generations of such swarmers represent the gametophyte generation, which thus consists of a *population* of separate single cells. Eventually such cells function as gametes and fertilization reestablishes the diploid condition. Diploid zygotic cells subsequently grow or aggregate into plasmodial sporophytes (Fig. 21.5).

Among protozoa (Fig. 21.6), the usual method of vegetative reproduction is mitotic cell division. Sporulation is known to occur in Foraminifera, Radiolaria, and Sporozoa. In these organisms, a vegetative cell first becomes multinucleate and then undergoes multiple cytoplasmic fission. The cellular products, each containing one nucleus, represent spores. Such cells have been given different names in different sporulating forms.

Gametic reproduction occurs universally among all protozoan groups, but some individual types are without sex (e.g., *Amoeba*). Fertilization is achieved either by *syngamy* (cell fusion), as in flagellate protozoa, or by *conjugation* (exchange of gamete nuclei) as in ciliate protozoa. Most protozoan life cycles are diplontic, but haplontic cycles occur in some of the Sporozoa and diplohaplontic cycles in some of the Foraminifera.

Sexual processes have been studied most in *Paramecium*, which has become one of the best known organisms of all kinds. Like ciliates generally, *Paramecium* is hermaphroditic, each organism producing both "male" and "female" gamete nuclei. Ordinarily, exchange of such nuclei during conjugation leads to cross-fertilization. Under certain circumstances, however, single organisms may be self-fertilized; that is, the two gamete nuclei within a given individual fuse together. One species, *Paramecium aurelia*, has been shown to consist of 16 distinct (but structurally indistinguishable) sexual varieties. Each variety in turn consists of two mating types, and conjugation requires one partner from each of these two types. Analogous sexual specializations are known to exist in other species of *Paramecium* and indeed in several other types of ciliates.

Fig. 21.5. The life cycle in a group of slime molds. A sclerotium is an encapsulated resting stage formed from a plasmodium and germinating back into a plasmodium. Swarm cells derived from the meiospore may alternate between amoeboid and flagellate states.

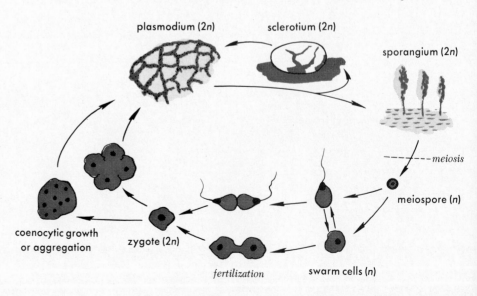

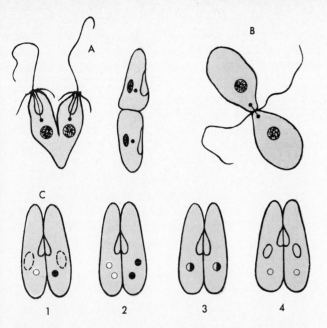

Fig. 21.6. Patterns of reproduction and sex in protozoa, diagrammatic. *A,* longitudinal fission as in zooflagellates and transverse fission as in ciliates. *B,* mating, as in zooflagellates. *C,* conjugation, as in ciliates: (1) macronuclear degeneration; (2) micronuclear division (after meiosis), resulting in "male" and "female" gamete nuclei in each individual; (3) nuclear exchange and fusion, resulting in diploid zygote nucleus in each individual; (4) division of the zygote nuclei, resulting in new micronuclei and macronuclei in each individual.

FUNGI

Vegetative reproduction in fungi occurs through mitotic nuclear divisions and cytoplasmic growth of the hyphae. Fragments of a mycelium may disperse and give rise elsewhere to whole new mycelia.

In the primitive aquatic fungi the spores are flagellate and they are formed more or less as in algae; that is, a cell subdivides internally and releases numerous small spore cells. In terrestrial fungi the spores are encapsulated. For example, in the bread-mold *Rhizopus* upright branch hyphae with expanded tips grow from many places in the mycelium (Fig. 21.7). The tips are fruiting bodies, or *sporangia*, in which spores are produced. Each such spore is encapsulated within a wall which turns black as the spore matures. After the spores are dispersed they may germinate into new mycelia.

The mycelia, sporangia, and spores of *Rhizopus* are all haploid; the life cycle here, as in many other fungi, is haplontic. A sexual process may occur when two mycelia live in close proximity. Each may then develop a short *suspensor* hypha, one growing toward the other. The tip of each such hypha becomes walled off as a multinucleate gametelike cell. When the two gametes meet, they fuse and a cyst wall is secreted around the fusion mass. In the interior, the nuclei pair off, one from one gamete joining one from the other. Such nuclear pairs fuse, forming diploid zygote nuclei. Unpaired nuclei degenerate. When the cyst germinates, its contents grow directly into an upright

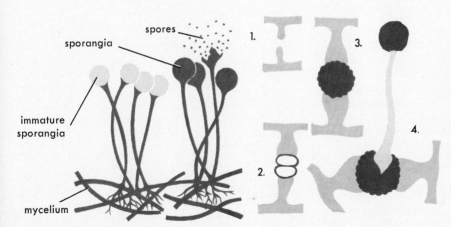

spores

sporangia

immature sporangia

mycelium

1.

2.

3.

4.

Fig. 21.7. Reproduction in bread molds. Left, sporulation. Note the horizontal threads of mycelium, stalks with ripening spore cases, and escape of spores from the cases. Right, sexuality. Note the mycelial outgrowth on two neighboring hyphae, contact and fusion of sex cells, formation of encysted zygote, and development of zygote into stalk with spore case.

hypha with a terminal sporangium. The zygote nuclei divide in the process and the first two divisions are meiotic. Numerous haploid nuclei are thereby formed, and these participate in spore formation in the sporangia. Mature spores then grow into new vegetative mycelia (see Fig. 21.7).

Haplontic life cycles are by no means the only ones among fungi. For example, most Ascomycetes and many Basidiomycetes exhibit cycles which are basically equivalent to diplohaplontic ones. In such fungi, the gamete-producing generation is represented by mycelia containing haploid nuclei (Fig. 21.8). If two mycelia of this type live side by side, a cytoplasmic connecting bridge may grow between them and nuclei from one mycelium may migrate through the bridge into the other. This is a mating process; the nuclei here represent "gametes." A hypha which now contains nuclei from both parental mycelia is roughly equivalent to a diploid stage. It grows into a more or less extensive mycelium which constitutes the spore-producing generation; from it develop special spore-forming hyphae. Such hyphae usually

become surrounded by other hyphae which develop into a fruiting body (as in the case of mushrooms, for example). At the ends of the spore-forming hyphae within a fruiting body, cells arise which will be asci in the Ascomycetes, basidia in the Basidiomycetes. In a developing ascus or basidium two gamete nuclei are present, each derived from one of the two original parent mycelia. The gamete nuclei fuse and the resulting single nucleus then undergoes meiosis. Haploid nuclei are so produced, and the cytoplasm surrounding each such nucleus is subsequently walled off. Distinct spore cells are formed in this manner— ascospores in an ascus, basidiospores in a basidium. These spores eventually scatter and when they germinate they give rise to new mycelia with haploid nuclei (Fig. 21.9).

In many Basidiomycetes, either the haploid or the diploid phase of the life cycle is greatly reduced or prolonged, often as an adaptation to a parasitic way of life. Among the numerous parasitic fungi, *rusts* and *smuts* exhibit particularly complex life histories. Rusts, for example, make use of several intermediate hosts

Fig. 21.8.   The life cycle in Ascomycetes and Basidiomycetes. If two uninucleate haploid mycelia grow side by side, mating may occur by the migration of nuclei from one mycelium through a bridge into the other mycelium (left). A binucleate (diploid) mycelium is so formed. From it then grow special spore-forming hyphae, which are usually surrounded by packed hyphae forming a fruiting body. In terminal cells of the spore-forming hyphae nuclear fusion occurs, meiosis takes place subsequently, and haploid spores are produced. The cell containing such spores is either an ascus or a basidium, depending on the fungal class. Liberated ascospores or basidiospores then germinate and form a new uninucleate mycelium.

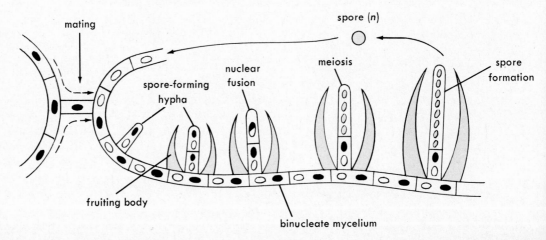

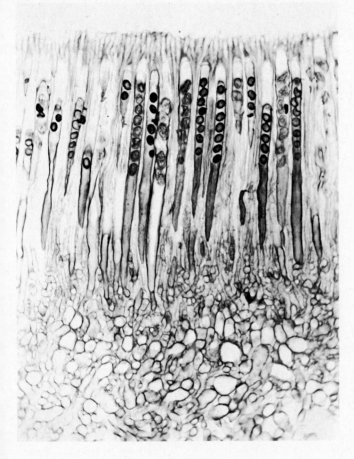

Fig. 21.9.   A layer of asci in a cup fungus, with asco-spores in the asci. See also Fig. 8.23. (Carolina Biological Supply Co.)

and they transfer from one host to the next by means of specially produced spores. Thus the black wheat rust fungus manufactures, in succession, *summer spores* on wheat, *winter spores* on wheat, *early spring spores* (haploid basidiospores) on wheat stubble or in soil, *spring spores* on the leaves of barberry bushes (such spores being formed after a sexual process), and then again summer spores on wheat. Each type of spore here develops into a mycelium which produces the next spore type in the series.

Bryophytes

The reproduction of all Metaphyta is characterized by the presence of multicellular sex *organs*, namely, *antheridia* and *archegonia*, in which distinct sperms and eggs are formed. Also universal are diplohaplontic life cycles in which the gametophyte generation is structurally *dissimilar* from the sporophyte generation. The gametophyte generation is dominant in the bryophytes, the sporophyte generation in the tracheophytes.

Vegetative reproduction is particularly highly developed in the bryophytes. As already noted in Chap. 9, for example, many bryophytes may form *gemma cups* from surface cells of the body (Fig. 9.2). The floor of such a cup continuously develops vegetative buds, or *gemmae*, each an upright spindle-shaped mass of cells attached by a tiny stalk. Gemmae are readily dislodged by rain drops; and if the gemmae are splashed to suitable ground, they develop into new plants.

The sex organs develop in different regions in dif-

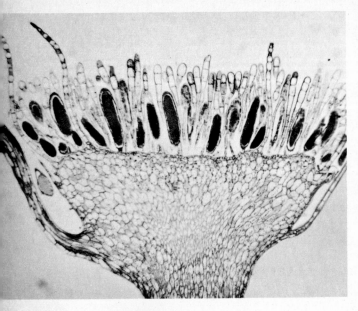

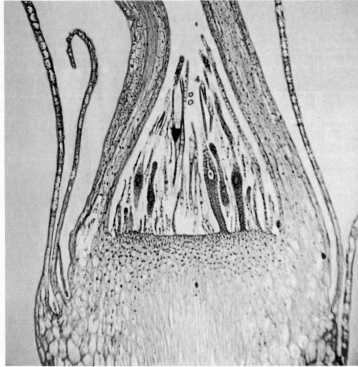

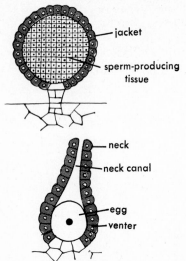

jacket

sperm-producing tissue

neck

neck canal

egg

venter

Fig. 21.10. The sex organs of bryophytes. Photos, longitudinal sections through the antheridial heads (left) and archegonial heads (right) of a moss gametophyte. Diagram, the structure of an antheridium and an archegonium. (Photographs courtesy of Dr. M. S. Fuller, University of California, Berkeley.)

ferent groups of bryophytes. In mosses, for example, the organs form at the tips of the leafy shoots (Fig. 21.10). A sperm-producing antheridium is more or less spherical and consists of an external protective layer and of sperm-forming cells in the interior. Each such interior cell matures into a biflagellate sperm. An archegonium is roughly flask-shaped. The expanded portion consists of a large egg in the interior and of a single layer of cells on the outside. This layer con-

tinues into the narrow portion of the sex organ as a canal which provides a sperm path to the egg.

All structures of a bryophyte mentioned so far represent the gametophyte generation (Fig. 21.11). The main bryophyte body, the leafy shoots, the sex organs, the gametes, all are haploid and constitute the sexual phase of the life cycle. The fertilized egg is diploid, however, and it represents the beginning of the diploid sporophyte generation.

In all bryophytes, fertilization depends on free water. Either water must form continuous films between nearby sex organs or fluid droplets must splash sperms to archegonia. After sperms enter an archegonium, one fertilizes the egg. The zygote remains in the female sex organ and grows into a diploid embryo which later matures into an adult sporophyte. Such a sporophyte consists of basal *foot* anchored in the female sex organ, a *stalk* of different lengths in different bryophyte groups, and a terminal *sporangium*, or spore-forming organ (Fig. 21.12).

Spore maturation in the sporangium includes the process of meiosis, which terminates the diploid phase of the life cycle. Mature spores are haploid and encapsulated. When the sporangium breaks open the spores escape and they eventually develop into new gametophytes. The pattern of this life cycle is outlined in Fig. 21.13.

In most bryophytes, the cells of a sporophyte are without chlorophyll. Consequently, sporophytes are generally parasitic and nutritionally dependent on the green gametophytes to which they remain attached.

Moreover, a sporophyte is short-lived compared to a gametophyte. For these reasons, the gametophyte generation clearly represents the main, dominant phase of the bryophyte life cycle.

Tracheophytes

Dominance of the haploid gametophyte, as in bryophytes, puts emphasis on the generation which produces the motile sperms. Therefore, regardless of how well adapted to land the gametophyte may be in other respects, it can never be really well adapted in its reproduction; gametic reproduction requires free external water for swimming sperms and this is not always available in a terrestrial environment. As we have seen, bryophytes "make do" by gearing their sperm release to wet periods.

Primitive tracheophytes actually cannot do much better. But they put the emphasis on the diploid sporophyte, not the gametophyte. The sporophyte produces encapsulated spores, which are excellently

Fig. 21.11. Sex-organ–bearing stalks in Marchantia. Left, stalk bearing fingerlike processes in which female sex organs are located. Right, structure containing male sex organs. (Carolina Biological Supply Co.)

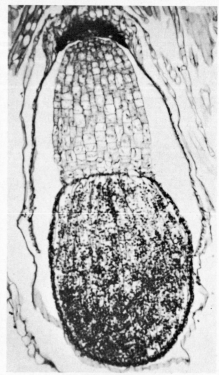

Fig. 21.12.   The sporophyte of bryophytes. Left, moss gametophytes bearing attached sporophytes on top. Right, the sporophyte of the liverwort *Marchantia*. The foot is at top of photo, the sporangium at bottom, and the stalk interconnects foot and sporangium. (Left, Carolina Biological Supply Co.; right, courtesy of Dr. M. S. Fuller, University of California, Berkeley.)

adapted to terrestrial conditions. And by reducing the gametophyte to microscopic dimensions and to a generally short-lived existence, they correspondingly reduce the water problem of the weak link in their life cycle. Moreover, deemphasis of the gametophyte also prepares the way for a complete circumvention of the water problem, realized in advanced tracheophytes through seeds. Thus, whereas the "familiar" plant in mosses and other bryophytes is a gametophyte, the familiar plant in all tracheophytes is a spore-producing organism.

THE EARLY PATTERN

The reproductive difficulties imposed on a land plant by a water-requiring gametophyte are clearly in evi-

dence in those tracheophytes which do not produce seeds, that is, the psilopsids, the lycopsids, the sphenopsids, and the ferns. In most of these, the sporophyte and gametophyte generations are separate green plants living in soil independently. But the gametophytes are exceedingly tiny, often near-microscopic ground-hugging plantlets, existing in moist, shaded places. They usually live only just long enough to produce sperms and eggs. The sporophytes on the other hand, being independent of free external water for reproduction, are large and generally perennial. Many grew to tree size in past ages; some ferns still do today. The life cycle of ferns may illustrate the reproductive pattern typical for this entire group of plants.

The plant customarily spoken of as a "fern" rep-

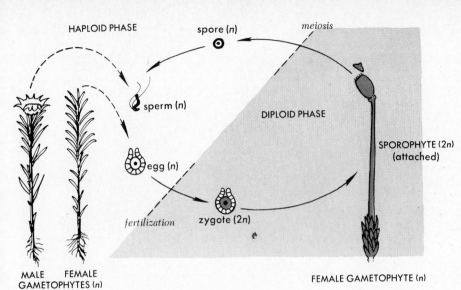

HAPLOID PHASE   spore (n)   *meiosis*

DIPLOID PHASE

sperm (n)

SPOROPHYTE (2n)
(attached)

egg (n)

fertilization   zygote (2n)

Fig. 21.13. The life cycle of a
bryophyte (moss).

MALE   FEMALE
GAMETOPHYTES (n)
(independent)

FEMALE GAMETOPHYTE (n)

resents the diploid sporophyte generation. It is large, leafy, green, and it persists the year round. Spore-forming structures develop at certain seasons of the year on the undersides of fern leaves (Fig. 21.14). A single cell on the lower surface of a leaf divides and produces a series of cells. These become arranged into a basal stalk and a terminal lens-shaped *sporangium*. Numerous sporangia usually arise from the same area of the leaf, and such a sporangial group is a *sorus*. It is covered over by a single-layered, often pigmented, shield of tissue, the *indusium*. Sori appear in regular double rows, one row on each side of a main leaf vein. Internally, a sporangium contains cells which undergo meiosis and give rise to encapsulated spores.

Sporangia eventually rupture, and the escaping spores later develop into haploid gametophytes. Though everyone has seen ferns, that is, sporophytes, few nonbiologists would be able to identify fern game-tophytes. Each is a green plantlet consisting principally of a tiny heart-shaped plate of tissue, flat on the ground and measuring not more than about $\frac{1}{4}$ inch across (Fig. 21.15). Several filaments projecting from the underside into the soil serve an absorptive function. This inconspicuous gametophyte, so unlike its large sporophytic partner, requires a moist, shady environ-ment. In size, way of life, and function, the fern

gametophyte is wholly comparable to a gametophyte of liverworts.

Sex organs develop on the gametophyte. In her-maphroditic species, male sex organs are usually located near the tip of the heart-shaped plant, female sex organs near the notch. In other species, male and female organs are formed in separate individuals. The

Fig. 21.14. A section through a fern leaf with a sorus on the underside. Stalks bearing spore cases project sideways, covered over by the indusium.

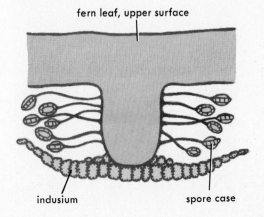

fern leaf, upper surface

indusium   spore case

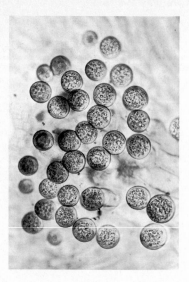
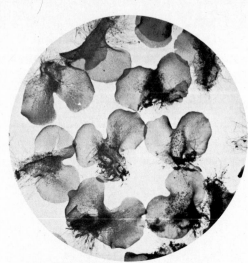

Fig. 21.15.   Middle, gametophytes of ferns. Left, fern antheridia. Right, fern archegonia. (General Biological Supply House, Inc.)

Fig. 21.16. Young fern sporophyte, still attached to remnants of gametophyte. (Courtesy of Dr. M. S. Fuller, University of California, Berkeley.)

haploid sex organs manufacture haploid eggs and haploid, flagellate sperms. The pattern of fertilization is the same as in bryophytes; that is, rain is required to provide a water path for the sperms.

The fertilized egg initiates a new diploid sporophyte generation. Retained within the female sex organ, the zygote divides and gives rise to a small sporophyte embryo. A tiny stem grows out from the female sex organ and curves into the soil, and a tiny embryonic leaf similarly shoots up (Fig. 21.16). At this stage the embryo does not yet possess chlorophyll but depends on food supplied by the gametophyte, to which it is still attached. But soon the embryonic fern leaf matures and greens, and thereafter the embryo is on its own. Indeed, the gametophyte presently degenerates and dies off, leaving the young sporophyte as a separate, independent plant.

The whole pattern of this life cycle is outlined in Fig. 21.17. Evidently, ferns and bryophytes do not differ too greatly in their gametophytes. Although ferns possess a highly developed sporophyte, well adapted to the general lack of free water on land, the gametophyte still poses a fundamental difficulty. Only the seed plants have fully solved this problem of the gametophyte.

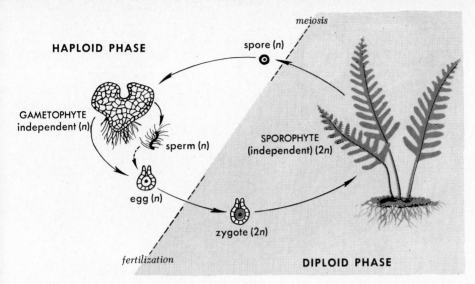

HAPLOID PHASE

meiosis

spore (n)

GAMETOPHYTE
independent (n)

sperm (n)

SPOROPHYTE
(independent) (2n)

egg (n)

zygote (2n)

fertilization

DIPLOID PHASE

Fig. 21.17.   Summary of the life
cycle of ferns.

THE SEED PLANT PATTERN

In all plants discussed so far, spores develop into gametophytes which carry either male or female or both types of sex organs. The plants here are said to be *homosporous;* that is, the spores are indistinguishable and one cannot tell ahead of time whether a given spore will become a male gametophyte, a female gametophyte, or a hermaphrodite.

In seed plants, by contrast, *two* kinds of spores are formed, one kind smaller than the other. The smaller *microspores*, produced in *microsporangia*, consistently give rise to male gametophytes, or *microgametophytes;* the larger *megaspores*, formed in *megasporangia*, develop into female gametophytes, or *megagametophytes*. Plants which produce two kinds of spores are said to be *heterosporous*. A heterosporous condition has evolved independently in several ancestral tracheophyte groups, and in one of the groups this condition has prepared the way for the later evolution of seeds.

The life cycle of a seed plant may therefore be considered to begin with sporophyte organisms which develop microsporangia and megasporangia (Fig. 21.18). Cells in these organs undergo meiosis and the products become microspores and megaspores, respectively.

Next, a microspore gives rise to a male gametophyte which consists of few cells only and which remains surrounded by the wall of the original microspore cell. Such a microgametophyte is a *pollen grain*. In analogous fashion, a megaspore gives rise to a few-celled female gametophyte. The latter does not leave the megasporangium in which it is produced. Megasporangia are often called *ovules*.

Third, pollen grains are dispersed from the microsporangia and are carried by wind or animals to the ovules. Such dispersion, leading eventually to contact between a pollen grain and an ovule, is called *pollination*.

Fourth, the male gametophyte within a pollen grain develops a *pollen tube*. In its tip certain nuclei come to function as sperm nuclei. The pollen tube digests its way to the female gametophyte, where one of the cells has matured into an egg. The tip of the pollen tube makes contact with this egg. A sperm nucleus then enters the egg and accomplishes *fertilization*. Note that pollination and fertilization are distinct and separate events; several months may in some cases intervene between them. Note also that it is the pollen tube which circumvents the requirement of free water in fertilization. The success of seed plants therefore rests in large measure on the evolutionary development of such tubes.

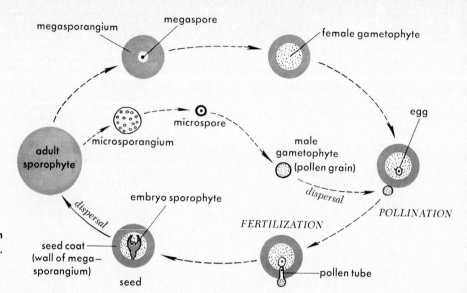

Fig. 21.18. The basic pattern of reproduction in seed plants.

Fifth, the fertilized egg, the female gametophyte, the surrounding wall of the megaspore, and the surrounding tissues of the ovule, all together constitute a *seed*. Within a seed, the zygote develops into a new sporophyte embryo. Through subsequent dispersion of the seed from the parent sporophyte and through seed germination, the young sporophyte becomes an independent plant. Thus the gametophyte generation remains hidden throughout and the grossly visible reproductive pattern of a seed plant becomes sporophyte → seed → sporophyte.

GYMNOSPERMS

In virtually all of these seed plants the reproductive structures form in *cones*. In a pine, for example, two kinds of cones develop, one kind smaller than the other. In the smaller variety, the underside of each cone leaf bears two microsporangia in which microspores are formed (Fig. 21.19). Each microspore possesses a wall composed of two layers. The outer one subsequently separates partially and forms two conspicuous "wings." Within its wall, the microspore cell divides and forms one small and one large cell. The small cell divides once more, producing two *prothallial cells*. These represent the whole vegetative

portion of the male gametophyte. They eventually disintegrate and play no further role. The larger cell also divides, forming one smaller *generative cell* and one larger *tube cell*. At such a stage of development a pollen grain is mature and is shed from the microsporangium.

In the larger variety of pine cones, scalelike cone leaves bear ovules (Fig. 21.20). An ovule is bounded on the outside by an *integument* layer, which is extended on one side into two flaps, the *micropylar arms*. Between the arms the integument leaves a narrow canal, the *micropyle*, which leads into the ovule. Deep within the ovule, a single cell undergoes meiosis. Of the four haploid cells so produced, three degenerate and the remaining one is the megaspore.

When pollination occurs, some pollen grains usually fall into the space between the micropylar arms. In this region the ovule secretes a *pollination fluid*, which traps pollen grains and permits them to float into the micropyle. Pollen grains so come to make contact with the inner tissues of the ovule. After pollination, the external tips of the cone leaves fuse to one another and this seals off the whole cone.

Subsequent events within a pine ovule occur exceedingly slowly; about a year elapses between pollination and fertilization. During this time, the whole cone and its contents increase in size. The megaspore enlarges and elongates. The megaspore nucleus divides repeatedly, until some 2,000 haploid nuclei are present. Cell walls are then laid down between the nuclei, and in this way the megaspore is transformed into a multicellular female gametophyte. On the side of the micropyle a few highly reduced sex organs develop, each with an egg (Fig. 21.21).

In the meantime, the pollen grain resting against the ovule develops also. The tube cell of each pollen grain elongates slowly, producing a pollen tube. This tube secretes enzymes which digest a path through ovule tissue. The generative cell of the male gameto-

phyte divides, and the two resulting cells migrate toward the tip of the pollen tube. The nucleus of one of these cells later divides once again, forming two *sperm nuclei*. Fertilization occurs when a pollen tube penetrates into an egg and one sperm nucleus fuses with the egg nucleus. The diploid zygote so formed represents the beginning of a new sporophyte generation.

Repeated divisions soon transform the zygote into a sporophyte embryo with young root, stem, and two or more embryonic leaves called *cotyledons* (Fig. 21.22). The whole embryo is embedded in the remains of the female gametophyte tissue, which in

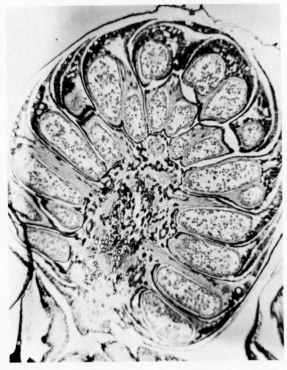

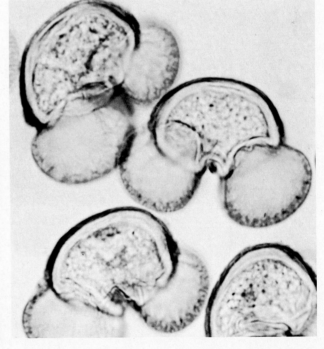

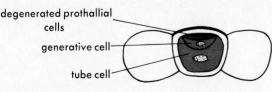

degenerated prothallial cells

generative cell

tube cell

mature pollen grain

Fig. 21.19. Section through a microsporangium-bearing pine cone and photo and diagram of pollen grains. (Section, courtesy of Dr. M. S. Fuller, University of California, Berkeley; pollen, Ward's Natural Science Establishment, Inc.)

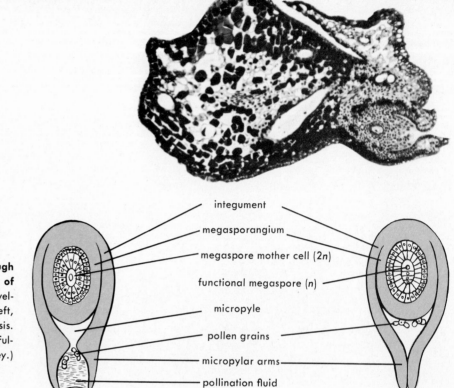

Fig. 21.20. Photo, section through a megasporangium-bearing scale of a pine cone. Diagrams, the early development of a megasporangium. Left, before meiosis; right, after meiosis. (Photograph courtesy of Dr. M. S. Fuller, University of California, Berkeley.)

integument

megasporangium

megaspore mother cell (2n)

functional megaspore (n)

micropyle

pollen grains

micropylar arms

pollination fluid

Fig. 21.21. The female gametophyte of pines. A, cell formation in the developing female gametophyte; B, the mature female gametophyte, with eggs.

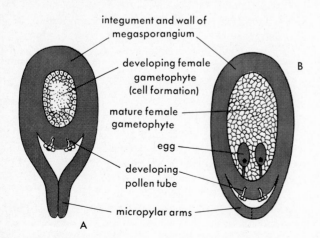

integument and wall of megasporangium

developing female gametophyte (cell formation)

mature female gametophyte

egg

developing pollen tube

micropylar arms

turn is surrounded by the remains of the ovule and the external integument. The latter has hardened by this time into a *seed coat*, and a flap of integument which extends away from the seed coat has matured into the "wing" of the seed.

Pine seeds are ripe several months after fertilization. At that time the cone leaves become brittle and spread open. The seeds are exposed in this manner and may be dispersed. The name "gymnosperm" indicates that these plants form "naked," exposed seeds. In gymnosperms and also in angiosperms, mature seeds may remain *dormant*, often for very long periods (even centuries in some cases). This is a major adaptive device, for if seeds were to germinate immediately after they were mature, the emerging seedlings would frequently find themselves in totally unsuitable environments. Actually, further development of a dormant seed appears to be triggered specifically by a favorable environment.

Not all gymnosperms require two or three years for seed formation like pines, in which pollination occurs one year and fertilization not until the next. In spruces, for example, the time interval between pollination and fertilization is only a few weeks. Many

Fig. 21.22. Longitudinal section through a seed, showing the central embryo and the surrounding remnants of the female gametophyte. The seed coat and the wing of the seed are not in the photo. (General Biological Supply House, Inc.)

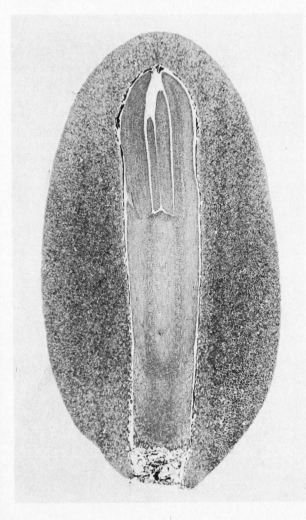

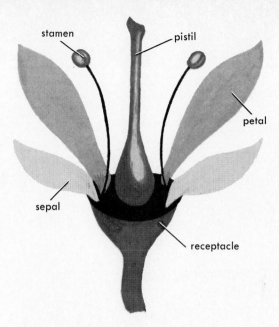

Fig. 21.23. Diagram of a simple flower.

other conifers similarly complete their whole reproduction in a single season. Such time variations notwithstanding, the reproductive processes themselves are basically the same in all gymnosperms.

ANGIOSPERMS

In this group of plants, the equivalents of gymnosperm cones are *flowers* (Fig. 21.23). A flower is formed on a *receptacle*, which is the terminal expanded part of a stem. From the receptacle arise a *calyx*, consisting of a whorl of *sepals;* a *corolla*, consisting of a whorl of *petals;* a circularly arranged set of *stamens;* and a central *pistil*. A stamen consists of a stalk and a terminal *anther*. The latter contains microsporangia. A pistil consists of a terminal *stigma*, a middle *style*, and an expanded basal *ovary*. Within the ovary are the ovules (Fig. 21.24).

Flowers may be with or without calyx or corolla. Where these leaves are present, they may or may not be pigmented (other than green) and they may or may not produce scents. Pigments and scents are familiar adaptations which attract various pollen-dispersing

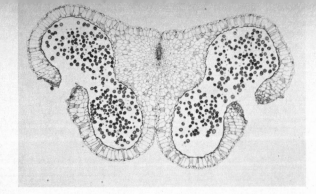

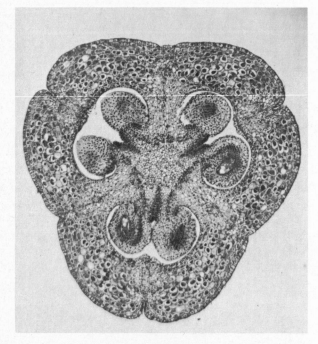

Fig. 21.24. Top, cross section through an anther of the lily. Note the two spore sacs, the openings in these sacs, and the microspores (pollen grains). Bottom, cross section through the ovary of a lily. Note the ovary wall (which will eventually give rise to the "meat" of a fruit) and the three pairs of ovules containing female gametophytes. (Ward's Natural Science Establishment, Inc.)

animals (bees, wasps, butterflies, moths, in some cases small birds, as well as men). Plants depending on animals for pollination generally also secrete abundant nectar (sugar water) in their flowers. Many ingenious structural devices have evolved whereby only particular animal types may have access to the nectar of a particular flower type. Potential "robbers" either cannot enter the flower or cannot reach the nectar stores. On the other hand, qualified animals such as

bees may find landing platforms, colored guide marks on petals, and other conveniences. As such animals reach for nectar deep down in the flower, they brush against stamens and pistil. In the process they pick up new pollen on their body surfaces or deposit pollen from other flowers visited earlier.

Some species of angiosperms are regularly *self-pollinating;* pollen grains fall on the stigma of the same flower and develop normally thereafter. In the majority of angiosperms, however, *cross-pollination* must occur. In such cases, many pollen grains undoubtedly do chance on the stigma of the same flower. But such pollen grains may not begin to develop at all or may develop abnormally. Events proceed normally only when pollen grains from one flower are transferred to the stigmas of other flowers of the same species.

In the anthers, formation of microspores occurs as in gymnosperms by meiosis. The microspore nucleus then divides once, producing a *generative nucleus* and a *tube nucleus.* The generative nucleus subsequently divides once more, forming two *sperm nuclei.* The whole male gametophyte in a pollen grain so consists of a single cell with three nuclei (Fig. 21.25).

An analogously condensed development occurs in the ovary, which may contain one or more ovules. In each ovule, as in gymnosperms, a micropyle leads

Fig. 21.25. The development of a microspore of angiosperms.

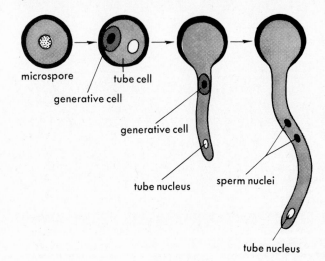

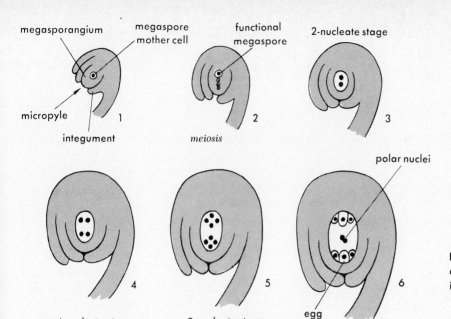

megasporangium
megaspore
mother cell
functional
megaspore
2-nucleate stage
micropyle
integument
meiosis
1
2
3

polar nuclei

4

5

6

4-nucleate stage

8-nucleate stage

egg

Fig. 21.26. The basic pattern of the development of a female gametophyte in angiosperms.

through the integument to the inner tissues (Fig. 21.26). Within the latter, a single cell undergoes meiosis and of the four resulting haploid cells one persists as a megaspore. In this megaspore, the nucleus then undergoes three divisions. Four of the resulting eight haploid nuclei come to be situated at one end of the spore cell, four at the other. Three of each group of four then become partitioned off as cells and the remaining two, the so-called *polar nuclei*, migrate to the center of what is now a seventh large middle cell. These seven cells constitute the entire female gametophyte. Sex organs are not formed at all. Instead, of the three gametophyte cells near the micropyle, one becomes an egg directly.

Pollen of angiosperms is dispersed partly by wind, partly by insects and other animals. Numerous pollen grains may land on a stigma of a pistil. The stigma is sticky and traps the pollen grains. Each then produces (usually) one pollen tube, which grows between the cells of the style toward the ovary. Such a tube usually enters an ovule through the micropyle and then digests a path through the ovule tissues. The tip of the tube contains the two sperm nuclei. Both are eventually discharged into the female gametophyte (Fig. 21.27).

Fig. 21.27. The growth of pollen tubes after pollination in angiosperms.

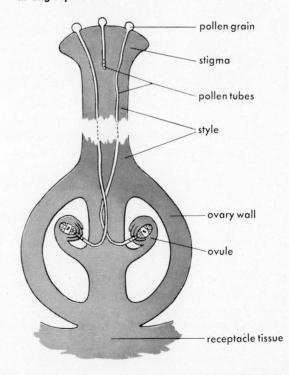

pollen grain

stigma

pollen tubes

style

ovary wall

ovule

receptacle tissue

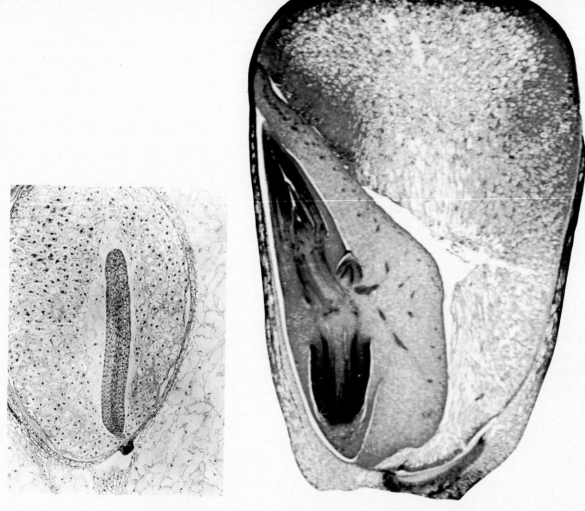

Fig. 21.28. Angiosperm embryos surrounded by endosperm within seeds. In the section through a corn kernel (seed) in right photo, note the embryo on left side, the endosperm on right and at top. (Left, courtesy of J. Limbach, Ripon Microslides; right, courtesy of Dr. M. S. Fuller, University of California, Berkeley.)

The next event is *double fertilization,* unique to the angiosperms. One of the sperm nuclei enters the egg and effects fertilization. The other sperm nucleus migrates to the two polar nuclei in the middle cell of the female gametophyte and all three of these nuclei now fuse together into a so-called *endosperm nucleus.* This nucleus, formed from two female nuclei and one male haploid nucleus, is *triploid;* that is, it contains three complete sets of chromosomes. The endosperm nucleus then divides repeatedly, cell walls are usually laid down between the nuclei, and the tissue so formed is the *endosperm.* It soon fills up the space formerly occupied by the female gametophyte. Endosperm cells accumulate food substances from the parent sporophyte.

While the endosperm develops, the zygote divides

and gives rise to a sporophyte embryo (Fig. 21.28). The latter possesses one or two cotyledons, depending on the subclass of angiosperms (see Chap. 9). The whole embryo is embedded in endosperm, and this tissue gradually contributes more or less of its food to the developing sporophyte. In a germinating seed, therefore, endosperm may or may not be present. If the endosperm is still extensive, the cotyledons are likely to be thin and leafy (e.g., squash, castor beans). But if the endosperm is absent, its substance is incorporated into the cotyledons and these are likely to be massive (e.g., peanuts, peas).

Soon after fertilization, the integuments around the developing embryos in an ovary harden into seed coats and much of the flower withers. On the contrary, the ovary and in some cases also parts of the receptacle enlarge rapidly and mature into a *fruit*. This structure may become *dry* and *fleshy*, and it hides the seeds within it. The name "angiosperm" indicates that these plants produce "hidden" seeds, embedded within fruits (Fig. 21.29).

Thus the reproduction of angiosperms is characterized by three major features not encountered in gymnosperms: the *flower* itself; double fertilization, resulting in the inclusion of *endosperm* tissue within seeds; and the *fruit*, which contains a number of seeds. Each of these evolutionary innovations is of pronounced adaptive value. The flower often promotes pollination by attracting insects. The endosperm nourishes the embryo. And the fruit promotes seed dispersal and seed germination; for fleshy fruits may be eaten by animals and seeds may be spit out or may be expelled undigested with the feces, in new locations. Dry fruits like nuts may be carried about by squirrels, for example, and may be left by them in some forgotten hiding place. Fruits with burrs, hooks, or wing blades are distributed widely by animals and wind. Fruits which simply fall to the ground eventually decay, and

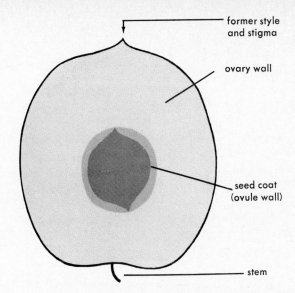

Fig. 21.29. **Diagram of a section through a fleshy fruit.**

former style and stigma

ovary wall

seed coat (ovule wall)

stem

this aids seed development by enriching a patch of soil.

We note that the solution to the problem of terrestrial reproduction is rather similar in seed plants and in terrestrial animals. As the next chapter will show, most terrestrial animals circumvent the need for external water by copulation and *internal* fertilization: a male animal deposits sperms directly into a female animal which contains mature eggs. In seed plants the depositing is done by wind or animals, but internal fertilization in a sense takes place also. As we have seen, a sporophyte produces microspores and, through them, sperms or sperm nuclei. Another sporophyte produces megaspores and, through them, eggs. The sperm nuclei then reach the eggs by means of pollen tubes, which are the plant equivalents of the copulating organs of animals.

Review questions

1. Review the basic life-cycle patterns of Monera. How can these organisms adapt without sexuality?

2. Describe reproductive processes among algae. Which groups of these organisms exhibit which type of life cycle?

3. Describe the processes of sporulation and gametic

reproduction in *Ulothrix*. Describe the process of gametic reproduction in (*a*) *Spirogyra*, (*b*) *Oedogonium*, and (*c*) *Fucus*. How does the degree of sexual definition differ in these three algal types?

4. Describe the life cycle of slime molds. Review the reproductive repertoire of protozoa. What reproductive processes occur in Phycomycetes?

5. Review the life cycle of Ascomycetes and contrast it with that of Basidiomycetes. What are basidia and how are they formed?

6. Describe the detailed life cycle of a bryophyte. In what respects is it (*a*) well, (*b*) poorly adapted to terrestrial life? Define: homospory, heterospory, microsporangium, megaspore, ovule.

7. Describe the detailed life cycle of a fern. Compare with the life cycle of bryophytes; what is similar and what is different? What are the adaptive advantages of a prolonged 2*n* phase?

8. Describe the basic life cycle of seed plants. In what ways is this pattern particularly advantageous for terrestrial life? Distinguish carefully between pollination and fertilization.

9. Describe the detailed life cycle of coniferous plants. Define seed, pollen tube, self-pollination, and cross pollination.

10. Describe the structure and adaptive significance of a flower. Define ovary, endosperm, fruit. Describe the detailed life cycle of flowering plants.

Suggested collateral readings

Delbruck, M., and M. Delbruck: Bacterial Viruses and Sex, *Sci. Am.*, vol. 179, 1948.

Grant, V.: The Fertilization of Flowers, *Sci. Am.*, vol. 184, 1951.

Koller, D.: Germination, *Sci. Am.*, vol. 200, 1959.

Wollman, E. L., and F. Jacob: Sexuality in Bacteria, *Sci. Am.*, vol. 195, 1956.

REPRODUCTION: METAZOA

22

The principal and often the only form of multiplication in Metazoa is gametic reproduction. Gamete formation occurs in multicellular sex organs and is accompanied by meiosis. The life cycle is therefore diplontic, mature gametes representing the only haploid phase. Fertilized eggs develop into distinct embryos. These may grow into adults directly or, as is more typical, may first become *larvae* and then adults.

Reproductive patterns

Vegetative reproduction occurs regularly in some animal groups as a normal process of propagation. It may take the form of fragmentation (as in some flatworms and sea anemones) or of budding of the parent animal (as in sponges, coelenterates, and other groups). Regenerative reproduction after injury is widespread (e.g., starfishes, earthworms, hydras), but in the majority of groups the capacity of regeneration is severely restricted. Pieces separated from the parent simply die, and in such cases the only remnant of vegetative reproduction is wound healing.

Species dispersal among animals is achieved by locomotion of the adults or the larvae. Sporulation is therefore largely superfluous and indeed does not occur among any motile animals. Even where the adults are sessile, moreover, only a few primitive groups such as sponges produce sporelike cells.

Whatever other forms of reproduction may or may not occur in given cases, gametic reproduction occurs in all cases. The sexes typically are separate, but hermaphroditism is common, particularly in sessile and sluggish animals. Virtually all hermaphroditic types are cross-fertilizing. Animal sex organs, or *gonads,* usually are components of distinct reproductive systems which include ducts leading from the sex organs to the exterior of the body. Gametes are formed from special groups of diploid cells in the gonads. Such cells become sperms or eggs by processes of maturation involving both the cell nucleus and the cytoplasm.

Nuclear maturation consists of meiosis. In a male gonad, or *testis,* meiosis in a diploid cell results in four haploid cells all of which become functional sperms. In a female gonad, or *ovary,* a diploid cell undergoes a first meiotic division and produces two cells. Of these, one is small and soon degenerates. Its remnants, now called the *first polar body,* remain attached to the other cell. This cell subsequently passes through the second meiotic division. Of the two cells produced here, one becomes the egg and the other again is small and degenerates. Its remnants form the *second polar body* which, like the first, remains attached to the egg. Each original diploid cell so gives rise to only one functional egg (Fig. 22.1).

In parallel with the meiotic division, cytoplasmic maturation takes place. In sperm-forming cells, much of the cytoplasm typically degenerates altogether. The nucleus enlarges into an oval *sperm head,* and the mature sperm retains only three structures having a cytoplasmic origin: a long posterior *sperm tail,* which serves as locomotor flagellum; a *middle piece,* which contains mitochondria and which joins the sperm tail with the sperm head; and an *acrosome,* a structure at the forward end of the sperm head, by means of which the sperm will make contact with an egg. As a result of losing all other cytoplasm, a mature sperm is among the smallest cells within the body.

Mature eggs, on the other hand, are among the largest cells; their cytoplasms have become specialized for the accumulation and storage of *yolk,* food reserves for the future embryos. The amount of yolk may be insignificant, as in mammals, where the embryo will be nourished by the female parent; or it may be comparatively enormous, as in birds, where yolk represents the very substance out of which an offspring bird will be constructed.

Like plants, most animals manufacture gametes only at specific times of the year, during *breeding seasons.* Some animals, however, notably mammals like apes and man, may produce gametes the year round. As in plants, sperms invariably require a water medium. Such a medium is always available for aquatic animals, sessile or motile. On land, the water problem in sperm distribution is reduced substantially by animal locomotion; terrestrial animals (all of which are motile) may migrate either toward one another or to natural bodies of water for sperm release. Indeed, only two basic patterns of mating and fertilization occur among animals. In *external fertilization,* mating partners come into more or less close proximity and *spawn,* that is, release sperms and eggs directly into water. Frequent chance collisions among the closely placed gametes then lead to many fertilizations. This pattern is characteristic of most aquatic animals and also of terrestrial animals such as frogs and toads, which migrate to permanent bodies of water for reproduction. The second pattern is *internal fertilization.* Mating partners here come into physical contact and a copulating organ of the male ejects swimming sperms directly into the reproductive system of the female. The female tissues then provide moisture for the sperms and the need for external water is thereby circumvented altogether. Internal fertilization is characteristic of most terrestrial animals, e.g., mammals, birds, reptiles, insects, spiders, and many worms.

Where fertilization is external, development of the zygotes into new adults takes place externally as well, in natural bodies of water. In many cases where fertilization is internal, the zygotes are released from the female parent and zygote development then also occurs externally. All animals in which the eggs are shed to the outside, either in an unfertilized or a fertilized state, are said to be *oviparous.* Among vertebrates, for example, many fishes are oviparous and externally fer-

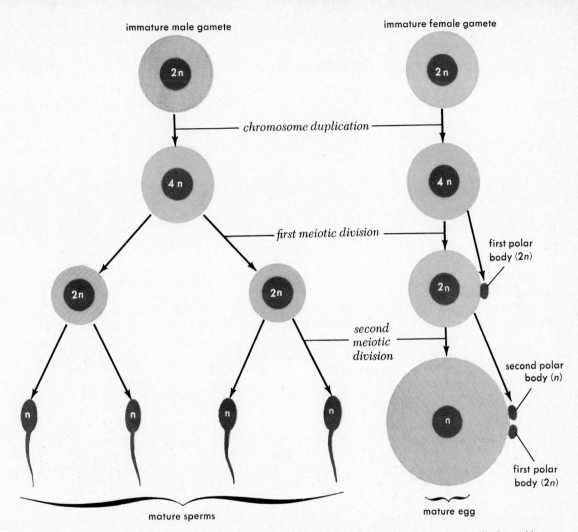

immature male gamete

immature female gamete

— *chromosome duplication* —

— *first meiotic division* —

first polar body (2n)

second meiotic division

second polar body (n)

first polar body (2n)

mature sperms

mature egg

Fig. 22.1.   Meiosis in males and females. In males, all four haploid cells formed become functional sperms. In females, one cell formed by the first meiotic division is small and degenerates and becomes the first polar body. Similarly, one cell formed by the second meiotic division becomes the second polar body. Thus only one cell matures as a functional egg.

tilizing, whereas all birds are oviparous and internally fertilizing. In all cases of oviparity, the eggs develop essentially on their own, food being supplied within each egg by the yolk. Eventually the embryos *hatch* as larvae or as miniature, immature adults. Such a pattern of events is characteristic for most animals (Fig. 22.2).

If the development of oviparous animals takes place in water, the zygotes often have coats of jelly around them (e.g., frog eggs) but are otherwise protected very little. Coats of this sort are secreted by the tissues of the female reproductive system before the eggs are laid. Zygotes developing on land possess more elaborate protection, particularly against evaporation.

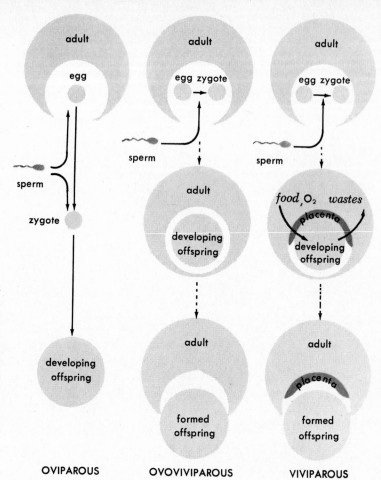

Fig. 22.2. In oviparous animals, fertilization is either external or internal, but the zygote is always external and development accordingly takes place externally. In ovoviviparous animals, fertilization and zygote development take place internally, but the maternal body does not otherwise contribute to offspring development; the young are born. In viviparous animals, fertilization and zygote development again occur internally, but the maternal body here does contribute importantly to offspring development, via a placenta; the young are born.

OVIPAROUS   **OVOVIVIPAROUS**   **VIVIPAROUS**

For example, earthworms, spiders, and insects such as grasshoppers and cockroaches form a cocoon or a hard casing around batches of just-laid fertilized eggs. Other insects and also reptiles and birds secrete shells around individual eggs after fertilization and before laying. As will be shown in a later section, the "land eggs" of reptiles and birds are adapted particularly well to terrestrial conditions.

Some animals are *ovoviviparous*. Fertilization in such cases is always internal, and the zygotes are then retained within the female reproductive system. Development therefore occurs inside the female. However, beyond providing a substantial measure of protection, the female body does not otherwise contribute to

zygote development; as in oviparous types, food is supplied by the yolk included within each egg. Ultimately, the young are *born* rather than hatched; that is, the females release fully formed animals, not eggs. Among vertebrates, some of the fishes, amphibia, and reptiles are ovoviviparous.

A third group of animals comprises *viviparous* types. In these, fertilization is again internal, zygotes are retained within the female, and the young are born as developed animals. However, the female body here influences the development of the young not merely by providing protection. It also supplies food and contributes to offspring metabolism generally in numerous and vital ways. Among vertebrates, the principal viviparous types are mammals. We shall examine some of the details of this particular reproductive pattern in the following sections.

The gametes

REPRODUCTIVE SYSTEMS

As in animals generally, the basic structural plan of the reproductive system of a mammal such as man is comparatively simple: a pair of gonads, ovaries or testes, connects with a system of channels which leads to the exterior of the body.

In human males, the testes are located in a *scrotum*, a skin sac between the legs (Fig. 22.3). Leading away from each testis is a *sperm duct*, greatly looped and coiled just outside the testis. This coiled portion stores sperms crowded out from the testis. During copulation, nerve impulses may bring about contraction of the muscular walls of the coiled part of the sperm duct. The collected sperms are then propelled forward, into a straight part of the duct. The latter leaves the scrotum and passes through the groin. It eventually

opens into the *urethra*, close to the point where the urinary bladder also opens into the urethra. Near its termination, the sperm duct receives lymphlike secretions from the *seminal vesicle* and the *prostate gland*. These secretions together with the sperms constitute *semen*. Note that urine and semen are expelled along the same exit path, the urethra, a channel which leads to the outside through the *penis*. Simultaneous discharges of urine and semen are prevented by reflexes.

Most vertebrates produce sperms only during an annual *breeding season*, but man and some other mammals form sperms the year round. In man, sperm-producing capacity develops at puberty and continues to old age, often until death. As in all vertebrates, sperm manufacture is under the control of hormones. Specialized cells in the testes secrete *androgens*, the male sex hormones. These hormones, *testosterone* most particularly, govern the proper functioning of the entire reproductive system. Moreover, they also maintain sex urge as well as various secondary sex characteristics—all those features which, apart from the reproductive organs themselves, distinguish males from females.

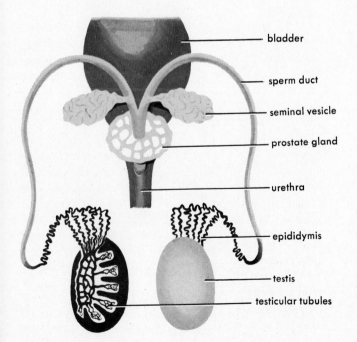

bladder

sperm duct

seminal vesicle

prostate gland

urethra

epididymis

testis

testicular tubules

Fig. 22.3. The male reproductive system, diagrammatic. Testis on left shown in section.

The manufacture of androgens in the testes is in turn under the control of pituitary gonadotropic hormones (see Chap. 17). Two such hormones are secreted by the pituitary: *FSH* and *LH*. The function of FSH in males is still obscure, but pituitary LH is known to be the hormone which stimulates the testes to produce androgens (Fig. 22.4). If the androgen concentration in blood becomes too high, the sex hormones inhibit the pituitary from producing more LH. Androgen secretion then declines. Conversely, if androgen concentrations are too low, the pituitary will not be inhibited, LH will therefore be produced in greater amount, and this increases the rate of androgen production. Through such feedback control, the androgen concentration in males is maintained automatically at a fairly steady level.

In females, the ovaries are situated at the back of the abdominal cavity, at hip level. They are partially enveloped by the funnel-shaped terminals of the *oviducts,* also called *Fallopian tubes.* These ciliated channels lead into the *uterus.* The young develop in this

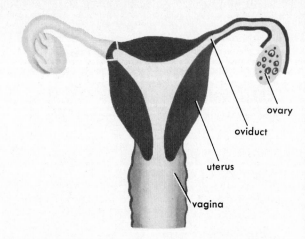

Fig. 22.5.   Diagram of the female reproductive system.

muscular organ, which may stretch and enlarge considerably. The mouth of the uterus opens into the *vagina,* and this channel leads to the outside (Fig. 22.5). Note that, in contrast to the arrangement in males, the reproductive tract in females is entirely separate from the urinary tract. Each of these duct systems in females leads to the outside through its own opening.

Like sperm production in males, egg production is under hormonal control. Most vertebrates form eggs only during an annual breeding season, but in mammals such as apes and man eggs can be produced the year round. The reproductive period begins at the time of puberty and in man it then lasts for about 30 years, to the time of *menopause.* During the egg-producing phase in most vertebrates, the rates of production are generally fairly high. In chickens, for example, eggs are laid at a rate of about one per day. By contrast, old-world monkeys, apes, and man manufacture eggs far more slowly; a rate of one per month is typical for human females, for example. Such rhythmic, month-long, egg-producing cycles are known as *menstrual* cycles, and they are governed by hormones.

MENSTRUAL CYCLES

The egg-producing tissues of an ovary are its outer layers. New cells manufactured by these layers are crowded into the interior of the ovary. In a given

Fig. 22.4.   The control of androgen secretion. LH is one of the gonadotropic hormones of the pituitary. Compare with Fig. 17.12. Arrow tipped with transverse double bar denotes inhibition.

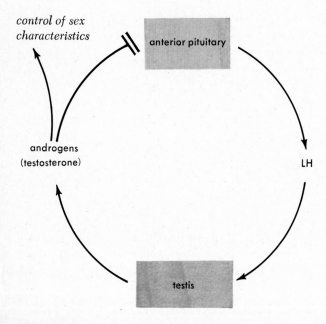

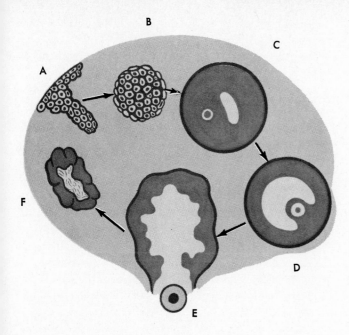

Fig. 22.6. The growth of an egg (diagrammatic). *A* and *B*, newly formed potential egg cells within the ovary. *C* and *D*, maturation of one of the cells into an egg and development of surrounding cells into a follicle. Note the enlarging follicular cavity. *E*, ovulation. *F*, the remnants of the follicle have transformed into a corpus luteum.

batch of newly produced cells, all of which are probably potential eggs, usually only one actually matures into a reproductive cell. Meiosis occurs in such a cell, and its cytoplasm enlarges and accumulates some yolk. The surrounding cells are inhibited in some unknown way from also maturing as eggs (Fig. 22.6).

However, these surrounding cells specialize as endocrine tissue and secrete *estrogens,* the female sex hormones. Like androgens in males, estrogens maintain the operation of the reproductive system, sex urge, and the secondary sex characteristics of females. The endocrine cells surrounding the egg become arranged into a *follicle,* a ball of tissue which soon develops a fluid-filled cavity. In such a follicle, the egg is located eccentrically, in a thickened region.

The gonadotropic hormones secreted by the pituitary gland, namely, FSH and LH, control the growth of follicles and the course of a menstrual cycle as a whole. Such a cycle may be considered to begin with FSH production by the pituitary. The name of this hormone, short for "*follicle-stimulating hormone,*" describes its function. Under its influence, a follicle grows, an egg matures within it, and the endocrine follicle cells secrete increasing amounts of estrogen (Fig. 22.7).

This last has two specific consequences. First, the increasing concentration of estrogen in the blood eventually reaches a level which *inhibits* the pituitary from secreting more FSH. Second, high concentrations of estrogen *stimulate* the pituitary to begin secreting

Fig. 22.7. The hormonal changes during the follicular phase of a menstrual cycle, leading to ovulation. Arrow tipped with double bar denotes inhibition.

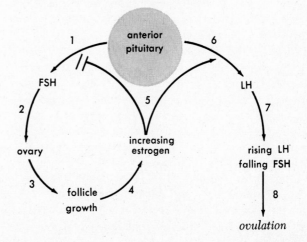

LH, the other gonadotropic hormone. In other words, continued growth of the follicle and the correlated rising estrogen output ultimately bring about a sharp fall in FSH concentration and a sharp rise in LH concentration.

These hormonal changes, occurring in man about two weeks after a follicle has begun to grow, are the specific stimulus for *ovulation*, or egg release. The ovary surface and the follicle wall both rupture and the mature egg falls out of the ovary (see Figs. 22.6 and 22.7).

An immediate consequence of ovulation is that the ruptured and eggless follicle in the ovary loses its fluid and collapses. Another consequence is that, since FSH production by the pituitary has ceased, the remnant of the follicle ceases to manufacture estrogen. Instead, under the specific influence of the LH now produced by the pituitary, the remnant of the follicle transforms into a yellowish body, the *corpus luteum*. The name "LH" stands for "*luteinizing hormone.*" Under the continuing influence of this hormone, the corpus luteum begins to secrete a new hormone of its own, namely, *progesterone*. Thus, ovulation marks the time when, owing to the change from FSH to LH secretion, an egg is released, the follicle becomes a corpus luteum, and estrogen production gives way to progesterone production.

Progesterone has a distinct effect in mammals. Being viviparous animals, mammals become *pregnant*, that is, the offspring develop within the female body, specifically in the uterus. Progesterone prepares the uterus to receive an egg and to house the developing offspring till birth. Progesterone may therefore be described as "pregnancy hormone." When an egg leaves the ovary during ovulation, it normally falls into the funnel of the oviduct. From there the egg is slowly propelled toward the uterus by the cilia which line the oviduct. The uterus in the meantime is readied for the arrival of the egg. Under the influence of progesterone, the inner lining of the uterus thickens, becomes greatly pitted with glandular pockets, and acquires a rich supply of blood capillaries. As a result, the inner surface of the uterus is transformed into a spongy carpet of particularly well-nourished tissue.

What happens next depends on whether the egg is fertilized or not. If fertilization does occur, the event normally takes place as the egg travels through the upper part of the oviduct. The fertilized egg then continues to migrate toward the ready uterus and arrives there some two days after ovulation.

If fertilization does not occur, the egg disintegrates when it is about halfway down the oviduct. In such a case the uterus will have been made ready for nothing. Progesterone continues to be produced in increasing quantities, and the concentration in blood eventually becomes so high that the hormone begins to have an inhibitory feedback effect on the pituitary. As a result, less and less LH is secreted and the corpus luteum correspondingly produces gradually less progesterone (Fig. 22.8). The corpus luteum actually begins to degenerate, and it ultimately secretes so little progesterone that the "ready" uterus can no longer remain ready. The newly formed spongy lining of the uterus wall distintegrates, tissue fragments separate away, and some blood escapes from torn capillary vessels. Over a period of a few days, all this debris is expelled through the vagina to the outside. This is *menstruation*. It begins some two weeks after ovulation. At this time, the pituitary resumes FSH production and a new month-long egg-producing cycle is initiated (Fig. 22.9).

Fig. 22.8. The hormonal changes during the luteal phase of a menstrual cycle, leading to menstruation.

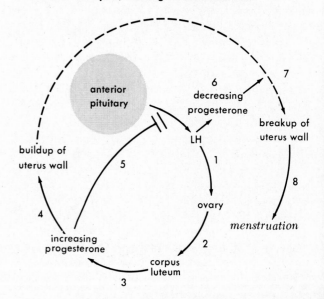

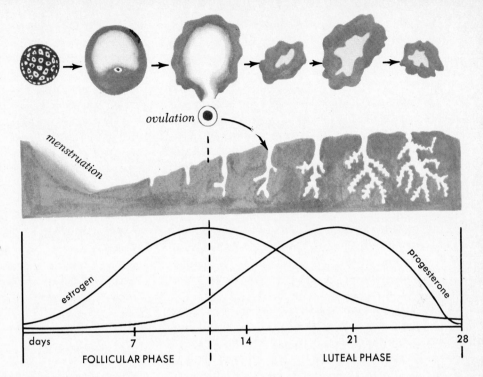

ovulation

menstruation

estrogen

progesterone

days	7	14	21	28

FOLLICULAR PHASE   LUTEAL PHASE

Fig. 22.9. Summary of some of the events during a menstrual cycle. Top, events in the ovary, indicating follicle growth, ovulation, and corpus luteum formation. Middle, events in the wall of the uterus. Bottom, variations in the sex hormone concentrations.

We note that the first two weeks or so of a menstrual cycle are dominated by FSH, estrogen, and the follicle, and that the second two weeks are dominated by LH, progesterone, and the corpus luteum. FSH and estrogen are components of one control cycle, LH and progesterone of another. These two hormonal cycles occur alternately, the termination of one being the stimulus for the initiation of the other. The net result is the rhythmic production of eggs.

As pointed out above, most animals are without menstrual cycles. With or without them, however, eggs in all cases set the stage for fertilization and for the subsequent *development* of a zygote.

The embryo

In animals which become pregnant, that is, in mammals, some aspects of embryonic development are quite unique; we shall discuss these below. Here we are concerned mainly with those events of development which occur in fundamentally similar fashion in all animals.

THE PROCESSES OF DEVELOPMENT

The transformation of a zygote into a whole adult animal is accomplished by two broad groups of processes, *morphogenesis* and *differentiation*.

One component of morphogenesis is increase in size, or *growth*. This may occur by increase in the *number* of living parts, by increase in the *size* of parts, by increase in the *spacing* of parts, or by two or all three of these in combination. The most significant form of growth usually is increase in the number of *cells*, brought about by mitotic divisions. Large animals actually differ from small ones mostly in cell number, not cell size.

A second component of morphogenesis is establishment of distinct animal *form*, specific for each species. One form-producing process is *differential growth*. Here the amounts and rates of growth are unequal in different body parts, or they differ for different directions of space. Such conditions lead to localized enlargements, diminutions, elongations, thickenings, altered contours, layers, solid masses, and other expressions of form.

In addition to differential growth, the form of a developing animal is shaped and molded by *form-regulating movements*. These produce actual shifts and migrations of growing parts relative to one another. Through such movements, parts may pile up in one region and become thinned out in others. Compact masses may spread out and form sheets, or sheets may fold and form ducts and cavities. As may be appreciated readily, any number of shapes may be produced by moving and rearranging the building blocks.

The net result of growth, differential growth, and form-regulating movements is the elaboration of an animal which possesses distinctly shaped and appropriately sized internal body parts and which has a particular external symmetry: *spherical, radial, bilateral,* or *asymmetrical.* All these aspects of morphogenesis may be said to represent the *architectural* component of development.

But development also includes an important *operational* component, namely, differentiation. For example, growth of a zygote does not simply produce an aggregate of many identical cells, but an aggregate of *mutually different* cells; some become nerve cells, some liver cells, some skin cells, etc. Yet all arise from the same cell mass of the zygote and all inherit the same genes from the zygote. Nevertheless, a multitude of differently specialized cells is formed. Moreover, most of these cells acquire their specializations gradually, and cells in the embryo change their structural and functional characteristics repeatedly before they become adult. We say that the parts of a developing animal *differentiate.*

How does differentiation come about? The process is not yet fully understood and indeed it is one of the most crucial unsolved problems in biology. Three general possibilities exist. First, cell differentiations might be a result of progressive changes in gene action. Genes themselves probably do not change during development, for, as already noted, their stability is an essential requirement for the preservation of species characteristics. But the *activity* of different genes could vary with time. For example, in a given cell some genes might become active at certain developmental stages, whereas others might become inactive. Such differential activity patterns might occur differently in different cells and this might contribute to differentiation.

Or, second, gene actions might remain the same, but the operations of the cytoplasm could become altered progressively. For example, one round of cytoplasmic reactions might use up a certain set of starting materials, and in the subsequent absence of these, similar reactions could then no longer take place. A next round of reactions would proceed with different starting materials and would therefore produce different endproducts. The net result could be progressive differentiation.

Or, third, nuclear and cytoplasmic changes might both occur, in reciprocal fashion. This is probably the likeliest possibility, and much current research is devoted to a study of this very complex key problem. For the present, therefore, we are limited to identifying and describing processes of differentiation wherever they occur, without being able to explain their underlying mechanisms. The following is just such a description.

THE COURSE OF DEVELOPMENT

The main steps in the development of an animal are described by the sequence: *fertilization → embryo → larva → adult* (Fig. 22.10). During the embryonic period, all basic structures and functions of the future adult body are elaborated in at least rough detail. In the majority of Metazoa, the embryonic phase typically terminates with a process of *hatching*, in which the embryo emerges from its original egg envelopes and becomes a free-living larva.

A larval phase is characteristic of virtually all animal phyla, but it is often absent in some of the more advanced subgroups within a phylum (e.g., reptiles, birds, and mammals among vertebrates). Larvae are temporary organisms having a variety of functions. For example, they may serve in geographic dispersal, especially if the adult is sessile or sluggish (e.g., clams, many worms, tunicates). Or they may serve as temporary feeding machines, which accumulate enough raw materials in the form of larval tissues to make lengthy further development possible (e.g., insect caterpillars). Or they may simply represent a developmental stage resembling a similar stage of ancestral organisms (e.g., frog tadpoles, which resemble the larvae of fishes to some extent).

Larvae eventually undergo *metamorphosis*, a more

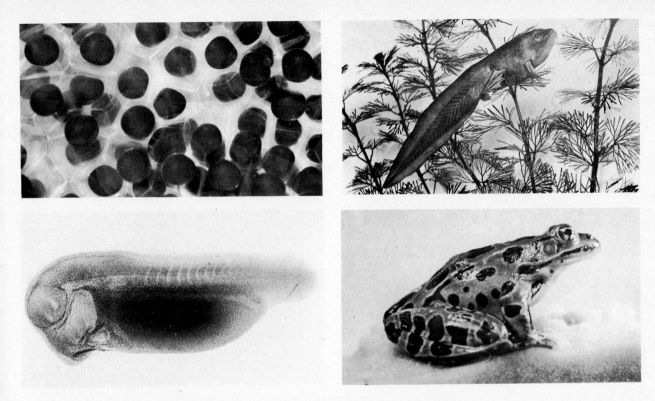

Fig. 22.10.   These stages of the life cycle of frogs symbolize the main stages in the sexual development of animals generally. Top left, egg; bottom left, embryo; top right, larva; bottom right, adult. (Eggs, Carolina Biological Supply Co.; tadpole, American Museum of Natural History; others, General Biological Supply House, Inc.)

or less gradual but in many cases quite sudden transformation into the adult condition. Note that this last phase in the developmental history of an individual is not any more static than preceding phases. On the contrary, as shown in the chapters on metabolism, the components of the adult are steadily being demolished and redesigned or replaced. In this continuing turnover, internal as well as external features become altered. Adolescence so passes into maturity, maturity into senescence, and only death brings development to a halt.

The first clearly visible event after fertilization (Fig. 22.11) is *cleavage*, the repeated division of the zygote into many cells. Growth does not occur during

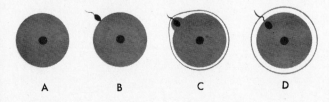

A   B   C   D

Fig. 22.11.   Diagrammatic representation of fertilization. A sperm enters an egg by being engulfed by the egg, through an egg cone which comes to surround the sperm (C). A so-called fertilization membrane lifts off the egg surface after a sperm has made contact. This prevents additional sperms from being engulfed (C and D). The sperm tail is left at the egg surface, and the sperm head (nucleus) alone migrates into the egg cytoplasm, where it fuses with the egg nucleus. An egg is fully fertilized only after sperm and egg nucleus have fused.

Fig. 22.12. Cleavage in frog eggs. Left to right, two-cell stage, eight-cell stage, and later stage. Note how cell size decreases with successive cleavage divisions. (Carolina Biological Supply Co.)

this phase. Therefore, as cleavage proceeds, the cells become progressively smaller. The original egg is a comparatively huge cell, and cleavage usually continues until the cells have a species-characteristic mature size (Fig. 22.12).

Abnormal cleavage in some animals occasionally leads to the formation of identical *twins*. The zygote divides, and the resulting cells do not remain together as is normal, but separate. In certain groups of animals, each such separate cell then may develop into a whole offspring. If the cells separate only partially, Siamese twins may be the result. Twinning processes may be duplicated experimentally with test animals such as fish, frogs, and others (Fig. 22.13).

The normal result of cleavage is a ball of a few hundred cells, called a *blastula*. This ball may be hollow or solid, and it represents a developmental stage characteristic of virtually all Metazoa (Fig. 22.14). Cell divisions continue in a blastula, and growth now occurs as well. The main subsequent developmental event is the transformation of the blastula into an embryo consisting of three distinct layers of tissue. This process of transformation is called *gastrulation*, and the three-layered result is the *gastrula*. It too is a developmental stage common to virtually all Metazoa.

Patterns of gastrulation vary widely. For purposes of illustration, we may examine events in the embryos of sea urchins and other echinoderms. In these, the blastula is a hollow, one-layered sphere. When gastrulation occurs, one side of this sphere *invaginates*, that is, becomes indented. A two-layered cup-shaped structure is formed in this manner. The resulting outer layer is called the *ectoderm* and the inner layer is the *endoderm*.

Later a third tissue layer, the *mesoderm*, arises between the ectoderm and the endoderm. As described

in Chap. 10, several major categories of animals may be distinguished on the basis of how mesoderm forms. Regardless of the method of formation, however, the fully formed gastrula is a hollow, triple-walled ball with an opening at one point (Fig. 22.15).

This opening is the *blastopore*, which marks the region of the future anus in enterocoelomates and the region of the future mouth in all other animals. A mouth or an anus will later break through at the opposite end of the gastrula. The interior space is the future alimentary cavity. The endoderm which encloses this space will develop into the alimentary system, the breathing system, and all glands and ducts associated

Fig. 22.13. X-ray photo of Siamese twinning in fish. Abnormalities like these result from incomplete divisions of cells during early cleavage. (American Museum of Natural History.)

Fig. 22.14. The early development of starfish embryos. Left to right, late cleavage; blastula; invagination, early gastrula; late gastrula, beginning of mesoderm formation, mesoderm formation under way. (General Biological Supply House, Inc.)

with these: liver, pancreas, salivary glands, trachea, etc. The ectoderm will give rise to the whole nervous system and to the skin, including hair, nails, and skin glands. The mesoderm will form the remaining parts of the body, namely, bones, muscles, and the circulatory, excretory, and reproductive systems. The endocrine system arises partly from ectoderm, partly from mesoderm, and partly from endoderm.

Clearly, the basic architectural design of the body becomes established with the formation of the gastrula. The precise ways in which subsequent transformations occur differ very widely, according to the character-

istics of the different animal species. In general, however, we may say that distinct organs and systems arise through the outfolding or infolding, the outpouching or inpouching, of portions of the three layers of the gastrula. For example, the nervous system of vertebrates forms by the infolding of a tube of tissue along the dorsal midline of the ectoderm (Fig. 22.16). Later, the eye develops in part as an outpouching from the anterior portion of the tubular nervous system. Limbs form by combined localized outpouchings from ectoderm and mesoderm. Lungs and digestive glands develop as outpouching from various levels of

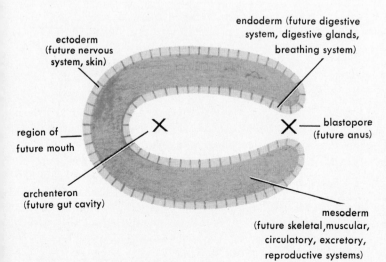

ectoderm
(future nervous
system, skin)

endoderm (future digestive
system, digestive glands,
breathing system)

region of ___
future mouth

blastopore
(future anus)

archenteron
(future gut cavity)

mesoderm
(future skeletal, muscular,
circulatory, excretory,
reproductive systems)

Fig. 22.15. The general structure of a vertebrate gastrula, and the adult organ systems formed by each of the primary germ layers (diagrammatic).

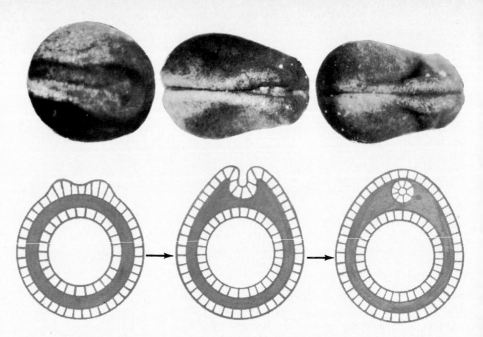

Fig. 22.16. The initial development of the nervous system in vertebrates (frogs). Top: left to right, dorsal views, progressive stages. The anterior ends of the embryos are toward the right. Bottom: diagrammatic cross sections corresponding to the stages shown above. (Photos, courtesy of Dr. Roberts Rugh, from "Experimental Embryology," Burgess Publishing Company.)

the endodermal tube. All other body parts develop analogously. The ultimate result of these processes of morphogenesis and differentiation is a fully formed embryo, clearly recognizable as a young stage of a particular species.

Experiments have shown how these orderly sequences of development may come about. Eye development in vertebrates provides a particularly striking example. As just noted above, the formation of an eye starts with the growing out of a pocket from the side of the future brain (Fig. 22.17). This pocket is narrow at the base and bulbous at the tip. Soon the bulbous portion invaginates, or indents, from the forward end and a double-layered cup is formed. The cup represents the future eyeball. As it grows outward from the brain, its rim comes into contact with the outer ectoderm layer which overlies the whole nervous system and which represents the future skin. Just where the eyecup rests against it, the ectoderm layer now begins to thicken. This thickening eventually grows into a ball of cells, which is nipped off toward the inside. It fits neatly into the mouth of the eyecup and represents the future lens. The cells of this ball and the ectoderm overlying them later become transparent. The basic structure of the eye is then established.

The following type of experiment has shown dramatically how these developmental processes are controlled. In amphibian embryos it is possible to cut off the eyecup and its stalk before they have grown very far. Eyecup and stalk may then be transplanted. For example, they may be inserted into a region just under the belly ectoderm of an embryo. Under such conditions the patch of belly ectoderm overlying the eyecup soon thickens, a ball of cells is nipped off toward the inside, and a lens differentiates. Moreover, lens and overlying skin become transparent. In effect, the transplanted structures have caused the formation of a structurally normal eye in a highly abnormal location (Fig. 22.18).

A common conclusion emerges from this and many similar types of experiments. One embryonic tissue layer interacts with an adjacent one and the latter is thereby induced to differentiate, to grow, to develop in a particular way. This developed tissue then interacts with another one in turn and induces it to develop. In such a manner, one tissue provides the stimulus for the development of the next. This phenomenon of *embryonic induction* consequently may account well for the orderly, properly timed, and properly spaced elaboration of body parts.

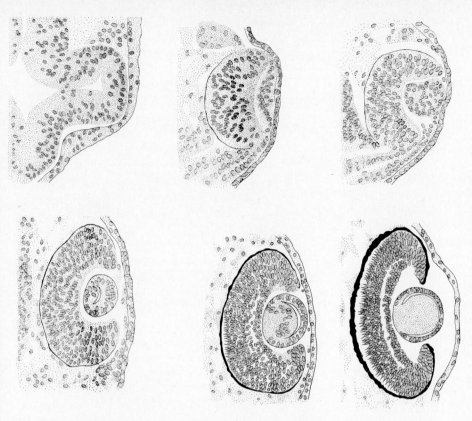

Fig. 22.17. Development of the vertebrate eye (amphibian; semidiagrammatic). This series of successive stages shows the outgrowth of a pocket from the brain, contact of this pocket with the outer body ectoderm, formation of an eyecup, gradual formation of a lens from the outer ectoderm, and development of the pigmented and other tissue layers of the eyeball. (Courtesy of Dr. D. Bodenstein, from originals of figs. 2 and 3, *J. Exptl. Zool.*, vol. 108, pp. 96 and 97, by permission.)

Fig. 22.18. Experiments in eye transplantation. Diagram, if an embryonic eyecup is excised from a donor embryo *A* and is transplanted into an abnormal location in a host embryo *B*, then a structurally perfect eye will develop at that abnormal location. Photo, a larva of the amphibian *Amblystoma*, with two supernumerary eyes grafted into abnormal locations. The procedure followed that outlined in the diagram, and the photo was taken 43 days after the transplant operation. (Photo from original fig. 16, S. R. Detwiler and R. H. Van Dyke, *J. Exptl. Zool.*, vol. 69, p. 157.)

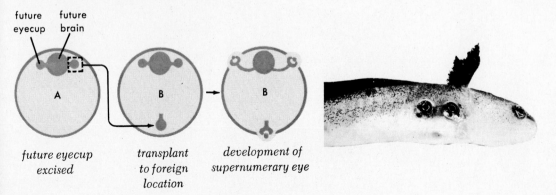

future eyecup   future brain

A

B

B

future eyecup excised   *transplant to foreign location*   *development of supernumerary eye*

The ultimate result of these occurrences is a fully formed embryo. It may later hatch and become a larva or may develop into a miniature adult directly. The latter alternative occurs in man and in mammals generally, where embryonic development as above is accompanied by the processes of pregnancy.

Pregnancy

As noted earlier, fertilization in man takes place shortly after ovulation, in the upper part of the oviduct. The zygote begins to develop immediately and is at the same time propelled toward the uterus. Within a day or two after fertilization, therefore, the uterus receives a young embryo composed of a few hundred cells. This embryo is deposited on the inner surface of the uterus wall, which has been readied for reception of the egg by progesterone.

The embryo next becomes *implanted* in the wall of the uterus, that is, it is gradually surrounded by uterus tissue (Fig. 22.19). Such implantation leads to a suppression of menstruation. Through still poorly identified nervous pathways, the presence of an embryo in the uterus wall is signaled via the brain to the pituitary, which continues to produce LH as a result.

The corpus luteum consequently continues to secrete progesterone. The thickened wall of the uterus then can be maintained without tissue disintegration and menstruation does not take place.

The early embryo, embedded and held fast within the wall of the uterus, soon comes to consist of two groups of cells. A central group represents the embryo proper. These cells develop according to patterns substantially as described in the preceding section. Surrounding this central embryo are cells which do not become part of the offspring body as such. Instead, the cells form into four so-called *extraembryonic membranes*. To appreciate the crucial function of these membranes, it is necessary to consider that they are an evolutionary reminder of the reptilian ancestry of mammals. Reptiles were the first vertebrates to lay eggs on land, and extraembryonic membranes evolved as specific adaptations to egg development under terrestrial conditions. Early reptilian stocks then gave rise independently to birds and mammals. Birds inherited the egg membranes virtually unchanged, but in most mammals the membranes came to function in new ways, in conjunction with development within the uterus.

Reptiles and birds are oviparous, and they lay shelled eggs. The shells are porous enough to permit

Fig. 22.19. Implantation of the egg in the uterus. The diagram shows position of egg relative to wall of uterus, at the time of implantation.

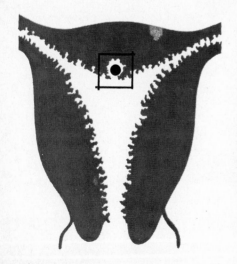
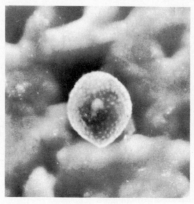

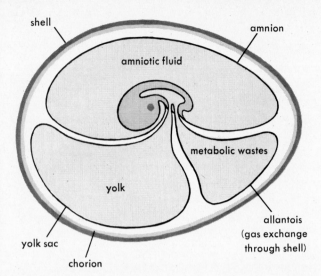

Fig. 22.20. The extraembryonic membranes in reptile and bird eggs. Note that yolk sac and allantois are large and functional.

shell

amnion

amniotic fluid

metabolic wastes

yolk

yolk sac

chorion

allantois (gas exchange through shell)

Mammals (with the exception of egg-laying mammals; see Chap. 10) are viviparous and do not produce egg shells. But the four extraembryonic membranes develop nevertheless (Fig. 22.21). In man, for example, the chorion again forms as an outer enclosure around the other membranes and the embryo; it is in direct contact with the tissue of the uterus. In one region the chorion develops numerous fingerlike outgrowths which branch extensively and erode paths through the spongy uterine wall. In this manner the tissues of the chorion and the uterus become attached to each other firmly. These interfingering and interlacing tissues are known as the *placenta*. When fully developed, the placenta functions both as a mechanical and as a metabolic connection between the embryo and the female body.

The allantois in mammals still serves as in reptiles and birds as an embryonic lung, except that now gas exchange occurs in the placenta, between the embryonic blood vessels of the allantois and the maternal blood vessels of the uterus. However, the allantois has

Fig. 22.21. The extraembryonic membranes in mammals and the placenta (diagrammatic). Note that yolk sac and allantois are rudimentary and collapsed.

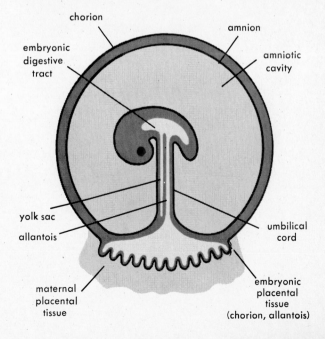

chorion

amnion

embryonic digestive tract

amniotic cavity

yolk sac

allantois

umbilical cord

maternal placental tissue

embryonic placental tissue (chorion, allantois)

aerial gas exchange, yet not porous enough to permit leakage of water. Just inside the egg shell and enclosing all interior structures lies one of the extraembryonic membranes, the *chorion* (Fig. 22.20). It prevents undue evaporation of water through the shell. A second membrane, the *amnion*, surrounds the developing embryo everywhere except on its ventral side. This membrane holds lymphlike fluid, the *amniotic fluid*, which bathes the embryo as in a "private pond." The fluid may be regarded as the equivalent of the freshwater ponds in which the ancestors of reptiles and birds developed. The two remaining membranes pouch out from the ventral side of the embryo, more specifically, from the alimentary tract. One of these is the *allantois*, which comes to lie against the egg shell, just inside the chorion. Blood vessels ramify through the allantois, and this membrane is the breathing structure of the embryo; gas exchange occurs between it and the air outside the shell. Also, the allantois serves as an embryonic urinary bladder in which metabolic wastes are stored up to the time of hatching. The second membrane on the ventral side is the *yolk sac*, which contains the ample food stores for development and which gradually gets smaller as the yolk is used up during the growth of the embryo.

entirely lost its ancestral function as urinary bladder; embryonic wastes now are carried off by the maternal blood in the placenta. The allantois in mammals is actually a collapsed, empty sac. This is true also of the yolk sac, food being supplied by maternal blood, again through the placenta. On the other hand, the fluid of the amnion still functions as in reptiles and birds as a "private pond" and shock absorber. As more and more amniotic fluid accumulates during the course of pregnancy, the amnion distends greatly and the surrounding chorion and uterus are stretched correspondingly. This enlargement, more than growth of the embryo itself, eventually leads to the characteristic bulging out of the abdomen of the pregnant female (Fig. 22.22).

Beginning to form after the early embryo has become implanted in the uterus, the placenta is usually fully developed by the twelfth week of pregnancy. In addition to its mechanical and metabolic functions, it also specializes as an endocrine organ. As the placenta grows, it manufactures slowly increasing amounts of estrogen and progesterone. Indeed, the progesterone output eventually becomes far greater than that of the corpus luteum. The latter actually degenerates and its hormone secretion subsides as the twelfth week of pregnancy approaches. From that time on, the placenta provides the main hormonal control of pregnancy; through its progesterone output it maintains its own existence. Interconnecting the placenta and the

Fig. 22.22. Diagram, the embryo within its membranes in the uterus: amnion on the inside, chorion on the outside. Photos, stages in embryonic development of man. Top left, approximately 25 days after fertilization. Top right, approximately 33 days old. Bottom left, approximately 6 weeks old. Bottom right, approximately 8 weeks old. (Photos courtesy of Dr. G. W. Corner and Department of Embryology, Carnegie Institution of Washington.)

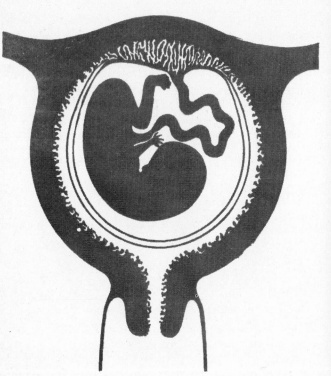 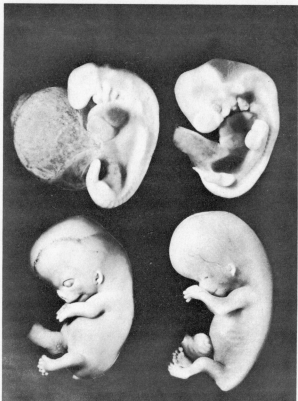

embryo proper and literally forming a life line is the *umbilical cord*. Within the cord is the empty yolk sac and the allantois, the latter carrying the blood vessels which transport nutrients and wastes to and from the embryo. The point of origin of the cord in the embryo leaves a permanent mark in the later offspring in the form of the navel.

With several exceptions, the duration of pregnancy in mammals is roughly proportional to adult size. For example, the period of pregnancy is three weeks in mice and 22 months in elephants. However, pregnancy lasts only a year, approximately, in whales.

Birth normally begins when the chorion and the amnion rupture and when the amniotic fluid escapes to the outside. Labor contractions of the uterine muscles then occur with increasing frequency and strength, pressing against the fetus and pushing it out through the vagina. Concurrently, the placenta loosens away from the wall of the uterus and the connection between

mother and offspring is thereby severed. An important result of this is that CO_2 produced by the offspring must accumulate in his own circulation. Within seconds or minutes, the concentration of the gas then becomes high enough to stimulate the breathing center of the newborn.

The loosened placenta, still connected to the umbilical cord, is expelled to the outside as the *afterbirth* within an hour or so after the offspring is expelled. Mammalian mothers, modern human ones excepted, bite the umbilical cord off their young and then generally eat the cord and the placenta.

After the birth of the offspring, normal menstrual cycles are generally not resumed as long as *nursing* continues. But once the offspring is weaned, FSH is formed again in quantity and a new follicle then begins to mature in the ovary. The reproductive machinery of the female then reverts to rhythmic nonpregnancy operation.

Review questions

1. What are the first and second polar bodies? Are they found in males as well as females? Explain. What is the general structure of a mature sperm and of a mature egg? In which animals is fertilization (*a*) external, (*b*) internal? Define oviparity, ovoviviparity, viviparity. In which vertebrates does each occur?

2. Review the structure of the reproductive system of human males and females. Where, specifically, are sperms and eggs produced? Describe the hormonal controls of sperm production. What is semen? What is a follicle and what is its structure?

3. Describe the hormonal controls and the process of follicle growth up to the time of ovulation. What events take place during ovulation? After ovulation, what happens to (*a*) the egg and (*b*) the follicle?

4. Describe the hormonal controls and the events in the uterus up to the time of menstruation. What happens during menstruation? Review the entire menstrual cycle from the standpoint of (*a*) hormonal control, (*b*) events in the ovary, and (*c*) events in the uterus.

5. Define morphogenesis, differential growth, form-regu-

lating movements, differentiation. What different types of symmetries are exhibited by living units? What is the relation between differentiation and specialization?

6. Describe the principal developmental phases in the life history of an organism. What events usually terminate (*a*) the embryonic period and (*b*) the larval period?

7. What events occur during the cleavage of an egg? Describe the processes leading to the formation of (*a*) a blastula and (*b*) a gastrula.

8. Define ectoderm, endoderm, mesoderm. How does mesoderm form in vertebrates? Which structural components of an adult vertebrate develop from each of the three embryonic layers?

9. By what general processes do the primary embryonic layers develop into adult structures? Illustrate this in the development of the eye. What role does induction play in such transformations?

10. Describe the location and function of the extraembryonic membranes in (*a*) reptiles and birds and (*b*) mammals. In which vertebrates and how is a placenta formed? What are the functions of a placenta?

Suggested collateral readings

Csapo, A.: Progesterone, *Sci. Am.*, vol. 198, 1958.

Dahlberg, G.: An Explanation of Twins, *Sci. Am.*, vol. 184, 1951.

Fischberg, M., and A. W. Blackler: How Cells Specialize, *Sci. Am.*, vol. 205, 1961.

Gray, G. W.: The Organizer, *Sci. Am.*, vol. 197, 1957.

Moog, F.: Up from the Embryo, *Sci. Am.*, vol. 182, 1950.

Pincus, G.: Fertilization in Mammals, *Sci. Am.*, vol. 184, 1951.

Reynolds, S. R. M.: The Umbilical Cord, *Sci. Am.*, vol. 187, 1952.

Tyler, A.: Fertilization and Antibodies, *Sci. Am.*, vol. 190, 1954.

Waddington, C. H.: How Do Cells Differentiate? *Sci. Am.*, vol. 189, 1953.

Wigglesworth, V. B.: Metamorphosis and Differentiation, *Sci. Am.*, vol. 200, 1959.

part **7**

The Functions of Life: Adaptation

On the molecular as on the organismic level, in structure as in function, every organism is *adapted* to its environment. For example, among thousands of shapes that a fish *might* posses, it actually possesses one which is well suited for rapid locomotion in water. A bird is cast in a form eminently suited for aerial life, yet its ancestry traces to fish. Over long periods of time, clearly, organisms may *change* their particular adaptations in response to new environments.

Based on steady-state control and reproduction, adaptation is brought about by three kinds of processes: *sex*, *heredity*, and *evolution*. Of these, the adaptive role of sex has already been discussed earlier. In this last series of chapters, therefore, we begin with an analysis of the adaptive roles of *heredity* and continue with a similar analysis of *evolution*.

HEREDITY

23

Like sex, heredity has adaptive value; for what an organism inherits will determine its survival potential in large measure. It should be clear here that organisms do *not* inherit blue eyes, clever minds, red blood, or any other trait. Organisms inherit the contents of reproductive cells, not traits. Visible traits and specializations then *develop*.

The key problem in studies of heredity is to explain the inheritance of *likeness* and of *variation:* how an offspring usually comes to resemble its parents in certain major respects but differs from the parents in many minor respects. Are such hereditary patterns in any way regular and predictable, and if so, what are the underlying principles? The first important studies of this sort were made in the last half of the nineteenth century by the Austrian monk Gregor Mendel. He discovered two basic rules of inheritance which laid the foundation for all later advances in understanding of processes of heredity.

Accordingly, this discussion of heredity will include an account of the rules of *Mendelian inheritance* and a survey of some of the processes of *non-Mendelian inheritance* brought to light since the time of Mendel.

Mendelian inheritance

THE CHROMOSOME THEORY

If two red-flowered snapdragon plants are mated, all offspring produced are exclusively red-flowered. Moreover, all later generations also develop only red flowers. Similarly, a mating of two white-flowered snapdragons yields exclusively white-flowered progeny in all subsequent generations. Red and white flower colors in this case are said to be *true-breeding* traits.

When a red-flowered snapdragon is mated with a white-flowered plant, all offspring develop *pink* flowers. In Mendel's time, it was generally supposed that results of this kind were due to a *blending* of traits. Thus if red and white plant pigments were mixed together, like paints, a pink color would be produced. But if blending really occurs, pinkness should be equally true-breeding; a mating of two pink-flowered plants should yield pink offspring exclusively.

However, the actual results of such a mating are strikingly different. Two pink-flowered parents consistently produce pink *and* red *and* white offspring. Numerically, an average of 50 per cent of the offspring are pink, roughly 25 per cent are red, and the remainder are white (Fig. 23.1). Evidently, pinkness does *not* breed true, for from pink can be re-created pure red and white as well as pink. Hence pink color cannot be a permanent blend of red and white.

It may be concluded that blending inheritance does not occur and that, instead, traits remain distinct and intact. They may become joined temporarily in one generation and may again become separated, or *segregated*, from one another in a following generation. Mendel was the first to reach such a conclusion, and this denial of blending was Mendel's most significant contribution. It ultimately reoriented the thinking about heredity completely and paved the way for all modern insights. Mendel himself supplied the first of such insights, for he not only negated the old interpretation but also postulated a new one.

He realized that traits trace back to the sperm and the egg which produce a plant, and he suspected that some specific components within the gametes controlled the later development of traits. Mendel called these hypothetical components "factors." For any given trait, he argued, a plant must inherit at least one factor from the sperm and one from the egg. Therefore, the offspring must possess at least two factors for each trait. When that offspring in turn becomes an adult and produces gametes, each gamete must similarly contribute *one* factor to the next generation. Hence, at some point before gamete production, two factors must be reduced to one. Mendel consequently postulated the existence of a factor-reducing process.

With this he in effect predicted the occurrence of meiosis. When near the end of the nineteenth century meiosis was actually discovered, it was recognized that the reduction of chromosomes at some point before fertilization matched precisely the postulated reduction of Mendel's factors. Chromosomes then came to be regarded as the carriers of the factors, and the *chromosome theory of heredity* so emerged. This theory has since received complete confirmation, and Mendel's factors become the genes of today.

Fig. 23.1. If a red-flowered snapdragon is mated with a white-flowered plant, all offspring will be pink-flowered. And if two of these pink-flowered plants are then mated in turn, the offspring will be red, pink, and white, in the ratios shown.

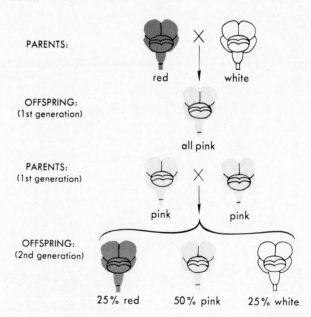

PARENTS:

red   ×   white

OFFSPRING:
(1st generation)

all pink

PARENTS:
(1st generation)

pink   ×   pink

OFFSPRING:
(2nd generation)

25% red   50% pink   25% white

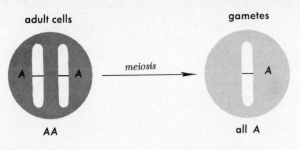

Fig. 23.2

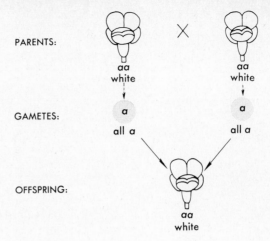

Fig. 23.4

SEGREGATION

Transmission of genes.   On the basis of the chromosome theory, we may interpret the snapdragon data above as follows. A true-breeding red-flowered plant possesses a pair of red-pigment-producing genes in each cell. These genes, which we may symbolize by the letters *AA*, are located on a given pair of chromosomes one of which is maternal and one paternal in origin. We say that the *genotype*, or gene content, of the plant is *AA* and that the *phenotype*, or visible appearance, is *red*. Before such a plant produces gametes, meiosis occurs. Mature gametes therefore contain only one of the two chromosomes, hence only one of the two genes (Fig. 23.2).

Note that it is entirely a matter of chance which of the two adult chromosomes will become incorporated

Fig. 23.3

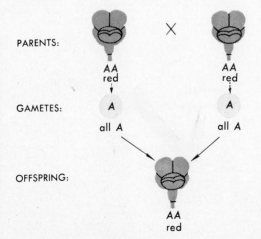

into a given gamete. Since both adult chromosomes here carry the same color gene, all gametes will be genetically alike in this respect. We may understand now why *AA* plants are true-breeding, that is, why a mating of *AA* × *AA* will produce only red-flowered, *AA* offspring (Fig. 23.3).

In precisely analogous manner, we may symbolize the genotype of a true-breeding white-flowered snapdragon as *aa*. The letters here represent genes which do not produce any pigment at all. The white coloration in such flowers is a result of this lack of pigment. A mating of two such plants will yield only white-flowered offspring (Fig. 23.4).

If we now mate a red-flowered and a white-flowered plant, *all* offspring will be *pink* (Fig. 23.5).

We may note here that an *Aa* offspring plant possesses only *one* pigment-producing gene per cell, namely, *A*. Such a cell consequently develops only *half* as much pigment as an *AA* cell, which possesses two pigment-producing genes. This lesser amount of pigment in the *Aa* offspring appears as a dilute red, i.e., pink.

If now two pink-flowered *Aa* plants are mated, after meiosis each plant will give rise to two types of gametes. Given the genes *Aa*, either the *A* gene or the *a* gene could become incorporated into any given gamete. What actually happens in each specific case is determined by chance. Hence if, as is usually the case

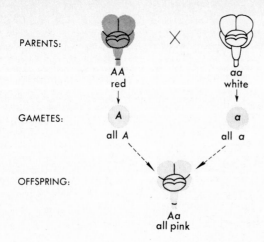

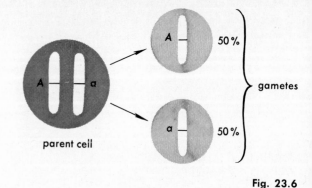

Fig. 23.6

Fig. 23.5

in plants, large numbers of gametes are produced, each possibility will be realized with roughly equal frequency. Consequently, approximately 50 per cent of the gametes will carry the *A* gene, the other 50 per cent the *a* gene. We may write: *Aa* parent ⟶ 50 per cent *A* gametes, 50 per cent *a* gametes (Fig. 23.6).

Now fertilization occurs. The are two genetically different sperm types and two genetically different egg types, and it is wholly a matter of chance which of the two sperm types fertilizes which of the two egg types.

If many fertilizations occur simultaneously, as is usually the case, then all possibilities will be realized with appropriate frequency (Fig. 23.7).

We note that half the offspring are pink-flowered and resemble their parents in this respect. One quarter are red-flowered, one quarter white-flowered, and these offspring resemble their grandparents. We may conclude that the visible results can be explained adequately on the basis of nonblending, freely segregating genes and the operations of chance.

Genetic dominance.   Genes like *A* and *a*, which control the same trait but produce different expressions of that trait, are called allelic genes, or *alleles.* In the

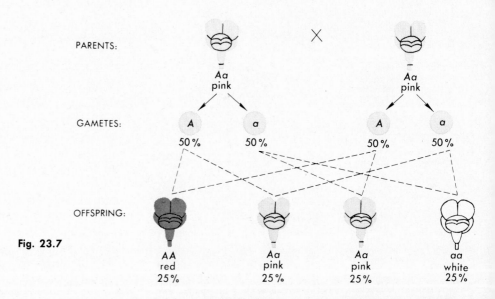

Fig. 23.7

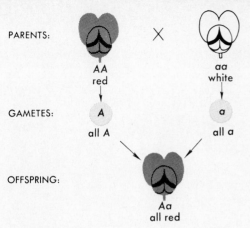

PARENTS: AA red × aa white

GAMETES: A all A a all a

OFFSPRING: Aa all red

Fig. 23.8

snapdragon example above, trait expression evidently depends on the number of *A* alleles. Presence of *A* in single dose, as in *Aa* plants, gives only half as much pigment as presence of *A* in double dose, as in *AA* plants. Most traits are affected in this way by gene dosage.

In some cases, however, a maximum trait may be produced even if an allele is present only in single dose. In garden peas, for example, as in snapdragons, true-breeding red-flowered plants may be symbolized as *AA*, true-breeding white-flowered plants as *aa*. But when two such plants are mated, *all* offspring are *red*, not pink (Fig. 23.8).

Evidently, the single *A* gene in *Aa* plants suffices to bring out the full red color. Two *A* genes, as in *AA*, do not produce substantially more redness. Therefore, if two red-flowered *Aa* plants are mated, three out of every four offspring will be red-flowered (Fig. 23.9).

Genes which produce a maximum trait even when present only in single dose, like the *A*'s of garden peas, are called *dominant* genes. They mask more or less completely the effect of other alleles, like the *a*'s of garden peas. These latter are called *recessive* alleles. Offspring in ratios of ¾ : ¼ are characteristic for matings involving dominant and recessive alleles, as above.

But complete dominance of this sort is far rarer than the allelic relationship illustrated above for snapdragons. There the *A* gene is said to be *partially* dominant, the *a* gene, *partially* recessive. Offspring ratios of ¼ : ½ : ¼ are then characteristic. We may note in this connection that allelic pairs like *AA* or *aa*, in which both genes are the same, are called *homozygous* combinations. By contrast, *Aa* pairs are called *heterozygous* combinations. For example, an *AA* genotype in garden peas is said to be "homozygous dominant."

In modern terminology, Mendel's first law, the *law of segregation*, may now be stated as follows: *Genes do not blend, but behave as independent units. They pass intact from one generation to the next, where they may or may not produce visible traits, depending on their dominance characteristics. And genes segregate at random, thereby producing predictable ratios of*

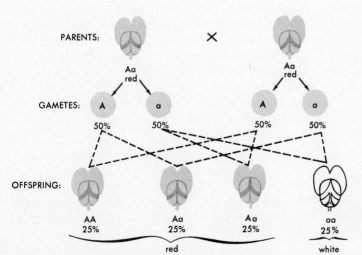

PARENTS: Aa red × Aa red

GAMETES: A 50% a 50% A 50% a 50%

OFFSPRING: AA 25% Aa 25% Aa 25% aa 25%

red white

Fig. 23.9

traits in the offspring. Implied in this law are chromosome reduction by meiosis and the operation of chance in the transmission of genes.

INDEPENDENT ASSORTMENT

Organisms do not express traits one at a time, but exhibit all their traits simultaneously. Analogously, genes are not inherited one at a time, but all of them are inherited together. Therefore, given certain parents, what will the offspring be like with respect to two or more simultaneous traits?

Mendel discovered a fundamental rule here. Phrased in modern terms, this *law of independent assortment* states: *The inheritance of a gene pair located on a given chromosome pair is unaffected by the simultaneous inheritance of other gene pairs located on other chromosome pairs.* In other words, two or more traits produced by genes located on two or more chromosome pairs "assort independently"; i.e., each trait will be expressed independently, as if no other traits were present.

Suppose we analyze, as Mendel did, the simultaneous inheritance of two traits of garden peas, *seed shape* and *seed color*. Seed shape can be either *round* or *wrinkled*. Round can be shown to be dominant over wrinkled, and the possible alleles can be symbolized as *R* for round and *r* for wrinkled. Therefore, on a given chromosome pair of peas is located either an *RR*, an *rr*, or an *Rr* pair of alleles. Similarly, *yellow* seed color (*Y*) is dominant over *green* seed color (*y*). Hence on another chromosome pair is located a *YY* or a *yy* or a *Yy* pair of alleles.

We now mate two *RrYy* plants, that is, individuals which are heterozygous for both traits (Fig. 23.10). After meiosis, each gamete will contain only *one* seed-

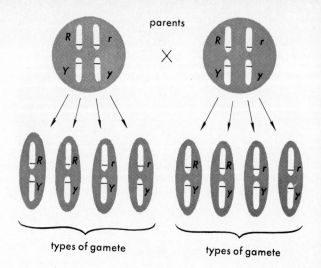

Fig. 23.11

shape gene and only *one* color gene. But which of each pair? The dominant or the recessive gene? This is a matter of chance. There are four possibilities. A gamete might contain the genes *R* and *Y*, or *R* and *y*, or *r* and *Y*, or *r* and *y*. Many gametes are produced; all four combinations will therefore occur with roughly equal frequency (Fig. 23.11).

Fertilization is also governed by chance. Consequently, *any* one of the four sperm types might fertilize *any* one of the four egg types. Hence there are 16 different ways in which fertilization can occur. If large numbers of fertilizations take place simultaneously, all 16 ways will be realized with roughly equal frequency. We may determine these 16 ways by using a grid where the gametes of one parent are put along a horizontal edge and the gametes of the other parent along a vertical edge (Fig. 23.12).

Among the 16 offspring types now formed, we find some individuals which contain *both* dominant genes at least once, some which contain one *or* the other of the dominant genes at least once, and some which contain none of the dominant genes. A count reveals round-yellow, round-green, wrinkled-yellow, and wrinkled-green to be present in a ratio of 9:3:3:1. This is the ratio Mendel actually obtained and which led him to formulate his law of independent assortment.

For he realized that if seed *shape* is counted alone,

Fig. 23.10

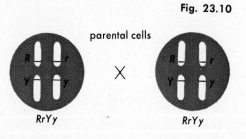

parental cells

RrYy   RrYy

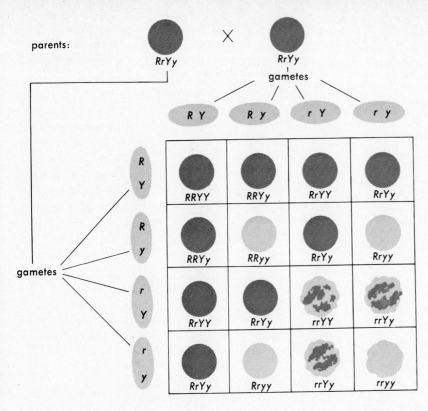

parents:

RrYy   ✕   RrYy

gametes

R Y   R y   r Y   r y

Fig. 23.12

there are 9 plus 3, or *12* plants out of every 16 which are round, and 3 plus 1, or *4* plants which are wrinkled. But 12:4 is a 3:1 ratio. Similarly, if seed *color* is counted alone, there are again *12* out of every 16 plants which are yellow and *4* which are green. Here too the ratio is 3:1. Accordingly, although the shape and color traits both are inherited simultaneously and yield a 9:3:3:1 overall ratio of offspring, each trait considered *separately* nevertheless gives a 3:1 ratio of offspring. Each trait therefore is inherited as if the other trait were not there at all; or as Mendel put it, the traits "assort independently," each obeying the law of segregation.

Mendel's second law applies specifically to gene pairs located on *different* chromosome pairs. But any given chromosome contains not just one gene, but anywhere from a few hundred to a few thousand genes. What is the inheritance pattern of two or more gene pairs located on the *same* chromosome pair? This question leads us beyond Mendel's two laws.

LINKAGE

Genes located within the same chromosome are said to be *linked:* as the chromosome is inherited, so are all its genes inherited. Such genes clearly do *not* assort independently, but are transmitted together in a block. The traits controlled by linked genes are similarly expressed in a block. For example, assume that in the heterozygote *AaBb* the two gene pairs are linked. When such an organism produces gametes, only *two* different gamete types are expected, 50 per cent of each (Fig. 23.13). We recall that if the gene pairs *Aa* and *Bb* were not linked, we should expect *four* gamete types through independent assortment, namely, *AB, ab, Ab,* and *aB,* 25 per cent of each.

Linkage studies were first undertaken by T. H. Morgan, a renowned American biologist of the early twentieth century. Experimenting with fruit flies, *Drosophila,* Morgan discovered a curious phenomenon. When genes were linked, the expected result of two

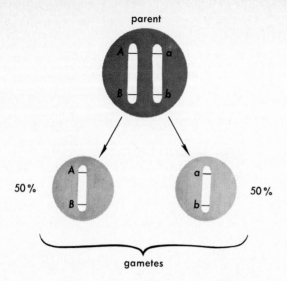

Fig. 23.13

gametes types in a 50:50 ratio was obtained relatively rarely. Instead, there were usually somewhat fewer than 50 per cent of each gamete type, and there were correspondingly small percentages of two additional, completely unexpected gamete types. For example, instead of obtaining 50 per cent *AB* and 50 per cent *ab* gametes, he would obtain, say, only 40 per cent each of *AB* and *ab* and, in addition, also 10 per cent each of the unexpected gamete types *Ab* and *aB* (Fig. 23.14).

If these four types had formed to an extent of about 25 per cent each, the experiment could have been regarded simply as a case without linkage, governed by Mendel's second law. But the actual results included significantly *more* than 25 per cent each of the expected gamete types and significantly *fewer* than 25 per cent each of the unexpected types.

To explain these odd results, Morgan proposed a new hypothesis. He postulated that, during meiosis, paired chromosomes in some cases might *twist around each other* and might break where they are twisted. The broken pieces might then fuse again in the "wrong" order (Fig. 23.15).

This would account for the large percentage of expected and the small percentage of unexpected gamete types. To test the validity of this hypothesis,

cells undergoing meiosis were examined carefully under the microscope: could chromosome twists and breaks actually be seen? They could indeed, and the phenomenon of *crossing over* was so proved.

The implications of this discovery were far-reaching. It was reasoned that the frequency of crossovers should be an index of the *distance* between two genes. If two genes on a chromosome are located near each other, the chances should be relatively small that a twist will occur between these close points. But if two genes are relatively far apart, then twists between these points should be rather frequent. In general, the frequency of crossovers should be proportional to the distance between two genes (Fig. 23.16).

Inasmuch as the crossover percentage of two genes could be determined by breeding experiments, it became possible to construct *gene maps* showing the actual location of given genes on a chromosome. Since Morgan's time, the exact position of few hundred genes has been mapped in the fruit fly. Smaller numbers of genes have similarly been located in corn plants, in mice, and in various other organisms. Many of these determinations have been corroborated by X-ray work. When irradiated, a chromosome may break into pieces and a small piece of this sort may be lost from a gamete. Offspring resulting from such deficient gametes will be abnormal in certain traits. In many cases, microscopic examination can show where a chromosome piece is missing and a trait so can be correlated with a particular spot on a chromosome.

A second implication of crossing over is that genes on a chromosome must be lined up single-file. Only if this is the case can linkage and crossing over occur as it actually does occur. This generalization has become known as the *law of the linear order of genes*. It

Fig. 23.14

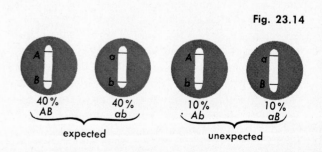

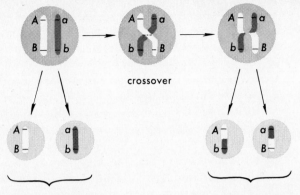

Fig. 23.15

expected types of gamete   unexpected types of gamete

constitutes the third major rule which governs Mendelian inheritance.

Thirdly, crossing over has provided a functional definition of "gene": *A gene is the smallest section of a chromosome within which crossovers do not take place.* The assumption here is that the minimum chromosome unit able to cross over is one *whole* gene, not a fractional part of one gene.

Lastly, a further implication of crossing over during meiosis is that meiosis is a *source of genetic variations.* For example, when a diploid cell in a testis undergoes meiosis and produces four haploid sperms, these four do not contain merely the same whole chromosomes as the original cell, even though redistributed. For if the original diploid cell possesses a chromosome pair M' and M'', then a given sperm will not simply receive either the M' or the M'' chromosome. Instead, as a result of crossing over, it will receive a quiltwork chromosome composed of various joined *pieces* of *both* M' and M''. Moreover, the original diploid cell possesses not only a single chromosome pair but several pairs, and each such pair is likely to be subjected to crossing over in an unpredictable fashion. Chances are therefore excellent that the four sperms will be genetically different from one another as well as from the original diploid cell. Genetic variations consequently are produced by both phases of sex, namely, by chromosome-doubling through fertilization as well as by chromosome reduction through meiosis.

The three rules of inheritance here outlined describe and predict the various results that can be obtained when different gene sets become joined through fertilization and are pooled in the zygote. Such pooling is often referred to as *sexual recombination,* and we may say that the genetic consequences of

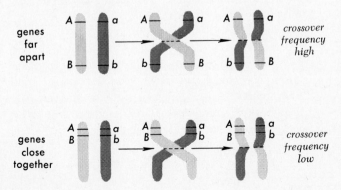

genes far apart

crossover frequency high

genes close together

crossover frequency low

Fig. 23.16. Crossover frequency in relation to gene distance. If two genes are far apart, crossing over between them is likely to occur rather frequently (top). But if genes are close together, crossing over between them is less likely. In general, the farther apart given genes are on a chromosome, the more frequent crossing over will be.

sexual recombination constitute Mendelian inheritance. The rules of Mendel and Morgan govern it. However, a great many hereditary events have been found which do not obey the three basic rules. Some of these non-Mendelian processes will be examined in the following section.

Non-Mendelian inheritance

Two examples of non-Mendelian heredity, not resulting from sexual recombination, are bacterial *transformation* and *transduction*. We have already referred to the first in Chap. 16. Transformation occurs, it will be recalled, by the experimental introduction of additional DNA into given bacteria (Fig. 16.10). Transduction is similar in principle, except that here DNA transfer is accomplished by viruses which infect bacteria. When a virus reproduces within an infected bacterium, pieces of bacterial DNA may on occasion be incorporated into the offspring viruses. If one of the latter subsequently infects a new bacterial host, additional bacterial genes are introduced into that host. As instances of non-Mendelian inheritance, transformation and transduction have strictly limited significance. Far more important, universally significant in all organisms, are *mutations*.

MUTATION

Any stable, inheritable change in the genetic material present in a cell constitutes a mutation. For example, the accidental doubling, tripling, etc., of the normal chromosome number represents a stable, transmissible change. This is a *chromosome mutation*. Accidental loss or addition of a whole chromosome, loss of a chromosome piece, fusion of such a piece with another chromosome, or fusion with the original chromosome in inverted position—these also are chromosome mutations. They occur on rare occasions in nature and they may be produced experimentally.

By far the most common type of mutation is a *point mutation*, a stable change of one gene (Fig. 23.17). Such mutations have provided us with another acceptable definition of "gene": a gene is that minimum part of a chromosome which, when it mutates, alters just one trait of a cell. Genes therefore may be investigated both as mutational units and as crossover units. (It follows that a gene is not a singularly definable object; what we mean by "a gene" depends entirely on the techniques we use to study it.)

It has been known for many years that mutational changes can be induced by high-energy radiation such as X rays. The frequency of mutation has been found to be directly proportional to the amount of radiation a cell receives. Are naturally occurring mutations similarly produced by radiation, e.g., by space radiation or by radioactive elements in the earth? Probably not entirely; it can be shown that the unavoidable natural radiation which affects all organisms is not sufficiently intense to account for the mutation frequency characteristic of genes generally. This frequency has been estimated as about 1 mutation per million cells, on the average. However, natural "background" radiation does produce some mutations. Most others probably represent errors in gene reproduction. Still others are undoubtedly caused by man-made radiation, which adds to and so increases the natural background radiation. Mutations can also be produced experimentally by physical agents other than radiations and by various chemical agents.

As far as can be ascertained, mutations appear to be completely random events. Any gene may mutate at any time, in unpredictable ways. A given gene may mutate several times in rapid succession, then not at all for considerable periods. It may mutate in one direction, then mutate back to its original state or in new directions. There is little question that *every* gene existing today is a *mutant* which has undergone many mutations during its past history.

The effect of a mutation on a trait is equally unpredictable. Some are "large" mutations, that is, they affect a major trait in a radical, drastic manner. Others are "small," with but little effect on a trait. Some mutations are dominant, producing immediate positive alterations of traits. Other mutations are recessive, and in diploid cells they remain masked by normal dominant alleles.

Most mutations are disadvantageous. Indeed, inasmuch as a living cell is an exceedingly complex,

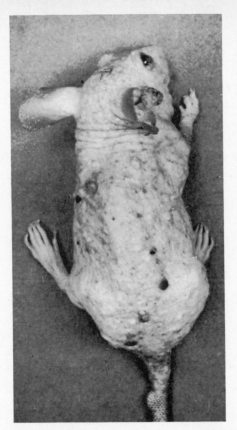
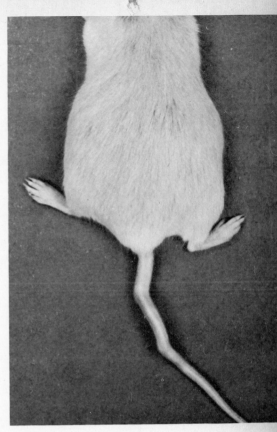

Fig. 23.17. Mutant types in mice. Left, the effects of the mutation "eyelessness." Middle, the effects of the mutation "hairlessness." Right, the effects of the "kinky-tail" mutation. Each of these alterations in structure is correlated with a single mutant gene; and the alterations are stable and inheritable. (Courtesy of Dr. H. B. Chase and R. Hughes, Brown University.)

very finely adjusted whole, it is to be expected that *any* permanent change in cellular properties would be more or less disruptive and harmful. In many cases, therefore, dominant mutations tend to be eliminated as soon as they arise, through death of the affected cell. In other cases, the effect of a dominant mutation (particularly a "small" dominant mutation) may become integrated successfully into cellular functions. Such a cell may then survive even though it exhibits an altered trait. By and large, however, recessive mutations are more likely to persist in diploid cells, since their effects may be masked by normal dominant alleles. Accumulated evidence ac-

tually shows that surviving mutations are very largely recessive ones.

A small percentage of mutants produces advantageous traits and new traits which are neither advantageous nor disadvantageous. Consider mutations in man for example. Many trillions of cells compose the human body and mutations occur at an average rate of 1 in every million cells. Therefore, several million mutations are likely to occur in each individual. Many of these may be lethal to the cells in which they occur and many others will remain masked by normal dominants. But some mutations may produce traits which do not kill a cell. Such new traits, arising in individual cells, are then transmitted to all cells formed from the original ones by division. For example, "beauty spots" probably develop in this manner.

Gene changes of this type, occurring in body cells generally, are known as *somatic mutations*. They affect the heredity of the cell progeny, that is, a patch of tissue at most. But in multicellular organisms such mutations have little direct bearing on the heredity of the individual. Entire multicellular offspring are affected only by so-called *germ mutations*, stable genetic changes in immature and mature reproductive cells. Such mutations will be transmitted to all cells composing the offspring. To the extent that germ mutations may be recessive and masked by normal dominants, the traits of the offspring will not be altered. But if the mutation is dominant or is an unmasked recessive, then a particular trait may be expressed in altered form. Provided such a new trait is not lethal, it will persist as an individual (and non-Mendelian) variation. Mutations may therefore affect the adaptation of an individual just as much as the sexual recombination of genes.

GENE INTERACTIONS

Inheriting certain genes is not automatically equivalent to developing certain traits; the development of traits is affected by the environment. Genes supply a reasonable promise, as it were, and the total environment of the genes subsequently permits or does not permit the translation of promise into reality.

The environment of genes includes, first of all, other genes, and it is well known that the genes in a cell often interact and cooperate in controlling a trait. One of the best illustrations of this is the trait of sexuality, which in numerous organisms is controlled not by individual genes acting separately but by whole chromosomes acting as functionally integrated units.

Sex determination. It has been known for a long time that the primary determiners of sex in various plants and animals are special *sex chromosomes*. These in turn control secondary determiners like sex hormones. The sex chromosomes are of two kinds, called *X* and *Y*. They differ in shape from each other and also from all other chromosomes, which are called *autosomes* for contrast. In human cells, for example, there are

22 pairs of autosomes and one pair of sex chromosomes. In females, both sex chromosomes are of the *X* type, but in males one is *X* and the other is *Y*. Therefore, we may symbolize the chromosome composition of female cells as $(44\ A + XX)$ and that of male cells as $(44\ A + XY)$.

All autosomes and *X* chromosomes carry genes. On the other hand, functioning genes are almost completely absent from *Y* chromosomes, which appear to be quite inert genetically. *Y* chromosomes may be lost from cells without appreciable interference with the normal expression of traits. In effect, therefore, cells of human males contain only 45 functional chromosomes, but female cells contain 46. This difference of one whole *X* chromosome, with its hundreds of genes, lies at the root of the sexual differences between males and females.

It can be shown that it is the ratio of autosomes to *X* chromosomes which is significant in the expression of sex. *Autosomes* promote the development of *maleness; X chromosomes* promote the development of *femaleness.* In a human $44\ A + XX$ cell, the total feminizing influence of the two *X* chromosomes outweighs the total masculinizing influence of the 44 autosomes. Individuals composed of such cells are females. But if the cells contains $44\ A + XY$, then the masculinizing effect of the 44 autosomes is sufficiently strong to override the feminizing effect of the single *X* chromosome. Such individuals are male.

The sexual nature of man, as of other animals, thus appears to depend on a particular *balance* between two genetic influences. If this is correct, should it not be possible to alter the expression of sex by experimentally altering the numerical balance between autosomes and *X* chromosomes? This is indeed possible. Experiments of this kind actually have given the first clues that chromosome balances play a role in sex determination.

In the fruit fly *Drosophila*, for example, the numbers of autosomes and *X* chromosomes in sperms and eggs can be varied by certain laboratory procedures. One may then obtain offspring characterized by normal paired sets of autosomes, but by *three X* chromosomes instead of two. These individuals grow into so-called *superfemales:* all sexual traits are greatly accentuated in the direction of femaleness. *Supermales* and *intersexes* may be produced analogously. In intersexes, sexual traits are intermediate between those of males and females. The chromosome balances are shown in Fig. 23.18. Paradoxically, supersexes and also intersexes are generally sterile; as a result of the abnormal chromosome numbers, meiosis occurs abnormally and the sperms and eggs then produced are defective.

In the light of such balances, we may appreciate readily how the sex of an offspring is inherited normally. For example, human females, 44 A + XX, give rise to eggs of which each contains 22 A + X after meiosis. Males, 44 A + XY, produce two kinds of sperms, namely, 22 A + X and 22 A + Y, in roughly equal numbers. Fertilization now occurs at random, that is, a sperm of either type may unite with an egg. Therefore, in about 50 per cent of the cases the result will be (22 A + X) + (22 A + X), or 44 A + XX, or female-producing zygotes. In the remaining 50 per cent of the cases, the zygotes will be (22 A + X) + (22 A + Y), or 44 A + XY, or male-producing.

Note that it is the prospective father who, at the moment of fertilization, determines the probable sex of the offspring. When only a single offspring is produced, there exists a 50:50 chance of its being a son or a daughter. When many offspring are produced, the number of males will generally equal the number of females.

Genetic systems. The example of genetic sex determination shows clearly that genes of one or more chromosomes may act in concert and control one complex trait. The implication is that genes are not simply independent "beads on a string" lined up haphazardly on chromosomes. On the contrary, the genes in every chromosome appear to interact in very specific ways, and the expression of traits is influenced by such interactions.

Many other illustrations of this principle are known. For example, it is possible by experimental means to change the position of given sections of a chromosome. Genes here are neither removed from nor added to a cell; only their position relative to one another is rearranged. Under such conditions the cell may nevertheless develop altered traits, a clear indication that genes normally interact with their neighbors.

The phenomenon of dominance provides another good illustration of the interdependence of genes. A

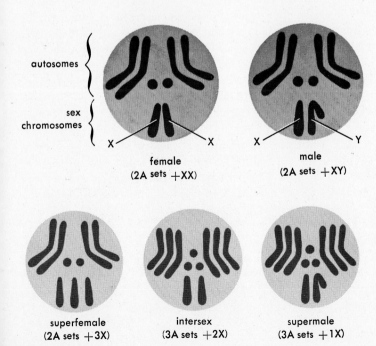

autosomes

sex chromosomes

X X
female
(2A sets +XX)

X Y
male
(2A sets +XY)

superfemale
(2A sets +3X)

intersex
(3A sets +2X)

supermale
(3A sets +1X)

Fig. 23.18. Top, the chromosomes of the fruit fly *Drosophila*. In each cell, $2n = 8$. Note the differences in the sex chromosomes of males and females. In man, $2n = 46$, sex-chromosome differences being as in fruit flies. Bottom, sex and chromosome balance in the fruit fly. The sexual character of an individual is determined by the specific balance of autosomes and X chromosomes.

dominant gene acts as it does not only because of its inherent characteristics, but also because other genes *permit* it to act in dominant fashion. If the functional characteristics of the recessive allele of a given dominant were to change, then the status of dominance of that gene would change correspondingly. And if the functional characteristics of any other genes in the cell were to change, then the status of dominance of that gene would again change.

Indeed, it is now well established that given genes boost, suppress, partially inhibit, or otherwise change the effects of other genes. For example, *modifier* genes are known which intensify or minimize the traits produced by other genes. Analogously, *suppressor* genes completely prevent traits produced by other genes from becoming expressed. Some genes affect not the traits produced by other genes but the other genes themselves. Among them are *operator* genes, which must be present if certain other genes are to function, and *regulator* genes, which apparently turn the action of other genes on and off. The functional integration of genes in a cell is actually so intimate and so complex that it becomes relatively meaningless to speak of "a" gene as if it were an independent, clearly distinct particle. Only the interacting totality of genes in a cell, called the *genome*, has functional reality.

This conclusion is reinforced further by very recent studies which have shown that genes actually are not the smallest hereditary units. A gene consists of DNA nucleotide chains, and small segments of such chains, each far smaller than a whole gene, may affect the expression of traits in demonstrable ways. When a gene mutates, for example, not all parts of the DNA chain become altered; a change in a small segment, consisting perhaps of not more than a single nucleotide, often suffices for the mutational effect. The name *muton* has been given to the smallest portion of a gene which may produce a mutational change, and a gene is envisaged to consist of numerous mutons in linear series. It has also been shown that blocks of adjoining mutons within a gene act cooperatively and form larger functional units called *cistrons*. If the cooperating mutons within a cistron happen to become disjoined in some way, the hereditary function of that cistron is abolished. But whole cistrons within a gene can become disjoined without loss of function. Such data show clearly that, in addition to interaction among genes, there is also considerable interaction of smaller functional units within genes.

Moreover, other genes and their subunits do not represent the whole environment of any given gene; the genetic environment also includes the cell cytoplasm, and it too influences gene expression greatly. In the cytoplasm, genes indirectly exercise their basic function: they control protein synthesis. We may regard proteins as the primary "traits" of a cell and indeed we may formulate a third acceptable definition of "gene" on this basis: a gene is that minimum section of a chromosome which controls the synthesis of a single protein. In recent years, genes have actually been studied extensively as units of biochemical action. In the form of enzymes or structural components, the proteins manufactured under gene control then bring about the development of various secondary, often visible traits. But such traits usually differ in different cell types even though the genes are the same in all. For example, *all* cells of a flowering plant possess flower-color genes, but only cells in the petals express that color. *All* cells of man possess eye-color genes, but only iris cells actually develop the color. Evidently, the cytoplasms of different cells react differently to the genes they contain and trait expression will differ correspondingly. The various *specializations* of cells and of larger body parts are the result.

So-called "inherited" diseases may be interpreted in a similar light. Certain mental diseases, diabetes, alcoholism, cancer, and many other abnormalities are known to "run in families." What is inherited here is not the disease itself. A child of diabetic ancestry is not automatically diabetic. However, *susceptibility* to disease may be inherited. The genes are present, but before the disease can become explicit, specific cellular and external environments must make gene expression possible. Analogously, a person who performs physical exercise regularly will develop strong muscles and so will acquire traits differing from those of a person who does not exercise. In both cases, however, the genes controlling muscular development may be the same.

We may therefore distinguish between *inherited* traits, controlled by genes, and noninherited, *acquired* traits, superimposed on the inherited ones and produced by environmental or developmental effects. And we are led to the fundamental conclusion that the actual, visible traits of an organism are always a product of inherited genes *and* of environment.

Thus, whereas the pre-Mendelians thought that *traits* were inherited and whereas the Mendelian era advanced to the concept that individual factors, or *genes*, were inherited, the present post-Mendelian era recognizes that actually neither traits nor genes are inherited. Instead, what are inherited are whole chromosome *sets*, coordinated *complexes* of genes,

subtly integrated and interacting *genetic systems*. Moreover, even genetic systems are not inherited by themselves but are transmitted within *whole* cells. The functional integration between genetic system and cell system is never lost, and it is biologically almost meaningless to consider one without the other. Ultimately, therefore, the smallest real unit of inheritance is one whole cell.

In the individual organisms, the interplay between sex, heredity, and environment results in adaptation of the organism. In the long reproductive successsion of organisms, this same interplay becomes *evolution*.

Review questions

1. What was meant by "blending inheritance"? Describe the experiments through which Mendel came to deny blending. What hypothesis did Mendel substitute for the blending concept? State the chromosome theory of heredity. What is the evidence that genes are actually contained within chromosomes?

2. Define genome, true-breeding, phenotype, genotype, allele, dominant gene, recessive gene, homozygous, heterozygous.

3. Review the experiments on inheritance of flower color in snapdragons in terms of genes and chromosomes. What are the quantitative results of the mating $Aa \times Aa$ if (*a*) *A* is dominant over *a*, (*b*) neither gene is dominant over the other?

4. In your own words, state the law of segregation. If *A* is dominant over *a*, what phenotype ratios of offspring are obtained from the following matings: (*a*) $Aa \times aa$, (*b*) $AA \times aa$, (*c*) $Aa \times Aa$, (*d*) $Aa \times AA$?

5. In your own words, state the law of independent assortment. By what kinds of breeding experiments, and by what reasoning, did Mendel come to discover this law? Interpret the law in terms of genes, meiosis, and gametes.

6. Define linkage. Why does inheritance of linked genes

not obey Mendel's second law? What were Morgan's observations which led him to the hypothesis of crossing over? Describe this hypothesis. How do crossover data permit the construction of gene maps? State the law of the linear order of genes. What definition of gene is based on the phenomenon of crossing over? Review other definitions.

7. Review the genetic basis of sex determination in man. What is the significance of a given numerical balance between autosomes and sex chromosomes?

8. What are transduction and transformation? In what organisms, and how, do these processes occur?

9. Distinguish between chromosome mutations and point mutations and between somatic mutations and germ mutations. What is the relation between mutation frequency and radiation intensity? What are the characteristics of mutations from the standpoint of (*a*) predictability, (*b*) functional relation to normal alleles, (*c*) effects on traits, and (*d*) relative advantage to the organism?

10. What are the sources of genetic variations? Distinguish between inherited and acquired variations. What contributions are made to the expression of traits by (*a*) genes, (*b*) the environment? What is an "inherited disease"?

Suggested collateral readings

Benzer, S.: The Fine Structure of the Gene, *Sci. Am.*, vol. 206, 1962.

Hollander, W. F.: Lethal Heredity, *Sci. Am.*, vol. 187, 1952.

Hotchkiss, R. D., and E. Weiss: Transformed Bacteria, *Sci. Am.*, vol. 195, 1956.

Ingram, V. M.: How Do Genes Act?, *Sci. Am.*, vol. 198, 1958.

Knight, C. A., and D. Fraser: The Mutation of Viruses, *Sci. Am.*, vol. 193, 1955.

Muller, H. J.: Radiation and Human Mutation, *Sci. Am.*, vol. 193, 1955.

Stern, C.: Man's Genetic Future, *Sci. Am.*, vol. 186, 1952.

Zinder, N. D.: Transduction in Bacteria, *Sci. Am.*, vol. 199, 1958.

EVOLUTION: THE MECHANISM

No biologist today seriously questions the principle that species
arise from preexisting species. Evolution on a small scale can
actually be brought about in the laboratory, and the forces
which drive and guide evolutionary processes are understood
quite thoroughly.

That evolution really occurs did not become definitely established till the nineteenth century. For long ages man was
unaware of the process, but he did wonder about the origin
of this kind and of other living creatures. Indeed, he developed
a succession of simple and rather crude theories about evolution. Unsupported by real evidence, these were ultimately
proved untenable one by one. Yet the early ideas occasionally
still color the views of those who are unacquainted with the
modern knowledge.

It is advisable, therefore, that we begin this chapter with
a brief survey of the historical *background* of evolutionary
thought. Based on such a perspective, we may then discuss the
forces of evolution, as these are understood today, and follow
with an analysis of the *nature of evolution*, as determined by
the underlying forces.

Background

EARLY NOTIONS

The earliest theory of organic creation is contained in the Old Testament: God made the world and its living inhabitants in six days, man coming last. On this were based the ideas of *spontaneous generation* and of *immutability of species*, which largely held sway until the eighteenth and nineteenth centuries. Each species was considered to have been created separately, completely developed, from dust, dirt, and other nonliving sources. And once so generated spontaneously, a species was held to be fixed and immutable, unable to change its characteristics.

In the sixth to fourth centuries B.C., Anaximander, Empedocles, and Aristotle independently considered the possibility that living forms might represent a *succession* rather than unrelated, randomly created types. However, the succession was thought of in an essentially philosophical way, as a progression from "less nearly perfect" to "more nearly perfect" forms. The *historical* nature of succession and the continuity of life were not yet recognized.

Francesco Redi, an Italian physician of the seventeenth century, was the first to obtain evidence against the idea of spontaneous generation, by showing experimentally that organisms could not arise from nonliving sources. Contrary to notions held at the time and earlier, Redi demonstrated that maggots would never form "spontaneously" in meat if flies were prevented from laying their eggs on the meat. But old beliefs die slowly, and it was not until the nineteenth century, chiefly through the work of Louis Pasteur, that the original notion of spontaneous generation finally ceased to be influential.

By this time, the idea of continuity and historical succession, or *evolution*, had occurred to a number of thinkers. Indeed, the first major theory of evolution was published in 1809. This was the theory of the French biologist Lamarck.

LAMARCK

To explain how evolution occurred, Lamarck proposed the two ideas of *use and disuse of parts* and of *inher-itance of acquired characteristics*. He had observed that if a part of an organism was used extensively, such a part would enlarge and become more efficient; and that if a structure was not fully employed, it would degenerate and atrophy. Therefore, by differential use and disuse of various parts during its lifetime, an organism would change to some extent and would acquire certain traits. Lamarck then thought that such acquired traits were inheritable and could be transmitted to offspring.

According to this Lamarckian scheme, evolution would come about somewhat as follows. Suppose a given short-necked ancestral animal feeds on tree leaves. As it clears off the lower levels of a tree, it stretches its neck to reach farther up. During a lifetime of stretching the neck becomes a little longer, and a slightly longer neck is then inherited by the offspring. These in turn feed on tree leaves and keep on stretching their necks; and so on, for many generations. Each generation acquires the gains of previous generations and itself adds a little to neck length. In time, a very long-necked animal is formed, something like a modern giraffe.

This theory was exceedingly successful and did much to spread the idea of evolution. But Lamarck's views ultimately proved to be untenable. That use and disuse *do* lead to acquired traits is quite correct. For example, it is common knowledge that much exercise builds powerful muscles. However, Lamarck was mistaken in assuming that such (nongenetic) acquired variations were inheritable. We may say categorically that *acquired characteristics are not inheritable*. They are effects produced by environment and development, not by genes (see Chap. 23). Only *genetic* characteristics are inheritable, and then only if such characteristics are controlled by the genes of the reproductive cells. What happens to cells other than reproductive cells through use and disuse, or in any other way for that matter, does not affect the genes of the gametes. Accordingly, although Lamarck observed some of the effects of use and disuse correctly in some cases, such effects cannot play a role in evolution.

One famous attempt at experimental refutation of Lamarckism was carried out by Weismann, an eminent biologist of the nineteenth century. The tails of mice were cut off for very many successive generations. According to Lamarck, such enforced disuse of tails should eventually have led to tailless mice. Yet mice in the last generation of the experiment still grew tails as long as their ancestors.

DARWIN AND WALLACE

The year in which Lamarck published his theory was also the year in which Charles Darwin was born. During his early life, Darwin undertook a 5-year-long circumglobal voyage as the biologist on the naval expeditionary ship *H.M.S. Beagle.* He made innumerable observations and collected a large number of different plants and animals in many parts of the world. Returning home, he spent nearly twenty years sifting and studying the collected data. In the course of this work, he found evidence for certain generalizations. Another biologist, Alfred Wallace, had been led independently to substantially the same generalizations, at the same time as Darwin. Darwin and Wallace together then announced a new theory of evolution, which was to supplant that of Lamarck. Darwin subsequently elaborated the new theory into book form. This famous work, entitled "On the Origin of Species by Means of Natural Selection, or the Preservation of Favored Races in the Struggle for Life," was published in 1859.

In essence, the Darwin-Wallace *theory of natural selection* is based on three observations and on two conclusions drawn from these observations.

Observation. Without environmental pressures, every species tends to multiply in geometric progression.

In other words, a population doubling its number in a first year possesses a sufficient reproductive potential to quadruple its number in a second year, to increase eightfold in a third year, etc.

Observation. But under field conditions, although fluctuations occur frequently, the size of a population remains remarkably constant over long periods of time.

We have already spoken of this in the discussion of food pyramids (Chap. 6).

Conclusion. Evidently, not all eggs and sperms will become zygotes; not all zygotes will become adults; and not all adults will survive and reproduce. Consequently, there must be a "struggle for existence."

Observation. Not all members of a species are alike; i.e., there exists considerable individual variation.

Conclusion. In the struggle for existence, therefore, individuals featuring favorable variations will enjoy a competitive advantage over others. They will survive in proportionately greater numbers and will produce offspring in proportionately greater numbers.

Darwin and Wallace thus identified the environment as the principal cause of natural selection. Through the processes above, the environment would gradually weed out organisms with unfavorable variations but preserve those with favorable variations. Over a long succession of generations and under the continued selective influence of the environment, a group of organisms would eventually have accumulated so many new, favorable variations that a new species would in effect have arisen from the ancestral stock.

Nonbiologists today often are under the impression that Darwin's and Wallace's theory is *the* modern theory of evolution. This is not the case. Indeed, Darwinism was challenged even during Darwin's lifetime. What, it was asked, is the *source* of the all-important individual variations? How do individual variations arise? Here Darwin actually could do no better than fall back on the Lamarckian idea of inheritance of acquired characteristics. Ironically, the correct answer regarding variations began to be formulated just six years after Darwin published his theory, when a monk named Mendel announced certain rules of inheritance. But Mendel's work went unheeded for more than thirty years and progress in understanding evolutionary mechanisms was retarded correspondingly.

Another objection to Darwinism concerned natural selection itself. If this process simply preserves or weeds out what already exists, it was asked, how can it ever create anything new? As we shall see, natural selection actually does create novelty. The earlier criticism arose in part because the meaning of Darwin's theory was—and still is—widely misinterpreted. Social philosophers of the time and other "press agents" and disseminators of "news," not biologists, thought that the essence of natural selection was described by the phrase "struggle for existence." They then coined alternative slogans like "survival of the fittest" and "elimination of the unfit." Natural selection so came to be conceived almost exclusively as a negative, destructive force. This had two unfortunate results. First, a major implication of Darwin's theory, namely, the creative role of natural selection, was missed; and, second, the wrong emphasis was often accepted in popular thinking as the last and final word concerning evolution. Even today, unfortunately, the mechanism of evolution is still commonly—and erroneously—thought to be a matter of "survival of the fittest."

By now, a full century after Darwin and Wallace, it has become clear that natural selection is preeminently a peaceful process and has very little to do with "struggle," "weeding out," or "the fittest." Also, natural selection is only a *part* of the evolutionary mechanism and we know that Darwin and Wallace, like Lamarck, were unsuccessful in identifying the genetic causes of evolutionary change. In short, Darwin and Wallace supplied an incomplete explanation, but as far as it went, theirs was the first to point in the right direction.

The modern theory of evolution is not the work of any one man. It evolved slowly during the first half of the current century, many biologists of various specializations contributing to it. The theory is the spiritual offspring of Mendel and of Darwin, but the family resemblance, though present, may not be immediately evident. We shall be concerned with this modern theory in what follows.

The forces of evolution

THE EVOLUTIONARY PROCESS

The medium of evolution is the *population*. The raw materials of the evolutionary process are the *inheritable variations* which appear among the individuals of such a population. And the mechanism of evolution may be described as *natural selection acting on the inheritable variations of a population.*

We already know from Chap. 6 that a popula-tion is a geographically localized group of organisms of the same species, in which the members interbreed preferentially with one another and also interbreed occasionally with members of neighboring populations. We may note now that the result of the close sexual communication within a population is a *free flow of genes*. Hereditary material present in a part of a population may in time spread to the whole population, through the gene-pooling and gene-combining effect of sex. Therefore, in the course of successive sexual generations, the total genetic content of a population may become shuffled and reshuffled thoroughly. We may say that a population possesses a given *gene pool* and that the interbreeding members of the population have free access to all components of that pool. Moreover, inasmuch as sister populations are in occasional reproductive contact, the gene pool of one population is connected also to the gene pools of sister populations. In this way, the total genetic content of an entire species continues to be shuffled about among the member organism.

Evolution operates via the gene pools of populations. We already know from Chap. 23 how changes in genetic systems, hence new inheritable traits may arise: by *sexual recombination* and by *mutation*. In each generation, some individuals may appear featuring new trait variations as a result of either recombinational or mutational processes. If these variant organisms survive and have offspring of their own, then their particular genetic innovations will persist in the gene pool of the population. In the course of successive generations, the genetic novelty may spread to many or all members of the population.

Whether or not such spreading actually takes place depends on natural selection. This term is synonymous with *differential reproduction*. Either "natural selection" or "differential reproduction" means simply that *some individuals of a population have more offspring than others.* Clearly, those which leave more offspring will contribute a proportionately greater percentage of individuals to the numerical total of the next generation than those which leave fewer offspring. If, therefore, differential reproduction continues in the same manner over many generations, the abundant reproducers will contribute a progressively larger number of individuals to the whole population. As a result, *their* genes will become preponderant in the gene pool of the population (Fig. 24.1).

Which individuals leave more offspring than others? Usually, but by no means necessarily, those that are *best adapted* to the environment. Being well adapted, such individuals on the whole are healthier and better fed, may find mates more readily, and may care for their offspring appropriately. However, circumstances may on occasion be such that comparatively poorly adapted individuals have the most offspring. Instances of this are sometimes encountered in human populations, for example. In any event, what counts most in evolution is not how well or how poorly an organism copes with its environment, but how many offspring it manages to leave. The more there are, the greater a role will the parental genes play in the total genetic content of the population. By and large, the well-adapted organism contributes most to the gene pool.

Therefore, if an inheritable variation appears in an organism and if, through differential reproduction in successive generations, the progeny of that organism becomes numerically more and more abundant, then a given genetic novelty will spread rapidly throughout the population. As a result, a new trait originating in one organism will have become a standard feature of the population as a whole.

This is the unit of evolutionary change. Many such unit changes must accumulate in a population before the organisms are sufficiently altered in structure or function to be established as a new species. All evolution operates through the basic process just described. In brief, it consists of:

1. appearance of inheritable variations by sexual recombination and mutation

2. spreading of these variations through a population, by differential reproduction in successive generations

Inasmuch as inheritable variations originate at random, evolutionary innovations similarly appear at

Fig. 24.1. **The effect of differential reproduction, or natural selection.** Assume that a variation arises in one individual of a parental generation (black dot) and that the variant organism is able to leave three offspring. Each nonvariant organism (white dot) on the other hand only manages to leave one offspring. The complexion of the population will then change as shown during subsequent generations; i.e., the variant type will represent a progressively larger fraction of the numerical total. Such spreading of variations, brought about by differential reproduction, constitutes natural selection.

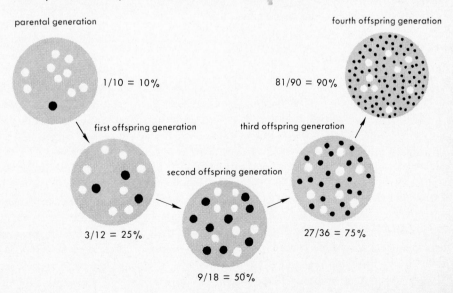

parental generation

1/10 = 10%

fourth offspring generation

81/90 = 90%

first offspring generation

third offspring generation

second offspring generation

3/12 = 25%

27/36 = 75%

9/18 = 50%

random. And inasmuch as the best reproducers are generally the best adapted, evolution as a whole is directed by adaptation and is oriented toward continued or improved adaptation.

Note that, in this modern view of evolution, *natural selection is fundamentally a creative force; its important effect is to spread genetic novelty,* hence new traits, through a population. It is also a peaceful force, involving *reproduction,* not "struggle for existence" or "survival of the fittest." Organisms actually struggle rather rarely. Indeed, animals try to avoid struggle and attempt to pursue life as inconspicuously as possible, eating when they can, reproducing when they can; and plants have never been seen to engage in struggles at all. Moreover, natural selection does not "eliminate the unfit." The "fit" may be the mightiest and grandest organism in the population, but it might happen to be sterile. And the "unfit" could be a sickly weakling, yet have numerous offspring. The point is that neither "survival" nor "elimination" is actually at issue. The only issue of consequence here is comparative reproductive success. Indirectly, to be sure, health, fitness, and even actual physical struggles may affect the reproductive success of organisms. To that extent, such factors can have evolutionary consequences. But what in Darwin's day was regarded as the whole of natural selection is now clearly recognized to have only a limited, indirect effect on evolution. The whole of natural selection, directly and indirectly, undoubtedly is differential reproduction.

THE GENETIC BASIS

From the preceding, we may describe evolution as a *progressive change of gene frequencies.* This means that, in the course of successive generations, the proportion of some genes in the population increases and the proportion of others decreases. For example, a mutation may at first be represented by a single gene, but if by natural selection this mutation spreads to more and more individuals, then its frequency increases whereas the frequency of the original unmutated gene decreases. Clearly, the *rates* with which gene frequencies change will be a measure of the *speed* of evolution. What determines such rates?

By experiment and calculation it can be shown that, *if mating is random, if mutations do not occur, and if the population is large, then gene frequencies in a population remain constant from generation to generation.* This generalization is known as the *Hardy-Weinberg law.* It is to the theory of evolution what Mendel's laws are to the theory of heredity.

The Hardy-Weinberg law indicates that, when a population is in genetic equilibrium, that is, when gene frequencies do not change, the rate of evolution is zero. That is, genes continue to be reshuffled by sexual recombination, and as a result individual variations continue to originate from this source. But the overall gene frequencies do not change. Of themselves, therefore, the variations are *not* being propagated differentially. Evolution consequently does not occur.

What does make evolution occur are deviations from the "ifs" specified in the Hardy-Weinberg law. First, mating is decidedly *not* random in most natural situations. Mates most often are deliberately chosen on the basis of health, strength, mentality, external appearance, or some other desirable traits. By and large, "desirable" traits are those which are adaptive, that is, which promise aid in survival. When two individuals with mutually desirable traits mate, their genes can spread via offspring through the population. By contrast, two individuals with mutually undesirable traits will not mate, and their genes therefore cannot spread. Evidently, nonrandom mating in a population means *natural selection* and uneven, nonrandom shuffling about of genes. Consequently, as some genes spread more than others, gene frequencies will become altered and a Hardy-Weinberg equilibrium will not be maintained. This represents evolutionary change. We say that a certain *intensity* of natural selection, or *selection pressure,* operates for or against given genes. In the course of many generations, even a very slight selection pressure affects the genetic makeup of a population substantially.

Second, mutations *do* occur in populations, and Hardy-Weinberg equilibria change for this reason also. Depending on whether a mutation has a beneficial or harmful effect on a trait, selection will be made either for or against the mutated gene. In either case gene frequencies will change, for the mutated gene will either increase or decrease in abundance.

Mutations in haploid organisms affect traits immediately. But the evolutionary effect of mutations in diploid organisms varies according to whether the gene changes are dominant or recessive. A newly originated dominant mutation will affect traits immediately, and selection for or against the mutation will take place at once. But if a mutation is recessive, it does not affect traits immediately. Natural selection therefore does not influence the mutation immediately either. This is the case with most mutations, since, as noted in Chap. 23, most actual mutations are recessive.

Nevertheless, recessive mutations may spread through a population. For example, an organism may carry a recessive mutant gene *a'*, and it may also carry a linked dominant gene *B* which produces an adaptively very desirable trait. Natural selection could then operate *for* the gene *B;* the organism possessing *B* might reproduce abundantly and its genes would spread through the population. This means that the mutant gene *a'* would be spread at the same time. Many recessive mutations actually do propagate in this way, by being inherited along with other, adaptively useful dominant genes.

Recessive mutants simply accumulate in the gene pool without visible effect. However, if two individuals carrying the same recessive mutation happen to mate, then one-fourth of their offspring will be homozygous recessive: $Aa' \times Aa' \longrightarrow 25$ per cent $a'a'$. These offspring will exhibit altered visible traits and natural selection will then affect the mutation directly.

Mutational effects in evolution also vary according to how greatly a given mutation influences a given trait. A "large" mutation which affects a vital trait in major ways is likely to be exceedingly harmful and will usually be lethal. For example, *any* change in the principal structure and function of the human heart is likely to cause immediate death. Indeed, large variations are usually eliminated as soon as they arise. By contrast, an organism may survive far more readily if a mutation is "small." Evolutionary alterations of organisms actually occur almost exclusively through the accumulation of *many, small* changes in traits, not through single, large changes.

The third condition affecting Hardy-Weinberg equilibria is population size. If a population is large, any regional imbalances of gene frequencies which may arise by chance are quickly smoothed out by the many random matings among the many individuals. The principle underlying this holds in statistical systems generally. In a coin-flipping experiment, for example, heads and tails will each come up 50 per cent of the time, but only if the number of throws is large. If only three or four throws are made, it is quite possible that *all* will come up heads, by chance alone. Analogously, gene combinations attain Hardy-Weinberg equilibria only if a population is large. In small groups, chance alone may produce major deviations.

We say that, in small populations, chance leads to *genetic drift,* that is, to the random establishment of genetic types which numerically are not in accordance with Hardy-Weinberg equilibria. Because genetic drift is governed solely by chance, natural selection plays little role. Genes here being propagated not for their adaptive value but because they happen to be picked for propagation by chance. The result is that, in small populations, nonadaptive and often bizarre traits become established. These may actually be harmful to the population and may promote its getting even smaller. Genetic drift is often observed among plants and animals on islands and in other small, reproductively isolated groups of organisms.

Evolution as it actually occurs must be interpreted in terms of the forces here described. That it in fact can be interpreted on this basis will become clear in the following.

The nature of evolution

SPECIATION

The key process to be explained is how unit evolutionary changes in a population eventually culminate in the origin of new species and higher taxonomic categories. A species, we recall, is a collection of populations within which reproductive communication is maintained by interbreeding. We may now define a species alternatively as a group of populations sharing the same gene pool. Within the pool a free flow of genes is maintained, but genetic flow between two such pools does not occur; a reproductive barrier isolates one species from another. The problem of speciation, therefore, is to show how reproductive barriers arise.

The pertinent factors here have already been outlined in Chap. 6. To recapitulate briefly, we have found that physical distance between two sister populations and other geographical isolating conditions, usually are the primary causes for an interruption of gene flow. To the geographical barriers then are added biological ones, through the gradual accumulation of evolutionary differences in the different populations. As a result, two populations do not interbreed even though at first they still could, and in time they become so different that they can no longer interbreed at all. Gene flow is then interrupted irreversibly. What started out as two populations of the same species has become two distinct and separate species.

Consciously or unconsciously making use of this principle of reproductive isolation, man has been and is now contributing to the evolution of many other organisms. Here may be found direct proof that evolution actually occurs and, indeed, that it operates according to the mechanism described above.

The most ancient evolution-directing effort of man is his successful *domestication* of various plants and animals. Darwin was the first to recognize the theoretical significance of domestication, and it was this, actually, which led him to his concept of natural selection. He reasoned that if man, by *artificial selection* and isolation, can transform wild varieties of given plants and animals into domesticated varieties, then perhaps *natural selection* and isolation, acting for far longer periods, can bring about even greater evolutionary transformations in nature. We know now that the domesticating process in fact does involve all the elements of natural evolution: first, deliberate physical, hence reproductive and genetic, isolation of a wild population by man; and second, long-continued, carefully controlled, differential reproduction of individuals "adapted" to human desires, that is, of individuals featuring traits considered desirable by man. The result is the creation of new strains, races, subspecies, and even species.

Furthermore, during the last few decades, rather rapid, man-directed evolution has taken place among certain viruses, bacteria, insects, various parasites, and other pest organisms. These live now in an environment in which antibiotics and numerous pest-killing drugs have become distinct hazards. And the organisms have evolved and are still evolving increasing resistance to such drugs. Indeed, the very rapid evolution of viruses and bacteria becomes a problem in research; laboratory populations of microorganisms may evolve resistance to a drug even while the drug is being tested. Because microorganisms have exceedingly short generation times, because their populations are physically small, compact, and easily reared, and because high mutation rates may be induced readily by X rays, they have become favorite test objects in evolution experiments.

Clearly, then, small-scale evolution unquestionably occurs and is observable directly. Moreover, it may be made to occur under conditions based on the postulated modern mechanism of evolution. That this mechanism actually operates as implied by theory is therefore no longer in doubt.

And we may note that the same mechanism is believed to operate in the transformation of species into genera, families, and other higher taxonomic categories. Creation of such a category out of a species is again envisaged to involve isolation and accumulation of small inheritable trait variations—only more of them than in the case of a species, and accumulating for a longer period of time.

CHARACTERISTICS OF EVOLUTION

Rates of Change.   Even on the species level, evolution is an exceedingly slow process. As noted, a very large number of very small variations of traits must accumulate, bit by bit over many generations, before a significant structural or functional alteration of organisms is in evidence. Moreover, genetic innovations occur at random, whereas natural selection is directed by adaptation. Therefore, if a substantial environmental change necessitates a correspondingly substantial adaptive change in a group of organisms, then the organisms must *await* the random appearance of appropriate genetic innovations. If useful innovations do not happen to arise by chance, then the organisms will not be able to readapt and will die out. Yet even if useful genetic novelty does arise in a given generation, there is no guarantee that more novelty of similar usefulness will originate in the next generation. In short, even though evolution may occur, it could occur too slowly to permit successful adaptation to changed environments.

The actual speeds of past evolution, though slow in all instances, have varied considerably for different types of organisms, differently at different times. As a rule, the more stable a given environment has been, the slower has been the evolution of the organisms living in it. Thus, terrestrial organisms by and large have evolved faster than marine organisms. Also, during periods of major geologic upheavals, e.g., in times of glaciation or of mountain building (see Chap. 25), evolution has been fairly rapid generally. On the other hand, in a few existing types of organisms, the rate of evolution has been practically zero for hundreds of millions of years. Horseshoe crabs, certain lampshells, and some of the radiolarian protozoa are among the oldest of such "living fossils" (see Fig. 10.26). In these and similar cases, the specific environment of the organisms has been stable enough to make the ancient way of life still possible.

Adaptive radiation. A general feature of evolution is the phenomenon of *adaptive radiation*. We have seen how, in speciation, one original parent species gives rise simultaneously to two or more descendant species. A similar pattern of *branching* descent characterizes evolution on all levels. A new type evolves, and it then becomes a potential ancestor for many different, *simultaneous* descendant lines. For example, the ancestral mammalian type has given rise simultaneously to several lines of grazing plains animals (e.g., horses, cattle, goats), to burrowing animals (e.g., moles), to flying animals (e.g., bats), to several lines of aquatic animals (e.g., whales, seals, sea cows), to animals living in trees (e.g., monkeys), to carnivorous predators (e.g., dogs, cats), and to many others. Evidently the original mammalian type branched out and exploited many different available environments and ways of life. Each descendant line thereby became adaptively specialized in a particular way. The sum of the various lines, all leading away from the common ancestral type, formed an "adaptive radiation."

Within each such line, furthermore, adaptive radiations of smaller scope can take place. For example, the line of tree-living mammals in time evolved several simultaneous sublines and subsublines. The specific

results today are animals as varied as monkeys, lemurs, tarsiers, apes, and men. Evidently, man did not "descend from the apes." Rather, apes and man have had a common ancestor, and they are *contemporary* members of the same adaptive radiation.

The important implication here is that evolution is *not* a "ladder" or a "scale." As already noted in Chap. 8, the pattern is more nearly that of a greatly branching bush, where the tips of all uppermost branches represent currently living species (see Fig. 8.1). Of these, none is "higher" or "lower" than any other. Instead, they are simply contemporary groups of different structure, function, and history.

Extinction. Not all the branches on the evolutionary bush ramify right to the top, but some terminate abruptly at various lower points; *extinction* has been a general feature of evolution. In many actual cases of extinction, the specific causes may never be known. But the general cause of all extinctions emerges from the nature of the evolutionary mechanism. That cause is change in environment, without rapid enough readaptation of organisms to the change. Evidently, unlike death, which is inherent in the life history of every individual, extinction is *not* a foregone conclusion inherent in the evolutionary history of every group. Rather, extinction occurs only if and when the group cannot make adaptive adjustments to environmental change (Fig. 24.2).

Such change need not necessarily be physical. For example, biological *competition* between two different types occupying the same territory often has led to the extinction of one. However, note that competition most often does not involve direct combat or "struggle." Characteristically, the competition is usually quite indirect, as when two different types of herbivores draw on the same limited supply of grass.

In past evolution, *extinction has been the more common the lower the taxonomic category.* Extinction of species and even of genera has been a nearly universal occurrence, but relatively few orders and still fewer classes have become extinct. And virtually all phyla that ever originated continue to be in existence today. The phylum evidently includes so broad and so far-flung an assemblage of different adaptive types that at least some of them have always persisted, re-

Fig. 24.2.   An animal which has become extinct relatively recently. The dodo survived till just a few hundred years ago. (American Museum of Natural History.)

gardless of how environments have changed. Species, on the other hand, are usually adapted rather narrowly to limited, circumscribed environments. The chances for extinction are therefore greater.

Replacement.   In conjunction with extinction, *replacement* has been another common occurrence in evolution. As noted, competition may be a direct cause for the replacement of one group in a given environment by another. For example, pouched marsupial mammals were very abundant in the Americas a few million years ago, but with the exception of forms like the opossum, they were replaced in the Western Hemisphere by the competing placental mammals. Competition is not a necessary prerequisite for replacement, however. A group may become extinct for some other reason and another group may then

evolve into the vacated environment and way of life. A good example of this is provided by the ichthyosaurs. These large, marine, fishlike reptiles became extinct some 100 million years ago, and their particular mode of living subsequently remained unused for about 40 million years. Dolphins and porpoises evolved then, and these mammals replaced the ichthyosaurs. Similar replacement occurred between the flying reptilian pterosaurs and the later mammalian bats.

Convergence and divergence.   The phenomenon of replacement is often accompanied by that of convergence, a frequent feature in evolution generally. We have seen how, in an adaptive radiation, a common ancestral type gives rise to two or more descendant lines, all adapted in different ways to different environments. Such development of dissimilar characteristics in closely related groups is often called evolutionary *divergence.* By contrast, when two or more *unrelated* groups adapt to the *same* type of environment, then their evolution is oriented in the same direction. Such organisms may come to resemble one another in one or more ways. Evolution of a common set of characteristics in groups of different ancestry is called *convergence* (Fig. 24.3).

For example, the development of wings in both pterosaurs and bats or of finlike appendages in both ichthyosaurs and dolphins illustrates evolutionary convergence. Similarly, the eyes of squids and of fish are remarkably alike. Squids and fish are not related directly. However, both groups comprise large, fast swimmers, and good eyes of a particular construction are a distinct advantage in the ways of life of both.

Opportunism.   Although the eyes of squids and fish are strikingly alike, they are by no means identical. Although the wings of pterosaurs and bats or of insects and birds are convergent, in the sense that all carry out the same functions of flying, the various wing types are quite different structurally and operate in different ways. Convergence leads to *similarity*, never to identity. Moreover, neither squids nor fish possess a theoretically "best" eye structure for fast swimmers, and none of the flying groups possesses a theoretically "best" wing design. Actually, the design of an organ or of an organism need not be theoretically "best" or

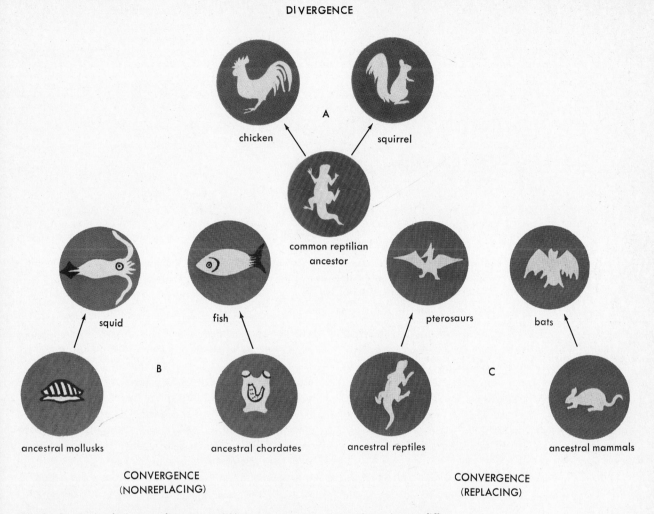

DIVERGENCE

A

chicken   squirrel

common reptilian
ancestor

squid   fish   pterosaurs   bats

B   C

ancestral mollusks   ancestral chordates   ancestral reptiles   ancestral mammals

CONVERGENCE
(NONREPLACING)

CONVERGENCE
(REPLACING)

**Fig. 24.3.   In evolutionary divergence (A), a common ancestor, gives rise to differ-
ent descendant lines.** In evolutionary convergence (B) and (C), relatively unrelated ancestors give rise to rather similar lines.

"most efficient." The design only needs to be practically workable and just efficient enough for a necessary function. In a way of life based on flying, wings of
some sort are clearly essential. But virtually all requirements for living can have *multiple* solutions, and so
long as a given solution works at all it does not matter
how the solution is arrived at. The various animal
wings do represent multiple solutions of the same problem, each evolved from a different starting point and
each functioning in a different way.

We are led to one of the most important and most
universal characteristics of evolution, that of *random
opportunism*. Evolution has produced not what is theoretically desirable or best, but what is practically *possible*. There has been no predetermined plan, no
striving for set "goals," but only the exploitation of
actually available opportunities offered by selection
among random hereditary changes. For example, it
might have been adaptively exceedingly useful for terrestrial plants to grow legs or for terrestrial animals to

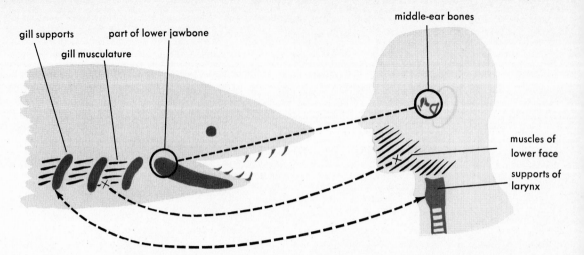

Fig. 24.4. Evolutionary opportunism. The diagram illustrates the evolutionary origin among ancestral fishes of one of the middle-ear bones, the muscles of the lower face, and laryngeal cartilages of men.

grow wheels. But neither occurred, because it could not occur. The ancestors simply did not possess the necessary structural and functional potential. However, they did possess the potential to evolve adequate, workable, alternative solutions. In the case of plants, already existing spores could be encapsulated and distributed by wind, and in the case of animals, already existing fins could be reshaped into walking legs.

Clearly, evolution can only remodel and build on what already exists, in small, successive steps. Since, given a long enough time span, *every* feature of *every* organism undergoes random variations in many different directions, opportunities for diverse evolutionary changes have been and still are very numerous. In man, for example, the bones of the middle ear have arisen opportunistically from pieces of earlier vertebrate jawbones. The musculature of the lower face has evolved from the gill muscles of ancestral fish. The voice box has developed from the gill bones of ancient fish (Fig. 24.4). Such instances of evolutionary opportunism are legion. We consequently conclude that specific organisms are *not* the result of any planned or predetermined course of creation. Instead, they are the result of a cumulative, opportunistic process of piece-by-piece building, based on preexisting organisms and governed entirely by natural selection acting on random variations.

Review questions

1. Describe the essential points of the evolutionary theories of (*a*) Lamarck, (*b*) Darwin and Wallace. How could the evolution of giraffes from short-necked ancestors be explained in terms of each of these two theories? What were the weaknesses of each theory?

2. What different kinds of inheritable variations may arise in organisms? Do such variations appear randomly or are they oriented toward usefulness? How do noninheritable variations arise and what role do they play in evolution?

3. Define the modern meaning of natural selection. Show how natural selection has little to do with "survival

of the fittest" or "struggle" or "weeding out" and how it is both a peaceful and a creative force. How does it happen that natural selection is oriented toward improved adaptation?

4. State the Hardy-Weinberg law. If a Hardy-Weinberg equilibrium exists in a population, what are the rate and amount of evolution?

5. What three conditions disturb Hardy-Weinberg equilibria? For each condition, show in what way such equilibria are disturbed and how evolution is therefore affected. How do recessive genes spread through a population? What is genetic drift, and where is it encountered?

6. Define "species" in genetic terms. Describe the process of speciation. What are some common geographical isolating conditions, and what is their effect on gene pools? How do reproductive barriers arise between populations?

7. Review some actual evidence for evolution. How have rates of evolution varied in the past? What is an adaptive radiation? Illustrate in the case of mammals.

8. How many and which implications are wholly erroneous in the following statement: "If we examine the evolutionary scale, we find that the lowly amoeba has given rise to higher forms such as man." Rephrase this statement into an appropriate number of correct ones.

9. What are the general causes of extinction? What has been the pattern of extinction on different taxonomic levels? What is evolutionary replacement? Distinguish between evolutionary divergence and convergence and give examples.

10. In what way is evolution randomly opportunistic? List 10 structural or functional features of man and determine for each (*a*) how it has evolved opportunistically and (*b*) that it cannot be labeled as being "theoretically best."

Suggested collateral readings

Crow, J. F.: Ionizing Radiation and Evolution, *Sci. Am.*, vol. 201, 1959.

Deevey, E. S.: The End of the Moas, *Sci. Am.*, vol. 190, 1954.

Deevey, E. S.: The Human Population, *Sci. Am.*, vol. 203, 1960.

Dobzhanski, T.: The Genetic Basis of Evolution, *Sci. Am.*, vol. 182, 1950.

Eiseley, L. C.: Charles Darwin, *Sci. Am.*, vol. 194, 1956.

Kettlewell, H. B. D.: Darwin's Missing Evidence, *Sci. Am.*, vol. 200, 1959.

Lack, D.: Darwin's Finches, *Sci. Am.*, vol. 188, 1953.

Ryan, F. J.: Evolution Observed, *Sci. Am.*, vol. 189, 1953.

EVOLUTION: THE PAST

25

One of the main lines of investigation which reveals the time course of past evolution is *paleontology*, the study of *fossils*. Representing the remains of formerly living plants and animals, fossils provide the most direct evidence of the kinds of organisms in existence at various earlier times. A second main line of investigation is *comparative morphology*, the study of the structure of presently living organisms. Being the products of past plants and animals, modern organisms reflect in their architecture the evolutionary history of their antecedents. All levels of structure embody the record of past evolution. Molecular and cellular evolution is revealed by studies in *comparative biochemistry* and *comparative cytology*, and tissue and organ evolution is revealed through *comparative embryology* and *comparative anatomy*.

Unfortunately, the fossil record does not go back more than 500 million years, a span of time representing only the last quarter or so of living history. Events during the crucial first three-quarters must therefore be inferred indirectly through a study of organisms now living.

The geologic record

FOSSILS

Fossils are any long-preserved remains of organisms. They may be skeletons or shells, perhaps recrystallized under heat and pressure and infiltrated with mineral deposits from surrounding rock. They may be footprints later petrified or the remnants of organisms trapped in arctic ice, amber, quicksand, gravel pits, tar pits, and swamps. Or they may be imprints of carbon black on rock, left when the soft parts of plants or animals vaporized under heat and pressure. Whenever a buried organism or any part of it becomes preserved in some way before it decays, it will be a fossil.

Fossils formed in the past are embedded in earth layers of different ages. In a geologically undisturbed section of the earth's crust, the deeper layers are the older layers. Material eroded from high-lying land gradually piles up on low land and on the sea bottom. A deep layer today therefore was on the surface in past ages and the earth's surface today will be a deep layer in the future. Fossils embedded in successive layers so provide a time picture of evolution. To be sure, deep-lying fossils are normally not accessible. But on occasion, a canyon-cutting river, an earthquake fracture, or an upbuckling and consequent breaking of the earth's crust may expose a cross section through the rock strata. Moreover, erosion gradually wears away top layers, exposing deeper rock. Geological changes of this sort have been sufficiently abundant to expose layers of all different ages in various parts of the world (Fig. 25.1).

How is the actual age of a rock layer determined? Very excellent clocks are built right into the earth's crust: radioactive substances. The disintegration rate of these substances is known accurately, as are the endproducts of disintegration. For example, a given quantity of radium is known to "decay" into lead in a certain span of time. When radium and lead are found together in one mass within a rock, the whole mass presumably had been radium originally, when the rock was formed. From the relative quantities of radium and lead present today, one can then calculate the time required for that much lead to form. This dates the rock.

An analogous principle underlies age determinations by potassium-argon dating and by radiocarbon dating. In the potassium-argon process, one measures how much of the unstable isotope potassium 40 has decayed into the isotope argon 40. Radiocarbon dating involves measurements of carbon 14, an isotope of "natural" carbon 12. Whereas the potassium-argon method can be used for dating fossils many millions of years old, the carbon 14 method is accurate only for fossils formed within the last 50,000 years. Fossils themselves often help in fixing the age of a rock layer. If such a layer contains a fossil which on the basis of other evidence is known to be of a definite age, then the whole layer, including all other fossils in it, is likely to be of the same general age.

Based on data obtained from radioactive and fossil clocks, geologists have constructed a *geologic time table* which indicates the age of successive earth layers and so provides a calendar of the earth's past history. This calendar consists of five successive main divisions, so-called *eras*. The last three of these are subdivided

Fig. 25.1. Rock layers of different ages are often exposed to view. The deeper a layer in the earth's crust, the older it is. (American Museum of Natural History.)

in turn into a number of successive *periods* (Table 10).

The beginning and terminal dates of the eras and periods have not been chosen arbitrarily but have been made to coincide with major geological events known to have occurred at those times. The transitions between eras in particular were times of great upheaval, characterized by mountain building and by severely fluctuating climates. For example, the transition from the Paleozoic to the Mesozoic dates the *Appalachian revolution*, during which the mountain range of that name was built up. By now, these mountains are already greatly reduced by erosion. Similarly, the transition between the Mesozoic and the Cenozoic was marked by the *Laramide revolution*, which produced the high mountain ranges of today: the Himalayas, the Rockies, the Andes, and the Alps.

THE PRECAMBRIAN ERA

The first geologic era, the immensely long Azoic, spans the period from the origin of the earth to the origin of life. Living history begins with the next era, the Precambrian.

TABLE 10
The geologic time table°

era	period	duration	beginning date
Cenozoic ("new life")	Quaternary	75 { 1	1
	Tertiary	74	75
Mesozoic ("middle life")	Cretaceous	60	135
	Jurassic	130 { 30	165
	Triassic	40	205
Paleozoic ("ancient life")	Permian	25	230
	Carboniferous	50	280
	Devonian	300 { 45	325
	Silurian	35	360
	Ordovician	65	425
	Cambrian	80	505
Precambrian		1,500	2,000
Azoic ("without life")		3,000	5,000

° All numbers refer to millions of years; older ages are toward bottom of table, younger ages toward top.

Fossils are not lacking altogether from these distant Precambrian ages. But the record is exceedingly fragmentary and it shows mainly that life, simple cellular life at least, already existed about 1 billion years ago. This must mean that the actual origin of life must have occurred earlier; we place it at about 2 billion years ago, at the start of the Precambrian. We also know how far evolution must have proceeded by the end of the Precambrian, for from that time on we have a continuous and abundant fossil record.

It is a very curious circumstance that rocks older than about 500 million years are so barren of fossils whereas rocks younger than that are comparatively rich in them. Many hypotheses have been proposed to account for this, but to date a satisfactory explanation has not been found. Did the Precambrian environment somehow preclude the formation of fossils? Were fossils destroyed in some way before the Paleozoic? Or is the Precambrian fossil record so scanty because the organisms then were still too unsubstantial to leave fossilizable remains? We simply cannot be sure.

But we *are* reasonably sure that Precambrian evolution must have brought about not only the origin of life and the origin of cells but also the origin of three of the four present main groups of organisms, namely, the Monera, the Protista, and the Metazoa. Moreover, practically all phyla within these three groups were in existence by the end of the Precambrian. To be sure, the organisms then representing these phyla were not the organisms of today; extinction and replacement by new types was still to occur many times. But the ancient types nevertheless did belong to the same phyla we recognize now. In what sequence these various ancient organisms evolved from the first cells must, in the absence of fossils, be inferred from the nature of presently living forms. In different contexts, we actually have already made such inferences in various earlier chapters.

Evidently, the long Precambrian spanned not only three-quarters of evolutionary time but also three-quarters of evolutionary substance. The organisms in existence at the end of the Precambrian probably were all aquatic. With the possible exception of some of the bacteria and some of the Protista, the land apparently had not been invaded as yet. The ensuing last quarter of evolution brought about principally a rich and extensive further diversification within the existing phyla. This produced replacement of ancient forms by new ones, including in each of the three main groups the evolution of types which could live on land. And among the land-adapted descendants of the Protista, more specifically the green algae, there were organisms which established a new main group, namely, the Metaphyta. These appear to have been the last to evolve among the four main categories now living.

Starting with the Cambrian period of the Paleozoic era, the course of evolution is documented fairly amply by fossils. These show that, on the phylum level, every group in existence in the Cambrian has persisted to the present. But on the species level, no group has persisted.

Plant evolution

The Cambrian and Ordovician periods lasted for almost half of the entire 300-million-year-long Paleozoic era. During this time, the seas and later also the fresh waters abounded with many diverse moneran, protistan, and animal types. The first truly terrestrial organisms appear in the fossil record of the Silurian. These were tracheophytes, specifically, psilopsids.

THE PALEOZOIC

In 1903, the French botanist Lignier proposed the hypothesis that the ancestors of the terrestrial tracheophytes were green algae with a branching, rather *Fucus*-like structure. Such an ancestral stock was postulated to have become terrestrial by development of an epidermis with cuticles and stomata; gradual straightening of some of the branches, leading to the formation of a main stem with smaller lateral branches; growth of some of the lowest branches into the ground as roots; development of vascular tissue in the interior of stem and root; and restriction of reproductive capacity to the terminals of stems. Lignier considered that the evolution of alga into tracheophyte might have occurred along sea or freshwater shores, where intermittent terrestrial conditions would have promoted the development of adaptations to land life (Fig. 25.2).

Later evidence has supported this hypothesis, which is now accepted quite widely. Numerous psilopsid fossils have been discovered which were structured more or less exactly as postulated by the Lignier hypothesis. A case in point is *Rhynia*, a Silurian fossil psilopsid which possessed rhizoids, forked upright branches about 1 foot in height, and terminal sporangia. Leaves were absent (Fig. 25.3).

Various other extinct psilopsids show clearly that these early plants could indeed have been ancestral to all other evolutionary lines of vascular plants. For example, the psilopsid *Asteroxylon* exhibited rootlike branches, numerous tiny leaves, and other characteristics which indicate a lycopsid direction of evolution. The sphenopsid direction is suggested by fossil plants such as *Hyenia*, which possessed small leaves arranged in nodal whorls. Several fossil psilopsids, among them *Pseudosporochnus*, point to the pteropsid direction of evolution. In these 9-foot-high treelike plants, the leaves were flattened and quite large, which may have foreshadowed a leaf structure characteristic of ferns.

By Devonian times, clearly defined lycopsids, sphenopsids, and pteropsids were already in existence and flourishing. The lycopsids were represented by the *lepidodendrids,* the giant club mosses (Fig. 25.4). All were huge trees up to 120 feet in height, with active secondary growth, leaves some 20 inches long, and cones up to 1 foot long. The "scale tree" *Lepidodendron* became particularly abundant, as did *Sigillaria*, the "seal tree." The 60-foot-high stem of this tree bore

Fig. 25.2. The Lignier hypothesis. Branching algae as in A may have evolved via stages as in B into primitive, rhizome-possessing tracheophytes as in C.

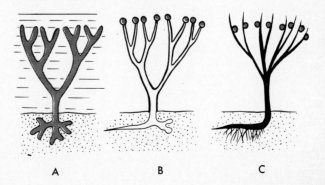

A   B   C

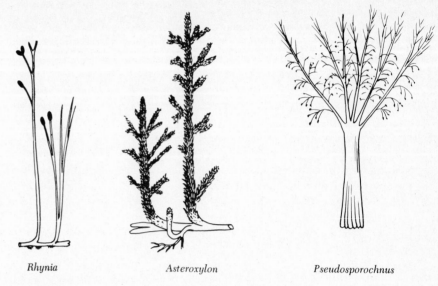

Fig. 25.3.   Fossil psilopsids. (Left and middle, after Kidston and Lang; right, after Krausel and Weyland.)

Rhynia   *Asteroxylon*   *Pseudosporochnus*

leaves in a terminal tuft which gave the plant the general appearance of a giant paintbrush. Some of the Devonian sphenopsids similarly were giant plants, in some cases forming trees up to 100 feet high (see Fig. 25.4).

But in comparison with the large lycopsids and sphenopsids, the pteropsids of the Devonian were still relatively small and had not yet attained the stature they were to achieve later. Fossil ferns were in existence, and some of them produced an adaptive radiation which included a line leading to the seed plants; fossil seed plants appear for the first time in late Devonian rocks. These seed plants were gymnosperms belonging to two groups, the *seed ferns* and the *fossil conifers*. The former (which were not really "ferns" despite their name) probably arose first and in turn gave rise to the latter (Fig. 25.5). But neither achieved prominence until the Carboniferous period.

During the Carboniferous, most of the tracheophytes which had evolved during the Devonian reached their peak abundance. Lycopsids and sphenopsids produced huge forests, and ferns too attained the stature of trees. Bryophytes appear for the first time in the fossil record of this period. It is possible that their evolution was promoted by the generally wet, tropical and subtropical conditions then prevailing over much of the earth. In addition, gymnosperms

came to be important members of the world's flora. The two already existing groups, seed ferns and fossil conifers, became dominant during the Carboniferous. A third gymnosperm group, the *fossil cycads*, evolved in this period from the seed ferns. The latter appear to have been the ancestors of all other gymnosperms, extinct as well as living, and they probably also gave rise later to the flowering plants. The Carboniferous is sometimes called the "age of seed ferns."

During the later part of the Carboniferous, many regions became so wet that they were transformed into vast tracts of swamps and marshes. In these, much of the woody flora of the time died. Later geological changes converted the bodies of the plants into coal. Hence the name of the whole period, "coal-bearing." The rich coal beds of Pennsylvania and West Virginia arose at that time.

Many of the plants survived, however, and persisted into the Permian. They were joined then by the newly evolved ginkgoes. The long Paleozoic eventually terminated with the geological upheavals of the Appalachian revolution, which in turn precipitated a so-called *Permo-Triassic crisis* among living organisms. This unstable time of transition was marked by widespread extinction of archaic forms and later replacement with rapidly evolving new types. Also, the total amount of life decreased temporarily, both in the sea and on land. Among plants, many groups became extinct: virtually all of the psilopsids, lepido-dendrids, and early sphenopsids, as well as many of the ancient ferns, gymnospermous seed ferns, and fossil conifers. Only remnant groups of psilopsids, lycopsids, and sphenopsids managed to survive, and their descendants still linger on as relics today. The surviving groups of ferns and gymnosperms soon began

Calamites

Fig. 25.4. Photos: fossil lycopsids. Left, reconstruction of *Lepidodendron;* right, reconstruction of *Sigillaria.* Diagrams: left, a fossil sphenopsid; right, a fossil fern. (Photos, Chicago Natural History Museum; diagrams, after Hirmer.)

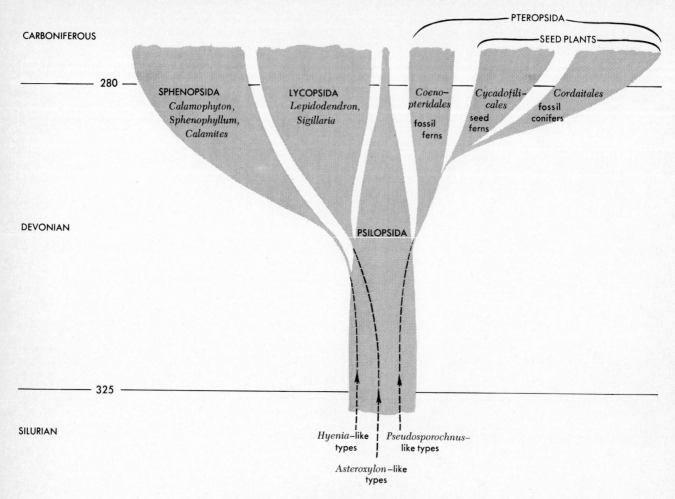

Fig. 25.5.   Summary of Devonian plant-fossil history. Technical and common names are given. The widths of the gray areas indicate the relative abundance of given groups at various time levels.

to flourish anew, however; they became the ancestors of the expanding flora of the new Mesozoic era (Fig. 25.6).

THE MESOZOIC

The Mesozoic as a whole is often called the "age of gymnosperms" in plant evolution (Fig. 25.7).

As noted, fossil cycads (*Bennettitales*) had evolved from the seed ferns and had already been in existence since the Carboniferous. This group reached its peak during the Jurassic, when it formed extensive forests. The trees were some 10 feet high, with terminal leaves almost as long as the tree trunk. Fossil cycads died out during the Cretaceous (and their ample remains may still be found, for example, in the Fossil Cycad National Monument in the Black Hills of South Dakota). The group was replaced on a reduced scale by the true cycads, probably evolved independently from seed ferns. Descendants of these plants are still living in various warm-climate areas today.

During the early part of the Mesozoic, the ginkgoes

steadily increased in abundance. They reached their peak during the Jurassic and early Cretaceous. Concurrently, new groups of coniferous gymnosperms came into ascendancy. These dominated the whole later part of the Mesozoic and included many of the presently living conifers: cypresses, yews, redwoods, and pines, for example.

But the forests formed by these large trees did not dominate the late Mesozoic landscape alone. They had to share space with the *angiosperms*, which produced a first extensive radiation at that time. Fragmentary fossils of angiosperms date back to the Jurassic, and the first ample finds occur in Cretaceous layers. The origin of angiosperms is quite obscure. The best guess at present is that they evolved from some seed fern

stock which had survived into the Mesozoic. As will become apparent below, the late Mesozoic expansion of angiosperms coincided with a similarly extensive radiation of insects. Most of the Mesozoic angiosperms were woody. They included many of the tree-forming types still living today, e.g., elms, oaks, maples, magnolias, and palms. Forests of these were already flourishing in the closing phases of the Mesozoic, when they began to rival the forests of conifers.

THE CENOZOIC

If the Mesozoic was the age of gymnosperms, the Cenozoic was unquestionably the "age of angiosperms" in plant evolution. The increasing dominance of

Fig. 25.6. Summary of late Paleozoic and early Mesozoic plant-fossil history. Fossil cycads are identified by their technical name, Bennettitales; modern cycads are labeled "cycads." Cordaitales are fossil conifers.

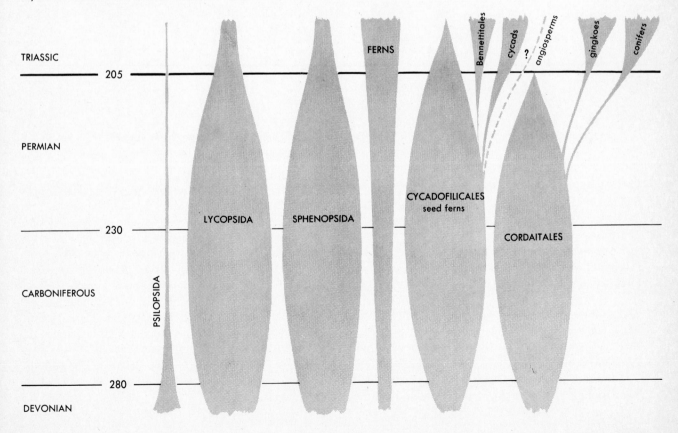

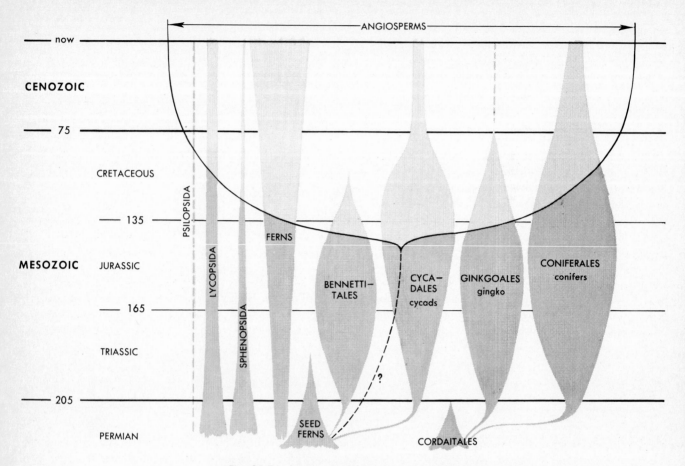

Fig. 25.7. **Summary of Mesozoic and Cenozoic plant-fossil history.** Fossil cycads are again identified as Bennettitales, and fossil conifers, as Cordaitales.

the angiosperms and the corresponding decline of the gymnosperms was in large measure a consequence of the Laramide revolution which terminated the Mesozoic.

As noted earlier, the main effect of the Laramide revolution was the formation of the high mountain ranges of today. Their emergence substantially changed the patterns of air circulation between ocean and land, and the new patterns led to new climatic conditions. For example, the east-west barrier of the Himalayas in Asia and of the Alps in Europe prevented warm south winds from reaching the northern portions of Eurasia. These regions became colder as a result. Such cooling in turn undoubtedly facilitated the de-

velopment of ice ages during the last million years (see Chap. 7).

High, even temperatures had predominated before the Laramide revolution, when much of the earth was tropical and subtropical and when the poles were ice-free. This was an advantageous climate which offered a continuous, uninterrupted growing season to plants. The early gymnosperms and angiosperms were well adapted to such conditions. They evolved secondary growth and accumulated more and more wood with each passing year. Indeed, fossil trees from the Mesozoic and early Cenozoic are without annual rings, indicating the existence of even, warm conditions.

But as climates became cooler during the later Cenozoic, distinct tropical, temperate, and cold polar zones became established. This meant that seed plants already living in the tropics could remain tropical but that species in other regions could not. Three choices were open to them. They could migrate to the tropics, or they could die and become extinct, or they could readapt right where they lived to the succession of winter and summer. All three possibilities were actually realized in different groups. Of the groups which did not migrate, many became extinct. The decline of gymnosperms traces to this time. Today only some 700 species are left, and these survive because they now manage to protect themselves against the cold through processes of winter-hardening. Many woody angiosperms similarly survive today in temperate and northern regions, but they have adapted to winter conditions by shedding their leaves. Even so, the luxuriant forests of gymnosperms and angiosperms once characteristic of northern regions thinned out and became less extensive. Fossil trees from the later Cenozoic do show annual rings like trees today, indicating clearly that uninterrupted year-round growth was no longer possible.

Furthermore, in response to late Cenozoic climates the surviving angiosperms of temperate and northern regions produced a whole new adaptive radiation. The plants of this radiation coped with the cool seasons in new ways: they became nonwoody herbaceous biennials and annuals. Winter then could not harm them, for during the winter they simply died and became nonexistent as mature plants. Thus the long-range consequences of the Laramide revolution were, first, the reduction of the woody seed plants in all regions except the tropics, and second, the gradual emergence of the modern small-bodied flowering herbs. These became dominant in the northern and arctic zones. Such areas today are inhabited by about 80 per cent of all the herbaceous angiosperms, whereas the tropics are inhabited by a similar percentage of all the woody angiosperms.

As we shall see shortly, the reduction of forests during the middle and late Cenozoic was to prove highly significant for animal evolution, human evolution in particular.

Animal evolution

As noted earlier, all metazoan phyla recognized today appear to have been already established 500 million years ago and all have persisted to the present. But not a single species has persisted. Indeed, the dominant theme of the animal fossil record is very extensive and repeated replacement within major groups and relatively few additions of new major groups.

THE PALEOZOIC

The land during the early Paleozoic remained free of animals, but animal life in the sea was already abundant. Sponges, coelenterates, brachiopods, bryozoa, echinoderms, mollusks, arthropods, and a large variety of worms were particularly common (Fig. 25.8). From the human standpoint, the most important event of the early Paleozoic was the rise of the subphylum Vertebrata. The chordate ancestors of vertebrates probably were marine tunicates, already present at the start of the Paleozoic. Some of the descendants of these ancestral tunicates later evolved into vertebrates, presumably in freshwater rivers. The first fossil vertebrates date to the late Ordovician. These were members of the class Agnatha, the *jawless fishes*. Lampreys and hagfishes are the only surviving descendants of these forms.

We recall that the first land organisms were Silurian psilopsids. Animals soon followed the plants to land; fossil scorpions from the late Silurian are the earliest known terrestrial animals. Other land arthropods appeared in the Devonian: spiderlike creatures, archaic mites, and probably the ancestors of insects. Moreover, at the very end of the Devonian the first terrestrial vertebrates made their appearance.

The Devonian as a whole is often called the "age of fishes" in animal evolution. During the early Silurian, ancestral jawless fishes had given rise to a new line, the *jawed fishes*, or *placoderms*. The name of this separate class of vertebrates refers to the armor plates with which the skins of these fishes were equipped (Fig. 25.9). The placoderms became abundant when the Devonian began, and they replaced the jawless

Fig. 25.8.   Seascapes of the early Paleozoic. Restorations. Top, Cambrian seas. Various algae, trilobites (ancient arthropods, in center foreground), eurypterids (ancient crustacea, in center background), sponges, jellyfish, brachiopods, and different types of worms are the most prominent organisms shown. Bottom, Ordovician seas. The large animal in foreground is a straight-shelled nautiloid, an ancient mollusk. (Top, American Museum of Natural History; bottom, Chicago Natural History Museum.)

fishes more or less completely. Some of the placoderms were small, but others reached lengths of 12 yards or more. Most exploited the possession of jaws by adopting a fiercely carnivorous way of life.

The dominance of the placoderms was relatively short-lived. Early during the Devonian, ancestral placoderms had given rise to two new lines of fishes which came to replace the later placoderms. By the end of the Devonian, placoderms had disappeared completely, the only vertebrate class (and one of the few classes of animals generally) which has become extinct.

The two new types of fishes evolved from early placoderms during the Devonian were the *cartilage*

Fig. 25.9.   Drawing of a placoderm. (Chicago Natural History Museum.)

fishes and the *bony fishes*, each representing a separate class (Fig. 25.10). The former includes sharks, skates, and rays. The latter soon radiated into several subgroups, and one of these, the *lobe-finned fishes*, included the ancestors of the *amphibia*, the first land vertebrates. As indicated by their name, the lobe-fins had fleshy appendages, usable to some extent as walking legs (Fig. 25.11). These fishes probably lived in fresh waters which dried out periodically, and their fins may have enabled them to crawl overland to other bodies of water. We may conclude, indeed, that terrestrial vertebrates arose not because certain fish preferred the land, but because they had to use the land if they were to survive as fish.

Thus, when the Devonian came to a close, sharks dominated in the ocean and bony fishes in fresh waters. On land, terrestrial arthropods had become abundant and the first amphibia had made their appearance. Many of the land animals could shelter in the lycopsid and sphenopsid forests already established at that time.

In later Paleozoic times, the character of aquatic animal life did not change in major ways, but that of terrestrial life did. Additional terrestrial groups evolved from aquatic ancestors, and some other groups, already terrestrial, began to diversify. For example, insects produced extensive adaptive radiations at that time. Some of these ancient insect types reached sizes well above the modern maximum. A Permian dragonfly,

Fig. 25.10. Vertebrate evolution during the Paleozoic. The name of each group is shown roughly at the time level at which this group first appears in the fossil record.

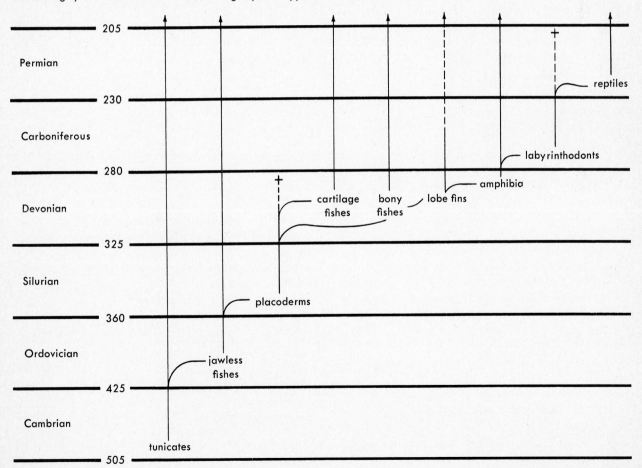

Fig. 25.11.   Left, restoration of fossil lobe-finned fishes. Right, reconstruction of *Diplovertebron*, a Permian amphibian labyrinthodont. (American Museum of Natural History.)

for example, is known to have had a wingspread of close to a yard.

Among vertebrates, the early amphibia gave rise to a large variety of more or less clumsy, often bizarre forms, the *labyrinthodonts* (see Figs. 25.10 and 25.11). During the Permian, however, most of these began to be replaced by members of a new vertebrate class, the *reptiles*. The latter had evolved from ancestral labyrinthodonts late during the Carboniferous and were represented at first by one main group, the *cotylosaurs*, or *stem reptiles*. These produced a major reptilian radiation during the Permian, which set the stage for a subsequent "age of reptiles" during the Mesozoic era.

As noted earlier, the Paleozoic era terminated with the Permo-Triassic crisis precipitated by the Appalachian revolution. This crisis was characterized as among plants by widespread extinction of archaic animal forms and by replacement and rapid evolution of new groups. In the sea, most of the once abundant invertebrate types disappeared and were replaced by newly evolved representatives. Similar replacement occurred among the cartilage and bony fishes. On land, the labyrinthodonts became extinct and the amphibian tradition so became limited to a small group of inconspicuous types, the direct ancestors of the modern salamanders, frogs, and toads. When the new Mesozoic era opened, reptiles were already dominant.

THE MESOZOIC

Several major evolutionary events occurred during this era. As pointed out earlier, the flowering plants arose during the Jurassic and underwent an explosive expansion during the Cretaceous which established them as the dominant land plants from then on. In parallel with this, insects reradiated enormously and their present importance traces to this Mesozoic expansion. An equally extensive radiation occurred among the bony fishes, which became the dominant animals of the aquatic environment, a status they still retain today.

The most spectacular Mesozoic event was the expansion of the reptiles. These animals not only evolved many different terrestrial ways of life but also invaded the water and the air. As a group they reigned supreme on earth for 130 million years, longer than any other animals to date. When their dominance was eventually broken, they were replaced by two new groups they themselves had given rise to, the birds and the mammals.

At the beginning of the Mesozoic, five major reptilian stocks were in existence, all evolved during the Permian from the stem reptiles. As Fig. 25.12 indicates, the members of these stocks did not all flourish at the same time. The Triassic was dominated largely by the ancestral *thecodonts* and the *therapsids*. The former were rather birdlike in appearance. They possessed large hind limbs for walking, an enormous supporting tail, and diminutive forelimbs, often not even long enough to shovel food into the mouth. Therapsids, on the other hand, walked on all fours, and some of them gave rise to true mammals during the late Triassic or early Jurassic. However, the new fur-bearing mammals still were greatly overshadowed by the reptiles; they remained small and inconspicuous during the rest of the Mesozoic, that is, for a period of about 80 or 90 million years.

During the Jurassic, *ichthyosaurs* became abundant in the ocean and one of the thecodont groups evolved into *birds*. Like the early mammals, the ancestral birds similarly remained inconspicuous during the whole remaining Mesozoic. They were overshadowed particularly by their thecodont kin, the pterosaurs. These flying reptiles had their heyday during the Cretaceous, the period when reptiles as a whole attained their greatest abundance and variety. *Plesiosaurs* then were common in the ocean, and the *dinosaurs* came into undisputed dominance on land.

The two dinosaurian groups, called the *Ornithischia* and the *Saurischia*, evolved from the thecodonts.

Not all dinosaurs were large, but some were enormous. The saurischian *Brontosaurus* was the largest land animal of all time, exceeded in size only by the modern blue whale. This dinosaur was herbivorous and it probably lived in swamps or lagoons, where it could support its 20- to 30-ton bulk in water. Another saurischian, the giant *Tyrannosaurus,* probably was the fiercest land carnivore of all time (Fig. 25.13).

As the Cretaceous came to a close, virtually all the reptilian multitude became extinct. Today the class is represented mainly by turtles, crocodiles, lizards, and snakes. The specific reasons for this large-scale dying out have been sought for a long time, but fully satisfactory explanations have not yet been found. Climatic changes at the end of the Mesozoic, coincident with the Laramide revolution, are believed to have played a decisive role.

THE CENOZOIC

Just as each geological era may be subdivided into periods, so each period in turn may be subdivided into epochs. The periods and epochs of the Cenozoic era are shown in Table 11.

The radiation of mammals and birds, made possible by the extinction of most of the reptiles, came to be the main feature of animal evolution during the Cenozoic. Terrestrial mammals replaced the dinosaurs; aquatic mammals eventually took the place of the former ichthyosaurs and plesiosaurs; and bats, but more especially birds, gained the air left free by the pterosaurs. The Cenozoic is often designated as the

TABLE 11
The epochs and periods of the Cenozoic era°

period	epoch	duration	beginning date
Quaternary	Recent	20,000 years	20,000 B.C.
	Pleistocene	1	1
Tertiary	Pliocene	11	12
	Miocene	16	28
	Oligocene	11	39
	Eocene	19	58
	Paleocene	17	75

° Unless otherwise stated, all figures refer to millions of years.

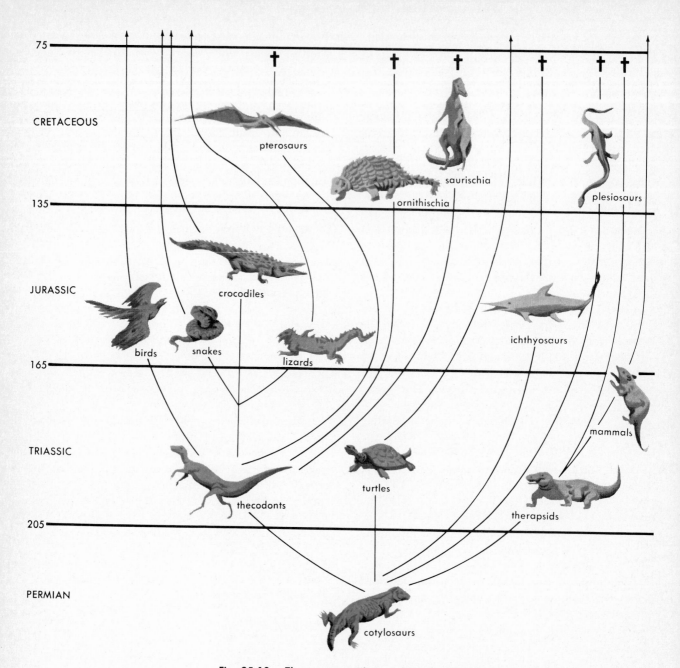

Fig. 25.12. The great reptilian radiation of the Mesozoic. Placement of groups corresponds roughly with the time of their greatest abundance.

"age of mammals"; it might equally well be called the "age of birds."

When the Cenozoic began, the great mammalian radiation was just getting under way. Three subclasses came into existence, as noted in Chap. 10, including a total of some two dozen independent lines (each ranked as an order). Most of these lines represented *placental* types, which now include the most familiar

Fig. 25.13.   Dinosaurs. Left, *Brontosaurus*. Right, *Tyrannosaurus*. (Left, American Museum of Natural History; right, Chicago Natural History Museum.)

mammals: cats, dogs, seals, and walruses; rodents; whales and dolphins; bats; moles and shrews; cattle, sheep, pigs, and camels; horses and zebras; elephants and tapirs; monkeys and men; and many others (Fig. 25.14).

The fossil record of this mammalian radiation is fairly extensive for most groups and extremely good for a few, such as horses and elephants. Each mammalian line descended from the common ancestral stock exploited a particular way of life available at the time.

Fig. 25.14.   Some of the main features of the mammalian radiation during the Cenozoic.

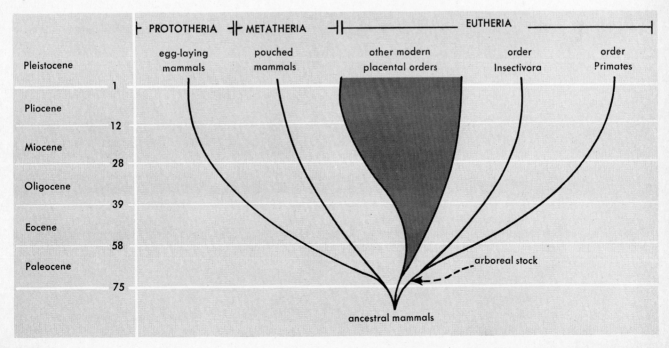

The animals came to occupy either a new environmental niche or one left free after the extinction of the Mesozoic reptiles. One mammalian line is of particular interest, for it eventually led to man. This line exploited a relatively new environmental possibility. Its members took to the trees, which then still formed vast forests, and adapted to an *arboreal* life.

Soon after such a stock of arboreal mammals had evolved during the early Paleocene, it produced two major sublines, the order *Insectivora* and the order *Primates*. The insect eaters today include shrews, moles, and hedgehogs, and the most familiar member of the primates is man. In the next section we shall trace the evolution of the primate stock in greater detail.

The evolution of man

THE PRIMATE RADIATION

As just noted, the ancestors of primates were arboreal and insect-eating. They were shrewlike in appearance, tiny, and like shrews today they were probably ferocious in behavior and ate ravenously and incessantly.

The first distinct primates evolved from such ancestral types during the Paleocene may be referred to as the *early prosimians*. Of the many lines which they in turn gave rise to, four major ones survive today (Fig. 25.15).

One of these four are the *modern prosimians*. The group includes the *lemurs* and the *aye-ayes*, found today largely on the island of Madagascar (Fig. 25.16). These animals still possess long snouts and long tails, but instead of claws they have flat nails, a general primate characteristic. It is likely that nails are a specific adaptation to arboreal life, for nails probably interfere less with locomotion along tree branches than long claws. The modern prosimians also include the *tarsiers* of Southern Asia and Indonesia. In these animals, the snout has receded considerably and a fairly well-defined face has appeared. Moreover, the eyes, which in lemurs are still more or less on the side, have moved well into the face. As a result, tarsiers may focus on one point with both eyes; they are endowed with stereoscopic vision and efficient depth perception.

These features are additional adaptations to a

Fig. 25.15. Diagram of the radiation of primates.

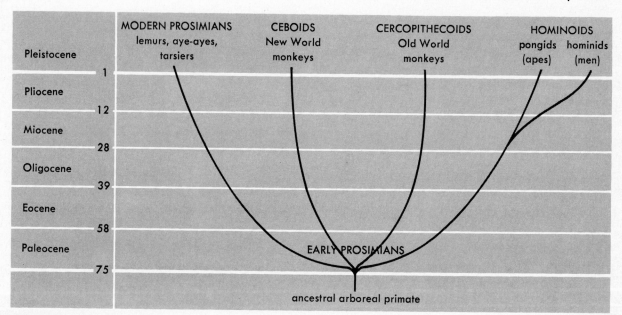

Fig. 25.16. Left, a modern lemur from Madagascar. Right, modern tarsier from Indonesia. (American Museum of Natural History.)

tree-dwelling existence. In a plains animal such as a horse, for example, the eyes are located advantageously on the side, where they enable the animal to scout the open environment even while grazing. But among the branches of a tree, lateral vision is less important. Quite the contrary, it becomes important to look ahead along a branch, almost a necessary requirement if balance is to be retained during locomotion. Note also that tarsiers possess fairly well-defined fingers, with a gripping pad at the end of each.

The second of the main groups descended from the early prosimians comprises the *New World monkeys*. They attained their present diversity during the Oligocene and Miocene and are found today in South and Central America. The animals are characterized by long, strong tails, which are used as fifth limbs. The third main group evolved independently from Paleocene prosimians consists of *Old World monkeys*. They too radiated during the Oligocene and Miocene, and they now live in Africa and Asia. These monkeys possess tails, but they are not used as limbs.

In both groups of monkeys, adaptations to arboreal life have evolved a good deal farther than in modern prosimians. A monkey possesses a very well-developed face, stereoscopic vision, and independently movable fingers on all four limbs. Moreover, it possesses opposable thumbs, which allow it to grip tree branches very firmly. Also, limbs may be rotated freely within their

sockets. In a plains animal like a horse, limbs move predominantly back and forth. The limb sockets here permit very little lateral play, an energy-saving feature in running. In jumping among tree branches, on the other hand, freely movable limbs are clearly advantageous.

Correlated with such skeletal specializations to arboreal life, monkeys have also evolved important muscular, sensory, and neural adaptations. Through a general enlargement of the cerebral cortex and a particular enlargement of the optic lobes, monkeys have become capable of precision timing, of judging distances to the inch, and of coordinating limb and finger muscles in new, complex ways. In turn, increase in brain size has led to a quickness of mind and a level of intelligence well above the prosimian average. The evolution of intelligence has been correlated particularly with the improvement of eye-limb coordination, and we may note that primate intelligence is thus likewise a result of the arboreal way of life.

Trends of the same kind, but developed very much farther than in monkeys, are apparent also in the fourth group of living primates. Descended independently from Paleocene prosimians, this group comprises the so-called *hominoids*. During the early Miocene, some 30 million years ago, the hominoid line branched into two main sublines. One of these led to the *pongids*, or apes, the other to the *hominids*, the family of man and manlike types (see Fig. 25.15). Both groups are characterized by the absence of an external tail and by an increase in body size over the average of other primates. Moreover, the brain of pongids and hominids is still further enlarged and elaborated functionally.

Apes are represented today by four genera: gibbons, orangutans, chimpanzees, and gorillas. The group is fundamentally arboreal, but modern apes include types which have abandoned the arboreal way of life more or less completely. For example, orangutans and especially chimpanzees can be quite at home out of trees. Gorillas are ground animals altogether, using trees as little as men. Correlated with this abandonment of life in trees is a tendency toward more or less two-legged walking and toward a more or less upright posture. In such a way of life on the ground, arboreal adaptations can be used to advantage. For example, the long arms of a gorilla need not participate in locomotion and become free to perform other tasks.

These trends became very much more elaborated in the hominids, the line leading to man. After branching away from the common hominoid stock during the Miocene, the hominids left the trees completely. Forelimbs remained adapted for gripping, but the feet evolved into flat walking platforms. Undoubtedly, it was this total freeing of arms and fingers for many new functions which made possible the evolution of the most basic human characteristics. For, correlated with new opportunities for exceedingly complex hand-eye coordination, brain size enlarged still further and intelligence increased spectacularly. We note that the modern human type could not have evolved if the ancestral type had not first been specialized for life in trees.

What prompted our Miocene ancestors, along with some of the early apes, to abandon arboreal life? As pointed out earlier, the progressively cooler climates during the Cenozoic led to a thinning out of forests. In many regions, therefore, continuous overhead canopies of branches and foliage disappeared. As a result, our prehuman ancestors would have had to travel on the ground if they wished to move from one stand of trees to another. Such forced excursions may well have been fraught with considerable danger, for saber-toothed carnivores and other large mammals dominated the ground at those times. Consequently, ability to dash quickly across open spaces may have had great selective value, and this may have oriented the evolution of running feet in the human direction. Moreover, strong muscles would be required to move the hind limbs in new ways. Indeed, a unique trait of the human line is the possession of such muscles, partly in the form of enlarged buttocks.

It is conceivable, therefore, that the hominids came out of the trees because they had to. Life on the ground then promoted the gradual evolution of running feet, bipedal locomotion, newly functioning forelimbs, complex hand-eye coordination, and powerful brains.

THE HOMINID RADIATION

After the hominid stock had separated from the pongid stock at about the beginning of the Miocene, the hominid group must have given rise to an adaptive radiation of its own. The detailed pattern of this hominid radiation is unknown, but that it occurred can be inferred from available fossil evidence. To be sure, this evidence is tantalizingly scanty; we can trace the recent evolution of almost any mammal far better than our own. Nevertheless, such fossils as have been found to date show clearly that the known members of the hominid radiation, including ourselves, do not appear to be related directly. In other words, other known hominids are related to us somewhat as uncles or cousins (Fig. 25.17).

With the exception of the line leading to ourselves, all other lines of the hominid radiation have become extinct at various periods during the last 30 million years. Apart from their biological distinctions, given fossil hominids are defined as prehuman or truly human on the basis of evidence relating to cultural achievements. Any hominid which *made* tools in addition to using them can be called a "man." If a hominid only used stones or sticks found ready-made in his environment, he is considered prehuman; if he deliberately fashioned natural objects into patterned tools, no matter how crude, he is considered human. By this criterion, quite a few hominid types were men.

The early parts of hominid history are almost

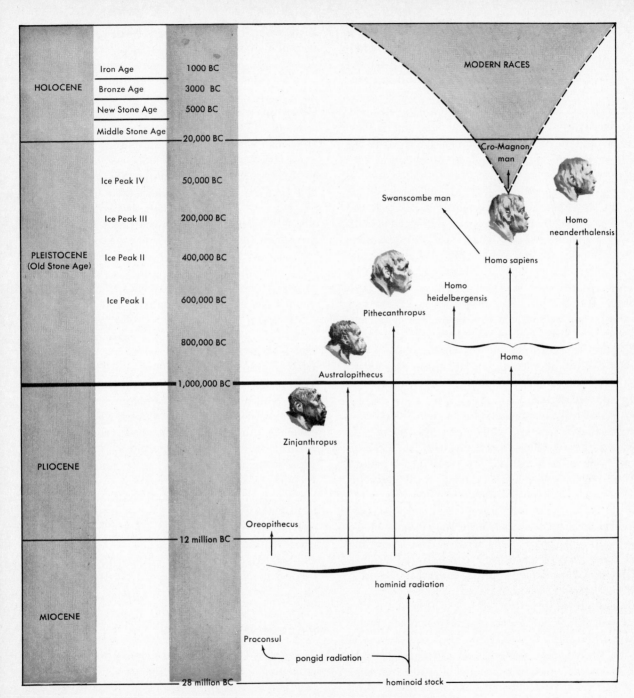

Fig. 25.17. The hominid radiation and some of its principal known members. Each hominid type is shown roughly at a time level at which that type is known to have existed. The detailed interrelations of the various hominid lines are unknown. *Proconsul* is an early type believed to have been fairly closely related to the common ancestral stock from which both apes and men arose.

completely unknown. A primate fairly closely related to the hominid radiation is *Oreopithecus*, the "mountain ape," whose remains were found in northern Italy. This primate dates back some 10 million years, to the early Pliocene. The teeth and the organization of the jaw of *Oreopithecus* were distinctly hominid, but in other respects the animal was still apelike.

Beyond these finds, the hominid record of the Tertiary is blank, with the notable exception of *Zinjanthropus*, the "East Africa man," discovered in Tanganyika. *Zinjanthropus* lived 1¾ million years ago, in the late Pliocene. This hominid made tools and thus was a true man. The tools included wooden clubs and stone hammers, with which *Zinjanthropus* killed small animals and broke open their bones. The diet was mainly coarse vegetation, however, as the large molars clearly indicate. Bone structure in the skull reveals that the head was held very erect and that jaw muscles were attached as in modern man, suggesting that *Zinjanthropus* probably knew speech. On the other hand, a forehead was virtually absent; the volume of the brain could not have been larger than 600 cubic centimeters, comparable to the brain volume of a modern gorilla.

All other known hominid fossils are of Pleistocene origin, that is, not older than 1 million years. The oldest of these includes *Australopithecus*, the "southern ape," whose remains date back roughly 1 million years or somewhat less. Although these hominids thus lived much later than *Zinjanthropus*, they probably were not as far advanced. For example, they apparently did not make tools. Their brain volume averaged 600 cubic centimeters, and the skulls and skeletons reveal a mixture of apelike and manlike traits. Some investigators regard *Australopithecus* to be fairly closely related to the line which gave rise to modern man.

A more recent and comparatively much better known hominid is *Pithecanthropus*, a true man who made tools of stone and bone and used fire for cooking. Remains of several species of *Pithecanthropus* were found in Java and China and were shown to be about 500,000 years old. The brain volume of this "erect apeman" averaged 900 to 1,000 cubic centimeters. Like several other hominids, *Pithecanthropus* probably practiced cannibalism. His fossil remains

include separate skullcaps detached cleanly from the rest of the skeleton; sheer accident does not appear to have caused such neat separations.

The first representative of the genus Homo, to which we belong, may have been *Homo heidelbergensis*, the Heidelberg man. Like *Pithecanthropus*, he lived about 500,000 years ago. Unfortunately, Heidelberg man is known only from one fossil jaw, and his status therefore cannot be fully assessed. Far more complete information is available about the Neanderthal man, who appears to have been an early representative of our own species, *Homo sapiens* (Fig. 25.18). Neanderthal man probably arose some 150,000 years ago, flourished during the period of the last ice age, and became extinct only about 25,000 years ago, when the ice sheets began to retreat. The brain of the Neanderthalers had a volume of 1,450 cubic centimeters, which compares with a volume of only 1,350 cubic centimeters for modern man. The Neanderthal brain was also proportioned differently; the skull jutted out in back, where we are relatively rounded, and the forehead was low and receding. Heavy brow ridges were present and the jaw was massive and virtually without chin.

Culturally, the Neanderthalers were Stone Age cavemen. All Pleistocene hominids are generally regarded as belonging to the *Old Stone Age*. But whereas earlier hominids made only crude stone implements, Neanderthal man fashioned a variety of weapons, tools, hunting axes and clubs, and household equipment. Yet he was still a nomad living from hand to mouth and he had neither agriculture nor domesticated animals. He did not make pottery and did not leave any art. His territory covered most of Europe, with fringe populations along the African and Asian coasts of the Mediterranean.

MODERN MAN

The time of origin of our own species cannot be pinpointed very precisely. The oldest representative of *Homo sapiens* appears to be the *Swanscombe man*, known only through a few skull bones. These remains are believed to be from 500,000 to 250,000 years old.

Later groups include *Cro-Magnon man*, who lived

Fig. 25.18. Restoration of a Neanderthal group. (Chicago Natural History Museum.)

from about 50,000 to 20,000 years ago and who may have caused the extinction of Neanderthal man in Europe. Cro-Magnon was 6 feet tall on the average, with a brain volume of about 1,700 cubic centimeters. In addition to stone implements, Cro-Magnon used bone needles with which he may have sewn animal skins into crude garments. The dog became his companion, and he was a cave-dwelling hunter who also painted remarkable murals on cave walls.

Cro-Magnon man was a contemporary of other groups of *Homo sapiens* living in different parts of the world. The racial division of modern man into *caucasoids*, *negroids*, and *mongoloids* may have taken place then. However, any original racial traits became diluted or obliterated fairly rapidly, through interbreeding among the extensively migrating human populations. None of the present human types represents a "pure" race.

By the time the Pleistocene came to a close, some 20,000 or 25,000 years ago, all species of Homo other than *Homo sapiens* had become extinct. The ice started to retreat, milder climates gradually supervened, and eventually man no longer needed to shelter in caves. For the next 15,000 years he produced what is known as the *Middle Stone Age* culture. It was characterized chiefly by great improvements in stone tools.

The *New Stone Age* began about 5,000 B.C., about the time Abraham settled in Canaan (see Fig. 25.17). A great cultural revolution took place then. Man learned to fashion pottery; he developed agriculture; and he was able to domesticate animals. From that period on, modern civilization moved on with rapid strides. By 3,000 B.C. man had entered the *Bronze Age*. Some 2,000 years later the *Iron Age* began. And not very long afterward man discovered steam, electricity, and now the atom and outer space. Measured by geological standards, the hairy beast which lumbered down from the trees 30 million years ago turned into a college professor in a flash.

That modern man has evolved through the operation of the same forces which produced all other organisms is clear. And it should also be clear that this organism is by far the most remarkable product of evolution. Man is sometimes described rather offhandedly as being "just" another animal. Often, on the contrary, he is considered to be so radically distinct that the appellation "animal" assumes the character of an insult. Neither view is justified.

Man certainly *is* an animal, but an animal with very unique attributes. At some stage during this evolution, his rate of embryonic development slowed down and his whole life cycle became stretched out in duration. Thus man became perhaps the longest-lived of all animals. As a result, another uniquely human characteristic emerged, namely, a proportionately very long *youth*. A chimpanzee, mature after a few years of life, may reach death at age twenty, when man is only beginning to be an adult. Man therefore has *time* to be young and to learn, and in his learning capacity man is also unique.

Learning presupposes a powerful brain, and in this department man clearly has no equal. The most characteristically human traits depend directly or indirectly on man's brain. Man is far more individualized in personality and behavior than any other creature. He displays a greater range of emotions than any other animal, and he is the only animal able to laugh, to weep, and to know beauty. Moreover, the human capacities of planning ahead, of having reasoned purposes, and of making considered choices far outclass anything similar among other animals.

Above all, only man has *traditions* and only he *accumulates* knowledge over successive generations. This transmission of knowledge occurs by nonbiological means, and we actually deal here with a new kind of evolution. The old is biological evolution, its vehicle being the gene. The new is social evolution, its vehicle being spoken and written *speech*. Man is quite unique in having evolved and in continuing to evolve through inherited traditions passed on not only by genes, but also by words.

Conceivably, this changeover from the merely biological to the human may have as much future significance as the earlier changeover, 2 billion years ago, from the inorganic to the biological. The first transition gave rise to totally new opportunities through which matter became organized into wealth of previously nonexistent arrangements. The recent transition may create new possibilities of like scope. But the realization of this potential is now in the hands of man; for with the coming of man, the chance operations of nature have begun to be modified and manipulated by human purpose. The activities of man block chance increasingly. Man's fate will therefore be decided by man's purpose.

Review questions

1. What is a fossil? How can the age of a fossil be determined? Review the names and dates of the geologic eras and periods. What were the Appalachian and Laramide revolutions? List the major groups of plants not yet in existence 500 million years ago.

2. Review Lignier's hypothesis regarding the origin of tracheophytes. Cite fossil evidence in support of the view that psilopsids were ancestral to all other vascular plants.

3. Describe the key events of plant evolution during the Silurian and the Devonian periods. Which pteropsid groups were in existence by the end of the Devonian?

4. Describe the key events of plant evolution during the Carboniferous and the Permian periods. What were the seed ferns? Which other plant groups are they believed to have given rise to?

5. Describe the causes and events of the Permo-Triassic crisis. At what date did it take place? Review the key events of plant evolution during (*a*) the Mesozoic era and (*b*) the Cenozoic era. What were the consequences of the Laramide revolution on plants?

6. Describe the key events of animal evolution during the (*a*) Cambrian-Ordovician, (*b*) Silurian-Devonian, (*c*) Carboniferous-Permian. Review the course of vertebrate evolution during the entire Paleozoic.

7. Describe the main events of animal evolution during the Mesozoic and Cenozoic. Review the principal features and the time pattern of the Mesozoic reptilian radiation.

8. Describe the principal features of the Cenozoic mammalian radiation, with special attention to the origin of primates. Describe the major features of the primate radiation and name living animals representing each of the main lines. When and from where did the line leading to man branch off?

9. Describe the various adaptations of each of the primate stocks to arboreal life. Which structural, functional, and behavioristic features of man trace back specifically to

the arboreal way of life of his ancestors? How does the hominoid line differ from other descendants of early prosimians? How does the hominid line differ from the pongid line?

10. Describe the known members of the hominid radiation. When was each of them probably in existence?

Roughly when did *Homo sapiens* arise? Review the biological characteristics which *Homo sapiens* shares with (*a*) all other hominids, (*b*) all other hominoids, (*c*) all other primates, (*d*) all other mammals. Review in detail the biological characteristics which distinguish man uniquely from all other animals.

Suggested collateral readings

Abelson, P. H.: Paleobiochemistry, *Sci. Am.*, vol. 195, 1956.

Clark, J. D.: Early Man in Africa, *Sci. Am.*, vol. 199, 1958.

Colbert, E. H.: The Ancestors of Mammals, *Sci. Am.*, vol. 180, 1949.

Deevey, E. S.: Radiocarbon Dating, *Sci. Am.*, vol. 186, 1952.

Dobzhansky, T.: The Present Evolution of Man, *Sci. Am.*, vol. 203, 1960.

Glaessner, M. F.: Pre-Cambrian Animals, *Sci. Am.*, vol. 204, 1961.

Janssen, R. E.: The Beginnings of Coal, *Sci. Am.*, vol. 179, 1948.

Millot, J.: Coelacanth, *Sci. Am.*, vol. 193, 1955.

Washburn, S. L.: Tools and Human Evolution, *Sci. Am.*, vol. 203, 1960.

Weckler, J. E.: Neanderthal Man, *Sci. Am.*, vol. 197, 1957.

GLOSSARY [1]

[1] The system of indicating pronunciation is used by permission of the publishers of Webster's New Collegiate Dictionary. Copyright 1949, 1951, 1953, 1956, 1958 by G. & C. Merriam Co.

abscission (ăb·sĭzh′ŭn) [L. *abscindere*, to cut off]: separation of a body part from a plant, particularly after a special layer of cells weakens and dies.

acoel, acoelomate (a·sēl′) [Gr. *a*, not, + *koilos*, cavity]: (1) without coelom; (2) an animal without coelom, i.e., flatworms, proboscis worms.

acrosome (ăk′rô·sōm) [Gr. *akros*, outermost, + *soma*, body]: structure at the tip of the sperm head (nucleus) which makes contact with the egg during fertilization.

adenosine *(di-, tri-) phosphate (ADP, ATP)* (a·děn′ō·sēn): phosphorylated organic compounds functioning in energy transfers within cells.

adipose (ăd′ĭ·pōs) [L. *adipis*, fat]: fat, fatty, fat-storing tissue.

adrenal, adrenalin (ăd·rē′năl, ăd·rēn′ăl·ĭn) [L. *ad*, to, + *renalis*, kidney]: (1) endocrine gland; (2) the hormone produced by the adrenal medulla.

adventitious (ăd′věn·tĭsh′ŭs): appearing not in usual place; as in adventitious root, which may sprout from anywhere on a stem.

aerobe, aerobic (ā′ĕr·ōb, —ō′bĭk) [Gr. *aeros*, air, + *bios*, life]: (1) oxygen-requiring organism; (2) pertaining to oxygen-dependent form of respiration.

Agnatha (ăg′nà·thà) [Gr. *a*, not, + *gnathos*, jaw]: jawless fishes, a class of vertebrates including lampreys and hagfishes.

alga (ăl′gà), *pl. algae* (—jē): any member of a superphylum of protists; blue-green, green, golden-brown, brown, red algae.

allantois (ă·lăn′tô·ĭs) [Gr. *allantoeidēs*, sausage-shaped]: one of the extraembryonic membranes in reptiles, birds, and mammals; functions as embryonic urinary bladder or as carrier of blood vessels to and from placenta.

allele (ă·lēl′) [Gr. *allēlōn*, of one another]: one of a group of alternative genes which may occupy a given locus on a chromosome; a dominant and its correlated recessive are allelic genes.

alveolus (ăl·vē′ô·lŭs), *pl. alveoli* (—lī) [L. dim. of *alveus*, a hollow]: a small cavity or pit, e.g., a microscopic air sac of the lungs.

amnion (ăm′nĭ·ŏn) [Gr. dim. of *amnos*, lamb]: one of the extraembryonic membranes in reptiles, birds, and mammals, forming a sac around the embryo.

amylase (ăm′ĭ·lās) [L. *amylum*, starch]: an enzyme promoting the decomposition of polysaccharides into smaller carbohydrate units.

anaerobe, anaerobic (ăn·ā′ĕr·ōb, —ō′bĭk) [Gr. *an*, not, + *aeros* + *bios*]: (1) an oxygen-independent organism; (2) pertaining to an oxygen-independent form of respiration.

anaphase (ăn′à·fāz) [Gr. *ana*, up, + *phasis*, appearance]: a stage in mitotic cell division, characterized by the migration of chromosome sets toward the spindle poles.

anatomy (à·năt′ô·mĭ) [Gr. *ana*, up, + *temnein*, to cut]: the gross structure of an organism, or the science which deals with gross structure; a branch of the science of morphology.

androgen (ăn′drô·jĕn) [Gr. *andros*, man, + *genēs*, born]: one of a group of male sex hormones.

angiosperm (ăn′jĭ·ô·spûrm′) [Gr. *angeion*, a vessel, + *sperma*, seed]: a member of a class of tracheophytic plants, characterized by the possession of flowers and fruits; a flowering plant.

annelid, Annelida (ăn′ĕ·lĭd) [L. *anellus*, a ring]: (1) a segmented worm; (2) the phylum of segmented worms.

anther (ăn′thĕr) [Gr. *anthos*, flower]: the microsporangia in a stamen of flowering plants.

antheridium (ăn′thĕr·ĭd′ĭ·ŭm) [Gr. *anthēros*, flowery]: the sperm-producing organ of plants.

anthocyanin (ăn′thō·sī′à·nĭn) [Gr. *anthos*, flower, + *kyanos*, blue]: a water-soluble pigment in plants, producing red, purple, and blue colors.

antibody (ăn′tĭ·bŏd′ĭ): a substance, produced within an organism, which opposes the action of another substance; in specific usage, an antibody is a globulin type of protein which combines and renders harmless an antigen, i.e., a foreign protein introduced into an organism by infectious processes.

antigen (ăn′tĭ·jĕn): a foreign substance, usually protein in nature, which elicits the formation of specific antibodies within an organism.

apical (ăp′ĭ·kăl) [L. *apex*, tip]: belonging to an apex, being at or near the tip; as in apical meristem, the embryonic plant tissue at the tip of root or stem.

archegonium (är′kē·gō′nĭ·ŭm) [Gr. *archegonos*, first of a race]: the egg-producing organ of plants.

archenteron (är·kĕn′tĕr·ŏn) [Gr. *archein*, to be first, + *enteron*, gut]: the central cavity of a gastrula, lined by endoderm, representing the future digestive cavity of the adult.

arthropod, Arthropoda (är′thro·pŏd, är·thrŏp′ô·dà) [Gr. *arthron*, joint + *podos*, foot]: (1) a jointed-legged invertebrate, such as an insect or a crustacean; (2) the phylum of jointed-legged invertebrates.

ascus (ăs′kŭs) [Gr. *askos*, a bladder]: the tubular spore sac of a class of fungi.

atactostele (ă·tăkt'ô·stēl) [Gr. *a*, without + *tassein*, to arrange]: type of stele in which vascular bundles are scattered throughout stem, as in monocots.

atom (ăt'ŭm) [Gr. *atomos*, indivisible]: the smallest whole unit of a chemical element; composed of given numbers of protons, neutrons, and other particles which form an atomic nucleus, and of given numbers of electrons, which orbit around the nucleus.

auricle (ô'rĭ·k'l) [L. dim. of *auris*, ear]: a chamber of the heart receiving blood from the circulation and pumping it into a ventricle.

autosome (ô'tô·sōm) [Gr. *autos*, self, + *soma*, body]: any chromosome which is not a sex chromosome.

autotroph, autotrophism (ô'tô·trŏf', —ĭz'm) [Gr. *autos*, self, + *trophos*, feeder]: (1) an organism which manufactures organic nutrients from inorganic raw materials; (2) a form of nutrition in which only inorganic substances are required as raw materials.

auxin (ôk'sĭn) [Gr. *auxein*, to increase]: a plant hormone promoting cell elongation, hence growth.

axon (ăk'sŏn): an outgrowth of a nerve cell, conducting impulses away from the cell body; a type of nerve fiber.

bacillus (bà·sĭl'ŭs) [L. dim. of *baculum*, rod]: any rod-shaped bacterium.

bacteriophage (băk·tēr'ĭ·ô·fāj) [*bacterium* + Gr. *phagein*, to eat]: one of a group of viruses which infect, parasitize, and eventually kill bacteria.

bacterium (băk·tēr'ĭ·ŭm) [Gr. dim. of *baktron*, a staff]: a small, typically unicellular organism characterized by the absence of a formed nucleus; genetic material is dispersed in clumps through the cytoplasm.

basidium (bà·sĭd'ĭ·ŭm) [Gr. dim. of *basis*, base]: a spore-bearing organ of a class of fungi.

benthos, benthonic (bĕn'thŏs) [Gr., depth of the sea]: (1) collective term for organisms living along the bottoms of oceans and lakes; (2) adjective.

beriberi (bĕr'ĭ·bĕr'ĭ) [Singhalese *beri*, weakness]: disease produced by deficiency of vitamin B_1 (thiamine).

bicuspid (bī·kŭs'pĭd) [L. *bi*, two, + *cuspis*, point]: ending in two points, as in bicuspid heart valve, two flaps of tissue guarding opening between left auricle and left ventricle; see also *mitral*.

blastopore (blăs'tô·pōr): opening connecting archenteron of gastrula with outside; represents future mouth in some animals, future anus in others.

blastula (blăs'tū·là): stage in early animal development, when embryo is a hollow and in some cases a solid sphere of cells.

bronchus, bronchiole (brŏng'kŭs, brŏng'kĭ·ōl) [Gr. *bronchos*, windpipe]: (1) a main branch of the trachea; (2) a smaller branch of a bronchus.

bryophyte, Bryophyta (brī'ô·fĭt) [Gr. *bryon*, moss, + *phyton*, a plant]: (1) a moss, liverwort, or hornwort; (2) phylum name.

cambium (kăm'bĭ·ŭm) [L., exchange]: embryonic tissue in roots and stems of tracheophytes, giving rise to secondary xylem and phloem.

carbohydrate, carbohydrase (kăr'bô·hī'drāt): (1) an organic compound consisting of a chain of carbon atoms to which hydrogen and oxygen, present in a 2:1 ratio, are attached; (2) an enzyme promoting the synthesis or decomposition of a carbohydrate.

carotene, carotenoids (kăr'ô·tēn, kà·rŏt'ê·noid) [L. *carota*, carrot]: (1) a pigment producing cream-yellow to carrot-orange colors; precursor of vitamin A; (2) a class of pigments of which carotene is a member.

catalysis, catalyst, catalytic (kà·tăl'ĭ·sĭs) [Gr. *katalysis*, dissolution]: (1) acceleration of a chemical reaction by a substance which does not become part of the end-product; (2) a substance which accelerates a reaction as above; (3) adjective.

Cenozoic (sē'nô·zō'ĭk) [Gr. *kainos*, recent, + *zōē*, life]: geological era after the Mesozoic, dating approximately from 75 million years ago to present.

centriole (sĕn'trĭ·ōl): cytoplasmic body forming spindle pole during mitosis and meiosis; present in cells of many Protista and most Metazoa.

centromere (sĕn'trô·mēr): region on chromosome at which spindle fibril is attached during mitosis and meiosis.

cerebellum (sĕr'ê·bĕl'ŭm) [L. dim. of *cerebrum*]: a part of the vertebrate brain, controlling muscular coordination.

cerebrum (sĕr'ê·brŭm) [L., brain]: a part of the vertebrate brain, especially large in mammals; controls many voluntary functions and is seat of higher mental capacities.

chemosynthesis (kĕm'ô·sĭn'thê·sĭs): a form of autotrophic nutrition in certain bacteria, in which energy for the manufacture of carbohydrates is obtained from inorganic raw materials.

chitin (kī'tĭn): a horny organic substance forming the exo-skeleton of arthropods, the epidermal cuticle of many other invertebrates, and the cell wall of certain Protista.

chloroplast, chlorophyll, chlorophyte (klō'rô—) [Gr. *chloros*, green]: (1) chlorophyll-containing plastid; (2) green light-trapping pigment essential as electron donor in photosynthesis; (3) a green alga, member of the phylum Chlorophyta.

Chondrichthyes (kŏn·drĭk'thĭ·ēz) [Gr. *chondros*, cartilage, + *ichthyos*, fish]: fishes with cartilage skeleton, a class of vertebrates comprising sharks, skates, rays, and related types.

Chordata (kôr·dā'tȧ) [L. *chorda*, cord]: animal phylum in which all members possess notochord, dorsal nerve cord, and pharyngeal gill slits at least at some stage of the life cycle; three subphyla, the Urochordata, the Cephalochordata, and the Vertebrata.

chorion (kō'rĭ·ŏn) [Gr.]: one of the extraembryonic membranes in reptiles, birds, and mammals; forms outer cover around embryo and all other membranes and in mammals contributes to structure of placenta.

chromosome (krō'mō·sōm) [Gr. *chroma*, color, + *soma*, body]: gene-containing filamentous body in cell nucleus, becoming conspicuous during mitosis and meiosis.

chrysophyte, Chrysophyta (krĭs'ō·fīt) [Gr. *chrysos*, gold, + *phyton*, a plant]: (1) a golden-brown alga, e.g., a diatom; (2) phylum name.

cilium (sĭl'ĭ·ŭm): microscopic bristlelike variant of a flagellum, present on surfaces of many cell types and capable of vibratory motion; functions in cellular locomotion and in creation of currents in water.

coccus (kŏk'ŭs), *pl. cocci* (kŏk'sī) [Gr. *kokkos*, a grain]: a spherical bacterium.

cochlea (kŏk'lē·ȧ) [Gr. *kochlias*, snail]: part of the inner ear, coiled like a snail shell.

coelenterate (sê·lĕn'tēr·at) [Gr. *koilos*, hollow, + *enteron*, gut]: an invertebrate animal possessing a single alimentary opening and tentacles with sting cells; e.g., jellyfish, corals, sea anemones, hydroids.

coelom (sē'lŏm) [Gr. *koilōma*, a hollow]: body cavity of animals, lined entirely by mesoderm.

coenocyte (sē'nō·sīt) [Gr. *koinos* + *kytos*, vessel] a multinucleate cell, found particularly among Protista.

coenzyme (kō·ĕn'zīm): a substance required if a given enzyme is to be active.

colloid (kŏl'oid) [Gr. *kolla*, glue]: a substance divided into fine particles, where each particle is larger than a particle of a true solution but smaller than one in a coarse suspension.

commensal, commensalism (kŏ·mĕn'sȧl, —ĭz'm) [L. *cum*, with, + *mensa*, table]: (1) an organism living symbiotically with a host, where the host neither benefits nor suffers from the association; (2) noun.

conjugation (kŏn·jōō·gā'shŭn) [L. *conjugare*, to unite]: a mating process characterized by the temporary fusion of the mating partners; occurs particularly in unicellular organisms.

corpus luteum (kôr'pŭs lū'tê·ŭm), *pl. corpora lutea* [L.]: progesterone-secreting bodies in vertebrate ovaries formed from remanants of follicles after ovulation.

cortex (kôr'tĕks), *pl. cortices* [L., bark]: the outer tissue layers of an organ or body part, e.g., adrenal cortex, cerebral cortex; also, in plants, the tissue underneath the epidermis.

cotyledon (kŏt'ĭ·lē'dŭn) [Gr. *kotylēdōn*, a cup shape]: the first leaf of a seed plant, developed by the embryo within the seed.

cyanophyte, Cyanophyta (sī·ăn'ō·fīt) [Gr. *kyanos*, dark blue, + *phyton*, plant]: (1) a blue-green alga; (2) phylum name.

cyclosis (sī·klō'sĭs) [Gr. *kyklos*, circle]: circular streaming and eddying of cytoplasm.

cytochrome, cytoplasm (sī'to—) [Gr. *krytos*, vessel]: (1) one of a group of hydrogen carriers in aerobic respiration. (2) the living matter of a cell between cell membrane and nucleus.

deamination (dē·ămĭ·nā'shŭn): removal of an amino group, especially from an amino acid.

deciduous (dê·sĭd'û·ŭs) [L. *decidere*, to fall off]: to fall off at maturity, as in plants which shed foliage during the autumn.

dendrite (dĕn'drīt) [Gr. *dendron*, tree]: filamentous outgrowth of a nerve cell, conducting nerve impulses from its free end toward the cell body.

denitrify, denitrification (dē·nī'trĭ·fī): (1) to convert nitrates to ammonia and molecular nitrogen, as by denitrifying bacteria; (2) noun.

deoxyribose (dē·ŏk'sĭ·rī'bōs): a 5-carbon sugar having one oxygen atom less than parent-sugar ribose; component of deoxyribose nucleic acid (DNA).

diabetes (dī'ȧ·bē'têz) [Gr. *diabainein*, to pass through]: abnormal condition marked by insufficiency of insulin, sugar excretion in urine, low blood-glucose levels.

diastole (dī·ăs'tô·lē) [Gr. *diastolē*, moved apart]: phase of relaxation of auricles or ventricles, during which they fill with blood; preceded and succeeded by systole, i.e., contraction.

dictyostele (dīk'tĭ·ô·stē'lē): a type of stele in which the vascular tissue is arranged in cylindrically placed bundles.

diplohaplontic (dĭp'lō·hăp·lŏn'tĭk) [Gr. *diploos*, double, + *haploos*, single]: designating a life cycle with meiosis at spore formation, i.e., with alternation of diploid and haploid generations.

diploid (dĭp'loid): a chromosome number twice that characteristic of a gamete of a given species.

diplontic (dĭp·lŏn′tĭk): designating a life cycle with meiosis at gamete formation, i.e., with diploid adults.

disaccharide (dī·săk′a·rĭd) [Gr. *dis*, twice, + *sakcharon*, sugar]: a sugar composed of two monosaccharides; usually refers to 12-carbon sugars.

DNA: abbreviation of deoxyribose nucleic acid.

DPN: abbreviation of diphosphopyridine nucleotide: a hydrogen carrier in respiration.

duodenum (dū′ô·dē′nŭm) [L. *duodeni*, twelve each]: most anterior portion of the small intestine, continuation of the stomach; bile duct and pancreatic duct open into it.

echinoderm, Echinodermata (ê·kĭ′nô·dûrm) [Gr. *echinos*, urchin, + *derma*, skin]: (1) one of the spiny-skinned animals, i.e., starfishes, sea urchins, brittle stars, sea cucumbers, sea lilies; (2) phylum name.

ectoderm, ectoparasite, (ĕk′tô—) [Gr. *ektos*, outside]: (1) outer tissue layer of an embryo; (2) a parasite attached to the outside of a host.

egestion (ê·jĕs′chŭn) [L. *egerere*, to discharge]: the elimination from the alimentary system of unusable and undigested material.

electrolyte (ê·lĕk′trô·līt) [Gr. *ēlektron*, amber, + *lytos*, soluble]: a substance which dissociates into ions in aqueous solution and so makes possible the conduction of electric current through the solution.

element (ĕl′ê·mĕnt): one of about 100 distinct natural or man-made types of matter, which, singly or in combination, compose all materials of the universe; an atom is the smallest representative unit of an element.

embryo (ĕm′brĭ·ō): [Gr. *en*, in, + *bryein*, to swell, teem]: an early developmental stage of an organism, produced from a fertilized egg and contained within a reproductive organ.

endergonic (ĕn′dĕr·gŏ·nĭk): energy-requiring, as in a chemical reaction.

endocrine (ĕn′dô·krīn) [Gr. *endon*, within, + *krinein*, to separate]: applied to type of gland which releases secretion not through a duct but directly into blood or lymph; functionally equivalent to hormone-producing.

endoderm, endodermis (ĕn′dô·dûrm): (1) inner tissue layer of an embryo, (2) single layer of tissue in a root or stem which separates the cortex from the stele.

energy (ĕn′ẽr·jĭ) [Gr. *energos*, active]: capacity to do work; the time rate of doing work is called power.

enterocoel, enterocoelomate (ĕn′tẽr·ô·sēl′) [Gr. *enteron*, gut, + *koilos*, hollow]: (1) a coelom formed by the outpouching of a mesodermal sac from the endoderm; (2) an animal possessing an enterocoel, e.g., echinoderms, vertebrates.

enzyme (ĕn′zīm) [Gr. *en*, in, + *zymē*, leaven]: a protein produced within an organism, capable of accelerating a particular chemical reaction; a type of catalyst.

epidermis (ĕp′ĭ·dûr′mĭs) [Gr. *epi*, over, + *derma*, skin]: the outermost surface tissue of an organism.

epithelium (ĕp′ĭ·thē′lĭ·ŭm) [Gr. *epi* + *thēlē*, nipple]: an animal tissue type in which the cells are packed tightly together, leaving little intercellular space.

esophagus (ê·sŏf′a·gŭs) [Gr. *oisō*, I shall carry, + *phagein*, to eat]: part of alimentary tract connecting pharynx and stomach.

estrogen (ĕs′trô·jĕn) [Gr. *oistros*, frenzy, + *genēs*, born]: one of a group of female sex hormones, produced by a follicle.

exergonic (ĕk′sẽr·gŏ·nĭk): energy-yielding, as in a chemical reaction.

exocrine (ĕk′sô·krīn) [Gr. *exō*, outside, + *krinein*, to separate]: applied to type of gland which releases secretion through a duct.

fermentation (fûr′mĕn·tā′shŭn): synonym for anaerobic respiration, i.e., fuel combustion in the absence of oxygen.

fibril (fī′brĭl) [L. dim. of *fibra*, thread]: a strand or filament produced by cells and located within cells.

flagellate, flagellum (flăj′ê·lāt, —ŭm) [L., whip]: (1) equipped with one or more flagella; an organism possessing flagella; (2) a microscopic, whiplike filament serving as locomotor structure in flagellate cells.

florigen (flō′rĭ·jĕn) [L. *flos*, flower, + Gr. *genēs*, born]: flowering hormone, believed to be produced as a result of appropriate photoperiodic treatment of plants.

follicle (fŏl′ĭ·k′l) [L. *folliculus*, small ball]: hollow ball of cells in the mammalian ovary containing a maturing egg.

fovea centralis (fō′vê·a·sĕn·trā′lĭs) [L., central pit]: small area in the optic center of the retina; only cone cells are present here.

gamete (găm′ēt) [Gr. *gamein*, to marry]: reproductive cell which must fuse with another before it can develop; sex cell.

gametophyte (găm·ē′tô·fīt): a gamete-producing organism or plant; phase of life cycle in diplohaplontic organisms which alternates with a sporophyte phase.

ganglion (găng′glĭ·ŭn) [Gr., a swelling]: a collection of cell bodies of neurons located outside the brain or the spinal cord.

gastrula, gastrulation (găs′trŏŏ·lá, —lā′shŭn): (1) a two-layered and later three-layered stage in the embryonic development of animals; (2) the process of gastrula formation.

gemma (jĕm′á) [L., a bud]: vegetative bud in bryophytes, capable of developing into whole plant.

gene (jēn) [Gr. *genēs*, born]: a segment of a chromosome, definable in operational terms: repository of genetic information.

genome (jēn′ōm): the totality of genes in a haploid set of chromosomes, hence the sum of all different genes in a cell.

genotype (jĕn′ō·tīp): the particular set of genes present in an organism and its cells; the genetic constitution.

genus (jē′nŭs) [L., race]: a rank category in taxonomic classification, between species and family; a group of very closely related species.

geotropism (jē·ŏt′rō·pĭz˙m) [Gr. *gē*, earth, + *tropē*, a turning]: behavior governed and oriented by gravity, i.e., growth of roots toward center of earth.

glomerulus (glō·mĕr′û·lŭs) [L. dim. of *glomus*, ball]: a small meshwork of blood capillaries found in the cup-shaped capsule of a nephron.

glottis (glŏt′ĭs) [Gr. *glōssa*, tongue]: slitlike opening in the larynx, formed by the vocal cords.

gonad (gōn′ăd) [Gr. *gonē*, generator]: collective term for the testes and ovaries of animals.

granum (grăn′ŭm) [L., grain]: a functional unit of a chloroplast; smallest particle capable of carrying out photosynthesis.

gymnosperm (jĭm′nō·spûrm) [Gr. *gymnos*, naked, + *sperma*, seed]: a plant belonging to a class of seed plants in which the seeds are not enclosed in an ovary; includes the conifers.

haemoglobin (hē′mô·glō′bĭn) [Gr. *haima*, blood, + L. *globus*, globe]: oxygen-carrying constituent of red blood corpuscles; consists of red pigment haeme and protein globin.

haploid (hăp′loid) [Gr. *haploos*, single, simple]: a chromosome number characteristic of a mature gamete of a given species.

haplontic (hăp·lŏn′tĭk): designating a life cycle with zygotic meiosis and haploid adults.

herbaceous (hûr·bā′shŭs) [L. *herbaceus*, grassy]: having the characteristics of an herb; contrasts with woody.

hermaphrodite (hûr·măf′rô·dīt) [fr. Gr. Hermes + Aphrodite]: an organism possessing both male and female reproductive structures.

heterosporous (hĕt′ĕr·ŏs′pôrŭs): producing two different types of spores, viz., microspores and megaspores; microspores give rise to male gametophytes, megaspores to female gametophytes.

heterotroph, heterotrophism (hĕt′ĕr·ō·trŏf) [Gr. *heteros* + *trophos*, feeder]: (1) an organism which must obtain both inorganic and organic raw materials from the environment; (2) form of nutrition characteristic of heterotrophs.

heterozygote, heterozygous (hĕt′ĕr·ō·zī′gōt) [Gr. *heteros* + *zygōtos*, yoked]: (1) an organism in which a pair of alleles for a given trait consists of different (e.g., dominant and recessive) kinds of genes; (2) adjective.

holotroph, holotrophism (hō′lō·trŏf) [Gr. *holos*, whole, + *trophos*, feeder]: (1) a bulk-feeding organism in which nutrition includes the process of alimentation; an animal; (2) form of nutrition characteristic of animals.

hominid (hŏm′ĭ·nĭd) [L. *homo*, man]: a living or extinct man or manlike type; the family of man or pertaining to this family.

hominoid (hŏm′ĭ·noid) [L. *homo*, man]: a superfamily including hominids, the family of man, and pongids, the family of apes, living or extinct.

homosporous (hō·mŏs′pô·rŭs): producing spores of the same size or form.

homozygote, homozygous (hō′mô·zī′gōt) [Gr. *homos*, same, + *zygōtos*]: (1) an organism in which a pair of alleles for a given trait consists of the same (e.g., either dominant or recessive, but not both) kinds of genes; (2) adjective.

hormone (hôr′mōn) [Gr. *hormaein*, to excite]: a growth factor produced within an organism and affecting another part of that organism.

hybrid (hī′brĭd) [L. *hibrida*, offspring of tame sow and wild boar]: an organism which is heterozygous for one or more (usually many) gene pairs.

hydrolysis (hī·drŏl′ĭ·sĭs) [Gr. *hydōr*, water + *lysis*, a loosening]: dissolution through the agency of water; especially decomposition of a chemical by the addition of water.

hydroponics (hī′drō·pŏn′ĭks) [Gr. *hydōr* + *ponos*, labor]: growing plants without soil by immersing the roots in a nutrient-rich water medium.

hypertonic (hī′pĕr·tŏn′ĭk): exerting greater osmotic pull than the medium on the other side of a semipermeable membrane, hence possessing a greater concentration of particles and acquiring water during osmosis.

hypha (hī′fá) [Gr. *hyphē*, a web]: a filamentous structural unit of a fungus; a meshwork of hyphae forms a mycelium.

hypotonic (hī′pô·tŏn′ĭk) exerting lesser osmotic pull than the medium on the other side of a semipermeable membrane; hence possessing a lesser concentration of particles and losing water during osmosis.

ichthyosaur (ĭk′thĭ·ô·sôr) [Gr. *ichthyos*, fish, + *sauros*, lizard]: extinct marine Mesozoic reptile, with fish-shaped body and porpoiselike snout.

indusium (ĭn·dū′zĭ·ŭm) [L., undergarment]: in ferns, tissue covering sori.

ingestion (ĭn·jĕs′chŭn) [L. *ingerere*, to put in]: intake of food from the environment into the alimentary system.

insulin (ĭn′sū·lĭn) [L. *insula*, island]: a hormone produced by the islets of Langerhans in the pancreas; promotes the conversion of blood glucose into tissue glycogen.

integument (ĭn·tĕg′ū·mĕnt) [L. *integere*, to cover]: covering; external coat, skin.

invagination (ĭn·văj′ĭ·nā′shŭn) [L. *in*—, in, + *vagina*, sheath]: local infolding of a layer of tissue, leading to the formation of a pouch or sac; as in invagination during gastrulation.

ion, ionization (ī′ŏn, —ĭ·zā′shŭn) [Gr. *ienai*, to go]: (1) an electrically charged atom or group of atoms; (2) addition or removal of electrons from atoms.

isotonic (ī′sô·tŏn′ĭk): exerting the same osmotic pull as the medium on the other side of a semipermeable membrane, hence possessing the same concentration of particles.

larva (lär′va), *pl. larvae* (—vē) [L., mask]: period in developmental history of animals, between embryo and adult; the larval period begins at hatching and terminates at metamorphosis.

larynx (lăr′ĭngks) [Gr.]: voice box; sound-producing organ in mammals.

lenticel (lĕn′tĭ·sĕl) [F. *lenticelle*, little lentil]: porous region in cork of woody stem, aiding gas exchange.

leucocyte (lū′kô·sīt) [Gr. *leukos*, white, + *kytos*, vessel]: a type of white blood cell, characterized by a beaded, elongated nucleus.

leucoplast (lū′kô·plăst) [Gr. *leukos*, white]: an unpigmented plastid.

lichen (lī′kĕn) [Gr. *leichēn*]: a symbiotic, mutualistic association of an algal type and a fungal type.

lipase (lī′pās) [Gr. *lipos*, fat]: an enzyme promoting the conversion of fat into fatty acids and glycerin, or the reverse.

lycopsid (lī·kŏp′sĭd) [Gr. *lykos*, wolf]: a member of a subphylum of tracheophytes; the club mosses.

lymph (lĭmf) [L. *lympha*, goddess of moisture]: the body fluid outside the blood circulation; leaks out of and eventually returns to the blood circulation.

madreporite (măd′rê·pô·rīt) [It. *madre*, mother, + *poro*, passage]: a sievelike opening on the upper surface of echinoderms, connecting the water-vascular system with the outside.

marsupial (mär·sū′pĭ·ăl) [Gr. *marsypion*, little bag]: a pouched mammal, member of the mammalian subclass Metatheria.

medulla (mê·dŭl′a) [L.]: the inner tissue layers of an organ or body part, e.g., adrenal medulla; the medulla oblongata is a region of the hindbrain which connects with the spinal cord.

medusa (mê·dū′sa): the free-swimming stage in the life cycle of coelenterates; a jellyfish.

megagametophyte (mĕg′a·ga·mē′tô·fīt) [Gr. *megas*, great]: in heterosporous plants, the gametophyte produced by a megaspore; the female gametophyte.

megaspore (mĕg′a·spōr): a spore formed in a megasporangium and developing into a megagametophyte.

meiosis (mī·ō′sĭs) [Gr. *meioun*, to make smaller]: process occurring at different points in the life cycles of different organisms in which the chromosome number is reduced by half; compensates for the chromosome-doubling effect of fertilization.

menopause (mĕn′ô·pôz) [Gr. *menos*, month, + *pauein*, to cause to cease]: the time at the end of the reproductive period of (human) females when menstrual cycles cease to occur.

menstruation (mĕn′strōō·ā′shŭn) [L. *mensis*, month]: the discharge of uterine tissue and blood from the vagina, at the end of a menstrual cycle in which fertilization has not occurred.

meristem (mĕr′ĭ·stĕm) [Gr. *meristos*, divided]: embryonic issue in plants, capable of giving rise to additional tissues.

mesoderm (mĕs′ô·dûrm) [Gr. *mesos*, middle, + *derma*, skin]: the middle tissue layers of an animal embryo, between ectoderm and endoderm.

mesogloea (mĕs′ô·glē′a) [Gr. *mesos* + *gloios*, glutinous substance]: the jellylike layer between the ectoderm and endoderm of coelenterates and comb jellies.

mesophyll (mĕs′ô·fĭl) [Gr. *mesos* + *phyllon*, leaf]: tissue in the interior of leaves, composed of chlorophyll-containing cells.

metabolism (mê·tăb′ô·lĭz′m) [Gr. *metabolē*, change]: a group of life-sustaining processes including principally nutrition, production of energy (respiration), and synthesis of more living substance.

metamorphosis (mĕt′ȧ·môr′fô·sĭs) [Gr. *metamorphoun*, to transform]: the transformation of a larva into an adult.

metaphase (mĕt′ȧ·fāz) [Gr. *meta*, between]: a stage during mitotic cell division in which the chromosomes line up in a plane at right angles to the spindle axis.

Metaphyta (mē·tăf′ĭ·tȧ): a major category of living organisms, consisting of the phyla Bryophyta and Tracheophyta.

Metazoa (mĕt′ȧ·zō′ȧ): a major category of living organisms, consisting of all multicellular animals.

microgametophyte (mīkrŏ-): in heterosporous plants, the gametophyte produced by a microspore; the male gametophyte.

micron (mī′krŏn), *pl. microns, micra* [Gr. *mikros*, small]: one-thousandth part of a millimeter, a unit of microscopic length.

micropyle (mī′krŏ·pīl) [Gr. *mikros* + *pilē*, gate]: an opening in the integument of an ovule, permitting entry of a pollen grain or pollen tube.

microspore (mī′krŏ·spōr): a spore formed in a microsporangium and developing into a microgametophyte; equivalent to pollen grain.

mitochondrion (mī′tô·kŏn′drĭ·ŏn) [Gr. *mitos*, thread, + *chondros, grain*]: a particulate constituent of cytoplasm; the site of respiration.

mitosis (mī·tō′sĭs) [Gr. *mitos*, thread]: a form of nuclear division characterized by complex chromosome movements and exact chromosome duplication.

molecule (mŏl′ô·kūl) [L. *moles*, mass]: a compound in which the atoms are held together by covalent bonds.

Mollusca, mollusk (mŏ·lŭs′kȧ, mŏl′ŭsk) [L. *molluscus*, soft]: (1) a phylum of schizocoelomate animals; comprises chitons, snails, clams, squids, and others; (2) a member of the phylum Mollusca.

Monera (mŏn·ē′rȧ) [Gr. *monos*, alone]: a major category of living organisms, comprising the bacteria and the blue-green algae.

monosaccharide (mŏn′ô·săk′ȧ·rīd) [Gr. *monos* + *sakcharon*, sugar]: a simple sugar such as 5- and 6-carbon sugars.

morphogenesis (môr′fô·jĕn′ê·sĭs) [Gr. *morphē*, form, + *genĕs*, born]: development of size, form, and other architectural features of organisms.

morphology (môr·fŏl′ô·jĭ) [Gr. *morphē* + *logos*, study]: the study or science of structure, at any level of organization, e.g., cytology, study of cell structure; histology, study of tissue structure; anatomy, study of gross structure of organisms.

mucosa (mù·kō′sȧ) [L. *mucosus*, mucus]: a mucus-secreting membrane, e.g., the inner lining of the intestine.

mutation (mù·tā′shŭn) [L. *mutare*, to change]: a stable change of a gene, such that the changed condition is inherited by offspring cells.

mycelium (mī·sē′lĭ·ŭm) [Gr. *mykēs*, mushroom]: the vegetative portion of a fungus, consisting of a meshwork of hyphae.

Mycophyta (mī′kô·fī′tȧ) [Gr. *mykēs* + *phyton*, plant]: the phylum comprising the fungi.

myelin (mī′ĕ·lĭn) [Gr. *myelos*, marrow]: a fatty material which surrounds the axons of nerve cells in the central nervous system.

myxophyte, Myxophyta (mĭk′sô·fīt, mĭks·ŏf′ĭ·ta): (1) a member of the phylum of slime molds; (2) phylum name.

nekton (nĕk′tŏn) [Gr. *nēktos*, swimming]: collective term for the actively swimming organisms in the ocean.

nematode (nĕm′ȧ·tōd) [Gr. *nēmatos*, thread]: a roundworm, member of the pseudocoelomate phylum Nematoda.

nephric, nephron (nĕf′rĭk, —rŏn) [Gr. *nephros*, kidney]: (1) pertaining to a nephron; (2) a functional unit of the vertebrate kidney.

neuron (nū′rŏn) [Gr., nerve]: nerve cell, including cyton, dendrites, and axons.

nitrify, nitrification (nī′trĭ·fī, —fĭ·kā′shŭn): (1) to convert ammonia and nitrites to nitrates, as by nitrifying bacteria; (2) noun.

notochord (nō′tô·kôrd) [Gr. *nōton*, the back, + L. *chorda*, cord]: longitudinal elastic rod of cells serving as internal skeleton in the embryos of all chordates and in the adults of some; in most adult chordates the notochord is replaced by a vertebral column.

nucleic acid (nū·klē′ĭk): one of a class of molecules composed of joined nucleotide complexes; the principal types are deoxyribose nucleic acid (DNA) and ribose nucleic acid (RNA).

nucleolus (nū·klē′ô·lŭs): an RNA-containing body within the nucleus of a cell; a derivative of chromosomes.

nucleotide (nū′klē·ô·tīd): a molecule consisting of joined phosphate, 5-carbon sugar (either ribose or deoxyribose), and a purine or a pyrimidine (adenine, guanine, uracil, thymine, or cytosine).

nucleus (nū′klē·ŭs) [L., a kernel]: a body present in all cell types except the bacteria and the blue-green algae and consisting of external nuclear membrane, interior nuclear sap, and chromosomes and nucleoli suspended in the sap.

organ (ôr′găn) [fr. Gr. *organon*]: a group of different tissues joined structurally and cooperating functionally to perform a composite task.

osmosis (ŏs·mō′sĭs) [Gr. *ōsmos*, impulse]: the process in which water migrates through a semipermeable membrane, from a side containing a lesser concentration of particles to the side containing a greater concentration; migration continues until particle concentrations are equal on both sides.

Osteichthyes (ŏs·tê·ĭk′thĭ·ēz) [Gr. *osteon*, bone]: a class of vertebrates, comprising the bony fishes.

ovary (ō′và·rĭ) [L. *ovum*, egg]: (1) the egg-producing organ of female animals; (2) the ovule(megasporangium)-containing organ of flowering plants.

oviparity, oviparous (ō′vĭ·păr′ĭ·tĭ, ô·vĭp′à·rŭs) [L. *ovum* + *parere*, to bring forth]: (1) animal reproductive pattern in which eggs are released by the female; offspring development therefore occurs outside the maternal body; (2) adjective.

ovoviviparity, ovoviviparous (ō′vō·vĭv′ĭ·păr′ĭ·tĭ, ō′vôvĭ·vĭp′·à·rŭs): (1) animal reproductive pattern in which eggs develop within the maternal body, but without nutritive or other metabolic aid by the female parent; offspring are born as miniature adults; (2) adjective.

ovule (ō′vūl): the integument-covered megasporangium of a seed plant.

oxidation (ŏk′sĭ·dā′shŭn): internal rearrangement of a molecule so as to create a high-energy bond; often achieved by dehydrogenation.

paleontology (pā′lê·ŏn·tŏl′ô·gĭ) [Gr. *palaios*, old, + *onta*, existing things]: study of past geological times, principally by means of fossils.

Paleozoic (pā′lê·ô·zō′ĭk) [Gr. *palaios* + *zōē*, life]: the geological era between the Precambrian and the Mesozoic, dating approximately from 500 to 200 million years ago.

parasite (păr′à·sĭt) [Gr. *para*, beside, + *sitos*, food]: an organism which lives symbiotically on or within a host organism, more or less detrimental to the host.

parenchyma (pà·rĕng′kĭ·mà) [Gr. *para* + *en*, in, + *chein*, to pour]: designating a type of cell in plants, relatively little specialized.

parthenogenesis (pär′thê·nô·jĕn′ê·sĭs) [Gr. *parthenos*, virgin, + *genēs*, born]: development of an egg without fertilization; occurs naturally in some organisms (e.g., rotifers) and may be induced artificially in others (e.g., frogs).

pathogenic (păth′ô·jĕn′ĭk) [Gr. *pathos*, suffering, + *genēs*]: disease-producing, e.g., many bacteria, fungi, and other parasites.

pelagic (pê·lăj′ĭk) [Gr. *pelagos*, ocean]: oceanic habitat zone, comprising the open water of an ocean basin.

pepsin (pĕp′sĭn) [Gr. *peptein*, to digest]: a protein-digesting enzyme present in gastric juice.

pericycle (pĕr′ĭ·sī′k'l) [Gr. *perikyklos*, spherical]: a tissue layer composed of parenchyma cells surrounding the vascular tissues of the stele; may be reduced or absent in stems.

peristalsis (pĕr′ĭ·stăl′sĭs) [Gr. *peristaltikos*, compressing]: successive contraction and relaxation of tubular organs such as the alimentary tract, resulting in a wavelike propagation of a transverse constriction.

petiole (pĕt′ĭ·ōl) [L. *petiolus*, little foot]: leafstalk; the slender stem by which a leaf blade is attached to a branch or a stem.

pH: a symbol denoting the relative concentration of hydrogen ions in a solution; pH values run from 0 to 14, and the lower the value, the more acid is a solution, i.e., the more hydrogen ions it contains.

Phaeophyta (fē′ô·fī′t·à): the phylum of brown algae.

pharynx (făr′ĭngks) [Gr.]: the part of the alimentary tract between mouth cavity and esophagus; it is also part of the air channel from nose to larynx.

phellem (fĕl′ĕm) [Gr. *phellos*, cork]: cork, the exterior product of the cork cambium.

phenotype (fē′nô·tīp) [Gr. *phainein*, to show]: the physical appearance of an organism resulting from its genetic constitution (genotype).

phloem (flō′ĕm) [Gr. *phloos*, bark]: one of the vascular tissues in tracheophytic plants; consists of sieve tubes and companion cells and transports organic nutrients both up and down.

photolysis (fô·tŏl′ĭ·sĭs) [Gr. *phōtos*, light, + *lysis*, a loosening]: a component process of photosynthesis in which water is dissociated and the hydrogen is joined to TPN under the indirect influence of solar energy.

photosynthesis (fô′tô·sĭn′thê·sĭs) [Gr. *phōtos*, light, + *syn*, together, + *tithenai*, to place]: process in which energy of light and chlorophyll are used to manufacture carbohydrates out of carbon dioxide and water.

phototropism (fô·tŏt′rô·pĭz'm) [Gr. *phōtos* + *tropē*, a turning]: behavior oriented by light, e.g., growth of plant stems toward light source.

phrenic (frĕn′ĭk) [Gr. *phrenos*, diaphragm]: pertaining to the diaphragm, e.g., phrenic nerve, innervating the diaphragm.

phylum (fī′lŭm), pl. *phyla* [Gr. *phylon*, race, tribe]: a category of taxonomic classification, ranked above class.

physiology (fĭz′ĭ·ŏl′ô·jĭ) [Gr. *physis*, nature, + *logos*, study]: study of living processes, activities, and functions generally; contrasts with morphology, the study of structure.

pituitary (pĭ·tū′ĭ·tĕrĭ) [L. *pituita*, phlegm]: a composite endocrine gland in vertebrates, attached ventrally to the brain; composed of anterior, intermediate, and posterior lobes, each representing a functionally separate gland.

placenta (plȧ·sĕn′tȧ) [L., cake]: a tissue complex formed in part from the inner lining of the uterus and in part from the chorion of the embryo; develops in most mammals and serves as mechanical, metabolic, and endocrine connection between the adult female and the embryo during pregnancy.

placoderm (plăk′ō·dûrm) [Gr. *plakos*, flat plate, + *derma*, skin]: a member of a class of Devonian vertebrates (fishes), all now extinct; ancestral to cartilage and bony fishes.

plankton (plăngk′tŏn) [Gr. *planktos*, wandering]: collective term for the passively floating or drifting flora and fauna of a body of water; consists largely of microscopic organisms.

plasmodium (plăz·mō′dĭ·ŭm) [Gr. *plasma*, form]: multinucleate amoeboid mass, representing aggregated diploid phase in certain slime molds.

plastid (plăs′tĭd) [Gr. *plastēs*, a molder]: a cytoplasmic, often pigmented body in cells; three types are leucoplasts, chromoplasts, and chloroplasts.

Platyhelminthes (plăt′ĭ·hĕl·mĭn′thēz) [Gr. *platys*, flat, + *helminthos*, worm]: flatworms, a phylum of acoelomate animals; comprises planarians, flukes, and tapeworms.

-ploid (-ploid) [Gr. *-ploos*, -fold]: the number of chromosome sets per cell, e.g., haploid, diploid.

polyp (pŏl′ĭp) [L. *polypus*, many-footed]: the sessile stage in the life cycle of coelenterates.

polysaccharide (pŏl′ĭ·săk′ȧ·rīd): a carbohydrate composed of many joined monosaccharide units, e.g., glycogen, starch, cellulose, all formed out of glucose units.

Porifera (po·rĭf′ẽr·ȧ) [L. *porus*, pore, + *ferre*, to bear]: the phylum of sponges.

progesterone (prō·jĕs′tẽr·ōn): hormone secreted by the corpus luteum and the placenta; prepares the uterus for the reception of a fertilized egg and later maintains the capacity of the uterus to hold the embryo.

prophase (prō′fāz′): a stage during mitotic division in which the chromosomes become distinct and a spindle forms.

prosimian (prō·sĭm′ĭ·ăn) [L. *pro*, before, + *simia*, ape]: an ancestral primate and certain of primitive living primates, e.g., a lemur, a tarsier.

protein (prō′tē·ĭn) [Gr. *prōteios*, primary]: one of a class of organic compounds composed of many joined amino acids.

Protista (prō·tĭs′tȧ) [Gr. *prōtistos*, first]: a major category of living organisms, including all groups of algae, slime molds, protozoa, and fungi.

protoplasm (prō′tō·plăz′m) [Gr. *prōtos* + *plasma*, form, mold]: synonym for living matter, living material, or living substance.

protostele (prō′tō·stēl′) [Gr. *prōtos* + *stēlē*, upright post]: a general type of stele in which the vascular tissues form a solid central aggregation within the stem or root, phloem being outside the xylem.

protozoon (prō′tō·zō′ŏn) [Gr. *protos* + *zōion*, animal]: a member of either of four protistan phyla (Mastigophora, Sarcodina, Ciliophora, Sporozoa).

pseudocoel, pseudocoelomate (sū′dō·sēl, —ō·māt) [Gr. *pseudēs*, false]: (1) an internal body cavity lined not by mesoderm but by ectoderm and endoderm; (2) an animal possessing a pseudocoel, e.g., rotifers, roundworms.

pseudopodium (sū′dō·pō′dĭ·ŭm): a temporary cytoplasmic protrusion from an amoeboid cell; functions in locomotion and feeding.

Psilopsida (sī·lŏp′sĭ·dȧ) [Gr. *psilos*, bare]: a subphylum of tracheophytes; includes the earliest representatives of the vascular plants.

Pteropsida (tē·rŏp′sĭ·dȧ) [Gr. *pteridos*, fern]: a subphylum of tracheophytes; includes ferns and all seed plants, i.e., large-leafed vascular plants.

Pyrrophyta (pĭ·rŏf′ĭ·tȧ) [Gr. *pyros*, fire]: a phylum of algae.

recessive (rē·sĕs′ĭv) [L. *recedere*, to recede]: a functional attribute of genes; the effect of a recessive gene is masked if the allelic gene is dominant.

renal (rē′năl) [L. *renes*, kidneys]: pertaining to the kidney.

rennin (rĕn′ĭn) [Middle Engl. *rennen*, to run]: an enzyme present in gastric juice; promotes the coagulation of milk.

reticulum (rē·tĭk′ū·lŭm) [L. *reticulum*, little net]: a network or mesh of fibrils, fibers, or filaments, as in *endoplasmic reticulum* within cytoplasm.

retina (rĕt′ĭ·nȧ) [L. *rete*, a net]: the innermost tissue layer of the eyeball; contains the receptor cells sensitive to light.

rhizoid (rī′zoid) [Gr. *rhiza*, root]: rootlike absorptive filament.

rhizome (rī′zōm) [Gr. *rhizōma*, mass of roots]: underground stem.

Rhodophyta (rō·dŏf′ĭ·tȧ) [Gr. *rhodon*, rose, + *phyton*, plant]: the phylum of red algae.

ribosome (rī′bō·sōm): a submicroscopic cytoplasmic particle; contains RNA and is the site of protein synthesis.

Rotifera (rō·tĭf′ẽr·ȧ) [L. *rota*, wheel, + *ferre*, to bear]: a phylum of microscopic pseudocoelomate animals.

saccule (săk′ūl) [L. *sacculus*, little sack]: portion of the inner ear containing the receptors for the sense of static balance.

saprotroph (săp′rô·trōf) [Gr. *sapros*, rotten]: an organism subsisting on dead or decaying matter.

schizocoel, schizocoelomate (skĭz′ō·sēl) [Gr. *schizein*, to split]: (1) a coelom formed by a splitting of embryonic mesoderm; (2) an animal possessing a schizocoel, e.g., mollusks, annelids, arthropods.

Schizophyta (skĭz′ŏf′ĭ·tà) [Gr. *schizein* + *phyton*, plant]: the phylum of bacteria.

sclera (sklē′rà) [Gr. *sklēros*, hard]: the outermost coat of the eyeball, continuous with the cornea.

serum (sē′ŭm) [L.]: the fluid remaining after removal of fibrinogen from blood plasma.

sinus (sī′nŭs) [L., a curve]: a cavity, recess, or depression, especially in bone.

siphon (sī′fŏn) [Gr. *siphōn*, a pipe]: tubular structure for drawing in or ejecting fluids, as in mollusks, tunicates.

siphonostele (sī′fô·nô·stēl): a general type of stele in which the vascular tissues are arranged around a central pith or a central hollow cavity.

sorus (sō′rŭs) [Gr. *soros*, heap]: a cluster of sporangia on a fern leaf.

species (spē′shĭz), *pl. species* (spē′shēz) [L. kind, sort]: a category of taxonomic classification, below genus rank, defined by breeding potential or gene flow: interbreeding and gene flow occur among the members of a species but not between members of different species.

Sphenopsida (sfê·nŏp′sĭ·dà) [Gr. *sphēn*, a wedge]: a subphylum of tracheophytes; includes the horsetails.

spirillum (spī·rĭl′ŭm) [L. *spirilla*, little coil]: any bacterium possessing a wavy, coiled, or spiral body.

sporangium (spô·răn′jĭ·ŭm): a spore-producing structure, unicellular or multicellular.

spore (spōr) [Gr. *spora*, a seed]: a reproductive cell capable of developing into an adult directly.

sporophyte (spōr′ô·fīt): a spore-producing organism; phase of diplohaplontic life cycle which alternates with a gametophyte phase.

stamen (stā′mĕn) [L., a thread]: the microspore-producing organ of a flower; consists of stalk and anther.

stele (stēl) [Gr. *stēlē*, upright post]: collective term for those portions of stem and root which contain vascular tissues and, where present, pericycle and pith.

stimulus (stĭm′û·lŭs) [L.]: any environmental change which activates a receptor.

stipule (stĭp′ūl) [L. *stipula*, stalk]: one of a pair of appendages at the base of the petiole in many plants.

stoma (stō′mà) *pl. stomata* [Gr., a mouth]: a microscopic opening in the epidermis of a leaf, formed by a pair of guard cells; interconnects the interior air spaces of a leaf with the external atmosphere.

suberin (sū′bĕr·ĭn) [L. *suber*, cork tree]: a waterproofing material secreted by cork and endodermis cells.

symbiont, symbiosis (sĭm′bĭ·ŏnt, sĭm′bĭ·ō′sĭs) [Gr. *syn*, with, + *bios*, life]: (1) an organism which lives in symbiotic association with another; (2) the intimate living together of two organisms of different species, for mutual or one-sided benefit; the principal variants are mutualism, commensalism, and parasitism.

synapse (sĭ·năps′) [Gr. *synapsis*, conjunction]: the microscopic space between the axon terminal of one neuron and the dendrite terminal of another adjacent neuron.

syncytium (sĭn·sĭ′shĭ·ŭm) [Gr. *syn* + *kytos*, vessel]: a multinucleate animal tissue without internal cell boundaries.

synthesis (sĭn′thê·sĭs) [Gr. *syn* + *tithenai*, to place]: the joining of two or more molecules resulting in a single larger molecule.

systole (sĭs′tô·lē) [Gr. *syn* + *stellein*, to place]: the phase of contraction of auricles or ventricles, during which blood is pumped forward along the circulation path.

taiga (tī′gà) [Russ.]: terrestrial habitat zone characterized by large tracts of coniferous forests, long, cold winters, and short summers; bounded in the north by tundra; found particularly in Canada, northern Europe, and Siberia.

taxonomy (tăks·ŏn′ô·mĭ) [Gr. *taxis*, arrangement + *nomos*, law]: classification of organisms, based as far as possible on natural relationships.

telophase (tĕl′ô·fāz) [Gr. *telos*, end]: a stage in mitotic division during which two nuclei form; usually accompanied by partitioning of cytoplasm.

testis (tĕs′tĭs) [L.]: male reproductive organ of animals; produces sperms.

tetrapyrrol (tĕt′rà·pī′rŏl): a molecule consisting of four united pyrrol units, each of the latter being a five-membered ring of carbon and nitrogen; the four pyrrols may be joined linearly or as a larger ring; tetrapyrrols include pigments such as chlorophyll.

thallus (thăl′ŭs) [Gr., young shoot]: a body without differentiation into root, stem, and leaf, usually flat and prostrate, sometimes filamentous; name applied mainly to some fungi, algae, and bryophytes.

thrombin (thrŏm′bĭn) [Gr. *thrombos*, clot]: substance participating in blood clotting; formed from prothrombin and in turn converts fibrinogen into fibrin.

thymus (thī′mŭs) [fr. Gr.]: a lymphoid gland in most young and many adult vertebrates; disappears in man at puberty; located in lower throat and upper part of thorax.

tissue (tĭsh′ū) [L. *texere*, to weave]: an aggregate of cells of similar structure performing similar functions.

trachea, tracheal (trā′kē·à) [Gr. *trachys*, rough]: (1) air-conducting tube, as in windpipe of mammals and breathing system of insects; (2) adjective.

tracheid (trā′kē·ĭd): plant cell type; a conducting component of xylem.

tracheophyte, Tracheophyta (trā′kē·ô·fĭt): (1) a vascular plant, i.e., one possessing xylem and phloem; (2) phylum name.

transpiration (trăn′spĭ·rā′shŭn) [L. *trans*, across, + *spirare*, to breathe]: evaporation of water from leaves or other exposed surfaces.

trophic (trŏf′ĭk) [Gr. *trophos*, feeder]: pertaining to nutrition, i.e., autotrophic, heterotrophic.

tropic, tropism (trŏp′ĭk) [Gr. *tropē*, a turning]: (1) pertaining to behavior or action brought about by specific stimuli, i.e., phototropic (light-oriented growing), gonadotropic (stimulating the gonads); (2) noun.

trypsin (trĭp′sĭn) [Gr. *tryein*, to wear down]: enzyme promoting digestion of proteins; acts in small intestine, but produced as inactive trypsinogen by pancreas.

tuber (tū′bēr) [L., knob]: a short, fleshy underground stem with buds, e.g., potato.

tundra (tōōn′drà) [Russ.]: terrestrial habitat zone, between taiga in south and polar region in north, characterized by absence of trees, short growing season, and frozen ground during much of the year.

turgor (tûr′gŏr) [L. *turgere*, to swell]: the distention of a cell by its fluid content.

umbilicus (ŭm·bĭl′ĭ·kŭs) [L.]: the navel; during pregnancy, an umbilical cord connects the placenta with the offspring, and the point of connection with the offspring later becomes the navel.

urea (ŭ·rē′à) [Gr. *ouron*, urine]: an organic compound formed in the liver out of ammonia and carbon dioxide and excreted by the kidneys.

ureter (ŭ·rē′tēr) [fr. Gr.]: duct carrying urine from a kidney to the urinary bladder.

urethra (ŭ·rē′thrà) [fr. Gr.]: duct carrying urine from the urinary bladder to the outside of the body; in the males of most mammals, the urethra also leads sperms to the outside during copulation.

uterus (ū′tēr·ŭs) [L., womb]: enlarged region of the female reproductive duct in which offspring develops during pregnancy and receives maternal nourishment.

utricle (ū′trĭ·k′l) [L. *utriculus*, little bag]: portion of the inner ear containing the receptors for dynamic body balance.

vacuole (văk′ū·ōl) [L. *vacuus*, empty]: a small, usually spherical space within a cell, bounded by a membrane and containing fluid, solid matter, or both.

vagus (vā′gŭs) [L., wandering]: the tenth cranial nerve; it is a mixed nerve, innervating many organs in the chest and the abdomen.

ventricle (vĕn′trĭ·k′l) [L. *ventriculus*, the stomach]: a chamber of the heart which receives blood from an auricle and pumps out blood from the heart.

vernalization (vûr′năl·ĭ·zā′shŭn) [L. *vernalis*, spring]: induction of flowering by cold (or heat) treatment of seeds or later developmental stages.

villus (vĭl′ŭs), *pl. villi* [L., a tuft of hair]: a tiny finger-like process projecting from the intestinal lining into the cavity of the gut.

virus (vī′rŭs) [L., slimy liquid, poison]: a submicroscopic noncellular particle, composed of a nucleic acid core and a protein shell; parasitic, and within a host cell it may reproduce and mutate.

vitamin (vī′tà·mĭn) [L. *vita*, life]: one of a class of organic growth factors contributing to the formation or action of cellular enzymes.

viviparity, viviparous (vĭv′ĭ·păr′ĭ·tĭ, vī·vĭp′à·rŭs) [L. *vivus*, alive, + *parere*, to bring forth]: (1) reproductive pattern in which eggs develop within female body with metabolic aid of maternal parent; offspring are born as miniature adults; (2) adjective.

xanthophyll (zăn′thô·fĭl) [Gr. *xanthos*, yellow, + *phyllon*, leaf]: one of a group of yellow pigments; members of the carotenoid group.

xylem (zī′lĕm) [Gr. *xylon*, wood]: tissue which conducts water from roots upward; consists of tracheids, vessels, and other cell types; in bulk represents wood.

zygote (zī′gōt) [Gr. *zygōtos*, yoked]: the cell resulting from the sexual fusion of two gametes; a fertilized egg.

INDEX